A Great Lakes Wetland Flora

A complete guide to the
aquatic and wetland plants
of the Upper Midwest

Second Edition

Steve W. Chadde

PocketFlora Press
Laurium, Michigan

What would the world be, once bereft
Of wet and wildness? Let them be left,
O let them be left, wildness and wet;
Long live the weeds and wilderness yet.
—GERARD MANLEY HOPKINS

A Great Lakes Wetland Flora.

A complete guide to the aquatic and wetland plants
of the Upper Midwest.

Second Edition

Copyright © 2002 by Steve W. Chadde
All rights reserved. Printed in the United States of America.

ISBN: 0-9651385-5-0

Library of Congress Control Number: 2002090348

Publisher's Cataloging-in-Publication Data

Chadde, Steve W. (Steve William), 1955–
2nd ed: A Great Lakes wetland flora : a complete guide to the aquatic
and wetland plants of the Upper Midwest (Second Edition) / Steve W.
Chadde
    648 p.   cm.
    Includes bibliographical references and index.
    ISBN 0-9651385-5-0
    1. Wetland Plants—Middle West   2. Plants—Identification
    I. Title.
    QK938.M3   2002
    581.5´26325—dc19

                                                2002090348

HOW TO ORDER
Copies may be ordered from PocketFlora Press, 436 Hecla Street,
Laurium, MI 49913; telephone (906) 337-0716; fax (586) 314-4295. An
order form is included in the back of the book. Orders may also be
placed online at our website, www.pocketflora.com, or by sending an e-
mail to info@pocketflora.com.

Visit us online at http://www.pocketflora.com

Contents

Introduction

A GREAT LAKES WETLAND FLORA is a comprehensive manual on the identification, habitats, and distribution of the vascular plants found in the aquatic and wetland environments of the Great Lakes region. The Second Edition features improved keys, updated descriptions, and many new illustrations. Nomenclature of plant families, genera and species generally conforms to that of the published volumes (as of 2002) of *The Flora of North America* series (Vols. 2, 3, 22) and the *Synthesis of the North American Flora* (Kartesz 1999).

Over 900 plant species within 113 plant families are described in the Flora. Aquatic and wetland plants found in Minnesota, Wisconsin, Michigan, northern Illinois, and northern Indiana are included, with general applicability of the Flora to the surrounding region as well, including adjacent portions of Ontario, Ohio, Indiana, Illinois, Iowa, and North and South Dakota. For convenience, the terms *wetland* or *wetland plant* are sometimes used to also include aquatic situations (the open water of lakes, ponds, rivers and streams) and aquatic plants.

The intended user of this Flora is the botanist, ecologist, natural resource manager, consultant, or other scientist engaged in wetland studies. However, this book was also written for the person simply interested in plants, or in the ecology, conservation, or aesthetic beauty provided by wetlands. To this end, the use of technical terminology has been minimized when possible, while still allowing the reader to accurately identify unknown plant specimens. A glossary of botanical terms is provided as Appendix A; abbreviations and symbols used are defined in Appendix B.

☞ See **Appendix C** for definitions of the wetland indicator categories.

Plants were first chosen for inclusion in this work according to their wetland indicator status, a classification system developed by the U.S. Fish and Wildlife Service (Reed 1988). Although a revised, updated list has been under preparation for a number of years, the 1988 status indicators continue to be widely used in wetland determination and delineation studies throughout the United States.

All species occurring in the Great Lakes region with a wetland status indicator of Obligate (OBL) or Facultative Wetland (FACW) were included. In addition, a number of species more typical of drier habitats (Facultative species [FAC] and Facultative Upland species [FACU]) were included, based on published reports of their occurrence in wetlands, or on the author's own encounters with them in the region's wetlands.

The result is a floristic guide for the upper midwest region that is applicable to the aquatic plants of lakes, ponds, rivers, and streams, the plants of the adjoining wetlands, and to the plants found in the transition area, or ecotone, between wetlands and the surrounding uplands. Descriptions of the various wetland vegetation types in each of these settings begin on page 6.

For coverage of all vascular plants in the Great Lakes region, refer to the 3-volume *Michigan Flora* (Voss 1972, 1985, 1996), or the second edition of the *Manual of Vascular Plants of Northeastern United States and Adjacent Canada* (Gleason and Cronquist 1991), and the *Illustrated Companion to Gleason and Cronquist's Manual* (Holmgren and others 1998). *Plants of the Chicago Region* (Swink and Wilhelm 1994) is the definitive reference for southern portions of the region. These publications, plus *Vascular Plants of Minnesota: A Checklist and Atlas* (Ownbey and Morley 1991), provided regional distribution information for most of the species. Since the publication of the first edition in 1998, online species distribution information has also become available. Notable is the website of the of Wisconsin State Herbarium (http://wiscinfo.doit.wisc.edu/herbarium/).

Natural heritage programs located in each state in the region provided information on uncommon species (state or federally listed as endangered or threatened), and sightings of endangered and threatened taxa should be reported to them. Non-vascular plants (mosses, liverworts) are not included in this Flora, although their importance as indicators of water chemistry and hydrologic conditions should be considered when conducting wetland studies. The standard reference for the region is *Mosses of Eastern North America* (Crum and Anderson 1981).

▶Wetlands Defined

In general, wetlands are lands where water saturation is the primary factor determining the nature of soil that will develop and the types of plant and animals that will occur there (Cowardin and others 1979). Wetlands occur as transitional areas between upland and aquatic ecosystems, and are covered by shallow water, or have a water table that is usually at or near the ground surface.

Wetlands will have at least one, and often all of the following three attributes regarding their vegetation, soils and hydrology:

• *The land supports (at least periodically) plants that are predominantly "hydrophytes."* Hydrophytes are plants growing in water, or on soil that is at least periodically deficient in oxygen as a result of high water content.

• *The soils are largely undrained, "hydric" soils.* Hydric soils are soils that are flooded or saturated long enough during the growing season so that anaerobic conditions develop in the upper portion of the soil.

   • *Water will either permanently or periodically cover the area during some or all of the growing season each year.*

A wetland definition used by the U.S. Army Corps of Engineers in its regulatory program is: "Wetlands are those areas inundated or saturated by surface or groundwater at a frequency and duration sufficient to support, and that under normal circumstances do support, a prevalence of vegetation typically adapted for life in saturated soil conditions. Wetlands generally include swamps, marshes, bogs, and similar areas."

▶Aquatic plants

Plants of open water areas—aquatic plants—include those species found in lakes, ponds, rivers, streams, and springs. They occur as either free-floating plants on the water surface, such as the duckweeds (*Lemna*) and water-meal (*Wolffia*), or float below the water surface, as in coontail (*Ceratophyllum*) and common bladderwort (*Utricularia vulgaris*). Aquatic species also occur as submergent plants anchored to the bottom substrate by roots or rhizomes. Submergent species may be entirely underwater as in water-milfoil (*Myriophyllum*), or have leaves floating on the water surface (water-lilies, *Nuphar*). Some aquatic species have differently shaped underwater and floating leaves, as in a number of pondweeds (*Potamogeton*).

▶Wetland Plants

Wetland species are intermediate between truly aquatic species and plants adapted to the moist or dry conditions of upland environments. Wetland species occur in habitats generally referred to as bogs, fens, marshes, swamps, thickets, and wet meadows, among others. Soils of these habitats may be organic (composed of decaying plant remains, or "peat"), of mineral origin, or a combination of both. Wetlands may be covered with shallow water for all or part of the year, or simply wet for a portion of the growing season.

On sites covered by shallow water, a group of wetland plant species termed *emergent* occur. These plants are rooted in soil but their stems and leaves are partly or entirely above the water surface. This large group includes many of the sedges (*Carex*), bulrushes (*Scirpus*), bur-reeds (*Sparganium*), rushes (*Juncus*), grasses (Poaceae) and the cat-tails (*Typha*).

A second large group of wetland species are those occurring on soils which are moist or even saturated throughout the year but are rarely covered by standing water. These sites include wetlands such as moist or wet meadows and low prairie. Many of the herbaceous dicots ("wildflowers") included in the Flora occur in these types of wetlands, especially on the drier margins. Species typically found in drier habitats are occasionally found in these wetlands as well, but are often restricted to hummocks slightly elevated above the surrounding lower, wetter areas.

Excluded from this Flora are species which occur only rarely in wetlands. For example, a number of upland plants are found on sites which may be wet for only a short time in the spring following snowmelt or runoff. Under the U.S. Fish and Wildlife Service classification ystem, these would generally be classified as either Facultative Upland (FACU) or Obligate Upland (UPL) species.

▶Using the Flora

The Flora is organized as follows:
- • **Wetland types of the Great Lakes region** - Major aquatic and wetland types of the Great Lakes region are described, including a simple key for field classification of each type.
- • **Family keys** - A key to each plant family covered in the Flora, based on vegetative and floral characteristics, is included. This is followed by a simplified key to just the woody plants (trees, shrubs and vines) found in the region's wetlands.
- • **Species descriptions** - The bulk of the Flora is the description and illustration of each plant species, and keys leading to each species' identification. Presented first are the group of families comprising the **Ferns and Fern Allies** (true ferns, horsetails, clubmosses), followed by the **Gymnosperms** (conifers), and the **Angiosperms** (which make up the majority of the species described). The Angiosperms are further subdivided into two groups—the **Dicots** and the **Monocots**. Within each of these sections, families are ordered alphabetically, as are the genera (plural of genus) within each family, and the species within each genus.

A standard format is used for each species description. Following the scientific name is a common name and the species' wetland indicator status (see Appendix C for definitions). Features of the plant—its lifeform (annual, perennial, herb, grass, etc.), stem and leaf characteristics, features of the flower and fruit, and a range of months when the species generally flowers—are next described. Synonyms for the species (other formerly accepted scientific names) are listed in italics. Habitats where the plant generally occurs are described, followed by the known geographic range of the species, first in the Great Lakes region, then across North America (traveling from east to west, then southward). If a species is listed as endangered or threatened within a state, it is noted in the sidebar adjacent to each description.

- **Appendix A** - A glossary of technical terms used in the Flora.
- **Appendix B** - A list of abbreviations used.
- **Appendix C** - A summary of the wetland indicator status (OBL, FACW, etc.) for all species included in the Flora.
- **Appendix D** - Common plant species associated with each wetland type.
- **Index** - A list of scientific and common names for plant families, genera and species. Synonyms are listed in italics.

▶Plant Names

Each species of plant has a unique name made up of three parts. The first part is the genus to which a species belong; the second part is termed the specific epithet. The name is followed by the name of the person or persons who first named a species, and are often abbreviated. For example, "L." refers to Carolus Linnaeus, the 18th-century Swedish botanist considered the father of modern plant taxonomy. Together the two form the scientific, or botanical name of the species.

▶Identifying Unknown Plants

The keys are the first step in identifying an unknown plant specimen. The keys are termed "dichotomous," meaning that the reader must choose between one of two leads which form a "couplet" at each step in the key. The lead is chosen which best describes the plant being identified and the user proceeds to the number following the lead in the key. The process is continued until the family, genus, and ultimately species are identified.

For a completely unknown plant (one in which even the family is unknown), start with the Family Keys (page 16). For families having only one genus or species in the Flora, these will be identified here as well. Once the family is identified, turn to the genus key. If the family is recognized for an unknown plant, begin identification with the genus key. Once the genus has been determined, use the species key to identify the specimen. In addition to the keys, use the description of the plant and its habitat and range information to verify your identification. With practice, the characters of many families and genera will be recognizable on sight, greatly reducing the time spent keying.

Equipment needs are minimal for successful identification—a 10–20 magnification hand lens and a ruler with mm scale (a ruler is also printed on the last page of the index). For some species, as in the Sedge Family (Cyperaceae), a more powerful dissecting microscope is useful for examining the smaller plant parts often needed for positive identification. When a microscope is available, plants may be collected, pressed and dried, and identified indoors at a later date.

Whenever possible, plants should be examined by leaving them rooted rather than uprooting or tearing off pieces to examine at eye level. This is especially important when working in wetlands, home to a disproportionate number of rare and uncommon plant species.

Open Bog (Poor Fen) with scattered trees of black spruce, summer. Typical northern peatland in Michigan's Upper Peninsula. Tawny cotton-grass (*Eriophorum virginicum*) is present in foreground; other members of Sedge Family (Cyperaceae) such as running bog sedge (*Carex oligosperma*) are common. Shrubs include members of Heath Family (Ericaceae), and include leatherleaf (*Chamaedaphne calyculata*), bog-rosemary (*Andromeda glaucophylla*), Labrador-tea (*Ledum groenlandicum*) and small cranberry (*Vaccinium oxycoccos*). Sphagnum moss covers nearly all of the ground surface.

Wetland Types of the Great Lakes Region

Wetlands occur across the Great Lakes region in a wide variety of physical settings and under a large range of climatic conditions. As a result, wetlands vary markedly in their size, appearance and composition. Wetlands of northern portions of the region differ from their southern counterparts as the vegetation changes from a "prairie-forest province" in the south, to a "northern forest province" in the north (Curtis 1971). Northern areas, for example, feature extensive areas covered by conifer swamps of black spruce (*Picea mariana*), tamarack (*Larix laricina*), and northern white cedar (*Thuja occidentalis*), and by various types of shrub-dominated and herbaceous wetlands, including alder thickets, sedge meadows, and open bogs.

Southward, floodplain forests along major rivers, and marshes and sedge meadows are common. In southern areas of the region, calcareous fens associated with upwelling groundwater are an unusual wetland type and home to a large number of uncommon plants. In north-central Minnesota, the Red Lake area supports a vast peatland. Continuing west onto the eastern edge of the Great Plains, rolling grasslands are interspersed with low prairie and prairie pothole ponds.

☞ Typical plant species associated with each wetland type are listed in **Appendix D**.

The following key is a basic classification of the wetland types found in the Great Lakes region. It is based in part on *Vegetation of Wisconsin* (Curtis 1971) and *Wetland Plants and Plant Communities of Minnesota and Wisconsin* (Eggers and Reed 1997). Descriptions of each type follow the key.

▶Key to Wetland Types of the Great Lakes Region

1 Open water areas of lakes, ponds, rivers and streams; vegetation is absent, or aquatic plants with underwater or floating leaves are present . . . . **OPEN WATER COMMUNITIES**
1 Wetland types of shallow water areas or on saturated or moist soil; trees, shrubs or herbaceous plants are dominant **2**

2 Wetlands of shallow depressions, flats, or lakeshores; standing water may be present for several weeks each year, then drying; herbaceous plants dominant . . . . **SEASONALLY WET BASIN OR SHORE**
2 Standing water present, or soils saturated for all or most of growing season **3**

3 Woody plants (trees and shrubs) dominant (greater than about 50 percent canopy cover) **4**
3 Herbaceous plants dominant, woody plants sparse; trees, if present, are stunted and mostly small in diameter (less than about 15 cm wide) and less than 5–6 m tall **11**

4 Trees dominant; overstory canopy ± closed by mature trees **5**
4 Shrubs dominant; mature trees absent or sparse and not forming a closed canopy **8**

5 Hardwood trees dominant; soils are alluvial deposits, poorly drained mineral soils, or sometimes organic . . . (**WET HARDWOOD FOREST**) **6**
5 Conifers such as tamarack (*Larix laricina*), black spruce (*Picea mariana*), or northern white cedar (*Thuja occidentalis*) dominant; soils usually highly organic **7**

6 Forests adjacent to rivers on alluvial soils, mostly central and southern portions of the region. Silver maple (*Acer saccharinum*), American elm (*Ulmus americana*), river birch, (*Betula nigra*) green ash (*Fraxinus pennsylvanica*), black willow (*Salix nigra*) or eastern cottonwood (*Populus deltoides*) are typical dominants . . . . **FLOODPLAIN FOREST**
6 Forests of low-lying basins and kettles, with poorly drained mineral or organic soils, mostly central and northern areas. Black ash (*Fraxinus nigra*), red maple (*Acer rubrum*) or silver maple are typical dominants; northern white cedar may be common . . . . **HARDWOOD SWAMP**

7 Tamarack and/or black spruce dominant; sphagnum moss forms a nearly continuous carpet; soils are organic and acid . . **CONIFER BOG**
7 Northern white cedar or tamarack dominant; sphagnum moss may be present but not a forming a continuous ground cover; soils with a high organic content, usually neutral to alkaline . . **CONIFER SWAMP**

8 Tall shrubs (mostly more than 1 m high) dominant; sphagnum moss may be present but not forming a continuous mat . . . . (**SHRUB WETLAND**) **9**
8 Low shrubs (mostly less than 1 m high) dominant; sphagnum moss present, or sparse or absent **10**

9 Speckled or tag alder (*Alnus incana*) dominant; occurring mostly in north and central areas of region . . . . **ALDER THICKET**
9 Dogwoods (*Cornus sericea, C. amomum*), willows (*Salix*), or other tall shrubs dominant; occurring throughout the region . . . . **SHRUB-CARR**

10 Evergreen shrubs of the Heath Family (Ericaceae) such as leatherleaf (*Chamaedaphne calyculata*), bog-rosemary (*Andromeda glaucophylla*), Labrador-tea (*Ledum groenlandicum*), or small cranberry (*Vaccinium oxycoccos*) dominant or common; sphagnum moss forming a ± continuous carpet . . . . **OPEN BOG (POOR FEN)**
10 Deciduous shrubs, especially shrubby cinquefoil (*Potentilla fruticosa*), dominant; sites often sloping and maintained by a spring-fed supply of calcium-rich water; other calcium-indicating plants present; sphagnum moss absent or sparse . . . . **CALCAREOUS FEN**

11 Dominant plants sedges (*Carex*) and other members of the Cyperaceae, cat-tails (*Typha*), and large emergent species such as bur-reed (*Sparganium*), bulrush (*Scirpus*), and water plantain (*Alisma*) **12**
11 Dominant plants are grasses (Poaceae) or plants of calcium-rich sites **14**

12 Cat-tails, bulrushes (*Scirpus*), water plantain (*Alisma*), arrowheads

(*Sagittaria*), pickerelweed (*Pontederia*), giant bur-reed, or emergent lake sedges (for example, *Carex lacustris, C. utriculata*) dominant; sites have standing water for all or most of growing season (sometimes drying to surface in summer or fall) . . . . **MARSH**

12 Sedges (primarily *Carex*) dominant; water level often falling below ground surface during growing season **13**

13 Sedges dominant; sphagnum moss may be present but not a continuous carpet; soils saturated most of growing season, acid to alkaline . . . . **SEDGE MEADOW**

13 Sphagnum moss forming a ± continuous mat; soils are acid peats; pitcher plants (*Sarracenia purpurea*), sundews (*Drosera*), sedges (such as *Carex oligosperma*), cottongrass (*Eriophorum*), and shrubs of the Heath Family (Ericaceae) are typically present . . . . **OPEN BOG** . . . . **(POOR FEN)**

14 Wetlands often on sloping sites, with a spring-fed supply of calcium-rich water; species indicative of calcium-rich sites, such as fen star sedge (*Carex sterilis*), marsh-muhly (*Muhlenbergia glomerata*), and Ohio goldenrod (*Solidago ohioensis*) dominant . . . **CALCAREOUS FEN**

14 Wetlands with water mainly from rainfall, springs, or surface drainage; calcium-indicating species not dominant; sites have standing water or are saturated during all or part of growing season . . **15**

15 Wetlands with saturated soils (rarely with standing water; plants such as bluejoint (*Calamagrostis canadensis*), redtop (*Agrostis stolonifera*), reed canarygrass (*Phalaris arundinacea*), and smooth goldenrod (*Solidago gigantea*) dominant. . . . . **WET MEADOW**

15 Wetlands with standing water or saturated soil during the growing season; prairie grasses such as big bluestem (*Andropogon gerardii*), prairie cordgrass (*Spartina pectinata*), and prairie lowland species present . . . . **LOW PRAIRIE**

▶Open Water Communities

These plant communities occur in shallow to deep water of lakes, ponds, rivers and streams. Plants are free-floating, or submergent (anchored to the bottom and with underwater and/or floating leaves). A controlling factor of these communities is that water levels remain deep enough so that emergent vegetation typical of marshes is unable to establish.

▶Marshes

Marshes are dominated by emergent plants growing in permanent or nearly permanent shallow to deep water. **Shallow water marshes** are covered with up to about 15 cm of water for all or most of the growing season, but water levels may sometimes drop to the soil surface. **Deep marshes** have standing water between 15 and 100 cm or more deep during most of the growing season. A mix of emergent species and aquatic species of the adjoining open water are present.

▶Sedge Meadows

Sedge meadows are dominated by members of the Sedge Family (Cyperaceae), with grasses (Poaceae) and rushes (*Juncus*) often present. Other herbaceous species are usually present only as scattered individuals. Because of differences in their species composition, sedge meadows can be subdivided into those occurring in northern portions of the region and those occurring southward. Soils are typically organic deposits (peat or muck), and saturated throughout the growing season. Common tussock sedge (*Carex stricta*) is a major component of sedge meadows, forming large hummocks composed of a mass of roots and rhizomes. Periodic fires may help maintain the dominance of the sedges by killing invading shrubs and trees.

▶Wet Meadows

Wet meadows occur on saturated soils, and are dominated by grasses (especially *Calamagrostis canadensis*) and other types of perennial herbaceous plants. Soils may be inundated for brief periods (1–2 weeks) in the spring following snowmelt or during floods. Shrubs occur only as scattered plants.

▶Low Prairie

Low prairies are dominated by grasses and grasslike plants. These communities are similar to wet meadows but are dominated by native grasses and other herbaceous species characteristic of the prairie. Low prairie communities primarily occur in southern and western portions of the Great Lakes region, but are occasional in northern areas on sandy plains or in wet swales.

▶Calcareous Fens

Calcareous fens are an uncommon wetland type in the Great Lakes region. They typically develop on sites that are sloping and with a steady flow of groundwater rich in calcium and magnesium bicarbonates (Curtis 1971). The calcium and magnesium bicarbonates precipitate out at the ground surface, leading to a highly alkaline soil. Such conditions are tolerated by a fairly small group of plants termed "calciphiles." Sphagnum mosses are absent or sparse. Due to their uniqueness, calcareous fens often support a large number of uncommon plant species.

▶Open Bogs

Open bogs are found most commonly in northern portions of the

Great Lakes region, but also occur as small relict features in the south. Technically, true bogs are extremely nutrient-poor, receiving nutrients only from precipitation. Many of the region's bogs may better be termed "poor fens," but given the widespread use of the term among scientists and general public alike, "bog" is used throughout this book. Bogs have a characteristic, nearly continuous carpet of sphagnum moss, and are dominated by shrubs of the Heath Family (Ericaceae; especially *Chamaedaphne calyculata*), members of the Sedge Family (Cyperaceae), and scattered herbs such as pitcher plant (*Sarracenia purpurea*) and sundew (*Drosera*). Scattered, stunted trees of black spruce (*Picea mariana*) and tamarack (*Larix laricina*) may be present; this type of bog is sometimes termed "muskeg." Soils are composed entirely of saturated organic peat.

▶Conifer Bogs

Conifer bogs are similar to open bogs except that trees of black spruce and/or tamarack are predominant. *Sphagnum* moss carpets the ground surface. Shrubs of the Heath Family (Ericaceae), sedges, and a small number of other species occur. Soils are organic, saturated peats.

▶Shrub-Carrs

Shrub-carrs are dominated by tall shrubs. Soils are organic peat or muck, or alluvial soils of floodplains, and are often saturated throughout the growing season, and sometimes inundated during floods. Willows (*Salix*) and dogwoods (*Cornus*) are especially characteristic.

▶Alder Thickets

Alder thickets are a tall, deciduous shrub community similar to shrub-carrs except that speckled or tag alder (*Alnus incana*) is dominant, and often forming dense colonies. Alder thickets are common in northern portions of the Great Lakes region along rivers and streams, or along the wet margins of marshes, sedge meadows and bogs.

▶Hardwood Swamps

Hardwood swamps are dominated by deciduous trees such as black ash (*Fraxinus nigra*), red maple (*Acer rubrum*), and yellow birch (*Betula alleghaniensis*). Southward, silver maple (*Acer saccharinum*) increases in importance; northward, northern white cedar (*Thuja occidentalis*) may be present. American elm (*Ulmus americana*) may be present, but in greatly reduced numbers than formerly due to losses from Dutch elm disease. Soils are saturated during much of the growing season, and may be covered with shallow water in spring.

▸Conifer Swamps

Conifer swamps are forested wetlands dominated primarily by tamarack (*Larix laricina*) and black spruce (*Picea mariana*). In areas where the water is not as stagnant and in areas underlain by limestone, northern white cedar (*Thuja occidentalis*) may form dense stands. Conifer swamps occur almost entirely in northern portions of the Great Lakes region. Soils are usually peat or muck, and vary in reaction from acidic and nutrient-poor, to neutral or alkaline and relatively fertile. Tamarack is most abundant on acid soils, while northern white cedar is most common on neutral or alkaline soils. Soils are typically saturated much of the growing season, and sometimes covered with shallow water. *Sphagnum* moss may be present, but does not usually form a continuous mat.

▸Floodplain Forests

Floodplain forests are dominated by deciduous hardwood trees growing on alluvial soils along rivers. These forests often have standing water during the spring, with water levels dropping to the surface (or below) in summer and fall. Typical trees include silver maple (*Acer saccharinum*), green ash (*Fraxinus pennsylvanica*), black willow (*Salix nigra*), eastern cottonwood (*Populus deltoides*), and river birch (*Betula nigra*). The diversity of the undergrowth is high, as flood waters remove and deposit alluvium, creating microhabitats suitable for many species.

▸Seasonally Flooded Basins

Seasonally flooded basins are poorly drained, shallow depressions in glacial deposits (kettles), low spots in outwash plains, or depressions in floodplains. The basins may have standing water for a few weeks in the spring or for short periods following heavy rains. Soils are typically dry, however, for much of the growing season. South in the region, attempts are made to cultivate the basins, and in combination with the fluctuating water level, these areas are often dominated by a wide array of annual or weedy plant species.

Open Water, Marsh, and Sedge Meadow communities, summer. Many aquatic and wetland plant species are present in this productive pond located in Michigan's Upper Peninsula, including white water-lily (*Nymphaea odorata*), water-shield (*Brasenia schreberi*), buckbean (*Menyanthes trifoliata*), various species of pondweed (*Potamogeton*), softstem bulrush (*Scirpus validus*), three-way sedge (*Dulichium arundinaceum*), and common cat-tail (*Typha latifolia*). Adjacent to the pond is a sedge meadow dominated by common tussock sedge (*Carex stricta*), common lakeshore sedge (*Carex lacustris*), and bluejoint (*Calamagrostis canadensis*); sweet gale (*Myrica gale*) is a common shrub at the water's edge.

Sedge Meadow community, summer. Typical growth-form of common tussock sedge (*Carex stricta*), a dominant component of sedge meadows. The large hummocks, up to 1 m tall, are composed of plant roots and the previous years' leaves.

Open bog, late spring. Overall species diversity is low due to the saturated, acidic, organic soil. Common are Heath Family (Ericaceae) shrubs such as leatherleaf (*Chamaedaphne calyculata*), bog-rosemary (*Andromeda glaucophylla*). and small cranberry (*Vaccinium oxycoccos*). Herbaceous species within the Sedge Family (Cyperaceae) include running bog sedge (*Carex oligosperma*), tussock cotton-grass (*Eriophorum vaginatum*), few-flowered bog sedge (*Carex pauciflora*), and poor sedge (*Carex paupercula*). Other herbaceous species include pod-grass (*Scheuchzeria palustris*), round-leaved sundew (*Drosera rotundifolia*), pitcher-plant (*Sarracenia purpurea*), and leafless bladderwort (*Utriculata cornuta*). Scattered trees of black spruce (*Picea mariana*) have established atop the slightly drier hummocks. *Sphagnum* moss forms a nearly continuous ground cover.

Open Bog or "muskeg", late spring. Tamarack (*Larix laricina*) and scattered black spruce (*Picea mariana*) are present but stunted in size due to saturated, anaerobic soil conditions. Common shrubs include leatherleaf (*Chamaedaphne calyculata*), bog-laurel (*Kalmia polifolia*), and Labrador-tea (*Ledum groenlandicum*). Dominant herbaceous species include running bog sedge (*Carex oligosperma*), tussock cotton-grass (*Eriophorum vaginatum*), and other members of the Sedge Family (Cyperaceae). *Sphagnum* moss forms a nearly continuous cover across the organic soil.

Hardwood Swamp, early spring. Black ash (*Fraxinus nigra*) is the dominant tree; red maple (*Acer rubrum*) is also present. Marsh-marigold (*Caltha palustris*) is common in the undergrowth, with scattered plants of several species of violet (*Viola*), three-seeded bog sedge (*Carex trisperma*), rough sedge (*Carex scabrata*), sensitive fern (*Onoclea sensibilis*), and orange touch-me-not or jewelweed (*Impatiens capensis*).

Alder thicket, summer. Speckled or Tag alder (*Alnus incana*) is a common, colony-forming shrub adjacent to streams, lakes, bogs, and marshes, especially in northern portions of the Great Lakes region. This wetland type is best developed on well-aerated soils where water is not stagnant. Grasses such as bluejoint (*Calamagrostis canadensis*) and reed canary-grass (*Phalaris arundinacea*), and large sedges such as beaked sedge (*Carex utriculata*) and fringed sedge (*Carex crinita*) are common.

Family Keys

☞ A
simplified
key to just
the woody
plants (trees,
shrubs, and
vines) begins
on page 36.

THIS KEY, based in part on that of Gleason and Cronquist (1991), will lead to each plant family included in the Flora. In cases where the key is specific to a particular genus or species, these are noted in italics. Begin identifying an unknown plant by first using the Key to Groups and Families below. After identifying the family, turn to the page number for the family and continue keying the plant using the genus and species keys provided after the family description.

▶Key to Groups and Families

1 Plants herbaceous (not woody), reproducing by spores . . . .
. . . .**Key 1 - FERNS AND FERN ALLIES**
1 Trees, shrubs or herbs; reproducing by seeds (conifers and flowering plants) **2**

2 Trees or shrubs with needlelike or scalelike, usually evergreen leaves; seeds in a dry cone, not inside an ovary . . . .**Key 2 - CONIFERS**
2 Trees, shrubs, or herbs; leaves usually deciduous; seeds inside an ovary which matures into the fruit . . . .**(Angiosperms) 3**

3 Plants with unusual or specialized features. The Lemnaceae (Duckweed Family), Asteraceae (Aster Family), Orchidaceae (Orchid Family), and Asclepiadaceae (Milkweed Family) will key here **4**
3 "Typical" trees, shrubs, or herbs **7**

4 Plants very small, floating in still water or stranded on wet shores; stem and leaf not differentiated; roots absent or 1–several from leaf underside . . . . .Lᴇᴍɴᴀᴄᴇᴀᴇ (Duckweed Family) p. 511
4 Plants larger; stems and leaves present **5**

5 Flowers clustered into a head on a plate-like receptacle, the head resembling a single flower . . . . .Aꜱᴛᴇʀᴀᴄᴇᴀᴇ (Aster Family) p. 100
5 Flowers not as above; stamens, style and stigma are highly modified and joined into a special structure at center of flower **6**

6 Flowers irregular, the lower petal different than the other 2 petals (or rarely the upper petal different); ovary inferior . . . . .Oʀᴄʜɪᴅᴀᴄᴇᴀᴇ
. . . .(Orchid Family) p. 521
6 Flowers regular, the 5 petals alike; ovary superior; fruit a podlike follicle containing many seeds, the seeds tufted with hairs . . . .
. . . . .Aꜱᴄʟᴇᴘɪᴀᴅᴀᴄᴇᴀᴇ (Milkweed Family) p. 99

7 Herbaceous plants with undivided, usually narrow leaves, main veins parallel; petals and sepals in 3s or multiples of 3 .**Key 3 - MONOCOTS**
7 Plants herbaceous or woody; leaves simple or divided, veins usually in a net-like pattern; petals and sepals usually equal to or in multiples of 2, 4 or 5 . . . .**Key 4 - DICOTS**

▶Key 1 - Ferns and Fern Allies

Divisions Lycopodiophyta, Equisetophyta, and Polypodiophyta (Clubmosses, Horsetails and Ferns)

1 Plants 1–2 cm long, floating on water surface; leaves very small (Azolla mexicana) . . . . .AZOLLACEAE (Azolla Family) p. 42
1 Plants rooted in soil or muck; leaves large or small **2**

2 Leaves small and narrow, 1-2 mm wide, simple, often scalelike . . .**3**
2 Leaves broader, 3 cm or more long, often large and dissected **6**

3 Stems hollow, grooved lengthwise and jointed, usually easily pulled apart at the nodes; leaves reduced to a whorl of papery scales in at each node; plants with simple or branched stems; sporangia in a terminal cone (*Equisetum*) . . .EQUISETACEAE (Horsetail Family) p. 52
3 Stems and leaves not as above; spores at plant base, in leaf axils, or in a terminal cone **4**

4 Leaves grasslike, 5–15 cm long, joined in a cormlike base; spores borne in a pocket at base of each leaf; plants rooted in mud and often underwater (*Isoetes*) . . . . .ISOETACEAE (Quillwort Family) p. 58
4 Leaves small, less than 2 cm long; plants spreading by rhizomes or trailing stems and resembling large mosses; spores in upper leaf axils or in terminal cones **5**

5 Spores in 4-sided cones; of 2 types, either of many very small male spores, or of a few larger female spores; leaves with a ligule (small projection near base of leaf) . . . . SELAGINELLACEAE
. . . . (Selaginella Family) p. 70
5 Spores in round cones (in cross-section) or in upper leaf axils; only 1 type of spore present; leaves without a ligule . . . . .LYCOPODIACEAE
. . . .(Clubmoss Family) p. 60

6 Leaves on long stalks; divided like a 4-leaf clover, sometimes floating on water surface; plants rooted in mud (*Marsilea*) . . .MARSILACEAE
. . . .(Water-clover Family) p. 63
6 Leaves not clover-like **7**

7 Plants with a small, erect stem and fleshy roots; spores borne on a specialized fertile spike or panicle that rises from the upper surface of the leaf . . . . .OPHIOGLOSSACEAE (Adder's tongue Family) p. 64
7 Plants larger, with fibrous roots and spreading by short or long rhizomes; spores borne in clusters (sori) on leaf undersides or on completely fertile leaves **8**

8 Spores borne in clusters on modified leaves, not in clusters on leaf undersides **9**
8 Spores borne in clusters (sori) on leaf undersides **10**

9 Plants large and upright, to 1 m high or more; common; spores borne on completely fertile leaf segments (*Osmunda*) . . . . .OSMUNDACEAE
. . . .(Royal Fern Family) p. 67
9 Plants trailing; entering our range only in sw Michigan where rare and local (*Lygodium palmatum*) . . . . .SCHIZAEACEAE
. . . .(Curly Grass Family) p. 69

10 Sori long and narrow, in 2 chain-like rows, 1 on each side of leaf midvein, covered by a flap (indusium) that opens toward the midvein; uncommon in s Michigan (*Woodwardia virginica*) . . BLECHNACEAE . . . .(Deer-Fern Family) p. 43

10 Sori not as above; if flap-like indusium present, then opening away from midvein; most species widespread and common **11**

11 Leaf midribs, and veins with sparse to dense covering of transparent hairs; fronds arising singly from widely creeping rhizomes .THELYPTERIDACEAE (Marsh Fern Family) p. 72

11 Leaf midribs and veins lacking transparent hairs; in most species (all but *Onoclea sensibilis*), fronds clumped from short rootstocks . . . . .DRYOPTERIDACEAE (Wood Fern Family) p. 44

▶Key 2 - Conifers

Division Pinophyta / Gymnosperms

1 Leaves scalelike, pressed flat to the stem (*Thuja occidentalis*) . . . . .CUPRESSACEAE (Cypress Family) p. 76

1 Leaves needlelike, often borne in clusters . . . . .PINACEAE (Pine Family) p. 77

▶Key 3 - Monocots

Division Magnoliophyta / Flowering Plants (Class Liliopsida / Monocots)

1 Sepals and petals (perianth) absent or reduced to scales or bristles, never petal-like in size or color **2**

1 Sepals and petals present **17**

2 Flowers in axils of chaffy scales larger than the flower; sepals and petals absent or reduced to bristles or small scales; flowers in regular heads or spikes **3**

2 Flowers not in chaffy bracts, or if bracts present, the flower equal or larger in size and not hidden by the bracts **5**

3 Plants with a basal cluster of narrow linear leaves and an upright stalk tipped by a single, button-like head (*Eriocaulon aquaticum*) . . . . .ERIOCAULACEAE (Pipewort Family) p. 489

3 Plants with leaves on stem (these sometimes reduced to scales), or plants with several to many heads or spikes **4**

4 Leaves usually 2-ranked around stem; stems usually hollow, round, or flat, and never triangular in cross-section; leaf sheath usually open on side opposite blade . . . . .POACEAE (Grass Family) p. 541

4 Leaves usually 3-ranked (sometimes reduced to scales); stems usually solid and pithy and triangular in cross-section; leaf sheath usually closed .CYPERACEAE (Sedge Family) p. 397

5 Plants aquatic, leaves submerged or floating and becoming limp when withdrawn from water; flowers underwater, floating, or sometimes raised slightly above water surface **6**

5 Plants of land or shallow water, leaves and flowers normally above water surface **11**

6 Flowers small and inconspicuous, single to several from leaf axils **7**
6 Flowers in heads or spikes **10**

7 Leaves alternate, or sometimes uppermost leaves opposite **8**
7 Leaves all opposite (or whorled) **9**

8 Widespread plants of mostly fresh water; flowers with 4 sepals and 4 stamens . . . . .POTAMOGETONACEAE (Pondweed Family) p. 578
8 Uncommon plants of brackish water (in our region known from only wc Minnesota and e UP of Michigan (*Ruppia maritima*) . . . . .RUPPIACEAE (Ditch-grass Family) p. 592

9 Leaves 1–4 cm long, tapering from base to a long point, margins with minute, spiny teeth; flowers with 1 ovary (*Najas*) . . . . .NAJADACEAE (Water-nymph Family) p. 518
9 Leaves 3–10 cm long, threadlike, margins not spiny; flowers usually with 4 ovaries . . . . .ZANNICHELLIACEAE . . . .(Horned Pondweed Family) p. 603

10 Flowers in globe-shaped heads; upper heads male (and deciduous), lower heads female (and persistent) (*Sparganium*) . .SPARGANIACEAE . . . .(Bur-reed Family) p. 594
10 Flower heads or spikes all alike; flowers perfect (with both male and female parts) . . . . .POTAMOGETONACEAE (Pondweed Family) p. 578

11 Flowers tiny, in spikes or heads surrounded by a large white or colored bract (spathe); leaves broad . .ARACEAE (Arum Family) p. 392
11 Flowers not surrounded by a large spathe; leaves ± linear **12**

12 Flowers many, in long spikes **13**
12 Flowers in globe-shaped heads, racemes, or loose, open clusters .**15**

13 Spike appearing to be from side of stem (*Acorus calamus*) . . . . .ACORACEAE (Sweet Flag Family) p. 386
13 Spike erect at end of stem **14**

14 Top of spike slender, made up of male flowers; lower spike broader and of female flowers (*Typha*) .TYPHACEAE (Cat-tail Family) p. 599
14 Spike uniform; flowers both male and female (Triglochin) . . . . .JUNCAGINACEAE (Arrow-grass Family) p. 510

15 Flowers either male or female, with male in upper clusters, female in lower clusters (*Sparganium*) . . . . .SPARGANIACEAE . . . .(Bur-reed Family) p. 594
15 Flowers with both male and female parts **16**

16 Flowers with 1 ovary; fruit a 3-parted capsule (*Juncus*) .JUNCACEAE . . . .(Rush Family) p. 497
16 Flowers with 3 or 6 ovaries; fruit separating into segments when mature (*Triglochin*) . .JUNCAGINACEAE (Arrow-grass Family) p. 510

17 Flowers either male or female, on same or separate plants **18**
17 Flowers with both male and female parts **20**

18 Flowers with 3 green sepals and 3 white or pinkish petals . . . . .ALISMATACEAE (Water-Plantain Family) p. 387
18 Sepals and petals ± same color **19**

19 Aquatic plants, mostly underwater; stamens 3–12 . . . . .HYDROCHARITACEAE (Frog's-bit Family) p. 490
19 Land plants; stamens 3–6 . . . . .LILIACEAE (Lily Family) p. 515

20 Ovary inferior (located below sepals and petals) **21**
20 Ovary or ovaries superior (attached above sepals and petals); plants aquatic and on land **23**

21 Aquatic plants; leaves underwater or floating .HYDROCHARITACEAE . . . .(Frog's-bit Family) p. 490
21 Plants emergent in shallow water or on wet soils **22**

22 Stamens 3 . . . . .IRIDACEAE (Iris Family) p. 493
22 Stamens 6 . . . . .LILIACEAE (Lily Family) p. 515

23 Flowers with 1 ovary **24**
23 Flowers with 2 or more ovaries **28**

24 Flowers radially symmetric (regular) **25**
24 Flowers irregular, not radially symmetric . . . . . . .PONTEDERIACEAE . . . .(Water-hyacinth Family) p. 576

25 Sepals green; petals variously colored **26**
25 Sepals and petals with same appearance **27**

26 Stamens 3 (or sometimes 2) (*Xyris*) . . . . .XYRIDACEAE . . . .(Yellow-eyed Grass Family) p. 601
26 Stamens 6 . . . . .LILIACEAE (Lily Family) p. 515

27 Petals 6, united into a tube; stamens 3; plants underwater or on muddy shores . . .PONTEDERIACEAE (Water-hyacinth Family) p. 508
27 Stamens 6; plants of drier sites . . . . .LILIACEAE (Lily Family) p. 515

28 Leaves all from base of plant and alternate on stem; flowers with 3 pistils (*Scheuchzeria palustris*) . . . . .SCHEUCHZERIACEAE . . . .(Scheuchzeria Family) p. 593
28 Leaves all from base of plant; pistils 3 to many **29**

29 Flowers with 3 green sepals and 3 white or pinkish petals; flowers in panicles or umbels . .ALISMATACEAE (Water-Plantain Family) p. 387
29 Flowers with 6 pink petals, the outer 3 smaller and darker pink than the inner; flowers in an umbel (*Butomus umbellatus*) .BUTOMACEAE . . . .(Flowering Rush Family) p. 395

▶Key 4 - Dicots

Division Magnoliophyta / Flowering Plants (Class Magnoliopsida / Dicots)

▶Group Keys

▶Group 1

Trees, shrubs, and woody vines.

4 Trees, petals separate, not joined; flowers either male or female; stamens 8; ovary superior (*Acer*) . . .ACERACEAE (Maple Family) p. 83
4 Shrubs; flowers perfect, with both male and female parts; stamens 5; ovary inferior (*Lonicera*) . . . . .CAPRIFOLIACEAE
. . . .(Honeysuckle Family) p. 170

5 Stamens usually 2; ovary not lobed (*Fraxinus*) . . . . .OLEACEAE
. . . .(Olive Family) p. 269
5 Stamens usually 8; ovary distinctly 2-lobed (*Acer*) . . . . .ACERACEAE
. . . .(Maple Family) p. 83

6 Leaves compound **7**
6 Leaves simple **11**

7 Plants vinelike and trailing (*Clematis*) . . . . .RANUNCULACEAE
. . . .(Buttercup Family) p. 302
7 Plants not vinelike **8**

8 Petals present **9**
8 Petals absent **10**

9 Shrubs; petals united (*Sambucus*) . . . . .CAPRIFOLIACEAE
. . . .(Honeysuckle Family) p. 170
9 Trees; petals separate (*Aesculus glabra*) . . . . . .HIPPOCASTANACEAE
. . . .(Horse-chestnut Family) p. 234

10 Stamens 2; ovary not lobed (*Fraxinus*) . . . . .OLEACEAE
. . . .(Olive Family) p. 269
10 Stamens 8; ovary 2-lobed (*Acer negundo*) . . . . .ACERACEAE
. . . .(Maple Family) p. 83

11 More stamens than petals or petal lobes **12**
11 Stamens equal or less than number of petals or petal lobes **14**

12 Petals joined . . . . .ERICACEAE (Heath Family)
12 Petals separate **13**

13 Stamens 8–10 (*Decodon verticillatus*) . . . . .LYTHRACEAE
. . . .(Loosestrife Family) p. 255
13 Stamens numerous (*Hypericum kalmianum*) . . . . .CLUSIACEAE
. . . .(St. John's-wort Family) p. 186

14 Petals separate (*Cornus*) . . . .CORNACEAE (Dogwood Family) p. 191
14 Petals joined **15**

15 Flowers in many-flowered, globe-shaped heads; leaves entire; shrub of southern part of our region, more common southward (*Cephalanthus occidentalis*) . . . . .RUBIACEAE (Madder Family) p. 331
15 Flowers not in dense heads; leaves entire, toothed, or lobed . . . . . .
. . . . .CAPRIFOLIACEAE (Honeysuckle Family) p. 170

16 Plants with either male or female flowers but not both on same plant (dioecious) **17**
16 Plants with male and female flowers on same plant; flowers either perfect (with both male and female parts), or imperfect (flowers single sex only) **25**

17 Woody climbing vines (*Vitis riparia*) . . . . .Vitaceae
. . . .(Grape Family) p. 384
17 Trees or shrubs **18**

18 Flowers in catkins; individual flowers small **19**
18 Flowers not in catkins; flowers often large and showy **20**

19 Trees or shrubs; twigs not covered with resinous dots . .Salicaceae
. . . .(Willow Family) p. 335
19 Shrubs; twigs densely covered with resinous dots (*Myrica gale*) . . . .
. . . . .Myricaceae (Bayberry Family) p. 263

20 Small shrub; leaves cylindric, short, 3–8 mm long; rare in northern
part of region mostly near Lake Superior (*Empetrum nigrum*) . . . . .
. . . . .Empetraceae (Crowberry Family) p. 202
20 Mostly larger shrubs; leaves much larger **21**

21 Sepals and petals absent or not different from one another (tepals);
tepals 6 and petal-like, yellow; stamens 9; shrub of sw Mich (*Lindera
benzoin*) . . . . .Lauraceae (Laurel Family) p. 247
21 Female flowers with sepals and petals, although sepals sometimes
very small **22**

22 Flowers in a large terminal panicle (*Toxicodendron vernix*) . . . .
. . . . .Anacardiaceae (Cashew Family) p. 86
22 Flowers 1 to several from leaf axils **23**

23 Style very short . . . . .Aquifoliaceae (Holly Family) p. 96
23 Style relatively long **24**

24 Style long, curved at tip; tree of se Wisc and s Mich (*Nyssa sylvatica*)
. . . . .Cornaceae (Dogwood Family) p. 191
24 Style of female flower divided above its middle; shrubs or small trees
. . . . .Rhamnaceae (Buckthorn Family) p. 315

25 Flowers small, either male or female, never perfect; male flowers in
catkins or round heads **26**
25 Flowers mostly perfect, sometimes large and showy, not grouped into
catkins or globe-shaped heads **30**

26 Male flowers in crowded, globe-shaped heads; tree of s Wisc and s
Mich (more common southward) (*Platanus occidentalis*) . . . .
. . . . .Platanaceae (Plane-tree Family) p. 281
26 Male flowers in cylindric catkins **27**

27 Female flowers 1, or several in clusters **28**
27 Female flowers more numerous; cone-like, or arranged into catkins or
heads **29**

28 Leaves pinnately compound; tree of s Mich (*Carya laciniosa*) . . . . .
. . . . .Juglandaceae (Walnut Family) p. 236
28 Leaves not compound; margin wavy or lobed (*Quercus*) .Fagaceae
. . . .(Beech Family) p. 215

29 Female flowers 2 or 3 behind each catkin scale . . . . .Betulaceae
. . . .(Birch Family) p. 145
29 Female flowers 1 behind each catkin scale (*Myrica gale*) . . . .
. . . . .Myricaceae (Bayberry Family) p. 263

30 Petals and sepals absent or in a single series, the petals and sepals not distinct from one another **31**
30 Petals and sepals present and clearly distinct from each other . . .**37**

31 Stamens about 10, petals tiny (*Nyssa sylvatica*) . . . . . .CORNACEAE
. . . .(Dogwood Family) p. 191
31 Stamens as many as number of petal and sepal lobes **32**

32 Style 1, sometimes branched **33**
32 Styles 2–3 . . . .**36**

33 Vines (*Vitis riparia*) . . . . .VITACEAE (Grape Family) p. 384
33 Shrubs or small trees **34**

34 Flowers in clusters at ends of branches (*Cornus*) . . . . . .CORNACEAE
. . . .(Dogwood Family) p. 191
34 Flowers from leaf axils or on short lateral branches **35**

35 Style not branched, stigma 1   .AQUIFOLIACEAE (Holly Family) p. 96
35 Style 2–4-parted, stigmas 2–4 . . . . .RHAMNACEAE
. . . .(Buckthorn Family) p. 315

36 Shrub; stems stout, very pricky; uncommon plant of Isle Royale and north shore of Lake Superior (*Oplopanax horridus*) . . .ARALIACEAE
. . . .(Ginseng Family) p. 98
36 Tree, stems and twigs not prickly; widespread in our region; . . . . . .
. . . . .ULMACEAE (Elm Family) p. 370

37 Ovaries 3 or more; stamens more than 10 . . . . .ROSACEAE
. . . .(Rose Family) p. 317
37 Ovary 1 . . . .**38**

38 Petals 1 (*Amorpha fruticosa*) . . . . .FABACEAE
. . . .(Pea or Bean Family) p. 212
38 Petals more than 1; flowers ± regular **39**

39 Petals joined **40**
39 Petals free **43**

40 Stamens more in number than corolla lobes **41**
40 Stamens equal to number of corolla lobes **42**

41 Stamens joined into 1 group at base (*Styrax americanus*) STYRACEAE
. . . .(Storax Family) p. 369
41 Stamens not joined at their base   .ERICACEAE (Heath Family) p. 203

42 Style well-developed . . . . .ERICACEAE (Heath Family) p. 203
42 Style short, the stigma ± stalkless . . . . .AQUIFOLIACEAE
. . . .(Holly Family) p. 96

43 Ovary inferior **44**
43 Ovary superior **47**

44 Stamens 2x or more than number of petals **45**
44 Stamens equal number of petals **46**

45 Style 1 (*Vaccinium*) . . . . .ERICACEAE (Heath Family) p. 203

45 Styles 2–5 . . . . .ROSACEAE (Rose Family) p. 317

46 Petals 4 . . . . .CORNACEAE (Dogwood Family) p. 191
46 Petals 5 (*Ribes*) . . . .GROSSULARIACEAE (Gooseberry Family) p. 224

47 Leaves short and cylindric, less than 1 cm long (*Empetrum nigrum*)
. . . . .EMPETRACEAE (Crowberry Family) p. 202
47 Leaves flat and broader **48**

48 Leaves compound (*Toxicodendron vernix*) . . . . . . .ANACARDIACEAE
. . . .(Cashew Family) p. 86
48 Leaves simple **49**

49 Stamens number more than petals ERICACEAE (Heath Family) p. 203
49 Stamens number as many as petals **50**

50 Flowers in clusters at ends of stems; leaf margins rolled under, leaf
underside densely hairy (*Ledum*) .ERICACEAE (Heath Family) p. 203
50 Flowers from leaf axils; leaf margins not rolled under, leaves not
densely hairy below **51**

51 Style 3-parted; stamens opposite the petals (*Rhamnus*) RHAMNACEAE
. . . .(Buckthorn Family) p. 315
51 Style very short; stamens alternate with the petals . . . .
. . . . .AQUIFOLIACEAE (Holly Family) p. 96

▶Group 2

Herbaceous plants; flowers either male or female (imperfect).

1 Leaves absent or reduced to small scales (*Salicornia rubra*) . . . .
. . . . .CHENOPODIACEAE (Goosefoot Family) p. 183
1 Leaves not reduced to scales **2**

2 Aquatic plants; leaves dissected into threadlike segments **3**
2 Leaves not dissected into threadlike segments **4**

3 Leaves pinnately dissected . . . . HALORAGACEAE
. . . .(Water-milfoil Family) p. 229
3 Leaves palmately dissected (*Ceratophyllum*) . . .CERATOPHYLLACEAE
. . . .(Hornwort Family) p. 181

4 Leaves simple, not compound **5**
4 Leaves compound **17**

5 Leaves all from base of plant **6**
5 Leaves all or mostly along stem **7**

6 Flowers in short or long spikes . . . . .PLANTAGINACEAE
. . . .(Plantain Family) p. 279
6 Flowers in small panicles (*Rumex*) . . . . .POLYGONACEAE
. . . .(Smartweed Family) p. 285

7 Leaves whorled or opposite **8**
7 Leaves alternate **13**

8 Flowers single **9**
8 Flowers in clusters from leaf axils or at ends of stems **10**

9 Leaves whorled (*Hippuris vulgaris*) . . . . .Hɪᴘᴘᴜʀɪᴅᴀᴄᴇᴀᴇ
. . . .(Mare's-tail Family) p. 235
9 Leaves opposite .Cᴀʟʟɪᴛʀɪᴄʜᴀᴄᴇᴀᴇ (Water-starwort Family) p. 164

10 Flower clusters from leaf axils **11**
10 Flowers in clusters at ends of stems **12**

11 Leaf margins entire . . . . .Pʟᴀɴᴛᴀɢɪɴᴀᴄᴇᴀᴇ (Plantain Family) p. 279
11 Leaf margins toothed . . . . .Uʀᴛɪᴄᴀᴄᴇᴀᴇ (Nettle Family) p. 371

12 Stamens 3, style 1 . . . . . . .Vᴀʟᴇʀɪᴀɴᴀᴄᴇᴀᴇ (Valerian Family) p. 374
12 Stamens 10, styles mostly 5 (*Silene*) . . . . .Cᴀʀʏᴏᴘʜʏʟʟᴀᴄᴇᴀᴇ
. . . .(Pink Family) p. 176

13 Sepals and petals present **14**
13 Petals absent **16**

14 Plants vining and with tendrils . . . . .Cᴜʀᴄᴜʀʙɪᴛᴀᴄᴇᴀᴇ
. . . .(Gourd Family) p. 196
14 Plants not vining; tendrils absent **15**

15 Flowers in a panicle at end of stem (*Napaea*) . . . . . . .Mᴀʟᴠᴀᴄᴇᴀᴇ
. . . .(Mallow Family) p. 259
15 Flowers single (*Rubus*) . . . . .Rᴏsᴀᴄᴇᴀᴇ (Rose Family) p. 317

16 Sepals dry and chaffy . .Aᴍᴀʀᴀɴᴛʜᴀᴄᴇᴀᴇ (Amaranth Family) p. 85
16 Sepals often absent, herbaceous (*Atriplex, Chenopodium*) . . . .
. . . . .Cʜᴇɴᴏᴘᴏᴅɪᴀᴄᴇᴀᴇ (Goosefoot Family) p. 183

17 Leaves divided into 3 leaflets (*Clematis*) . . . . .Rᴀɴᴜɴᴄᴜʟᴀᴄᴇᴀᴇ
. . . .(Buttercup Family) p. 302
17 Leaves divided into more than 3 leaflets **18**

18 Stem leaves alternate (*Thalictrum*) . . . . .Rᴀɴᴜɴᴄᴜʟᴀᴄᴇᴀᴇ
. . . .(Buttercup Family) p. 302
18 Stem leaves opposite . . . . .Vᴀʟᴇʀɪᴀɴᴀᴄᴇᴀᴇ (Valerian Family) p. 374

▶Group 3

Herbaceous plants; flowers with both male and female parts (perfect); flowers without petals or sepals.

1 Plants underwater or sometimes stranded on shores Hᴀʟᴏʀᴀɢᴀᴄᴇᴀᴇ
. . . .(Water-milfoil Family) p. 229
1 Land plants or of shallow water only **2**

2 Leaves deeply lobed or compound . . . . .Rᴀɴᴜɴᴄᴜʟᴀᴄᴇᴀᴇ
. . . .(Buttercup Family) p. 302
2 Leaves simple, margins entire **3**

3 Leaves whorled, linear (*Hippuris vulgaris*) . . . . . . .Hɪᴘᴘᴜʀɪᴅᴀᴄᴇᴀᴇ
. . . .(Mare's-tail Family) p. 235

3 Leaves alternate, heart-shaped (*Saururus cernuus*) . . . SAURURACEAE
. . . . (Lizard's-tail Family) p. 351

▶Group 4

Herbaceous plants; flowers with both male and female parts (perfect); petals and sepals not different (in 1 series); ovary inferior.

1 Stamens number more than sepals and petals **2**
1 Stamens less than or equal to number of sepals and petals **4**

2 Stamens many; stipules large (*Sanguisorba canadensis*) . .ROSACEAE
. . . .(Rose Family) p. 317
2 Stamens 4–8; plants in water or on wet soils; stipules ± absent . . .**3**

3 Leaves broadly ovate (*Chrysoplenium americanum*) SAXIFRAGACEAE
. . . .(Saxifrage Family) p. 352
3 Leaves linear or divided into linear segments . . . . .HALORAGACEAE
. . . .(Water-milfoil Family) p. 229

4 Leaves from base of plant or alternate **5**
4 Leaves opposite or whorled **10**

5 Stamens 4 or less; perianth lobes 3 or 4 . . . .**6**
5 Stamens 5; perianth lobes 5 . . . .**9**

6 Leaves with large stipules (*Sanguisorba canadensis*) . . . . .ROSACEAE
. . . .(Rose Family) p. 317
6 Stipules absent **7**

7 Stamens 3; perianth lobes 3 . . . . .HALORAGACEAE
. . . .(Water-milfoil Family) p. 229
7 Stamens 4; perianth lobes 4 . . . .**8**

8 Leaves broadly ovate, margins with rounded teeth (*Chrysoplenium americanum*) . . . . .SAXIFRAGACEAE (Saxifrage Family) p. 352
8 Leaves linear or lance-shaped, margins entire (*Ludwigia*) . . . .
. . . . .ONAGRACEAE (Evening-primrose Family) p. 271

9 Flowers single in leaf axils; leaf margins entire (*Geocaulon lividum*)
. . . . .SANTALACEAE (Sandalwood Family) p. 349
9 Flowers in heads or umbels; leaves usually dissected . . . .
. . . . .APIACEAE (Carrot Family) p. 88

10 Flowers densely clustered into heads at ends of stems (*Cornus*) . . . .
. . . . .CORNACEAE (Dogwood Family) p. 191
10 Flowers not in dense heads **11**

11 Leaves whorled (*Galium*) . . . . .RUBIACEAE (Madder Family) p. 331
11 Leaves opposite **12**

12 Flowers in clusters at ends of stems; stamens 3 . . . .VALERIANACEAE
. . . .(Valerian Family) p. 374
12 Flowers single or few from leaf axils; stamens 4 . . . .**13**

13 Style 1 (*Ludwigia*) .ONAGRACEAE (Evening-primrose Family) p. 271
13 Styles 2 (*Chrysoplenium americanum*) . . . . .SAXIFRAGACEAE
. . . .(Saxifrage Family) p. 352

▶Group 5

Herbaceous plants; flowers with both male and female parts (perfect); petals and sepals not different (in 1 series); ovary superior.

1 Each flower with more than 1 ovary; these sometimes joined up to their middle, free above **2**
1 Flowers with 1 ovary **3**

2 Ovaries of flowers joined up to their middle (*Penthorum sedoides*) .
. . . . .SAXIFRAGACEAE (Saxifrage Family) p. 352
2 Ovaries distinct, not joined . . . . .RANUNCULACEAE
. . . .(Buttercup Family) p. 302

3 Stamens more than 2x number of perianth lobes **4**
3 Stamens 2x or fewer than perianth lobes **5**

4 Leaves all at base of plant, modified into water-holding pitchers (*Sarracenia purpurea*) SARRACENIACEAE (Pitcher-plant Family) p. 350
4 Leaves not pitcher-like, large and heart-shaped, usually floating on water surface . . . . .NYMPHAEACEAE (Water-Lily Family) p. 265

5 Styles 2 or more **6**
5 Styles absent or 1 . . . .**10**

6 Leaves small and scalelike; plants of salty habitats (*Salicornia rubra*)
. . . . .CHENOPODIACEAE (Goosefoot Family) p. 183
6 Leaves not scalelike **7**

7 Leaves opposite or whorled **8**
7 Leaves alternate **9**

8 Leaf margins with shallow, rounded teeth (*Chrysoplenium americanum*) . . . . .SAXIFRAGACEAE (Saxifrage Family) p. 352
8 Leaf margins entire . . . . . .CARYOPHYLLACEAE (Pink Family) p. 176

9 Stipules present at base of each leaf and sheathing stem . . . .
. . . . .POLYGONACEAE (Smartweed Family) p. 285
9 Stipules absent . . . . .CHENOPODIACEAE (Goosefoot Family) p. 183

10 Stamens more numerous than perianth lobes **11**
10 Stamens as many or fewer than number of perianth lobes **12**

11 Leaves opposite (*Ammania coccinea*) . . . . .LYTHRACEAE
. . . .(Loosestrife Family) p. 255
11 Leaves alternate (*Cardamine*) . . . . .BRASSICACEAE
. . . .(Mustard Family) p. 153

12 Flowers in clusters at ends of stems . . . . .CARYOPHYLLACEAE
. . . .(Pink Family) p. 176
12 Flowers in clusters from leaf axils **13**

13 Perianth with 4 lobes . . . . . Lʏᴛʜʀᴀᴄᴇᴀᴇ (Loosestrife Family) p. 255
13 Perianth with 5 lobes (*Glaux maritima*) . . . . Pʀɪᴍᴜʟᴀᴄᴇᴀᴇ
. . . .(Primrose Family) p. 296

▶Group 6

Herbaceous plants; flowers with both male and female parts (perfect); petals and sepals present; each flower with 2 or more ovaries.

1 One style for each flower 2
1 Styles as many as ovaries, or styles absent 4

2 Petals ± separate, not joined; stamens many; ovaries 5 or more . . . .
. . . . Mᴀʟᴠᴀᴄᴇᴀᴇ (Mallow Family) p. 259
2 Petals joined; stamens 2–5; ovaries 4 3

3 Leaves opposite; stamens 2 or 4 . .Lᴀᴍɪᴀᴄᴇᴀᴇ (Mint Family) p. 237
3 Leaves alternate; stamens 5 .Bᴏʀᴀɢɪɴᴀᴄᴇᴀᴇ (Borage Family) p. 150

4 Flowers irregular (*Aconitum noveboracense*) . . . . .Rᴀɴᴜɴᴄᴜʟᴀᴄᴇᴀᴇ
. . . .(Buttercup Family) p. 302
4 Flowers regular 5

5 Sepals 3; petals 3 6
5 Sepals and petals each more than 3 7

6 Aquatic plants; leaves entire and floating, or leaves underwater and dissected . . . . .Cᴀʙᴏᴍʙᴀᴄᴇᴀᴇ (Water-Shield Family) p. 161
6 Plants of muddy shores; leaves opposite (*Crassula aquatica*) . . . . . .
. . . . .Cʀᴀssᴜʟᴀᴄᴇᴀᴇ (Stonecrop Family) p. 195

7 Leaves round, attached to petiole at center; flowers single, large, 1–2 dm wide (*Nelumbo lutea*) . . . . .Nᴇʟᴜᴍʙᴏɴᴀᴄᴇᴀᴇ
. . . .(Lotus-Lily Family) p. 264
7 Leaves not attached to petiole at center 8

8 Sepals not joined to form a cup . . . . .Rᴀɴᴜɴᴄᴜʟᴀᴄᴇᴀᴇ
. . . .(Buttercup Family) p. 302
8 Sepals joined and cuplike 9

9 Pistils as many or more than number of petals . . . . .Rᴏsᴀᴄᴇᴀᴇ
. . . .(Rose Family) p. 317
9 Pistils fewer than petals 10

10 Leaves entire or shallowly lobed . . . . .Sᴀxɪғʀᴀɢᴀᴄᴇᴀᴇ
. . . .(Saxifrage Family) p. 352
10 Leaves compond (*Agrimonia*) . . . . .Rᴏsᴀᴄᴇᴀᴇ (Rose Family) p. 317

▶Group 7

Herbaceous plants; flowers with both male and female parts (perfect); petals and sepals present; ovary inferior, 1 in each flower.

1 Stamens more than number of petals **2**
1 Stamens less than or equal to number of petals **6**

2 Style 1 . . . . **3**
2 Styles 2 . . . . **5**

3 Plants of moist soils . . . . .ONAGRACEAE
. . . .(Evening-primrose Family) p. 271
3 Aquatic plants or plants of wet, muddy shores **4**

4 Flowers small, not showy, white or green (*Myriophyllum*) . . . .
. . . . .HALORAGACEAE (Water-milfoil Family) p. 229
4 Flowers large and showy, yellow (*Ludwigia*) . . . . .ONAGRACEAE
. . . .(Evening-primrose Family) p. 271

5 Styles 2 . . . . .SAXIFRAGACEAE (Saxifrage Family) p. 352
5 Styles 3 (*Montia chamissoi*) . . . . .PORTULACACEAE
. . . .(Purslane Family) p. 295

6 Petals separate **7**
6 Petals joined for most of their length **14**

7 Petals 2; stamens 2 (*Circaea alpina*) . . . . .ONAGRACEAE
. . . .(Evening-primrose Family) p. 271
7 Petals 4 or 5; stamens 4 or 5 . . . .**8**

8 Petals 4 . . . .**9**
8 Petals 5 . . . .**11**

9 Plants with underwater leaves, these dissected into narrow segments
(*Myriophyllum*) . . . .HALORAGACEAE (Water-milfoil Family) p. 229
9 Underwater leaves absent, or if present, the leaves entire **10**

10 Leaves with normal blade (*Ludwigia*) . . . . .ONAGRACEAE
. . . .(Evening-primrose Family) p. 271
10 Leaves reduced to small scales (*Myriophyllum*) . . . .
. . . . .HALORAGACEAE (Water-milfoil Family) p. 229

11 Leaves entire **12**
11 Leaves dissected or compound **13**

12 Flowers in panicles . . . . .SAXIFRAGACEAE (Saxifrage Family) p. 352
12 Flowers in heads or umbels . . . . . .APIACEAE (Carrot Family) p. 88

13 Flowers in narrow, spikelike racemes (*Agrimonia*) . . . . . .ROSACEAE
. . . .(Rose Family) p. 317
13 Flowers in umbels . . . . .APIACEAE (Carrot Family) p. 88

14 Stem leaves alternate **15**
14 Stem leaves alternate or whorled, or leaves all from base of plant **17**

15 Flowers irregular (*Lobelia*) . . . . .CAMPANULACEAE
. . . .(Bellflower Family) p. 166
15 Flowers regular **16**

16 Flowers small, 2–3 mm wide (*Samolus floribundus*) . .PRIMULACEAE
. . . .(Primrose Family) p. 296

16 Flowers larger (Campanula aparinoides) . . . . . . .CAMPANULACEAE
. . . .(Bellflower Family) p. 166

17 Leaves in whorls of 3–8 (*Galium*) . . . . .RUBIACEAE
. . . .(Madder Family) p. 331
17 Leaves opposite along stem or all from base of plant **18**
18 Stamens 3 . . . . .VALERIANACEAE (Valerian Family) p. 374
18 Stamens 4 or 5 (*Linnaea borealis*) . . . . .CAPRIFOLIACEAE
. . . . (Honeysuckle Family) p. 170

▶**Group 8**

Herbaceous plants; flowers with both male and female parts (perfect); petals and sepals present; flowers regular, with a single superior ovary; stamens number more than petals or corolla lobes.

1 Stamens more than 2x number of petals **2**
1 Stamens 2x number of petals or less **4**

2 Aquatic plants with large leaves from base of plant NYMPHAEACEAE
. . . .(Water-Lily Family) p. 265
2 Land plants with alternate or opposite leaves along stem **3**

3 Leaves alternate . . . . .MALVACEAE (Mallow Family) p. 259
3 Leaves opposite . . . . . .CLUSIACEAE (St. John's-wort Family) p. 186

4 Stamens less than 2x number of petals **5**
4 Stamens exactly 2x number of petals **9**

5 Leaves opposite or whorled; styles 2–5 . . . .**6**
5 Leaves alternate; style1 . . . .**8**

6 Flowers yellow . . . . . . .CLUSIACEAE (St. John's-wort Family) p. 186
6 Flowers not yellow **7**

7 Stamens grouped into 3 clusters of 3 each (*Triadenum*) .CLUSIACEAE
. . . .(St. John's-wort Family) p. 186
7 Stamens not grouped together . . . . .CARYOPHYLLACEAE
. . . .(Pink Family) p. 176

8 Sepals 4; petals 4 . . . . .BRASSICACEAE (Mustard Family) p. 153
8 Sepals 5; petals 5 (*Senna hebecarpa*) . . . . .CAESALPINIACEAE
. . . .(Caesalpinia Family) p. 163

9 Petals 3 (*Crassula aquatica*) . . . . .CRASSULACEAE
. . . .(Stonecrop Family) p. 195
9 Petals 4 or more **10**

10 Leaves compound or divided to base **11**
10 Leaves simple, margins entire or shallowly toothed **12**

11 Leaves 3-parted; styles 5 (*Oxalis acetosella*) . . . . . . .OXALIDACEAE
. . . .(Wood Sorrel Family) p. 278
11 Styles 1; pinnately compound (*Senna hebecarpa*) .CAESALPINIACEAE
. . . .(Caesalpinia Family) p. 163

12 Style 1 . . . .**13**
12 Styles 2 or more **14**

13 Hypanthium present and urn-shaped (*Rhexia*)   .MELASTOMATACEAE
. . . .(Melastome Family) p. 261
13 Hypanthium absent . . . . . . .PYROLACEAE (Shinleaf Family) p. 301

14 Ovary lobed, each lobe tipped by a style . . . . .SAXIFRAGACEAE
. . . .(Saxifrage Family) p. 303
14 Ovary not lobed, the styles all from tip of ovary **14**

15 Flowers yellow (*Triadenum*) .CLUSIACEAE
. . . .(St. John's-wort Family) p. 186
15 Flowers white or pink-tinged . . . . .CARYOPHYLLACEAE
. . . .(Pink Family) p. 176

▶Group 9

Herbaceous plants; flowers with both male and female parts (perfect); petals and sepals present; flowers irregular, with a single superior ovary; stamens number more than petals or corolla lobes.

1 Sepals petal-like, or long and spurlike **2**
1 Sepals not petal-like, often green **3**

2 One sepal a spur or sac; leaf margins shallowly toothed . . . .
. . . . .BALSAMINACEAE (Touch-me-not Family) p. 143
2 Sepals not spurlike; leaves entire . . . . .POLYGALACEAE
. . . .(Milkwort Family) p. 284

3 Lower 2 petals joined for their length along lower margins, enclosing the stamens . . . . .FABACEAE (Pea or Bean Family) p. 212
3 Lower 2 petals not joined, or petals 1 . . . .**4**

4 Leaves compound . . .CAESALPINIACEAE (Caesalpinia Family) p. 163
4 Leaves simple, entire to lobed **5**

5 Styles 2 (*Saxifraga pensylvanica*) . . . . .SAXIFRAGACEAE
. . . .(Saxifrage Family) p. 352
5 Style 1 (*Lythrum*) . . . . . . .LYTHRACEAE (Loosestrife Family) p. 255

▶Group 10

Herbaceous plants; flowers with both male and female parts (perfect), with a single superior ovary; petals and sepals present; petals separate, not joined; stamens fewer or equal to number of petals.

1 Leaves opposite **2**
1 Leaves alternate or all from base of plant **9**

2 Sepals 2 or 3; petals 2 or 3 (*Elatine*) . . . . .ELATINACEAE
. . . .(Waterwort Family) p. 201
2 Sepals and petals each 4–6 or more **3**

3 Style 1 . . . .**4**
3 Styles 2–5 . . . .**6**

4 Flowers with well-developed hypanthium (cuplike structure around ovary) . . . . .LYTHRACEAE (Loosestrife Family) p. 255
4 Hypanthium absent **5**

5 Stamens opposite the petal lobes . . . . PRIMULACEAE . . . .(Primrose Family) p. 296
5 Stamens alternate with petal lobes . . . . .GENTIANACEAE . . . .(Gentian Family) p. 217

6 Ovary and capsule divided into 4–5 parts . . . . .LINACEAE . . . .(Flax Family) p. 254
6 Ovary and capsule 1-parted **7**

7 Flowers yellow (*Hypericum*) .CLUSIACEAE . . . .(St. John's-wort Family) p. 186
7 Flowers white to pink **8**

8 Petals joined at their base (*Sabatia angularis*) . . . . . .GENTIANACEAE . . . .(Gentian Family) p. 217
8 Petals free to base . . . . . . .CARYOPHYLLACEAE (Pink Family) p. 176

9 Styles 2 or more **10**
9 Styles 1 or absent **11**

10Leaves all from base of plant, covered with sticky, stalked glands . . . . .DROSERACEAE (Sundew Family) p. 198
10Leaves from stem, smooth . . . . LINACEAE (Flax Family) p. 254

11Hypanthium tube-shaped (*Lythrum*) . . . . .LYTHRACEAE . . . .(Loosestrife Family) p. 255
11Hypanthium absent **12**

12Flowers irregular, sometimes spurred . . . . .VIOLACEAE . . . .(Violet Family) p. 378
12Flowers regular, spur absent **13**

13Flowers single at ends of stems (*Parnassia*) . . . . . . .SAXIFRAGACEAE . . . .(Saxifrage Family) p. 352
13Flowers in a cluster at ends of stems (*Lysimachia*) . . .PRIMULACEAE . . . .(Primrose Family) p. 296

▶Group 11

Herbaceous plants; flowers with both male and female parts (perfect), with a single superior ovary; petals and sepals present; petals joined; stamens equal to number of petal lobes.

1 Leaves all from base of plant; flowers at end of naked stalk **2**
1 Leaves mostly along stem **3**

2 Flowers 4-parted, chaffy, in spikes or heads . . . . .PLANTAGINACEAE . . . .(Plantain Family) p. 279

2 Flowers 5-parted, not chaffy, in umbel at end of stem (*Primula mistassinica*) . . . . .PRIMULACEAE (Primrose Family) p. 296

3 Ovary deeply parted into 2 or 4 sections **4**
3 Ovary not parted **5**
4 Leaves opposite (*Mentha, Pycnanthemum*) . . . . .LAMIACEAE
. . . .(Mint Family) p. 237
4 Leaves alternate . . . . .BORAGINACEAE (Borage Family) p. 150

5 Leaves opposite or whorled **6**
5 Leaves alternate **11**

6 Flowers in crowded heads or spikes; corolla 4-lobed **7**
6 Flowers mostly not in dense heads (sometimes in short racemes);
corolla 4–12-lobed **8**

7 Flowers chaffy; leaves linear . . . . .PLANTAGINACEAE
. . . .(Plantain Family) p. 279
7 Flowers petal-like; leaves not linear (*Phyla lanceolata*) VERBENACEAE
. . . .(Vervain Family) p. 376

8 Stamens attached opposite the corolla lobes . . . . . . .PRIMULACEAE
. . . .(Primrose Family) p. 296
8 Stamens alternate with corolla lobes **9**

9 Corolla lobes 4 or 6–12 . . .GENTIANACEAE (Gentian Family) p. 217
9 Corolla lobes 5 . . . .**10**

10 Stigmas 1 . . . . .GENTIANACEAE (Gentian Family) p. 217
10 Stigmas 3 . . . . .POLEMONIACEAE (Phlox Family) p. 282

11 Leaves compound or dissected into leaflets **12**
11 Leaves entire, toothed, or with shallow lobes only **13**

12 Leaves divided into 3 leaflets (*Menyanthes trifoliata*) . . . .
. . . . .MENYANTHACEAE (Buckbean Family) p. 262
12 Leaves pinnately compound (*Polemonium*) . . . . . .POLEMONIACEAE
. . . .(Phlox Family p. 282

13 Leaves small and scalelike; corolla 4-lobed (*Bartonia*) . . . .
. . . . .GENTIANACEAE (Gentian Family) p. 217
13 Leaves not scalelike; corolla deeply 5-lobed (*Samolus floribundus*) .
. . . . .PRIMULACEAE (Primrose Family) p. 296

▶Group 12

**Herbaceous plants; flowers with both male and female parts (perfect),
with a single superior ovary; petals and sepals present; petals joined.
Flowers irregular, or stamens less than number of petal lobes.**

1 Corolla base a spur or sac **2**
1 Corolla not spurred or saclike **4**

2 Sepals joined, deeply 5-lobed **3**

2 Sepals 2-lobed (*Utricularia*) . . . . .LENTIBULARIACEAE
. . . .(Bladderwort Family) p. 248

3 Leaves all from base of plant; flowers single atop a naked stalk
(*Pinguicula*) . . . . .LENTIBULARIACEAE (Bladderwort Family) p. 248

3 Leaves mostly along stem . . . . .SCROPHULARIACEAE
. . . .(Figwort Family) p. 356

4 Leaves alternate or all from base of plant **5**
4 Leaves opposite or whorled **6**

5 Stamens 2 (*Veronica*) .SCROPHULARIACEAE (Figwort Family) p. 356
5 Stamens 4 . . . . .SCROPHULARIACEAE (Figwort Family) p. 356

6 Plants usually aromatic when rubbed; stems often 4-sided; ovary
deeply 4-parted . . . . .LAMIACEAE (Mint Family) p. 237
6 Plants not strongly scented; stems rarely 4-angled; ovary not deeply 4-
parted **7**

7 Stamens 2 . . . .**8**
7 Stamens 4 . . . .**9**

8 Flowers in spikes or racemes at ends of stems, or 1 or 2 together from
leaf axils . . . . .SCROPHULARIACEAE (Figwort Family) p. 356
8 Flowers in spikes from leaf axils (*Justicia americana*) ACANTHACEAE
. . . .(Acanthus Family) p. 82

9 Corolla ±regular (*Verbena hastata*) . . . . .VERBENACEAE
. . . .(Vervain Family) p. 376
9 Corolla lipped or irregular **10**

10 Flower in clusters from leaf axils (*Phyla lanceolata*) . .VERBENACEAE
. . . .(Vervain Family) p. 376
10 Flowers in clusters at ends of stems, or single from leaf axils **11**

11 Upper corolla lip absent (*Teucrium canadense*) . . . . . . .LAMIACEAE
. . . .(Mint Family) p. 237
11 Upper corolla lip well-developed . . . . .SCROPHULARIACEAE
. . . .(Figwort Family) p. 356

Woody Plant Key
Trees, Shrubs and Vines

THE FOLLOWING KEY includes the trees, shrubs and vines occurring in wetlands of the Great Lakes region. In some cases, only the genus is identified. To determine the species, use the species key for that genus.

▶Trees

1 Leaves needlelike or scalelike . . . .**(Conifers) 2**
1 Leaves broad and flat . . . .**(Hardwoods) 5**

2 Leaves in bundles of 10 or more and shed in the fall . . . .TAMARACK
. . . .(*Larix laricina*) p. 77
2 Leaves single and persistent **3**

3 Leaves overlapping and scalelike . . . . . . .NORTHERN WHITE CEDAR
. . . .(*Thuja occidentalis*) p. 76
3 Leaves needlelike or strap-shaped **4**

4 Leaves stiff, 4-sided in cross-section . . . . .SPRUCE
. . . .(*Picea*) p. 78
4 Leaves soft, flat in cross-section .BALSAM FIR (*Abies balsamea*) p. 77

5 Leaves compound (with 3 or more leaflets) **6**
5 Leaves simple **9**

6 Leaves alternate; uncommon tree of Michigan's southern Lower
Peninsula . . . . .SHELLBARK-HICKORY (*Carya laciniosa*) p. 236
6 Leaves opposite **7**

7 Leaves palmately compound . . . . .OHIO-BUCKEYE
. . . .(*Aesculus glabra*) p. 234
7 Leaves pinnately compound or with only 3 leaflets **8**

8 Leaflets 3-5; fruit a paired samara BOXELDER (*Acer negundo*) p. 83
8 Leaflets 7-11; samaras single . . . . .ASH (*Fraxinus*) p. 269

9 Leaves opposite . . . . .MAPLE (*Acer*) p. 83
9 Leaves alternate **10**

10 Leaves not toothed or lobed; tree of Michigan's southern Lower
Peninsula . . . . .BLACK GUM (*Nyssa sylvatica*) p. 193
10 Leaves toothed or lobed or both **11**

11 Leaves toothed but not lobed **12**
11 Leaves lobed **16**

12 Leaves asymmetrical at base (one lobe lower than other) . . . .
. . . . .AMERICAN ELM (*Ulmus americana*) p. 370
12 Leaves symmetrical at base (lobes equal) **13**

13 Leaves at least 4x as long as wide . . . . .WILLOW (*Salix*) p. 336
13 Leaves less than 4x as long as wide **14**

14 Leaves as wide as long or wider . . .COTTONWOOD (*Populus*) p. 335
14 Leaves longer than wide **15**

15 Leaf margins doubly toothed (the teeth themselves toothed) . . . . . .
. . . . .RIVER BIRCH (*Betula nigra*) p. 148
15 Leaf margins singly toothed . . . . . .COTTONWOOD (*Populus*) p. 335

16 Leaves palmately shallowly lobed and veined; fruit a round ball . . .
. . . . SYCAMORE (*Platanus occidentalis*) p. 281
16 Leaves shallowly to deeply lobed; if lobed more than halfway to middle, then also bristle-tipped; fruit an acorn . .OAK (*Quercus*) p. 215

▶Shrubs and vines

1 Leaves evergreen and persistent on plant **2**
1 Leaves deciduous, shed in the fall **8**

2 Leaves narrow, less than 5 mm wide **3**
2 Leaves broader, 5 mm or more wide **4**

3 Plants small and trailing; leaves elliptic, pointed or blunt-tipped; fruit a red cranberry; plants of sphagnum peatlands . . . . . . .CRANBERRY
. . . . .(*Vaccinium macrocarpon, V. oxycoccos, V. vitis-idaea*) p. 208
3 Plants forming mats; leaves narrow with inrolled margins; fruit a black berry; uncommon . . . . .BLACK CROWBERRY
. . . .(*Empetrum nigrum*) p. 202

4 Leaves opposite . . . . .BOG-LAUREL, SHEEP-LAUREL
. . . .(*Kalmia polifolia, K. angustifolia*) p. 206
4 Leaves alternate **5**

5 Leaf underside with a dense covering of white or brown hairs **6**
5 Leaf underside with only scattered hairs or with small scales **7**

6 Leaf underside with brown hairs; flowers cream-colored, in upright clusters . . . . .LABRADOR-TEA (*Ledum groenlandicum*) p. 206
6 Leaf underside with short white hairs; flowers white to pink, urn-shaped and drooping . . . . .BOG-ROSEMARY
. . . .(*Andromeda glaucophylla*) p. 203

7 Upright shrubs; leaf underside with scales; flowers 5-parted . . . . . .
. . . . .LEATHERLEAF (*Chamaedaphne calyculata*) p. 204
7 Small, trailing shrubs, leaf underside with scattered brown bristly hairs; flowers 4-parted . . . . .CREEPING SNOWBERRY
. . . .(*Gaultheria hispidula*) p. 205

8 Leaves opposite or whorled **9**
8 Leaves alternate on stem **16**

9 Leaves compound, divided into leaflets **10**
9 Leaves simple **11**

10 Vines . . . . .CLEMATIS (*Clematis*) p. 305

10 Shrubs . . . . .ELDER (*Sambucus*) p. 171

11 Most leaves opposite, some sub-opposite . . . . . . .BASKET WILLOW
. . . .(*Salix purpurea*) p. 347
11 All leaves opposite **12**

12 Leaf margins distinctly lobed . . . . . . .SQUASH-BERRY, WITHEROD,
. . . . .HIGH-BUSH CRANBERRY (*Viburnum*) p. 172
12 Leaf margins not lobed **13**

13 Leaves with translucent glandular dots on upper surface . . . .
. . . . . . .KALM'S ST. JOHN'S-WORT (*Hypericum kalmianum*) p. 188
13 Leaves without translucent glandular dots **14**

14 Leaves opposite or in whorls of 3 (or occasionally 4), flowers numerous, in a ball-shaped head atop a long stalk; fruits brown and nutlike
. . . . .BUTTONBUSH (*Cephalanthus occidentalis*) p. 331
14 Leaves strictly opposite; fruit white or colored and berrylike **15**

15 Leaf lateral veins noticeably curved toward tip; Flowers white, 4-part-
ed, stalkless with 4 white bracts, or in stalked clusters at ends of
branches . . . . .DOGWOOD (*Cornus*) p. 191
15 Leaf lateral veins not curved toward tip; flowers light yellow, 5-part-
ed, borne in pairs from leaf axils . .HONEYSUCKLE (*Lonicera*) p. 171

16 Leaves compound, divided into leaflets **17**
16 Leaves simple **22**

17 Leaflets 3 or 5, palmate or pinnate **18**
17 Leaflets 6 or more, pinnate **20**

18 Leaflets 3; margins entire or with a few coarse teeth; flowers many in
a branched inflorescence; fruit a whitish drupe; prickles absent . . . .
. . . . .COMMON POISON-IVY (*Toxicodendron radicans*) p.86
18 Leaflets 3 or 5; margins entire or coarselty toothed; flowers white,
pink, or yellow; prickles sometimes present on stems **19**

19 Leaf margins coarsely toothed; fruit a berry . . . .
. . . . .RASPBERRY, BLACKBERRY OR DEWBERRY (*Rubus*) p. 326
19 Leaflets narrow with entire margins, leaflets mostly 5, with upper 3
joined at base . . .SHRUBBY CINQUEFOIL (*Potentilla fruticosa*) p. 323

20 Stems with a pair of prickles at each node . . . . .SWAMP-ROSE
. . . .(*Rosa palustris*) p. 324
20 Stems without prickles **21**

21 Low, much-branched shrub less than 1 m high; leaflets 1–2 cm long,
narrow; flowers yellow and showy, 1–2.5 cm wide; fruit a capsule .
. . . . .SHRUBBY CINQUEFOIL (*Potentilla fruticosa*) p. 323
21 Taller shrubs; leaves 5 or more cm long; flowers small and green-yellow; fruit white and berrylike . . . . POISON-SUMAC
. . . . (*Toxicodendron vernix*) p. 86

22 Leaves deeply or shallowly lobed **23**
22 Leaves not lobed **27**

23 Woody vines . . . . .RIVERBANK GRAPE (*Vitis riparia*) p. 384

23 Shrubs . . . . **.24**

24 Stems without thorns or prickles . . . . **.25**
24 Stems thorny or prickly . . . . **.26**

25 Stems with bark peeling into papery strips; flowers white, many in terminal clusters; fruit a dry brown pod . . . . . . .EASTERN NINEBARK . . . .(*Physocarpus opuliformis*) p. 322
25 Bark not peeling into papery strips; flowers cream white, yellow or green-purple, in small clusters from leaf axils; fruit a red to black berry . . . . .CURRANT (*Ribes*) p. 224

26 Uncommon plant of Isle Royale and other islands near Lake Superior north shore; leaves large, 2–4 dm wide; leave underside and petiole with sharp, stout prickles .DEVIL'S CLUB . . . .(*Oplopanax horridus*) p. 98
26 Widespread plants; leaves smaller . . . . .GOOSEBERRY (*Ribes*) p. 224

27 Leaf margin entire . . . . **.28**
27 Leaf margin toothed or wavy . . . . **.33**

28 Leaves with resinous dots on both sides (especially underside) . . . . .BLACK HUCKLEBERRY (*Gaylussacia baccata*) p. 205
28 Leaves without resinous dots . . . . **.29**

29 Shrub of sw Michigan; leaves and fruit with spicy, lemony odor . . . . .SPICE-BUSH (*Lindera benzoin*) p. 247
29 Widely distributed shrubs; leaves and fruit not aromatic . . . . . . **.30**

30 Large shrubs, often over 1 m tall; buds covered by a single scale; flowers in catkins; male and female flowers on separate plants; fruit a capsule . . . . .WILLOW (*Salix*) p. 336
30 Bud scales absent or buds covered by 2 or more scales; flowers single or in several to many flowered clusters . . . . **.31**

31 Smaller shrubs, typically much less than 1 m; flowers bell-shaped, waxy white; fruit a blue or blue-black berry with many small seeds . . . . .BLUEBERRY (*Vaccinium*) p. 208
31 Taller shrubs, usually 2 m or more; flowers small; fruit a red-purple or crimson with several large seeds . . . . **.32**

32 Leaves tipped with a small, sharp point; flowers and fruit single on very thin, long stalks .MOUNTAIN-HOLLY . . . .(*Nemopanthus mucronata*) p. 96
32 Leaves pointed but without a small, sharp tip; flowers single or several in leaf axils; fruit on short stalks . . . . .GLOSSY BUCKTHORN (*Rhamnus frangula*) p. 315

33 Buds not covered by scales; shrub of n Ill and n Ind only, more common southward . .AMERICAN SNOWBELL (*Styrax americanus*) p. 369
33 Bud scales 1 or more . . . . **.34**

34 Buds covered by a single scale; flowers in catkins; fruit a capsule . . . . .WILLOW (*Salix*) p. 336
34 Buds covered by 2 or more scales; flowers various; if catkins present, fruit is hard and nutlike . . . . **.35**
35 Leaves aromatic when rubbed; leaves with rounded, toothed tip,

lower leaf margin entire, dotted on both sides with yellow glands . .
. . . . .Sweet gale (*Myrica gale*) p. 263
35 Leaves not aromatic **36**

36 Young twigs usually with glands; leaf margins coarsely toothed; fruit
in conelike, deciduous catkins . . . . .Swamp or Bog birch
. . . .(*Betula pumila*) p. 148
36 Glands absent; leaves various **37**

37 Leaf margins coarsely double-toothed or wavy Alder (*Alnus*) p. 145
37 Leaf margins not double-toothed or wavy **38**

38 Leaf midrib on upper surface of leaf with small dark glands . . . . . .
. . . . .Chokeberry (*Aronia*) p. 318
38 Glands absent from leaf blades or petioles **39**

39 Leaves with very short petioles, usually less than 5 mm long **40**
39 Leaves with longer petioles, 5-30 mm long **41**

40 Flowers single or several, bell-shaped; fruit a blue to blue-black berry
. . . . .Blueberry (*Vaccinium*) p. 208
40 Flowers small and numerous in upright, terminal clusters; fruit a persistent capsule .Spirea (*Spiraea*) p. 329

41 Flowers larger, pink-white, 1–4 at ends of short branches, or single
and terminal with single flowers from leaf axils; stalks 1–2 cm long
. . . . .Juneberry (*Amelanchier bartramiana*) p. 318
41 Flowers small and yellow-green, single or in several-flowered clusters
along branches, flower stalks short or absen **42**

42 Leaf margin with incurved, forward-pointing teeth; stipules persistent, dark-colored; fruit bright red, nearly stalkless . . .Winterberry
. . . .(*Ilex verticillata*) p. 96
42 Leaf margin with rounded, forward-pointing teeth; leaves with pronounced raised veins on underside; stipules present, narrow, but
falling before fruits mature; fruit purple-black and berrylike, stalked
. . . . .Buckthorn (*Rhamnus*) p. 315

Ferns & Fern-Allies

THE FERNS AND THEIR ALLIES in the Great Lakes region are classified into three major divisions (or phylla): **Pterophyta** (true ferns), **Lycophyta** (clubmosses), and **Sphenophyta** (horsetails). The Pterophyta are represented by eight families in wetlands of the Great Lakes region (Azollaceae, Blechnaceae, Dryopteridaceae, Marsilaceae, Ophioglossaceae, Osmundaceae, Schizaeaceae, Thelypteridaceae). Three families are included in the Lycophyta (Lycopodiaceae, Selaginellaceae, Isoetaceae). The Sphenophyta are represented by a single living family (Equisetaceae). ▶All ferns and fern-allies reproduce by spores, rather than seeds. The spore germinates and produces a tiny flattened thallus termed the *gametophyte*. The larger, leafy, spore-bearing plant (*sporophyte*) results from the fertilized egg produced by the female part of the gametophyte. The uncurling of the young leaf or frond is characteristic. The Lycophyta (clubmosses) bear their spores on specialized leaves (*sporophylls*). The Sphenophyta (horsetails) bear spores in terminal cone-like structures, either on typical green stems, or on specialized fertile stems which lack chlorophyll.

Cinnamon fern (*Osmunda cinnamomea*). Fertile leaf at left, sterile leaf at right.

Azollaceae
Azolla Family

▶**Azolla** Lam. / Mosquito-fern

Azolla mexicana Presl.
Mexican mosquito-fern   OBL

⚠
STATUS
Indiana - T

☞ Azolla is
an important
genus in rice-
producing
regions where
it is utilized as
a natural ferti-
lizer because of
its symbiosis
with nitrogen-
fixing bacteria.
The genus
was formerly
included in
the family
Salviniaceae.

Small annual aquatic fern; plants free-floating or forming floating mats several cm thick, sometimes stranded on mud; roots few and unbranched. **Stems** lying flat, 1–1.5 cm long, green or red, covered with small, alternate, overlapping leaves in 2 rows; **leaves** 2-lobed, the upper lobe to 1 mm long, emergent; lower lobe underwater and larger than the upper. **Sporangia** of 2 kinds; larger female megaspores (to 0.6 mm long) and tiny male spores (microsporangia), and borne in separate sporo-carps. **Sporocarps** usually paired on underwater lobes of some leaves. *A. caroliniana.* ❦ Quiet water of marshes, ponds, streams and ditches. ⊕ Uncommon along Miss River in sw Minn and s Wisc; ne Ill and nw Ind. Ind to Neb and BC, s to Tex, Calif and into Mex and S Amer.

Azolla mexicana
MEXICAN MOSQUITO-FERN

Blechnaceae
Deer-Fern Family

▶**Woodwardia** J. E. Smith / Chain-fern

Woodwardia virginica (L.) J. E. Smith
Virginia chain-fern   OBL

Fern; rhizomes stout, widely spreading and branching. **Leaves** deciduous, in rows from rhizomes; **blades** lance-shaped to oblong, tapered to a point, 35–70 cm long and 15–30 cm wide, 1-pinnate into 15–20 pairs of deeply cleft pinnae; pinna segments with thickened margins, veins forming a distinctive double row of enclosed spaces (areoles) along midvein, then separate and not joined out to margin; **petioles** as long as blades, purple-black and shiny at base, straw-colored above. Fertile leaves produced in summer, similar to sterile leaves, the long narrow **sori** forming chainlike rows along midveins of pinnae; **indusia** membranous and thin. ✺ Swamps, marshes, shallow ponds, open bogs, ditches; soils acidic to neutral. ⊕ c and s Mich, n Ind, rare in ne Ill (Lake County). NS to Ont and Mich, s along Atlantic coast to Fla and e Tex. ☞ Sometimes weedy in commercial cranberry bogs in e USA.

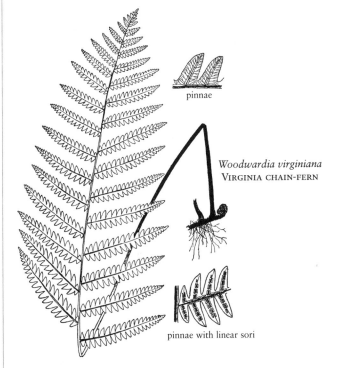

pinnae

Woodwardia virginiana
VIRGINIA CHAIN-FERN

pinnae with linear sori

Dryopteridaceae
Wood Fern Family

Medium to large ferns with scaly rhizomes. Fertile and sterile **leaves** mostly similar, usually divided or compound; **sori** (clusters of spore containers) present on lower leaf surface; **indusia** (covering over sori) present or absent.

▶**KEY TO DRYOPTERIDACEAE**

1 Leaves of two very different types (fertile and sterile) **2**
1 Leaves all similar. **3**

2 Leaves in large, vaselike clumps; fertile leaves 1-pinnate, surrounded by tall sterile leaves; veins of sterile leaves not netlike . . . .
. . . . *Matteuccia struthiopteris* / OSTRICH FERN
2 Leaves single or scattered along creeping rhizomes; fertile leaves 2-pinnate; veins of sterile leaves netlike . . . . *Onoclea sensibilis*
. . . . SENSITIVE FERN

3 Sori elongate, either straight or hook-shaped, indusia present **4**
3 Sori ± round, indusia present or absent **5**

4 Sori straight, blade 1-pinnate . . . . *Deparia acrostichioides*
. . . . SILVERY GLADE FERN
4 Sori curved or hook-shaped, blade 2-pinnate . *Athyrium filix-femina*
. . . . LADY FERN

5 Blade elongate, often with 'pealike' bulblets; indusium a hoodlike cover arching over spore clusters, attached at its base on side toward pinna midrib . . . . *Cystopteris bulbifera*
. . . . BULBLET FERN; BLADDER FERN
5 Blade various, bulblets absent; indusium round or kidney-shaped, attached at its center, or absent . . . . *Dryopteris* / WOOD FERN

▶**Athyrium** Roth / Lady fern

Athyrium filix-femina L.
Lady fern   FAC
Clumped fern, rhizomes short and ascending. **Leaves** deciduous, sterile and fertile leaves similar; petioles with brown, linear scales; blades elliptic, 2-pinnate, broadest at middle or slightly below middle; pinnae short-stalked or stalkless. **Sori** generally somewhat curved to hook-shaped, less often straight. *Athyrium angustum.* ≸ Common; moist deciduous woods, shrub thickets, streambanks, hummocks in swamps, wetland margins, and shaded rock outcrops. ⊕ Minn (but uncommon in sw), Wisc, Mich, Ill, Ind. ☞ A wide-ranging circumboreal species; our plants may be separated as var. *angustum,* which occurs in ne NAmer, s to NC, Mo and Neb.

▶**Cystopteris** Bernh. / Bladder fern

Cystopteris bulbifera (L.) Bernh.
Bulblet fern; Bladder fern   FACW-

Clumped fern, rhizomes short and thick. **Leaves** deciduous, 30–100 cm long, sterile and fertile leaves similar but sterile blades usually shorter than fertile; petioles much shorter than blades; **blades** lance-shaped, 6–15 cm wide at base, long tapered to tip, with 20–30 pairs of pinnae; the veins ending in a notch (sinus). **Sori** round, on a small vein; **indusia** hood-like and attached at its base, covered with scattered, short-stalked glands. **Green bulblets**, 4–5 mm wide, are produced on lower side of rachis (main stem of leaf) toward upper end of blade, these falling and forming new plants. ❦ Rocky streambanks, ravines, and moist, shaded, often calcium-rich rocks and cliffs. ⊕ n and e (especially se) Minn, Wisc, Mich and ne Ill. Nfld to Ont, Minn and SD, s to Ga and Tex. ☞ Distinguished from **fragile fern** (*C. fragilis*), a common fern of moist woods, by the blade broadest at base, most veins ending in a notch, and the small bulblets on underside of rachis. In fragile fern, the blade is broadest above its base, most veins end in a tooth, and bulblets are absent.

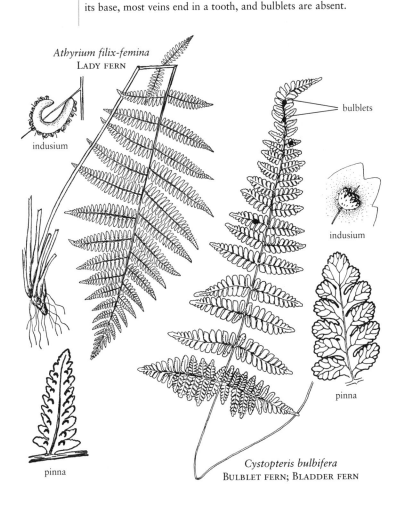

Athyrium filix-femina
LADY FERN

indusium

bulblets

indusium

pinna

pinna

Cystopteris bulbifera
BULBLET FERN; BLADDER FERN

▶**Deparia** Hooker & Greville / Glade Fern

Deparia acrostichioides (Swartz) M. Kato
  Silvery glade fern; Silvery spleenwort   FAC
Large fern from creeping rhizomes. **Leaves** deciduous, 50–100 cm long,
sterile and fertile leaves alike; petioles straw-colored (but dark red-brown
at base), with brown lance-shaped scales; blades lance-shaped to oblong
in outline, tapered at tip and distinctly narrowed toward base; deeply
lobed, the segments blunt to somewhat tapered at their tip, margins
entire to slightly lobed. **Sori** crowded, elongate, straight or sometimes
curved, the **indusia** silvery and shiny when young. *Athyrium thelypteri-
oides.* ❦ Moist, rich deciduous woods, especially in wetter swales and
depressions; streambanks; damp shady slopes. ⊕ Minn (extreme se
only), Wisc, Mich, Ill and Ind. NS and s Ont, w to Wisc and se Minn, s
to Ga and Ark.

▶**Dryopteris** Adans. / Wood-fern

Medium to large ferns; rhizomes short, stout and scaly, often covered
with old petiole bases. **Leaves** dark green, sometimes evergreen; petioles
shorter than blades, straw-colored or green, with chaffy scales near base.
Sterile and fertile leaves alike or slightly different; sterile leaves sometimes persisting over winter; blades 1–3 pinnate, the smallest segments
commonly toothed or lobed, veins simple to 1- or 2-branched. **Sori**
round, on underside veins of pinnae; **indusia** round to kidney-shaped.

▶**KEY TO DRYOPTERIS**

1 Blades narrowly oblong, the lowest pair of pinna triangular in outline; sterile and fertile leaves somewhat different, sterile leaves smaller than fertile leaves . . . . *D. cristata* / CRESTED WOOD-FERN
1 Blades broader; sterile and fertile leaves alike **2**

2 Blade more dissected, 2–3-pinnate **3**
2 Blade less dissected, 1–2-pinnate **4**

3 Leaves deciduous late in season; lowermost inner pinnule longer than
   next outer one and longer and wider than opposite upper pinnule .
   . . . . *D. carthusiana* / SPINULOSE WOOD-FERN
3 Leaves evergreen; lowermost inner pinnule shorter or equal to adjacent lower pinnule, not distinctly longer and wider than opposite
   upper pinnule . . . . *D. intermedia* / FANCY WOOD-FERN

4 Blades large, abruptly narrowed to a short, pointed tip; lowest pair of
   pinna with wavy outline . . . . . *D. goldiana* / GOLDIE'S WOOD-FERN
4 Blades gradually reduced to long, tapering tips **5**

5 Leaf blades mostly 2–3 dm wide, lowest pinna-pair narrowed at base;
   sw Mich only . . . . *D. celsa* / LOG-FERN
5 Leaf blades mostly less than 2 dm wide, lowest pinna-pair broadest at
   or near base; se Wisc, n Ind and Mich LP . . . . *D. clintoniana*
   . . . . CLINTON'S WOOD-FERN

☞ **Spinulose wood-fern** is similar to **fancy wood-fern** (*D. intermedia*) but the innermost lower pinnule of the basal pinnae is usually longer than the next outer one, and the leaves are more yellow-green in color than the blue-green, ± evergreen leaves of *D. intermedia*.

Dryopteris carthusiana (Villars) H. P. Fuchs
Spinulose wood-fern   FACW-

Clumped fern, rhizomes short-creeping. **Leaves** all alike, deciduous, smooth except for chaffy, pale brown scales near base of petioles; **blades** 2- to nearly 3-pinnate, 2–6 dm long and 1–4 dm wide, tapered to tip, slightly narrowed at base; pinnae usually 10–15 pairs, alternate to nearly opposite, narrowly lance-shaped; pinnules toothed to deeply lobed, mostly 5–40 mm long and 3–10 mm wide, the teeth tipped with a small spine; innermost lower pinnule longer than next outer one and 2–3x longer than opposite upper pinnule. **Sori** halfway between midvein and margin; **indusia** 1 mm wide, without stalked glands. *D. spinulosa.* ⚘ Moist to wet woods, hummocks in swamps, thickets; also drier sand dunes and ridges. ⊕ Minn (all but extreme w), Wisc, Mich, ne Ill and nw Ind. Labr to BC, s to NC, Ark, Neb and Wash.

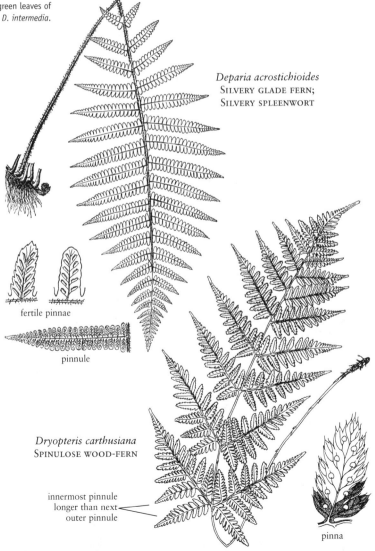

Deparia acrostichioides
SILVERY GLADE FERN;
SILVERY SPLEENWORT

fertile pinnae

pinnule

Dryopteris carthusiana
SPINULOSE WOOD-FERN

innermost pinnule longer than next outer pinnule

pinna

Dryopteris celsa (W. Palmer) Small
Log-fern   OBL

⚠
STATUS
Illinois - E
Michigan - T

Fern; rhizomes shallow, creeping, their tips covered by shiny brown or black scales. **Leaves** deciduous, to 12 dm long, all alike; **blades** 4–7 dm long and 2–3 dm wide, slightly narrowed at base and tapered gradually to tip; lower pinnae narrowed at base, upper pinnae oblong, uniformly long-tapering; **petioles** light-green, longer than blade, with scales having dark centers and paler margins. **Sori** midway between midvein and leaf margin; **indusia** smooth, 1 mm across. *D. goldiana* subsp. *celsa*. ❧ On rotting logs and humus-rich soils in wet woods, swamps, and near seeps. ⊕ Disjunct in sw Mich. NJ to s Ill and Mo, s to SC, n Ga and Ark; local and uncommon throughout its range.

Dryopteris clintoniana (D. C. Eat.) P. Dowel
Clinton's wood-fern   FACW+

Fern; rhizomes short-creeping, 5–7 mm wide. **Leaves** all ± alike, evergreen (or fertile leaves dying back in winter), 5–10 dm long; **blades** 3–8 dm long and 1–2 dm wide, slightly narrowed below and long-tapered to tip; pinnae long-triangular, gradually tapered to tip, with sharp-toothed segments; basal pinnae with a broad base, 1.5–2.5x longer than wide; **petioles** shorter than blades, scaly at base, scales brown or with darker brown center. **Sori** near midveins; **indusia** smooth, 1–2 mm wide. ❧ Swamps and wet woods. ⊕ LP of Mich, nw Ind, uncommon in se Wisc. Maine and Que to s Wisc, s to NJ, Pa, n Ohio and n Ind.

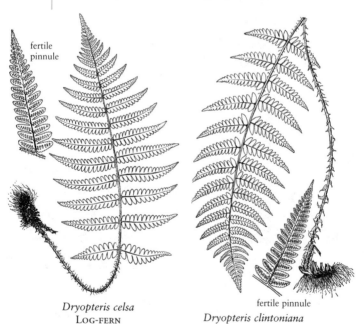

fertile
pinnule

Dryopteris celsa
LOG-FERN

fertile pinnule

Dryopteris clintoniana
CLINTON'S WOOD-FERN

Dryopteris cristata (L.) A. Gray
Crested wood-fern   OBL

Clumped fern, rhizomes short-creeping with ascending tips. Sterile and fertile **leaves** somewhat different, the outer sterile leaves waxy, persistent and smaller than inner fertile leaves; fertile leaves deciduous, 3–8 dm long. **Blades** 1-pinnate to nearly 2-pinnate, narrowly lance-shaped, 2–6 dm long and 7–15 cm wide, tapered to tip, narrowed at base; pinnae 5–9 cm long and to 4 cm wide, typically twisted to a nearly horizontal position, giving a "venetian blind" appearance to blades; pinnae segments to 20 mm long and 8 mm wide, with small spine-tipped teeth; **petioles** with sparse, pale brown, long-tapered scales. **Sori** round, midway between midvein and margin; **indusia** smooth, 1 mm wide. ❦ Swamps, thickets, open bogs, fens and seeps. ⊕ n and e Minn, Wisc, Mich, ne Ill and nw Ind. Circumboreal, in N Amer s to Va, Ark, Neb and Idaho.

Dryopteris goldiana (Hook.) A. Gray
Goldie's wood-fern   FAC

Clumped fern; rhizomes short-creeping, to 1 cm thick, densely scaly. **Leaves** to 1 m long; **blades** 30–60 cm long and 20–40 cm wide, deciduous late in season, the upper part abruptly narrowed to a small, tapered tip, the tip often mottled with white; pinnae with small, often rounded teeth; **petioles** brown, slightly shorter than blades, with narrow, pale brown scales 1–2 cm long, lower scales with a dark midstripe. **Sori** close to midveins, with a smooth **indusia** 1–2 mm across. ❦ Moist hardwood forests, shaded streambanks, talus slopes; soils rich in humus and usually neutral. ⊕ Uncommon in ec and se Minn; Wisc, Mich, ne Ill and nw Ind. NB and s Ont to Minn, s to Va, Ala and Mo.

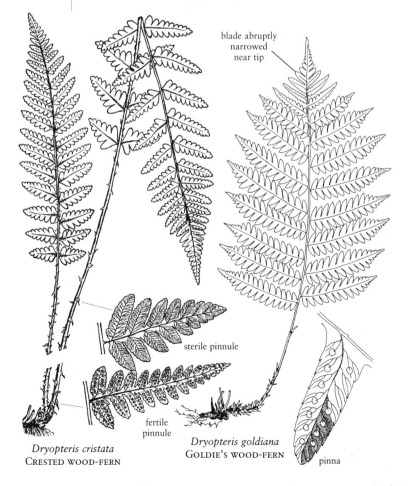

blade abruptly
narrowed
near tip

sterile pinnule

fertile
pinnule

Dryopteris cristata
CRESTED WOOD-FERN

Dryopteris goldiana
GOLDIE'S WOOD-FERN

pinna

Dryopteris intermedia (Muhl.) A. Gray
Fancy wood-fern   FAC

Clumped fern, rhizomes ascending. **Leaves** in an open vaselike cluster of evergreen leaves; **blades** broadest just above base and abruptly tapered near tip, 2–5 dm long and 1–2 dm wide, 2-pinnate; pinnae at right angles to stem, lowermost inner pinnule usually shorter than next outer pinnule, pinnules toothed and tipped with small spines; **petioles** 1/3 as long as blade, with pale brown scales with a darker center, petioles and stems with small, gland-tipped hairs. **Sori** midway between midvein and margin, the **indusia** 1 mm wide, covered with stalked glands. ❦ Moist hardwood and mixed hardwood-conifer forests, hummocks in swamps; soils rich in humus and slightly acid to neutral. ⊕ Common; ne and se Minn, Wisc, Mich, ne Ill and nw Ind. Nfld to Minn, s to Ga and Ark.

▶Matteuccia Todaro / Ostrich fern

Matteuccia struthiopteris (L.) Todaro
Ostrich fern   FACW

Large, colony-forming fern; rhizomes deep and long-creeping, black, scaly, producing erect leafy crowns. **Sterile leaves** upright, 1-pinnate, to 2 m tall and 15–50 cm wide; blades much longer than petioles, abruptly narrowed to tip, gradually tapered to base, stems ± hairy; each pinnae deeply divided into 20 or more pairs of pinnules, these 3–6 mm wide at base and rounded at tip; veins not netlike. **Fertile leaves** stiff and erect within a circle of sterile leaves, green at first, turning brown or black, much shorter than sterile leaves (to 6 dm tall), produced in mid to late summer and often persisting into following year; fertile blades 1-pinnate, pinnae upright or appressed, 2–6 cm long and 2–4 mm wide, the margins inrolled and covering the **sori; indusia** with a jagged margin. *Pteretis pensylvanica.* ❦ Wet and swampy woods, streambanks, seeps, and ditches. ⊕ Minn, Wisc, Mich; uncommon in ne Ill and nw Ind. Newf to Alaska, s to Va, Ohio, Mo, SD and BC; Europe.

▶Onoclea L. / Sensitive fern

Onoclea sensibilis L.
Sensitive fern   FACW

Medium fern, in clumps of several leaves, spreading by branching rhizomes and forming large patches. **Leaves** upright, with petioles about as long as blades. **Sterile leaves** deciduous, 1-pinnate at base, deeply cleft upward; the stem broader-winged toward the **tip**; blades 15–40 cm long and 15–35 cm wide, with 8–12 pairs of opposite pinnae, these deeply wavy-margined or coarsely toothed, 1–5 cm wide, with scattered white hairs on underside veins, the veins joined and netlike. **Fertile leaves** produced in late summer and persisting over winter, shorter than sterile leaves; fertile blades 1-pinnate, pinnae upright, divided into beadlike pinnules with inrolled margins covering the sori; veins not joined. **Sori** round and covered by a hoodlike **indusia**, becoming dry and hard. ❦ Swampy woods and low places in forests, wet meadows, calcareous fens, roadside ditches, wet or moist wheel ruts; sometimes weedy. ⊕ Minn (all but sw and extreme nw), Wisc, Mich, ne Ill and nw Ind. Newf to Man, s to Fla and Tex.

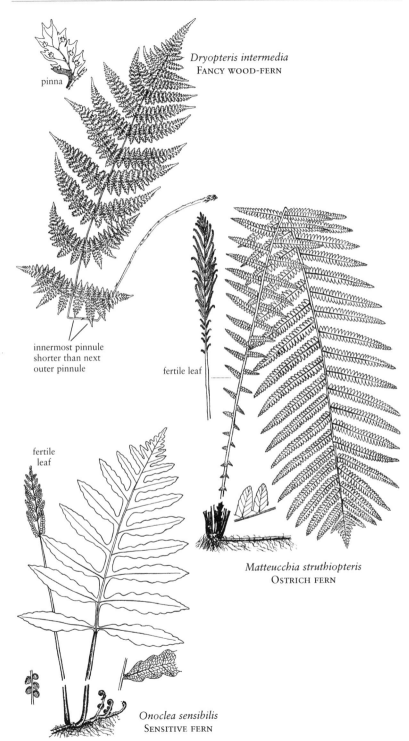

pinna

Dryopteris intermedia
FANCY WOOD-FERN

innermost pinnule
shorter than next
outer pinnule

fertile leaf

Matteucchia struthiopteris
OSTRICH FERN

fertile
leaf

Onoclea sensibilis
SENSITIVE FERN

Equisetaceae
Horsetail Family

▶**Equisetum** L. / Horsetail; Scouring-rush

☞ A stem cross-section is provided next to the description of each species. These are useful for identifying *Equisetum* in the field.

Rushlike herbs with dark rhizomes. **Stems** annual or perennial, grooved, usually with large central cavity and smaller outer cavities, unbranched or with whorls of branches at nodes. **Leaves** reduced to scales, united into a sheath at each node; top of sheath divided into dark-colored teeth. **Spores** in cones at tips of green or brown fertile stems.

▶**KEY TO EQUISETUM**

1 Stems evergreen; unbranched or with a few scattered branches, branches not in regular whorls (scouring rushes) **2**
1 Stems annual; usually with regular whorls of branches, sometimes unbranched (horsetails) **5**

2 Stems solid (central cavity absent); stems small, slender and sprawling . . . . *E. scirpoides* / DWARF SCOURING-RUSH
2 Stems hollow (central cavity present); stems larger, usually upright.**3**

3 Stems 1–3 dm tall, with 5–12 ridges, central cavity to 1/3 diameter of stem . . . . *E. variegatum* / VARIEGATED SCOURING RUSH
3 Stems usually taller, with 16–50 ridges, central cavity more than half diameter of stem **4**

4 Cones with a distinct, small sharp tip; stem sheaths with a black band at tip and base . . . . *E. hyemale* / COMMON SCOURING-RUSH
4 Cones blunt-tipped, sheaths with black band at tip only . . . . *E. laevigatum* / SMOOTH SCOURING-RUSH

5 Stems unbranched **6**
5 Stems with regular whorls of branches **10**

6 Stems green **7**
6 Stems brown or flesh-colored **8**

7 Stems with 9–25 shallow ridges; central cavity more than half diameter of stem; sheath teeth entirely black or with narrow white margins . . . . *E. fluviatile* / WATER-HORSETAIL
7 Stems with 5–10 strongly angled ridges; central cavity less than 1/3 diameter of stem; sheath teeth with white margins and dark centers . . . . *E. palustre* / MARSH-HORSETAIL

8 Sheath teeth papery and red-brown, teeth joined and forming several broad lobes . . . . *E. sylvaticum* / WOODLAND-HORSETAIL
8 Sheath teeth black or brown, not papery, separate or joined in more than 4 small groups **9**

9 Stems withering after spores mature, remaining unbranched . . . . *E. arvense* / COMMON OR FIELD HORSETAIL

9 Stems persistent, becoming branched and green . . . . *E. pratense*
. . . . Meadow-horsetail

10 First internode of each branch shorter than the subtending sheath of the main stem **11**
10 First internode of each branch equal or longer than the subtending sheath of the main stem **12**

11 Stems with 9–25 shallow ridges; central cavity more than half diameter of stem; sheath teeth more than 12, entirely black or with narrow white margins . . . . *E. fluviatile* / Water-horsetail
11 Stems with 5–10 strongly angled ridges; central cavity about same size as outer cavities; sheath teeth 5–6, with white margins and dark centers . . . . *E. palustre* / Marsh-horsetail

12 Stem branches themselves branched; sheath teeth papery and red-brown, teeth joined and forming several broad lobes . *E. sylvaticum*
. . . . Woodland-horsetail
12 Stem branches unbranched; sheath teeth black or brown, not papery, separate or joined in more than 4 small groups **13**

13 Stem branches ascending; teeth of branch sheaths gradually tapering to a slender tip . . . . *E. arvense* / Common or Field horsetail
13 Stem branches spreading; teeth of branch sheaths broadly triangular
. . . . *E. pratense* / Meadow-horsetail

Equisetum arvense L.

Common or Field horsetail   FAC

stem section

Stems annual, upright from creeping, branched, tuber-bearing rhizomes covered with dark hairs. Sterile and fertile stems unalike; **sterile stems** appearing in spring as fertile wither, green, regularly branched, 1–6 dm tall and 2–5 mm wide, with 10–14 shallow ridges, the ridges usually rough-to-touch; central cavity 1/3–2/3 stem diameter; **sheaths** with 6–14 persistent, black-brown teeth 1–2 mm long; **branches** numerous in dense whorls, usually without branchlets, upright or spreading, 3–5-angled, solid. **Fertile stems** flesh-colored, shorter than sterile stems and with larger sheaths, maturing in early spring and soon withering, unbranched, to 3 dm tall and 8 mm wide; sheaths with 8–12 dark brown teeth. **Cones** blunt-tipped, long-stalked at end of stem, 0.5–3 cm long. ☙ Streambanks, meadows, moist woods, ditches, roadsides and along railroads; calcareous fens in s part of region. ⊕ Very common; Minn, Wisc, Mich, n Ill and n Ind. Circumboreal, s in USA to all but Fla, Miss and La.

Equisetum fluviatile L.

Water-horsetail   OBL

stem section

Stems annual, fertile and sterile stems alike, to 1 m or more tall, from smooth, shiny, light brown, creeping rhizomes. Stems with 9–25 shallow, smooth ridges; central cavity large, about 4/5 stem diameter; **stem sheaths** green, 6–10 mm long; teeth 12–24, persistent, 2–3 mm long, dark brown to black, sometimes with narrow white margins; **branches** none or few, to many and regularly whorled from middle nodes, spreading, without branchlets, 4–6-angled, hollow. **Cones** 1–2 cm long at tips of stems, long-stalked, blunt-tipped, deciduous, maturing in summer. ☙ In standing water of marshes, ponds, peatlands, ditches and swales. ⊕ Minn (all but sw), Wisc, Mich, ne Ill and nw Ind. Circumboreal, s to Pa, WVa, Ohio, n Ill, Iowa, Neb, nw Mont and Ore.

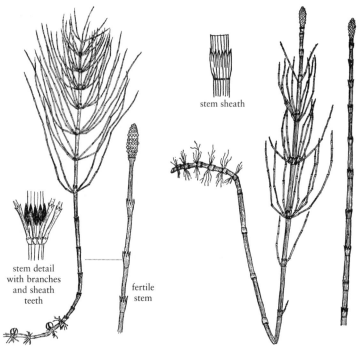

stem sheath

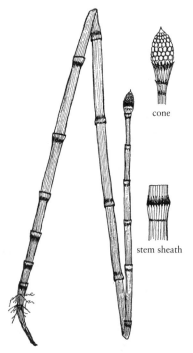

stem detail
with branches
and sheath
teeth

fertile
stem

Equisetum arvense
COMMON OR FIELD HORSETAIL

Equisetum fluviatile
WATER-HORSETAIL

cone

cone

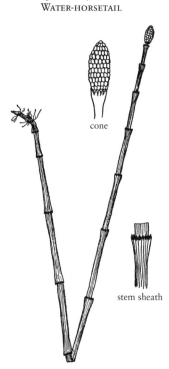

stem sheath

stem sheath

Equisetum hyemale
COMMON SCOURING-RUSH

Equisetum laevigatum
SMOOTH SCOURING-RUSH

Equisetum hyemale L.
Common scouring-rush   FACW-

☞ E. hymale was used by early settlers to scrub pots and pans.

stem section

Stems evergreen, persisting for more than 1 year, fertile and sterile stems alike, from black, slender rhizomes. Stems mostly unbranched or with few, short, upright **branches** from upper nodes, to 15 dm tall but usually shorter, 4–14 mm wide, with 14–50 rounded, very rough ridges; central cavity at least 3/4 stem diameter; stem **sheaths** 5–15 mm long, with a dark band at tip and usually also at base, the teeth dark brown to black with chaffy margin, 2–4 mm long, deciduous or persistent. **Cones** stalkless or short-stalked at tips of stems, sharp-pointed, eventually deciduous, 1–2.5 cm long, maturing in summer, or old stems sometimes developing branches with cones in the following spring. Ours are subspecies *affine*. *E. affine*. ॐ Often forming dense colonies in seeps, wet to moist meadows, shores and streambanks, ditches, roadsides and along railroads; usually where sandy or gravelly. ⊕ Minn (all but sw), Wisc, Mich, ne Ill and nw Ind. ± circumboreal, s to Fla, Tex and Calif; Mex and c Amer.

Equisetum laevigatum A. Braun
Smooth scouring-rush   FACW

stem section

Stems mostly annual, fertile and sterile stems alike, from brown or black rhizomes. Stems mostly unbranched or with a few upright branches, 3–10 dm tall and 3–8 mm wide, smooth and rather soft, with 10–32 ridges; central cavity 2/3–3/4 stem diameter; stem **sheaths** with a single dark band at tip, or rarely lowest sheaths with a dark band at base or entirely black; teeth dark brown or black with chaffy margins, free or partly joined in pairs, 1–4 mm long, soon deciduous. **Cones** short-stalked at tips of stems, rounded with a small sharp point, maturing in early summer and eventually deciduous. *E. kansanum*. ॐ Wet meadows, low prairie, streambanks, floodplains, seeps, and ditches, often where sandy or gravelly. ⊕ All but far ne Minn (most common c and s), most of Wisc (especially s), Mich, ne Ill and nw Ind. Que to s BC, s to Ohio, Ill, Mo, Tex and Calif; n Mex.

Equisetum palustre L.
Marsh-horsetail   FACW

stem section

Stems annual, erect, fertile and sterile stems alike, from creeping, branched, shiny black rhizomes. Stems 2–8 dm tall, with 5–10 pronounced ridges, the ridges mostly smooth; central cavity small, 1/6–1/3 stem diameter; **sheaths** green, loose and flared upward; teeth 5–6, free or partly joined, persistent, 3–7 mm long, brown to black, with pale, translucent margins; **branches** few and irregular, to many and whorled at upper nodes, upright, without branchlets, 5–6-angled, hollow. **Cones** long-stalked at tips of stems, 1–3 cm long, blunt-tipped, maturing in summer, deciduous. ॐ In shallow water, along wetland margins, streambanks and fens. ⊕ Sparse in n and ec Minn; local in nw, wc and se Wisc; Mich. Circumboreal, s to Pa, Neb, Mont and Wash.

Equisetum pratense Ehrh.
Meadow-horsetail   FACW

⚠ STATUS Illinois -T

Stems annual and erect, sterile and fertile stems unalike, from creeping, dull black rhizomes. Sterile stems regularly branched, 2–5 dm tall and 1–3 mm wide; 8–18-ridged, the ridges roughened by silica on middle and upper stem; central cavity 1/3–1/2 stem diameter; main stem **sheaths** 2–6 mm long, the teeth persistent, 1–2 mm long, free or partly joined in pairs, brown with white margins and a dark midstripe; **branches** slender, many in regular whorls from middle and upper nodes, without branchlets, hor-

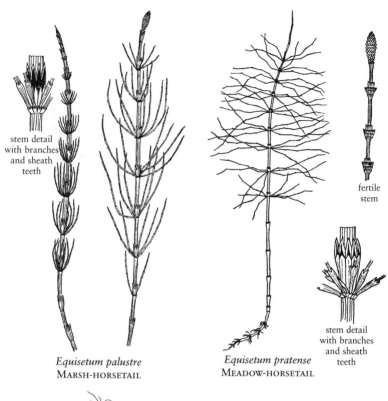

stem detail
with branches
and sheath
teeth

fertile
stem

stem detail
with branches
and sheath
teeth

Equisetum palustre
MARSH-HORSETAIL

Equisetum pratense
MEADOW-HORSETAIL

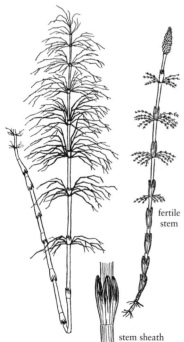

fertile
stem

stem sheath

Equisetum sylvaticum
WOODLAND-HORSETAIL

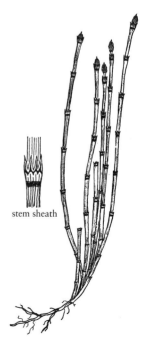

stem sheath

Equisetum variegatum
VARIEGATED SCOURING-RUSH

stem section

izontal or drooping, mostly 3-angled, solid. Fertile stems uncommon, appearing in early spring before sterile stems and persisting, at first unbranched, fleshy and brown (without chlorophyll), later becoming green at nodes and producing many small green branches, mostly 1–3 dm tall; sheaths and teeth about twice as long as on sterile stems. **Cones** long-stalked at tips of stems, to 2.5 cm long, blunt-tipped, deciduous. ❦ Moist woods, streambanks and meadows. ⊕ Minn (all but sw), Wisc (but uncommon in se), Mich. Circumboreal, s to NJ, SD, Idaho and s BC.

Equisetum scirpoides Michx.
Dwarf scouring-rush   FAC

⚠

STATUS
Illinois - E

stem section

Stems evergreen, very slender, fertile and sterile stems alike, from widely branching rhizomes. Stems 5–30 cm long and only 0.5–1 mm wide, in dense clusters, usually unbranched and zigzagged, upright or trailing; central cavity absent, 3 small outer cavities present; **sheaths** green with broad black band at tip, loose and flared above, with 3–4 teeth; teeth with white, chaffy margin, ± persistent, but tips usually soon deciduous. **Cones** black, small, 3–5 mm long, sharp-tipped. ❦ Mossy places and moist, shaded woods, the stems often partly buried in humus. ⊕ nc and e Minn, Wisc, Mich, ne Ill. Circumboreal, s to Conn, s Ill, SD and Wash.

Equisetum sylvaticum L.
Woodland-horsetail   FACW

⚠

STATUS
Illinois - E

stem section

Stems annual, erect, sterile and fertile stems unalike, from creeping, shiny light brown rhizomes, tubers occasionally present. Sterile stems green, 3–7 dm tall and 1.5–3 mm wide, with 10–18 ridges, rough-to-touch with sharp, hooked silica spines; central cavity 1/2–2/3 stem diameter; **sheaths** green at base, red-brown and flaring at tip; teeth brown, 3–5 mm long, joined in 3–5 broad lobes. Stems densely branched in regular whorls from the nodes, the **branches** themselves branched, often curving downward, 4–5-angled, solid. Fertile stems at first pink-brown (without chlorophyll), fleshy, unbranched, becoming green and branched as in sterile stems; sheaths and teeth larger than in sterile stems. **Cones** 1.5–3 cm long, stalked, blunt-tipped, deciduous. ❦ Wet or swampy woods, thickets, usually in partial shade. ⊕ Minn, Wisc (all but far s), Mich. Circumboreal, s to Md, WVa, Ky, Iowa, SD, nw Mont, n Idaho and s BC.

Equisetum variegatum Schleicher
Variegated scouring rush   FACW

⚠

STATUS
Indiana -E

stem section

Stems evergreen, fertile and sterile stems alike, from creeping, much-branched, smooth rhizomes. Stems 1–3 dm tall and 1–2.5 mm wide, with 5–12 shallow, rough ridges, branched near base and otherwise usually unbranched; central cavity 1/4–1/3 stem diameter, smaller outer cavities present; **sheaths** green at base with a broad black band above; teeth persistent, with a dark brown or black midstripe and wide white margins, abruptly narrowed to a hairlike, deciduous tip 0.5–1 mm long. **Cones** to 1 cm long, strongly sharp-tipped, maturing in summer or persisting unopened until following spring. Ours are var. *variegatum*. ❦ Lakeshores, streambanks, wet woods, moist meadows, fens, and ditches, moist sandy soil, frequent near Lake Michigan. ⊕ n and e Minn, Wisc, Mich, ne Ill and nw Ind. Circumboreal, s to Pa, Ill, Minn and Colo.

Isoetaceae
Quillwort Family

▶Isoetes L. / Quillwort

☞
Magnification
is needed to
see the
surface of
megaspores,
making field
identification
of quillwort
species
difficult.

Perennial aquatic or emergent herbs. **Leaves** simple, entire, linear, from a 2–3 lobed rhizome (corm). Outermost and innermost leaves typically sterile. Outer fertile leaves have a pocketlike structure (sporangia) bearing large whitish spores (megaspores; illustrated); inner fertile leaves have numerous small microspores. ☞ **Glade quillwort** (*Isoetes butleri* Engelm.), a species more common s of our region, is known from seasonally wet, calcium-rich prairie in ne Ill (⚠ state endangered). Glade quillwort has erect, twisted leaves to 20 cm long and less than 1 mm wide, sporangia 6–12 mm long, and is mostly restricted to areas underlain by limestone.

▶**KEY TO ISOETES**

1 Megaspores conspicuously covered with small spines . . . .
. . . . *I. echinospora* / SPINY-SPORED QUILLWORT
1 Megaspores not spiny **2**

2 Plants normally underwater; leaves without outer fibrous strands . .
. . . . *I. lacustris* / LAKE QUILLWORT
2 Plants underwater or on exposed, drying shores; leaves with 4 or
more fibrous strands **3**

3 Rare plant of s Mich; plants underwater or emergent; megaspores
with a raised, netlike surface . . . . *I. engelmannii*
. . . . ENGELMANN'S QUILLWORT
3 Rare plant of sw Minn; plants emergent and on drying shores; megaspores with numerous small bumps . . . . *I. melanopoda*
. . . . BLACK-FOOT QUILLWORT

Isoetes echinospora Durieu
Spiny-spored quillwort   OBL

☞ Our most
common
quillwort in
acidic lakes
and ponds.

Leaves linear, 7–25 or more, 5–15 cm long and 0.5–1.5 mm wide, usually erect, soft, bright green to yellow-green, tapered from base to a very long, slender tip, without peripheral strands from base; corm 2-lobed. **Sporangium** 4–8 mm long, usually brown-spotted when mature, half or more covered by a membranous flap (velum). **Megaspores** round, white, 0.3–0.6 mm wide, covered with short, sharp to blunt spines. *I. muricata.* ✿ Shallow water (to 1 m deep) of lakes, ponds and slow-moving rivers; plants rooted in mud, sand, or gravel. ⊕ ne, nc and ec Minn, n and c Wisc, Mich. Circumboreal, s to NJ, Pa, Ohio, Minn, Colo and n Calif.

megaspore

Isoetes engelmannii A. Braun
Engelmann's quillwort   OBL

⚠
STATUS
Indiana - E
Michigan - E

Leaves linear, 6–50 cm long and 0.5–2 mm wide, upright, not twisted, usually with 4 peripheral strands from base. **Sporangium** 6–13 mm long, pale, 1/3–2/3 covered by membranous flap (velum). **Megaspores** 0.4–0.6 mm wide, with a raised, netlike surface. ✿ Shallow water of ponds and

megaspore

megaspore

streams; plants usually underwater in spring, partly emergent later. ⊕ s Mich, Ind. NH and Mass occasionally to Ill, s to Fla, Ala and se Mo.

Isoetes lacustris L.
Lake quillwort   OBL

Leaves several to many, 5–20 cm long and 1–2 mm wide, stiff and erect or with leaf tips curved downward, dark green, fleshy and twisted, peripheral strands from base usually absent; corm 2-lobed. **Sporangium** to 5 mm long, usually not spotted; membranous flap (velum) covering up to half of sporangium. **Megaspores** round, white, 0.6–0.8 mm wide, with ridges forming an irregular netlike pattern. *I. macrospora*. ❦ Underwater in shallow to deep water of cold lakes, ponds and streams. ⊕ ne Minn, n Wisc, n Mich (and local in s Wisc and s Mich). Circumboreal, s to NY, Minn and Man; also mts of Va and Tenn.

Isoetes melanopoda Gay & Durieu
Black-foot quillwort   OBL

megaspore

Leaves 10–50 cm long and 0.5–2 mm wide, black at base with a pale line down middle of inner side, 4 peripheral strands from base usually present. **Sporangia** 5–20 mm long, brown-spotted when mature, up to 2/3 covered by membranous flap (velum). **Megaspores** 0.3–0.5 mm wide, covered with short, low ridges. ❦ Underwater to emergent in temporary ponds, wet streambanks, ditches and swales. ⊕ Rare in extreme sw Minn, once known from ne Ill. NJ occasionally to Ill, Minn and SD, s to Ga and Tex.

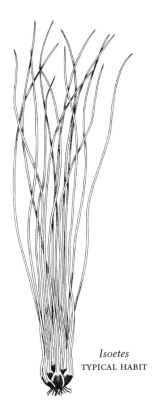

Isoetes
TYPICAL HABIT

Lycopodiaceae
Clubmoss Family

☞ Members of the Clubmoss Family were separated into several new genera in the *Flora of North America* (Vol. 2, 1993), and their treatment is followed here.

Low, trailing, evergreen, perennial herbs resembling large mosses. **Leaves** needlelike or scalelike, alternate or opposite on stem. Spore-bearing leaves (sporophylls) similar to vegetative leaves or in conelike clusters at tips of upright stems.

▶**KEY TO LYCOPODIACEAE**

1 Leafy horizontal stems absent; upright stems in clusters . . *Huperzia* . . . . Fɪʀ-ᴍᴏss

1 Leafy horizontal stems present and creeping on ground surface; upright stems borne singly along horizontal stems . . . *Lycopodiella* . . . . Bᴏɢ ᴄʟᴜʙᴍᴏss

▶**Huperzia** Bernhardi / Fir-moss

Low evergreen perennials with erect shoots; **leaves** spreading or appressed and upright. **Spores** borne at base of upper leaves.

▶**KEY TO HUPERZIA**

1 Leaves narrowly obovate with 1-8 irregular teeth; common plants of moist to wet conifer woods . . . . *H. lucidula* . . . . Sʜɪɴɪɴɢ ғɪʀ-ᴍᴏss

1 Leaves lance-shaped to oblong lance-shaped, margins entire or with 1-3 small teeth; uncommon species of wetland margins . . *H. selago* . . . . Nᴏʀᴛʜᴇʀɴ ғɪʀ-ᴍᴏss

Huperzia lucidula (Michaux) Trev.
Shining fir-moss   FAC+
Stems light green, creeping and rooting, upcurving stems forked several times, to 25 cm high and 2 mm wide (stem only), crowded with shiny dark green leaves which persist for more than one season. **Leaves** in mostly 6 rows, **spreading** or curved downward, in alternating groups of longer sterile and shorter fertile leaves, giving shoots a ragged look. Sterile leaves 6–12 mm long, toothed and broadest above middle; sporophylls barely widened and with small teeth or entire at tip. Small two-lobed buds (gemmae) produced in some upper leaf-axils; these may sprout into new plants after falling onto moist humus. *Lycopodium lucidulum.* ❦ Moist to wet conifer and hardwood forests. ⊕ nc and e Minn; Wisc, Mich, ne Ill and nw Ind. Nfld and Ont to Man and Minn, s to SC, n Ga and Ark.

leaf

Huperzia selago L.
Northern fir-moss   FACU-
Horizontal **stems** short; upright stems forked from base, 6–20 cm long and 2–3 mm wide (stem only). **Leaves** persistent, yellow-green, in 8–10 rows, 3–6 mm long and to 1 mm wide, swollen and concave at base, gradually tapered to tip, mostly without teeth, uniform in length; leaves appressed to stem, giving stems a smooth, cylindric outline. **Sporophylls**

leaf

similar to vegetative leaves; sporangia produced early in season in leaf axils, followed later by sterile leaves. Upper axils produce small, 2-lobed reproductive buds (gemmae). *Lycopodium selago.* ❦ An arctic tundra species of thickets, streambanks, cold woods and bog margins. ⊕ ne Minn, local in nw Wisc; n Mich. Circumboreal, s to Mass, NY, Ohio and Minn. ☞ A hybrid between *H. selago* and *H. lucidula* known as *H. buttersii* sometimes occurs.

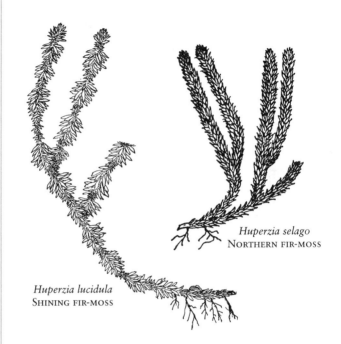

Huperzia selago
NORTHERN FIR-MOSS

Huperzia lucidula
SHINING FIR-MOSS

▶**Lycopodiella** Holub / Bog clubmoss

Low, creeping perennials of wet habitats. **Roots** located along underside of horizontal stems; horizontal stems lying flat or sometimes somewhat arched. Upright **shoots** unbranched, leafy, scattered along horizontal stems. **Leaves** narrowly lance-shaped, entire or with a few teeth. **Spores** borne in terminal, leafy cones.

▶**KEY TO LYCOPODIELLA**

1 Plants 5–10 cm high; leaves spreading; n and c portions of our region
. . . . *L. inundata* / NORTHERN BOG CLUBMOSS
1 Plants 10–30 cm high; leaves upright; sw Mich only . . . *L. appressa*
. . . . SOUTHERN BOG CLUBMOSS

Lycopodiella appressa (Chapman) Cranfill
Southern bog clubmoss   (OBL)

⚠
STATUS
Michigan - T

Stems elongate and trailing, deciduous except for evergreen buds. **Leaves** in many rows, those under trailing stems twisting upward, sparsely toothed and often with coarse hairs on leaf margins. **Fertile branches** 10–30 cm high and 1.5–5 mm wide, covered by upright leaves. **Cones** slender, 2.5–7 cm long and 3–8 mm wide, the sporophylls upright. *L. inundatum* var. *appressum, L. margueriteae, Lycopodium appressa.* ❦

sporophyll

⚠
STATUS
Illinois - E
Indiana - E

sporophyll

Wet shores and sphagnum peatlands. ⊕ Disjunct in sw Mich from main range along Atlantic coastal plain. Nfld and NS to Fla and Tex, inland to Va, NC, Tenn, Mo and Okla. ☞ Similar to **northern bog clubmoss** (*L. inundatum*) but fertile stems taller and margins of leaves often fringed with hairs.

Lycopodiella inundata L. Holub
Northern bog clubmoss   OBL

Stems elongate and trailing, deciduous but with evergreen buds at tips, rooting throughout. **Leaves** in 8–10 rows, those on underside of trailing stems twisted upward, margins ± entire. **Fertile branches** few, erect, to 1 dm high, with spreading leaves. **Cones** 1.5–5 cm long and 6–12 mm wide; sporophylls green, base widened and with a pair of teeth. *Lycopodium inundata.* ❦ Acid, open sphagnum bogs, wet sandy shores and streambanks; disturbed wetlands. ⊕ ne and ec Minn, n and c Wisc, Mich, ne Ill and nw Ind. Circumboreal, s to WVa, Ohio, n Ind, Minn and Wash.

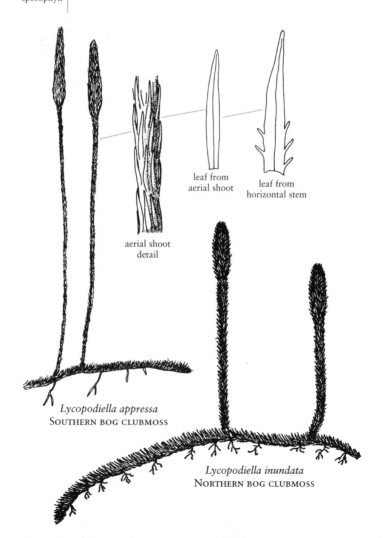

leaf from
aerial shoot

leaf from
horizontal stem

aerial shoot
detail

Lycopodiella appressa
SOUTHERN BOG CLUBMOSS

Lycopodiella inundata
NORTHERN BOG CLUBMOSS

Marsilaceae
Water-clover Family

▸**Marsilea** L. / Water-clover

Aquatic, perennial herbs, with slender rhizomes rooted in mud, sending up rows of **leaves** with long petioles and floating blades. **Blades** divided into 4 pinnae resembling a 4-leaf clover. Male and female **spores** in dark, hair-covered capsules (sporocarps) borne on stalks near base of petioles.

▸**KEY TO MARSILEA**

1 Rhizomes rooting along their entire length; leaves ± hairless; sporo-carps 2–3 on long, branched stalks; occasional in s Mich . . . . *M. quadrifolia* / EUROPEAN WATER-CLOVER
1 Rhizomes rooting only at nodes; leaves with appressed hairs; sporo-carps single on short, unbranched stalks; rare in sw Minn only (more common westward) . . . . *M. vestita* / HAIRY WATER-CLOVER

Marsilea quadrifolia L.

European water-clover   OBL

Creeping perennial. **Stem** a rhizome, rooting at nodes and with 1–3 roots between nodes; **petioles** 5–20 cm long, sparsely hairy to smooth; **blades** 5 to 20 mm long and about as wide, usually without hairs. **Sporangia** in 2–3 oval sporocarps 4–6 mm long, the sporocarps hairy when young, less so with age, on stalks to 2 cm long, stalks attached from 1–12 mm above base of petiole. ❧ Introduced and occasionally escaping to ponds and slow-moving streams. ⊕ s Mich. Me to Ill and Mo, s to Md and Ky.

Marsilea vestita Hook. & Grev.

Hairy water-clover   OBL

⚠
STATUS
Minnesota - E

Creeping perennial. **Stem** a slender rhizome, rooting only at nodes; **peti-oles** 2–20 cm long, sparsely hairy; **blades** floating or emergent, 5–20 mm long and 5–15 mm wide, usually hairy on both sides. **Sporangia** in a sin-gle oval sporocarp borne on a short stalk at or near base of petiole, the sporocarp brown, 4–7 mm long, covered with stiff, flat hairs; sori in 2 rows inside the sporocarp. *M. mucronata.* ❧ Shallow water or mud of temporary ponds, floodplains and ditches. ⊕ Rare in extreme sw Minn. Minn to s BC, s to La, Tex and Calif; Mex.

Marsilea quadrifolia
EUROPEAN WATER-
CLOVER

sporocarp

Marsilea vestita
HAIRY WATER-
CLOVER

sporocarp

Ophioglossaceae
Adder's-tongue Family

Perennial herbs from short, erect rhizomes having several fleshy roots. Plants produce 1 leaf each year on a single stalk (stipe), with bud for next year's leaf at base of stipe. **Leaves** divided into a fertile segment (sporophyll) and a sterile expanded blade. Sterile blades entire (*Ophioglossum*), or lobed or 1–3x pinnately divided (*Botrychium*). **Spores** in numerous round sporangia borne on simple or branched fertile blades.

▶**KEY TO OPHIOGLOSSACEAE**

1 Leaves dissected, veins forked but not joined; sporangia normally borne in a panicle . . . . *Botrychium* / GRAPE-FERN; MOONWORT
1 Leaves simple and entire, veins joined, forming a network; sporangia borne in a spike . . . . *Ophioglossum vulgatum*
. . . . NORTHERN ADDER'S-TONGUE

▶**Botrychium** Swartz / Grape-fern; Moonwort

Mostly small plants with 1 leaf, the blade divided into sterile and fetile segments. Sterile portion of blade pinnately divided or lobed, fertile portion branched to form a panicle bearing the sporangia.

▶**KEY TO BOTRYCHIUM**

1 Plants 50 cm or more tall; blade large and broadly triangular . . . . .
. . . . *B. virginianum* / RATTLESNAKE FERN
1 Plants smaller, less than 25 cm tall **2**

2 Blade broadly triangular in outline, dissected into narrow toothed segments (pinnae) . . . *B. lanceolatum* / LANCE-LEAVED GRAPE-FERN
2 Blade divided into 3–6 fan-shaped pairs . . *B. lunaria* / MOONWORT

Botrychium lanceolatum (S. G. Gmelin) Angström
Lance-leaved grape-fern   FACW

⚠
STATUS
Minnesota - T

Plants 6–30 cm tall, dark green, smooth, appearing in early summer and persisting to fall. **Stems** about 5x longer than blades; **blades** triangular in outline, 1–8 cm long and 1–5 cm wide, stalkless or on a short stalk to 6 mm long, divided into 2–5 pairs of sharp-pointed, toothed pinnae, lowermost pair the largest. Fertile segment 2–9 cm long, mostly twice pinnate, on a stalk 1–3 cm long. Ours are var. *angustisegmentum*. ❦ Moist humus-rich woods, hummocks in swamps, streambanks. ⊕ Rare in ec Minn, occasional in Wisc (especially nw) and Mich. Circumboreal, s to Va, Ohio, Minn, Colo and Wash. ☞ Var. *angustisegmentum* occurs from Nfld and Ont to Minn, becoming increasingly rare s to NJ and Ohio.

Botrychium lunaria (L.) Swartz
Moonwort   FACW

Plants 3–20 cm tall, rubbery-textured, appearing in late spring and withering in summer. **Leaf blades** 1.5–7 cm long and 1–3 cm wide, stalkless or on a short stalk to 5 mm long; pinnately divided into 3–6 pairs of stalkless pinnae, the pinnae fan-shaped, wider than long and without a midrib; petioles 1.5–3 cm long. Fertile segments 0.5–7 cm long, on stalks about as long as the segments. ⚘ Grassy meadows, sandy or gravelly lakeshores and streambanks, rock ledges and mossy talus; most common on ± neutral soils. ⊕ Uncommon in n Minn and along Lake Superior, Door Peninsula and extreme nw Wisc, Mich. Circumboreal, s to NY, Mich and Minn; also s Hemisphere. ☞ Several similar species of *Botrychium* have been described by W. H. Wagner including *B. campestre*, *B. minganense*, and *B. mormo*. For a complete discussion, see *Flora of North America*, Vol. 2 (1993).

Botrychium virginianum (L.) Swartz
Rattlesnake fern   FACU

Plants 40–75 cm tall, appearing in spring, withering in autumn, and not overwintering. **Blade** (trophophore) triangular, sessile, to 25 cm long and to 1.5x as wide, 3–4x pinnate, thin and herbaceous. Pinnae to 12 pairs, usually somewhat overlapping and slightly ascending; pinnules lance-shaped and deeply lobed, the lobes linear, sharply toothed and pointed at tip Spore-bearing portion (sporophore) 2-pinnate, 0.5–1.5x length of trophophore. ⚘ Occasional in swamps of cedar and black spruce; more common in moist deciduous woods. ⊕ Minn, Wisc, Mich, Ill, and Ind. Nfld to Alaska, s to Fl, Tex, and Ariz.

▸Ophioglossum L. / Adder's-tongue

Ophioglossum vulgatum L.
Northern adder's-tongue   FACW

Plants erect, 7–30 cm tall, from slender rhizomes. **Leaves** 1, entire, on a stalk 3–15 cm long; **blades** upright, oval to ovate, rounded to acute at tip, 3–8 cm long and 1–4 cm wide, conspicuously net-veined. **Sporangia** in 2 rows in a terminal, unbranched fertile segment, 1–5 cm long and 2–4 mm wide, on a stalk 6–15 cm long. Our plants are var. *pseudopodum*. *O. pycnostichium*, *O. pusillum*. ⚘ Wet sandy meadows and prairies, moist depressions, fens and wetland margins. ⊕ Local in nc and ec Minn; Wisc, Mich, ne Ill and nw Ind. Circumboreal in temperate zones; in N Amer from NS to Wash, scattered s to Va, Ohio, Ill, Iowa and Neb.

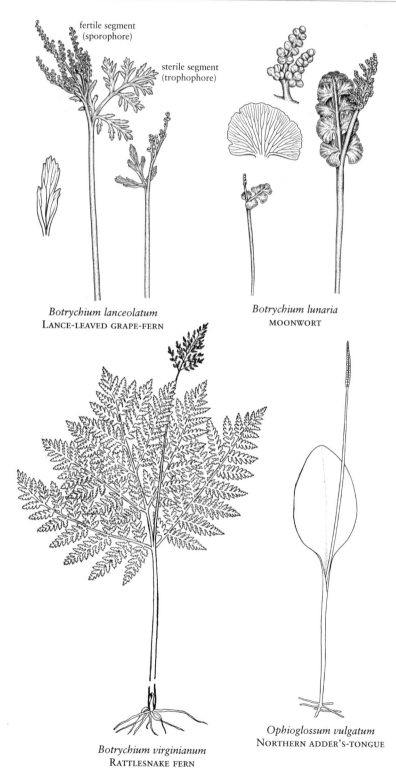

fertile segment
(sporophore)

sterile segment
(trophophore)

Botrychium lanceolatum
LANCE-LEAVED GRAPE-FERN

Botrychium lunaria
MOONWORT

Botrychium virginianum
RATTLESNAKE FERN

Ophioglossum vulgatum
NORTHERN ADDER'S-TONGUE

Osmundaceae
Royal Fern Family

▶**Osmunda** L. / Royal fern

Perennial ferns with large rootstocks and exposed crowns covered with old roots and stalks, sending up tufts of coarse leaves. **Leaves** 1–2-pinnate, differentiated into sterile and fertile segments. **Sporangia** in round clusters, spores green.

▶**KEY TO OSMUNDA**

1 Leaves 2-pinnate, pinnae ± entire; sporangia on upper half of fertile leaves . . . . *O. regalis* / ROYAL FERN
1 Leaves 1-pinnate, sterile pinnae deeply cleft; sporangia only near middle of fertile leaves, or fertile and sterile leaves separate **2**

2 Fertile and sterile leaves separate, fertile leaves cinnamon-colored, sterile leaves with a tuft of wool in axil of pinnae . . *O. cinnamomea* . . . . CINNAMON-FERN
2 Fertile pinnae near middle of vegetative leaves, with sterile pinnae above and below fertile portion, fertile portion green-black, pinnae mostly without tuft of wool in axil . . . . *O. claytoniana* . . . . INTERRUPTED FERN

Osmunda cinnamomea L.
Cinnamon-fern   FACW
Large clumped fern, to 1 m or more tall. **Blades** of sterile leaves to 30 cm wide, gradually tapered to tip, 1-pinnate, with conspicuous tuft of white or brown woolly hairs at base of each pinna, pinnae stalkless and deeply cleft into segments, with fringe of short hairs on margins; **petioles** densely hairy when young. **Fertile leaves** at center of crown, surrounded by taller sterile leaves, without leafy tissue, arising in spring or early summer and turning cinnamon brown, withering and inconspicuous by midsummer. ❦ Swamps, bog-margins, wooded streambanks, and low wet places; soils acid. ⊕ e Minn, Wisc, Mich, ne Ill and nw Ind. Labr to Minn, s to Fla, Tex, NM and tropical Amer.

Osmunda claytoniana L.
Interrupted fern   FAC+
Clumped fern to 1 m or more tall; often forming large colonies. Outer **leaves** usually sterile, inner leaves larger and with 2–5 pairs of fertile pinnae in middle of blade; fertile segments to 6 cm long and 2 cm wide and much smaller than vegetative segments above and below them; **sporangia** clusters at first green-black, turning dark brown and withering. **Blades** 4–10 dm long and 15–30 cm wide; pinnae stalkless and deeply cut into segments, with smooth or slightly hairy margins. **Petioles** covered with tufts of woolly hairs when young, becoming smooth or sparsely hairy with age, the hairs not forming tufts at pinna-bases (as in *O. cinnamomea*). ❦ Moist or seasonally wet depressions in forests, hummocks in swamps, low prairie, wet roadsides; often in drier places than *O. cinnamomea* or *O. regalis*. ⊕ e Minn, Wisc, Mich, ne Ill and nw Ind. Nfld to Ont and Minn, s to Ga and Ark; e Asia.

Osmunda regalis L.
Royal fern   OBL

Large fern to 1 m or more tall. **Blades** broadly ovate in outline, 4–8 dm long and to 3–5 dm wide, 2-pinnate into ± opposite divisions (pinnules), these well-spaced, oblong, rounded at tips, with entire or finely toothed margins. Fertile leaves with uppermost several pinnae replaced by sporangia clusters. **Petioles** smooth, green or red-green, to 3/4 length of blade. ※ Bogs, swamps, alder thickets and shallow pools; soils usually acidic. ⊕ ne and ec Minn, Wisc, Mich, ne Ill and nw Ind. Circumboreal, Nfld to Sask, s to Fla, Tex and tropical Amer.

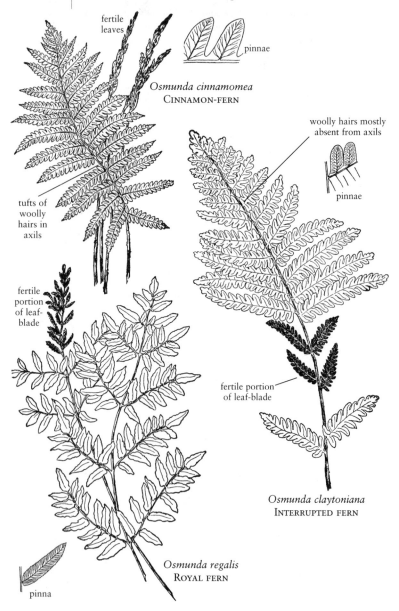

fertile leaves

pinnae

Osmunda cinnamomea
CINNAMON-FERN

woolly hairs mostly absent from axils

pinnae

tufts of woolly hairs in axils

fertile portion of leaf-blade

fertile portion of leaf-blade

Osmunda claytoniana
INTERRUPTED FERN

Osmunda regalis
ROYAL FERN

pinna

Schizaeaceae
Curly Grass Family

▶**Lygodium** Swartz / Climbing fern

Lygodium palmatum (Bernh.) Swartz
  American climbing fern   (FACW)

⚠
STATUS
Indiana - E
Michigan - E

Vining, climbing fern to 1 m or more long; rhizomes black, wiry, creeping and branching. **Leaves** delicate, evergreen, in rows from rhizomes;
blades yellow-green; pinnae of 2 types, the sterile pinnae on forked stalks
1–2 cm long, each division with a ± 6-lobed blade, 2–4 cm long and 3–6
cm wide; fertile pinnae repeatedly branched into small segments 3–5 mm
long and 1–2 mm wide, with 6–10 sporangia per segment. **Petioles** dark
brown. ≋ Moist thickets, seeps, and wetland margins; soils typically
sandy, humus-rich, and very acid. ⊕ Disjunct and rare in sw Mich and
Ind. Scattered locations from NH to Ohio, s to Fla and Miss.

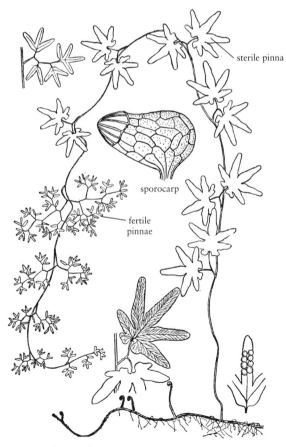

sterile pinna

sporocarp

fertile
pinnae

Lygodium palmatum / AMERICAN CLIMBING FERN

Selaginellaceae
Selaginella Family

▶**Selaginella** P. Beauv. / Spikemoss

Trailing, evergreen herbs with branched, leafy **stems**, rooting at branching points. **Leaves** small and overlapping. Spore-bearing leaves similar to vegetative leaves and clustered in cones at ends of branches. **Megaspores** 4 in each sporangium, yellow or white; microspores numerous and very small, red or yellow, covered with small spines.

▶ **TO SELAGINELLA**

1 Leaves in 4 rows, of 2 kinds: large and spreading, and small and appressed to stem, margins smooth; stems trailing with upright tips; cones 0.5–1 cm long . . . . *S. apoda* / MEADOW SPIKEMOSS
1 Leaves in many rows, all alike, with hairs on margins; fertile branches upright, cones 2–4 cm long . . . . *S. selaginoides*
. . . . NORTHERN SPIKEMOSS

Selaginella apoda (L.) Spring
Meadow spikemoss   FACW+

⚠
STATUS
Indiana - E

Plants forming large, yellow-green mats of branching, trailing stems with upright tips. **Stems** slender, to 0.4 mm wide. **Leaves** scalelike, in 4 rows, of 2 types, the larger leaves spreading, 1–2 mm long and 1 mm wide; the smaller leaves appressed to stem, up to 1 mm long and 0.5 mm wide. **Cones** 0.5–2 cm long, cylindric in 4 rows, the sporophylls similar to lateral leaves and slightly larger. **Megaspores** white, with a netlike surface. *S. eclipes.* ❦ Swamps, wet meadows, streambanks and springs, especially where calcium-rich. ⊕ e Wisc, Mich, ne Ill and nw Ind. s Que to Wisc, s to Fla and Tex.

Selaginella selaginoides (L.) Link
Northern spikemoss   FACW+

⚠
STATUS
Minnesota - E
Wisconsin - E

Plants forming small mats. Sterile **stems** prostrate, 2–5 cm long; fertile stems upright, deciduous, 5–10 cm high and 0.5 mm wide (stem only), changing upward into broader sporophylls. **Leaves** in multiple spiral rows, all alike, 2–4 mm long and l mm wide, with sharp tips and sparsely hairy margins. **Cones** ± cylindric but with 4 rounded angles, 1.5–3 cm long and to 5 mm wide. **Megaspores** yellow-white, with low rounded projections on the 3 flat surfaces. ❦ Streambanks and lakeshores; cool, mossy talus slopes; conifer bogs and swamps; moist dunes. ⊕ Rare in ne Minn and e Wisc (Door Peninsula); n Mich. Circumboreal, s to Nfld and NS, n Mich, n Minn, Colo and Wash

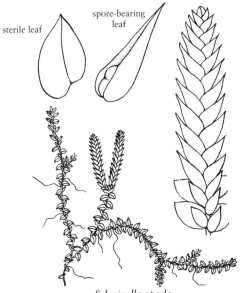

sterile leaf

spore-bearing leaf

Selaginella apoda
MEADOW SPIKEMOSS

spore-bearing leaf

Selaginella selaginoides
NORTHERN SPIKEMOSS

Thelypteridaceae
Marsh Fern Family

Ferns with creeping stems, plants from creeping stems and not forming vase-like clumps; **blades** 1-pinnate. **Sori** round to oblong; **indusia** absent in *Phegopteris*; present and tan-colored in *Thelypteris*.

▶**KEY TO THELYPTERIDACEAE**

1 Leaf blades broadly triangular in outline, broadest at base, lowermost pinnae directed downward; indusia absent . . *Phegopteris connectilis*
. . . . Northern beech-fern
1 Blades lance-shaped in outline, broadest above base; indusia present
. . . . *Thelypteris* / Marsh-fern

▶**Phegopteris** (C. Presl) Fee / Beech-fern

Phegopteris connectilis (Michaux) Watt
Northern beech-fern   UPL

⚠
STATUS
Illinois - E

Fern; rhizomes long, slender, scaly and densely hairy. **Leaves** triangular, 15–25 cm long and 6–15 cm wide; **blades** 1-pinnate, the pinnalike divisions joined by a wing along rachis, except for lowermost pair which are free and angled downward; pinnules oblong, rounded at tip, and usually hairy; **petioles** longer than blades, hairy, with narrow, brown scales. *Dryopteris phegopteris, Thelypteris phegopteris.* ⚘ Cool moist woods, thickets, streambanks, sphagnum moss hummocks, shaded rock crevices. ⊕ Common northward; ne, nc and extreme se Minn, Wisc, Mich; rare in Ill. Circumboreal, s to NC, Tenn, Iowa, nw Mont and Ore.

▶**Thelypteris** Schmidel / Marsh-fern

Small to medium ferns from slender rhizomes. **Leaves** ± hairy; **sori** small and round; **indusia** kidney- or horseshoe-shaped.

▶**KEY TO THELYPTERIS**

1 Veins of pinnae mostly forked; indusia fringed with hairs; widespread
. . . . *T. palustris* / Marsh-fern
1 Veins not forked; indusia with glands on margin; disjunct in driftless area of sw Wisc . . . . *T. simulata* / Massachusetts fern

---

Thelypteris palustris Schott
Marsh-fern   FACW+
Fern; rhizomes slender, spreading and branching. **Leaves** deciduous, erect, 20–60 cm long and to 15 cm wide; **blades** broadly lance-shaped, short-hairy on rachis and midveins, tapered to tip and only slightly narrowed at base; 1-pinnate, pinnae in 10–25 pairs, mostly alternate, narrowly lance-shaped, to 2 cm wide. Sterile and fertile leaves only slightly

different; sterile leaves thin and delicate, pinnules blunt-tipped, 3–5 mm wide, veins once-forked. Fertile leaves longer than sterile leaves; pinnules oblong, 2-4 mm wide, the margins rolled under, veins mostly 1-forked; **petioles** longer than blades, black at base, hairless and without scales. **Sori** round, located halfway between midvein and margin, sometimes partly covered by the rolled under margin; **indusia** irregular in shape, usually with a fringe of hairs. N Amer plants are var. *pubescens*. *Dryopteris thelypteris*. ≶ Swamps, low areas in forests, sedge meadows, forest depressions, open bogs, calcareous fens, marshes. ⊕ Minn (all but sw), Wisc, Mich, ne Ill and nw Ind. Newf to Man, s to Fla, Okla and e Tex.

Thelypteris simulata (Davenp.) Nieuwl.
Massachusetts fern   FACW

☞ Similar to **marsh-fern** (*T. palustris*) but lower pinnae in *T. simulata* are narrowed at base next to rachis (only slightly narrowed at base in *T. palustris*); veins in both sterile and fertile leaves of *T. simulata* are unbranched (veins in sterile leaves of *T. palustris* are mostly forked).

Fern; rhizomes creeping, 2–3 mm wide. Fertile leaves taller than sterile leaves; blades 20–40 cm long and 7–15 cm wide, tapered only slightly toward base, hairy on underside; pinnae cleft into oblong lobes which tend to fold together and upward in dry weather; petioles longer than blades, straw-colored, sparsely scaly. Sori round; indusia and lower surface of pinnules with red-orange glandular dots. Aspidium simulata, Dryopteris simulata. w Hummocks in bogs and swamps, usually in sphagnum moss; soils acid. c Disjunct in driftless area of sw Wisc from main range of NS s to Va and WVa.

fertile pinnae;
indusia absent

lower pinnule

Phegopteris connectilis
NORTHERN BEECH-FERN

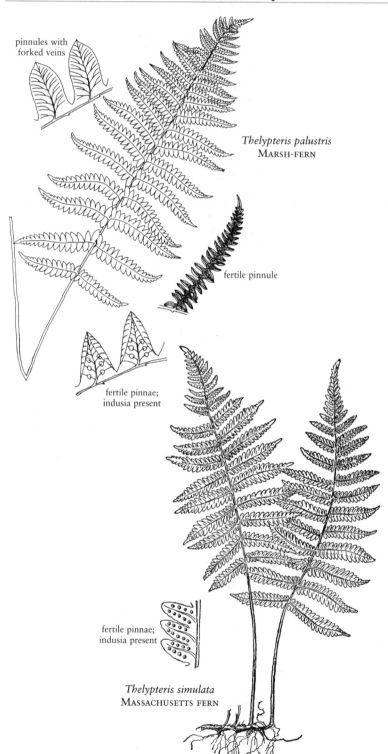

pinnules with
forked veins

Thelypteris palustris
MARSH-FERN

fertile pinnule

fertile pinnae;
indusia present

fertile pinnae;
indusia present

Thelypteris simulata
MASSACHUSETTS FERN

Conifers

ONIFERS belong to the Gymnosperms (Latin *gymn-* "naked," Greek *sperma*, "seed"), within the division Pinophyta (also termed the Gymnospermae). In contrast to the Angiosperms, the seed is not enclosed in an ovary (which develops into a fruit), but is exposed and attached to a cone or other structure. Two families are represented in Great Lakes wetlands: **Cupressaceae** (*Thuja occidentalis*), and **Pinaceae** (*Abies, Larix, Pinus, Picea*). In *Thuja*, the leaves are small, scalelike and appressed to the branches. The female cones are small, becoming brown with age. In Pinaceae, the leaves are needlelike, and either separate or grouped into bundles of two or more. The male and female flowers are borne separately on the same tree. The male flowers are borne in a herbaceous cone; the female flowers are in a woody cone with woody, overlapping scales.

Picea mariana
Black spruce
Pine Family
(Pinaceae)

Cupressaceae
Cypress Family

▶**Thuja** L. / Arbor-vitae

Thuja occidentalis L.

Northern white cedar; Arbor-vitae   FACW

Shade-tolerant tree to 20 m tall, cone-shaped with widely spreading branches, sometimes layered at base, trunk to 1 m wide or more, **bark** reddish or gray-brown, in long shreddy strips; **twigs** flattened, in fanlike sprays. **Leaves** scalelike and overlapping, 3–6 mm long and 1–2 mm wide, yellow-green, aromatic, persisting for 1–2 years. **Seed cones** small, brown, 1 cm long, maturing in fall and persisting over winter. ❦ Cold, poorly drained swamps where may *Thuja* form dense stands; soils neutral or basic, usually highly organic, water not stagnant. Also along streams, on gravelly and sandy shores of Great Lakes, and dry soils over limestone. ⊕ n and ec Minn (plus uncommon in extreme se), Wisc, Mich, local in ne Ill and nw Ind. NS and Que to Hudson Bay and Minn s to NJ, n Ind, n Ill and in mts to NC and Tenn.

Thuja occidentalis
NORTHERN WHITECEDAR; ARBOR-VITAE

Pinaceae
Pine Family

Resinous trees with evergreen or deciduous, needlelike leaves. Male and female cones separate but borne on same tree. Male cones small and soft, falling after pollen is shed. Female cones larger, with woody scales arranged in a spiral. Seeds on upper surface of scales. ☞ Although usually on well-drained soils in our area, **jack pine** (*Pinus banksiana*) and **eastern white pine** (*Pinus strobus*) are occasionally found in boggy habitats. When present they occur as stunted trees atop mossy hummocks. North of our region, jack pine is more typically a wetland species. **Eastern hemlock** (*Tsuga canadensis*) sometimes occurs on swamp margins and in seasonally wet forest depressions.

▶KEY TO PINACEAE

1 Leaves in clusters of 10–20; deciduous . . . . *Larix laricina*
. . . . TAMARACK; EASTERN LARCH
1 Leaves single and alternate on branches; persistent **2**

2 Leaves flattened in cross-section, soft; cones upright *Abies balsamea*
. . . . BALSAM FIR
2 Leaves 4-sided in cross-section, stiff; cones drooping. . . . . . . *Picea*
. . . . SPRUCE

▶**Abies** Miller / Fir

Abies balsamea (L.) Miller
  Balsam fir   FACW
Shade-tolerant tree to 25 m tall, crown spirelike, trunk to 6 dm wide; **bark** thin, smooth and gray, becoming brown and scaly with age; lower **branches** often drooping; **twigs** sparsely short-hairy. **Leaves** evergreen, linear, 12–25 mm long and 1–2 mm wide, blunt or with a small notch at tip, flat in cross-section, twisted at base and arranged in 1 plane (especially on lower branches), or spiraled on twigs. **Seed cones** 5–10 cm long and 1.5–3 cm wide, with broadly rounded scales. ❦ Cold boreal forests, swamps, and moist forests in n portion of the region; in s, mostly restricted to fens. ⊕ nc and ne Minn (plus local in se), n and c Wisc, n and c Mich. Nfld and NS to Alberta, s in mts to Va; Great Lakes.

▶**Larix** Miller / **Larch**

Larix laricina (Duroi) K. Koch
  Tamarack; Eastern larch   FACW

Shade-intolerant tree to 20 m tall, crown narrow, trunk to 6 dm wide; **bark** smooth and gray when young, becoming scaly and red-brown; **twigs** yellow-brown, ± horizontal or with upright tips. **Leaves** deciduous, in clusters of 10–20, linear, 1–2.5 cm long and less than 1 mm wide, soft,

blunt-tipped, bright green, turning yellow in fall. **Seed cones** 1–2 cm long and 0.5–1 cm wide, ripening in fall and persisting on trees for 1 year. ❦ Cold, poorly drained swamps, bogs and wet lakeshores; s in our region, confined to wet depressions. ⊕ n and c Minn (plus uncommon in se), Wisc, Mich, extreme ne Ill and nw Ind. Nfld and Labr to Alaska, s to n NJ, WVa, n Ohio, ne Ill and Minn.

▶**Picea** A. Dietr. / Spruce

Evergreen trees; **bark** thin and scaly, resin blisters common in white spruce (*P. glauca*). **Leaves** linear, square in cross-section, stiff, spreading in all directions around twig. **Cones** borne on last year's branches, drooping. **Seeds** wing-margined.

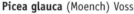

▶**KEY TO PICEA**

1 Leaves mostly 6–15 mm long; cones 1.5–3 cm long; twigs with fine
  hairs . . . . *Picea mariana* / BLACK SPRUCE
1 Leaves mostly 15–20 cm long; cones 2.5–6 cm long; twigs mostly
  without hairs . . . . *Picea glauca* / WHITE SPRUCE

Picea glauca (Moench) Voss
  White spruce   FACU
Moderately shade-tolerant tree to 30 m tall (often smaller), crown cone-like, trunk to 60 cm or more wide; **bark** thin, gray-brown; branches slightly drooping, hairless. **Leaves** evergreen, linear, 1.5–2 cm long, 4-angled in cross-section, stiff, waxy blue-green, sharp-tipped. **Cones** 2.5–6 cm long, scales fan-shaped, rounded at tip, the tip entire. ❦ Moist to sometimes wet forests; absent from wetlands where water is stagnant. ⊕ n Minn, n Wisc, UP and n LP of Mich. Nfld and Labr to Alaska, s to Maine, Mich, Minn, Mont and BC.

Picea mariana (Miller) BSP.
  Black spruce   FACW
Moderately shade-tolerant tree to 25 m tall (often smaller), crown narrow, often clublike at top, trunk to 25 cm wide; **bark** thin, scaly, gray-brown; **branches** short and drooping, often layered at base. **Leaves** evergreen, linear, 6–18 mm long, 4-angled in cross-section, stiff, waxy blue-green, mostly blunt-tipped. **Seed cones** 1.5–3 cm long, scales irregularly toothed, persisting for many years. ❦ Cold, acid, sphagnum bogs, swamps, and lakeshores; often where water is slow-moving and low in oxygen; less common in calcium-rich, well-aerated swamps dominated by **northern white cedar** (*Thuja occidentalis*). ⊕ n and ec Minn, n and c Wisc, n and c Mich (rare in s). Nfld and Labr to Alaska, s to NJ, Pa, Mich, Minn and BC. ☞ Distinguished from **white spruce** (*Picea glauca*) by its shorter needles, the branches with fine, white to red-brown hairs, the smaller, rounded seed cones with toothed scale margins, and its occurrence in generally wetter (and sometimes stagnant) habitats.

Abies balsamea
Balsam fir

Larix laricina
Tamarack;
Eastern Larch

Picea mariana
Black spruce

Picea glauca
White spruce

cone scales

Eupatorium maculatum
(Spotted joe-pye-weed) Asteraceae

Gentiana linearis (Narrow-leaved gentian)
Gentianaceae

Nymphaea odorata (White water-lily)
Nymphaeaceae

Salix bebbiana (Bebb's willow)
Salicaceae

Angiosperms - Dicots

ANGIOSPERMS (*angion-* "vessel," *sperm* "seed") form the world's largest group of vascular plants. Rather than cones as in the Gymnosperms, the reproductive structures are flowers, and seeds are enclosed in fruits that typically develop from the ovary. Angiosperms are divided into two subclasses, the **Dicotyledoneae** (sometimes termed the Magnoliopsida and often shortened to "Dicots") and the **Monocotyledoneae** (or Liliopsida, the Monocots, page 393). The names are derived from the presence of either one or two "seed leaves" or cotyledons. The Dicots are a large and diverse group of plants, and include a variety of trees, shrubs, and herbaceous species (these often simply called "wildflowers"). Monocots include familiar families such as the orchids (Orchidaceae), grasses (Poaceae), and sedges (Cyperaceae). Although not always clear-cut, Dicots and Monocots may be distinguished from one another by a combination of the following characters:

DICOTS
- Embryo with two cotyledons
- Flower parts in multiples of 4 or 5
- Major leaf veins netlike
- Stem vascular bundles in a ring
- Roots develop from radicle
- Secondary growth often present

MONOCOTS
- Embryo with single cotyledon
- Flower parts in multiples of 3
- Major leaf veins parallel
- Stem vacular bundles scattered
- Roots adventitious
- Secondary growth (wood) absent

Caltha palustris
Common marsh-marigold
Buttercup Family
(Ranunculaceae)

Acanthaceae
Acanthus Family

▶**Justicia** L. / Water-willow

Justicia americana (L.) M. Vahl
   American water-willow   OBL

⚠
STATUS
Michigan - T

Perennial herb, spreading by rhizomes and sometimes forming large colonies. **Stems** usually unbranched, smooth, 5–10 dm long. **Leaves** opposite, linear to lance-shaped, entire, 8–16 cm long and 10–25 mm wide, tapered to a tip, long-tapered to base, ± stalkless. **Flowers** in upright spikes on long stalks from upper leaf axils; spikes 1–3 cm long, crowded with flowers; sepals 5, green; petals 5, joined below into a tube, pale violet to purple, marked with darker purple on lower lip, 8–12 mm wide; stamens 2. **Fruit** a cylindric capsule 1–2 cm long; seeds 3 mm wide, covered with wartlike bumps. June–Aug. *Dianthera americana*. ≋ Shallow water, muddy pond and lakeshores, mud bars. ⊕ Local in se LP of Mich (mostly along Huron and Raisin Rivers), ne Ill and nw Ind. w Que to Ill, s to Ga, Kans and Tex.

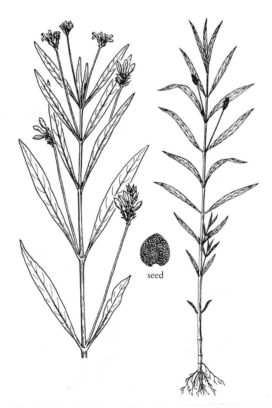

seed

Justicia americana / AMERICAN WATER-WILLOW

Aceraceae
Maple Family

☞ **Mountain
maple** (*Acer
spicatum*), a
large shrub,
sometimes
occurs in
conifer swamps
of the region.
It has large 3-
lobed leaves.

*Acer
spicatum*

☞ **Boxelder**
is distin-
guished from
the **ashes**
(*Fraxinus*)
by its paired
fruits (vs. sin-
gle in ash) and
its waxy-green
twigs.

☞ Distin-
guished from
silver maple
(*Acer sacchar-
inum*) by its
shallowly lobed
leaves vs.
deeply lobed in
silver maple.

▶**Acer** L. / Maple

Trees or shrubs. **Leaves** opposite, simple or compound. Male and female flowers borne on same or separate plants. **Flowers** with 5 sepals and 5 petals (sometimes absent), clustered into a raceme or umbel). **Fruit** a samara with 2 winged achenes joined at base.

▶KEY TO ACER

1 Leaves compound. . . . *A. negundo* / Boxelder; Ash-leaved maple
1 Leaves simple **2**

2 Leaves shallowly lobed, the terminal lobe broadest at its base; flowers with petals . . . . *A. rubrum* / Red maple
2 Leaves deeply lobed to middle of blade or below, the terminal lobe
narrowed at its base; flowers without petals . . . . . . *A. saccharinum*
. . . . Silver-maple; Soft maple

Acer negundo L.
Boxelder; Ash-leaved maple   FACW-
Tree to 20 m tall, the trunk soon dividing into widely spreading branches; **bark** brown, ridged when young, becoming deeply furrowed; **twigs**
smooth, green and often waxy-coated. **Leaves** opposite, compound,
leaflets 3–7, oval to ovate, coarsely toothed or shallowly lobed, upper
surface light green and smooth, underside pale green and smooth or
hairy. **Flowers** either male or female and on separate trees, appearing
with leaves in spring; petals absent; male flowers in drooping, umbel-like
clusters, female flowers in drooping racemes. **Fruit** a paired samara 3–4.5
cm long. ⚘ Floodplain forests, streambanks, shores; also fencerows,
drier woods and disturbed areas. ⊕ Common, especially in s and c part
of our region. Minn, Wisc, Mich, ne Ill and nw Ind. NH to Pacific coast,
s to Fla; local in Mex and c Amer.

Acer rubrum L.
Red maple   FAC
Tree to 25 m tall; **bark** gray and smooth when young, becoming darker
and scaly; **twigs** smooth, reddish with pale lenticels. **Leaves** opposite,
3–5-lobed (but not lobed to middle of blade), coarsely doubly toothed or
with a few small lobes, upper surface green and smooth, underside pale
green to white, smooth or hairy. **Flowers** either male or female, usually
on different trees but sometimes on same tree, in dense clusters, opening
before leaves in spring; sepals oblong, 1 mm long, petals narrower and
slightly longer. **Fruit** a paired samara, 1–2.5 cm long. ⚘ Floodplain
forests, swamps; also common in drier forests. ⊕ e and c Minn, Wisc,
Mich, ne Ill and nw Ind. Nfld to se Man, s to Fla and e Tex; absent from
c Ill, Iowa and n Mo.

Acer saccharinum L.
Silver-maple; Soft maple   FACW

Tree to 30 m tall; **bark** gray or silvery when young, becoming scaly; **twigs** red-brown, smooth. **Leaves** opposite, deeply 5-lobed to below middle of blade, sharply toothed, upper surface pale green and smooth, underside silvery white; petioles usually red-tinged. **Flowers** either male or female, usually on different trees but sometimes on same tree, in dense clusters, opening before leaves in spring. **Fruit** a paired samara, each fruit 3–5 cm long, falling in early to mid-summer. ❦ Floodplain forests, swamps, streambanks, shores, low areas in moist forests. ⊕ Minn, Wisc (but uncommon in far nw), Mich (especially s LP), ne Ill and nw Ind. NB and Que to Minn and e SD, s to Ga, w Fla, La and Okla.

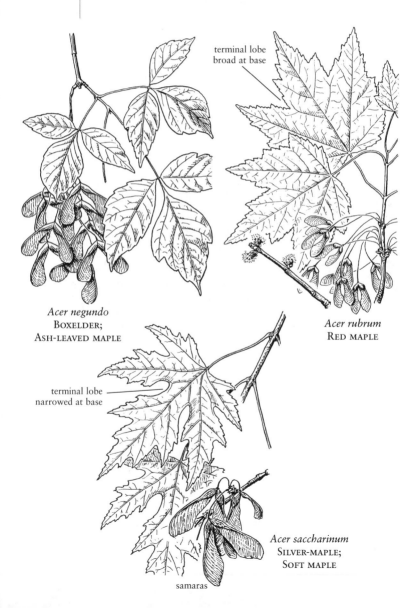

terminal lobe broad at base

Acer negundo
BOXELDER;
ASH-LEAVED MAPLE

Acer rubrum
RED MAPLE

terminal lobe narrowed at base

Acer saccharinum
SILVER-MAPLE;
SOFT MAPLE

samaras

Amaranthaceae
Amaranth Family

▶**Amaranthus** L. / Amaranth

Amaranthus tuberculatus (Moq.) Sauer
  Water hemp   OBL
Annual herb. **Stems** erect to spreading, usually much-branched, 2–15 dm
tall, usually hairless. **Leaves** alternate, ovate to lance-shaped, variable in
size, larger leaves 4–10 cm long, smaller leaves 1–4 cm long. **Flowers**
either male or female flowers and on different plants, in spikes from leaf
axils and at ends of stems; male flowers with 5 sepals, 2–3 mm long and
5 stamens; female flowers without sepals or petals (rarely with 1–2 small
sepals). **Fruit** a utricle 1–2 mm long; seeds red-brown, 1 mm wide.
July–Sept. *Acnida altissima*. ❁ Exposed muddy shores, streambanks,
swamps, wet meadows, ditches. ⊕ nc and s Minn, s Wisc, s LP of Mich,
ne Ill and nw Ind. Vt to ND, s to NJ, Ohio, Ark and Neb.

flower

Amaranthus tuberculatus / WATER HEMP

Anacardiaceae
Cashew Family

▶**Toxicodendron** Miller / Poison-sumac

Shrubs or vines. **Leaves** alternate, divided into 3 or more leaflets. **Flowers** in branched inflorescence; petals 5, green-white to yellowish. **Fruit** a white to yellowish drupe.

▶**KEY TO TOXICODENDRON**

1 Leaflets 3; margins entire or toothed . . . . *T. radicans*
. . . . COMMON POISON-IVY
1 Leaves 7–13; margins entire . . . . *T. vernix*
. . . . POISON-SUMAC

Toxicodendron radicans (L.) Kuntze.
Common poison-ivy   FAC+

Vine or low shrub. **Leaves** alternate, divided into 3 dull to shiny ovate to elliptic leaflets, 5–15 cm long; margins entire or with a few coarse teeth. **Flowers** green-white or yellowish, 25 or more in a branched inflorescence from leaf axil; petals 5. **Fruit** a white drupe, 3–5 mm wide, these often drooping. May–July. *Rhus radicans.* ☙ In n portion of region, occasional in swamps and moist rocky forests, more common along roadsides, clearings, and on sand dunes. Southward, found in floodplain forests, swamps and drier upland woods. ⊕ Minn, Wisc, Mich, Ill, Ind. NB and Que to Minn and SD, s to Fla and Tex.

Toxicodendron vernix (L.) Kuntze
Poison-sumac   OBL

Shrub or small tree to 5 m tall, often branched from base. **Leaves** alternate, divided into 7–13 leaflets, the **leaflets** oblong to oval, 4–6 cm long, tapered to a pointed tip; margins entire, smooth. **Flowers** small, white or green, in panicles to 2 dm long; sepals 5, joined at base; petals 5, not joined; stamens 5. **Fruit** a round, gray-white drupe, 4–5 mm wide. June–July. *Rhus vernix.* ☙ Tamarack swamps, thickets, floating bog mats and bog margins, often in partial shade. ⊕ ec Minn, c and s Wisc, Mich LP (especially c and s), ne Ill and nw Ind. s NS and Maine to sw Ont, s to Ohio, Ind and c Ill; also Atlantic coast from Del to Fla and Tex.

Toxicodendron radicans
COMMON POISON-IVY

Toxicodendron vernix
POISON-SUMAC

Apiaceae
Carrot Family

Biennial or perennial, aromatic herbs with hollow stems. **Leaves** alternate and sometimes also from base of plant, mostly compound; petioles sheathing stems. **Flowers** small, perfect (with both male and female parts), regular, in flat-topped or rounded umbrella-like clusters (umbels); sepals 5 or absent; petals 5, white or greenish. **Fruit** 2-chambered, separating into 2, 1-seeded fruits when mature.

▶**KEY TO APIACEAE**

1 Leaves simple . . . . *Hydrocotyle* / PENNYWORT
1 Leaves divided or compound **2**

2 Stems covered with woolly hairs; fruits and ovaries hairy . . . .
   . . . . *Heracleum lanatum* / COW-PARSNIP
2 Stems not covered with woolly hairs; fruits and ovaries hairless . . **3**

3 Lateral veins of the leaflets end in the notches (lobes or sinuses)
   between the teeth; or bulblets in upper leaf axils. . . . . *Cicuta*
   . . . . WATER-HEMLOCK
3 Lateral veins of the leaflets end in the teeth; bulblets absent **4**

4 Leaves finely divided, the smallest divisions deeply pinnately lobed;
   fruits winged, longer than wide . . . . *Conioselinum chinense*
   . . . . HEMLOCK-PARSLEY
4 Smallest divisions of leaves toothed; fruits various **5**

5 Divisions of stem leaves linear to narrowly lance-shaped, more than
   4x longer than wide **6**
5 Divisions of stem leaves broader, less than 4x longer than wide. . . **7**

6 Leaflets entire or with several coarse, irregularly spaced teeth . . . . .
   . . . . *Oxypolis rigidior* / COMMON WATER-DROPWORT
6 Leaflets finely toothed . . . . *Sium suave* / WATER-PARSNIP

7 Petiole sheaths large and inflated . . . . *Angelica atropurpurea*
   . . . . PURPLESTEM-ANGELICA
7 Petiole sheaths not inflated **8**

8 Large plants more than 1 m tall; stems with many purple spots; fruit
   with prominent ribs . . . . . *Conium maculatum* / POISON HEMLOCK
8 Smaller plants, less than 1 m tall, often partially underwater; stems
   not purple-spotted; fruit with indistinct ribs . . . . *Berula erecta*
   . . . . CUT-LEAF WATER PARSNIP

▶**Angelica** L. / Angelica

Angelica atropurpurea L.

Purplestem-angelica   OBL

Perennial herb. **Stems** stout, 2–3 m tall, ± smooth, often streaked with purple and green. **Leaves** alternate, lower leaves 3-parted, 1–3 dm long, on long petioles; upper leaves smaller, less compound, on shorter petioles, or reduced to bladeless sheaths; **leaflets** ovate to lance-shaped, smooth, 4–10 cm long; margins sharp toothed. **Flowers** in rounded small clusters (umbelets), these grouped into large rounded umbels 1–2 dm wide; petals white to green-white. **Fruit** oval, 4–6 mm long, winged. May–July. ❦ Springs, seeps, calcareous fens, streambanks, shores, marshes, sedge meadows, wet depressions in forests; often where calcium-rich. ⊕ e Minn (but local in ne), ec and s Wisc, LP of Mich (uncommon in UP), ne Ill and nw Ind. Labr to Minn, s to Del, WVa and Ill.

▶**Berula** Besser ex Koch / Water parsnip

Berula erecta (Huds.) Cov.

Cut-leaf water parsnip   OBL

⚠
STATUS
Michigan - T

Perennial herb. **Stems** erect to trailing, sparsely branched, 4–8 dm long, often rooting along trailing portion. **Leaves** alternate, 1-pinnate, basal leaves larger and less dissected than stem leaves, oblong, 5–20 cm long and 2–10 cm wide; **leaflets** lance-shaped to ovate; margins toothed or lobed. **Flowers** grouped into 5–15 small clusters (umbelets) 1 cm wide, these grouped into umbels 3–6 cm across; flowers white, 1–2 mm wide; sepals small or absent. **Fruit** oval or round, slightly flattened, 1–2 mm long, but seldom maturing. July–Sept. *B. pusilla.* ❦ Shallow water, springs, spring-fed streams, marshes, swamps, often where calcium-rich. ⊕ s Minn, s Wisc, w LP of Mich, ne Ill. NY and Ont to BC, occasional s to Fla, Mex, c Amer and Baja Calif; Europe.

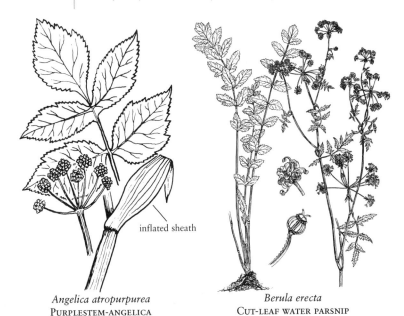

inflated sheath

Angelica atropurpurea
PURPLESTEM-ANGELICA

Berula erecta
CUT-LEAF WATER PARSNIP

▶Cicuta L. / Water-hemlock

CAUTION TOXIC!

Biennial or perennial toxic herbs. The tuberous roots, chambered **stem** base and young shoots of **common water-hemlock** (*Cicuta maculata*) are especially poisonous if eaten. **Leaves** alternate, 2–3-pinnate; **leaflets** narrow or lance-shaped, entire or toothed; leaf veins ending in the lobes (sinuses) and not at teeth as in other members of family. **Flowers** white or green, in few to many umbels. **Fruit** oval or round, ribbed.

▶**KEY TO CICUTA**

1 Upper leaflet axils usually with bulblets; leaflets narrow, to 5 mm wide . . . . *C. bulbifera* / BULBLET-BEARING WATER-HEMLOCK
1 Bulblets absent; leaflets usually much more than 5 mm wide. . . . . . .
. . . . *C. maculata* / COMMON WATER-HEMLOCK

CAUTION TOXIC!

Cicuta bulbifera L.
Bulblet-bearing water-hemlock   OBL

Biennial or perennial herb; fibrous-rooted or with a few thickened, tuber-like roots. **Stems** slender, upright, 3–10 dm tall, not thickened at base. **Leaves** alternate along stem, to 15 cm long and 10 cm wide, pinnately divided; **leaflets** mostly linear, 1–5 mm wide, margins sparsely toothed to entire; upper leaves reduced in size, undivided or with few segments, with 1 to several bulblets 1–3 mm long, in axils. **Flowers** white, in umbels 2–4 cm wide. **Fruit** round, 1–2 mm wide, but rarely maturing. Aug–Sept. ⚘ Streambanks, lake and pond shores, marshes, swamps, open bogs, thickets, springs and ditches. ⊕ Minn (all but sw), Wisc, Mich, ne Ill and nw Ind. Newf to BC, s to Va, Ill, Iowa, Neb and Ore.

CAUTION TOXIC!

Cicuta maculata L.
Common water-hemlock   OBL

Biennial or perennial herb. **Stems** single or several together, often branched, 1–2 m long, distinctly hollow above the chambered and tuberous-thickened base. **Leaves** from base of plant and alternate on stem, mostly 10–30 cm long and 5–20 cm wide; basal leaves larger and longer stalked than stem leaves; **leaflets** linear to lance-shaped, 3–10 cm long and 5–35 mm wide; margins toothed. **Flowers** white, in several to many umbels, these 6–12 cm wide in fruit, on stout stalks 5–15 cm long. **Fruit** round to ovate, 2–4 mm long, with prominent ribs. June–Sept. *C. douglasii.* ⚘ Wet meadows, marshes, swamps, moist to wet forests, thickets, shores, streambanks, springs. ⊕ Minn, Wisc, LP of Mich (uncommon in UP). Que to Alaska, s to Fla, Tex, Calif and n Mex.

Conioselinum Hoffm. / Hemlock-parsley

Conioselinum chinense (L.) BSP.
Hemlock-parsley   (OBL)

⚠
STATUS
Illinois - E
Indiana - E
Wisconsin - E

Perennial herb. **Stems** erect, slender to stout, 5–15 dm tall, smooth or often with short, rough hairs in flower head. **Leaves** alternate, triangular in outline, 1–3x pinnate, on short, winged stalks; **leaflets** lance-shaped, deeply lobed, 2–4 cm long. **Flowers** white, in long-stalked umbels 3–12 cm wide. **Fruit** oval or oblong, 2–5 mm long. Aug–Sept. ⚘ Tamarack swamps, floodplain forests, streambanks, fens. ⊕ se Wisc, s LP of Mich, ne Ill and n Ind. Labr and Nfld to Wisc, s to NC, Pa, Ind and Iowa.

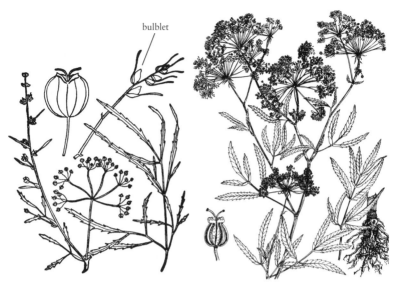

bulblet

Cicuta bulbifera
BULBLET-BEARING WATER-HEMLOCK

Cicuta maculata
COMMON WATER-HEMLOCK

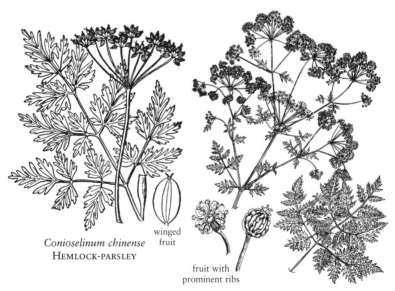

winged fruit

Conioselinum chinense
HEMLOCK-PARSLEY

fruit with prominent ribs

Conium maculatum
POISON HEMLOCK

▶**Conium** L. / Poison hemlock

Conium maculatum L.
Poison hemlock   FACW

🔲
CAUTION TOXIC!
Very poisonous,
fatal if eaten.

Biennial herb. **Stems** stout, branched, purple-spotted, 1–2 m long. **Leaves** alternate, 2–4 dm long, 3–4x pinnately divided, the **leaflets** toothed or sharply lobed. **Flowers** white, in many umbelets, these grouped in umbels to 6 cm wide. **Fruit** ovate, ribbed, 3 mm long. June–July. ⚘ Weed of shores, streambanks, waste ground and roadsides, especially on moist, fertile soil. ⊕ Occasional in Wisc, Mich, n Ill and n Ind. Introduced; now found throughout s Can and USA.

▶**Heracleum** L. / Cow-parsnip

Heracleum lanatum Michx.
Cow-parsnip   FACW

Large perennial herb. **Stems** stout, hairy, 1–2 m long. **Leaves** alternate, nearly round in outline, divided into 3 leaflets; **leaflets** 1–4 dm long and as wide, margins coarsely toothed. **Flowers** white, in large umbels, the terminal umbel 1–2 dm wide. **Fruit** obovate, 8–12 mm long and nearly as wide, often hairy. May–July. *H. maximum, H. sphondylium* subsp. *montanum.* ⚘ Streambanks, thickets, wet meadows, moist forest openings and disturbed areas. ⊕ Minn, Wisc, Mich, ne Ill and nw Ind. Labr to Alaska, s to Ga, Tex and Ariz; Siberia.

▶**Hydrocotyle** L. / Pennywort

Small perennial herbs. **Stems** prostrate and often rooting at nodes. **Leaves** round or kidney-shaped, with shallowly lobed margins and long petioles. **Flowers** small, white, in stalked or stalkless umbels. **Fruit** of 2 compressed carpels, ± round in outline. ☞ **Buttercup pennywort** (*H. ranunculoides* L. f.), an obligate wetland species more common s of our region, is rare in ne Ill (⚠ state endangered). It differs from **marsh pennywort** (*H. americana*) by its long-stalked umbels and deeply lobed leaves (vs. stalkless umbels and only shallowly lobed leaves in *H. americana;* see illustration, next page).

▶**KEY TO HYDROCOTYLE**

1 Leaf petiole attached to base of blade; flowers stalkless from leaf nodes . . . . *H. americana* / Marsh pennywort
1 Leaf petiole attached to center of blade; flowers at ends of long stalks . . . . *H. umbellata* / Water pennywort

---

Hydrocotyle americana L.
Marsh pennywort   OBL

⚠
STATUS
Indiana - E

Small perennial herb. **Stems** slender and creeping, 10–20 cm long. **Leaves** round to kidney-shaped, 1–5 cm wide; margins with 7–12 shallow lobes. **Flowers** white, in ± stalkless umbels from nodes; umbels 2–7-flowered. **Fruit** 1–2 mm wide, ribbed. June–Sept. ⚘ Conifer swamps, streambanks, shores, wet forest depressions. ⊕ Uncommon in ec and se Minn, Wisc, Mich, Ind. Nfld and Que to e Minn, s to NC, WVa, and Ind.

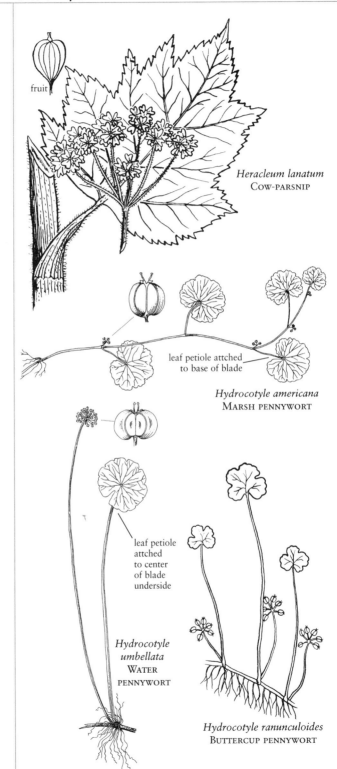

fruit

Heracleum lanatum
COW-PARSNIP

leaf petiole attched
to base of blade

Hydrocotyle americana
MARSH PENNYWORT

leaf petiole
attached
to center
of blade
underside

*Hydrocotyle
umbellata*
WATER
PENNYWORT

Hydrocotyle ranunculoides
BUTTERCUP PENNYWORT

Hydrocotyle umbellata L.
  Water pennywort   OBL
Smooth perennial herb. **Stems** creeping or floating in shallow water.
Leaves round, 3–6 cm wide, margins with rounded teeth or shallow
lobes; petioles 3–12 cm long, longer than leaves and attached to center
of blades. **Flowers** white, in umbels of 15–35 flowers, umbels on stalks
to 15 cm long. **Fruit** 2–3 mm wide, notched at both ends. Aug–Sept. ※
Streambanks, sandy shores, tamarack swamps; often in shallow water. ⊕
c and s LP of Mich, nw Ind. NS to Mich and n Ind, s to Fla and Tex;
Pacific coast and c Amer.

▶**Oxypolis** Raf. / Water-dropwort

Oxypolis rigidior (L.) Raf.
  Common water-dropwort   OBL
Perennial herb. Stems stout or slender, to 1.5 m long, with few branches
and leaves. Leaves 1-pinnate; leaflets 5–9, linear to oblong, 5–15 cm long
and 5–40 mm wide; margins entire or with scattered coarse teeth.
Flowers white, on stalks 5–20 mm long, in loose umbels to 15 cm wide.
Fruit rounded at ends, 4–6 mm long and 3–4 mm wide. July–Sept. O.
turgida. w Swamps, thickets, marshes, moist or wet prairie, calcareous
fens. c se Minn, s Wisc, s LP of Mich, ne Ill and nw Ind. e NY to s Ont
and s Minn, s to Fla and Tex. ☞ Similar to **water-parsnip** (*Sium suave*)
but differs in having entire to irregularly toothed leaves and a slightly
grooved stem, while *Sium* has finely toothed leaf margins and a more
deeply grooved stem.

▶**Sium** L. / Water-parsnip

Sium suave Walter
  Water-parsnip   OBL
Perennial emergent herb. **Stems** single, smooth, 5–20 dm long, strongly
ribbed upward; stem base thickened and hollow with cross-partitions.
Leaves 1-pinnate, on long, hollow stalks (shorter stalked above); **leaflets**
7–17 per leaf, linear to lance-shaped, 5–10 cm long and 3–15 mm wide;
margins with fine, sharp, forward-pointing teeth; finely dissected underwater leaves often present from spring to midsummer. **Flowers** white or
green-white, 1–2 mm wide, in stalked umbels 4–12 cm wide at ends of
stems and from side branches. **Fruit** oval, 2–3 mm long, with prominent
ribs. July–Sept. ※ Wet forest depressions, marshes, swamps, streambanks, pond and lake margins, ditches; usually in shallow water. ⊕
Minn, Wisc, Mich, ne Ill and nw Ind. Newf to BC, s to Fla, Tex and
Calif. ☞ A weak-stemmed form of *Sium suave* with simple leaves or
only a few leaflets is known from se Minn and sometimes considered a
separate species (*S. carsonii*).

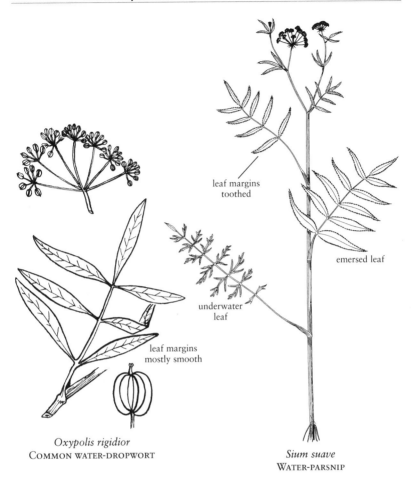

leaf margins
toothed

emersed leaf

underwater
leaf

leaf margins
mostly smooth

Oxypolis rigidior
COMMON WATER-DROPWORT

Sium suave
WATER-PARSNIP

Aquifoliaceae
Holly Family

Shrubs with alternate, simple **leaves**. **Flowers** from leaf axils, 4–8-part-ed, usually either male or female, sometimes perfect, on same (*Ilex*) or different (*Nemopanthus*) plants. **Fruit** a berrylike drupe.

▶**KEY TO AQUIFOLIACEAE**

1 Leaves tipped with a short, sharp point; margins mostly entire or with a few scattered teeth; petals linear . . . . . *Nemopanthus mucronatus*
. . . . Mountain-holly; Catberry
1 Leaves not tipped with a short, sharp point; margins toothed; petals oblong . . . . *Ilex verticillata* / Winterberry

---

▶**Ilex** L. / Holly

Ilex verticillata (L.) A. Gray
Winterberry   FACW+
Shrub to 5 m tall; **twigs** smooth, finely ridged. **Leaves** deciduous, alternate, obovate to oval, tapered to a tip, dull green above, paler below; margins with incurved teeth. **Flowers** small, green-white, on short stalks from leaf axils, opening before leaves fully expanded in spring; male flowers in crowded clusters, female flowers 1 or several in a group. **Fruit** a berrylike drupe, orange or red, 5–6 mm wide and persisting into winter. June. ❀ Swamps, open bogs, thickets, shores and streambanks. ⊕ e Minn, Wisc, Mich, ne Ill and nw Ind. Nfld and Que to Ont and Minn, s to Md, Ind and n Ill.

▶**Nemopanthus** Raf. / Mountain-holly

Nemopanthus mucronatus (L.) Loes.
Mountain-holly; Catberry   OBL
Much-branched shrub to 3 m tall; young **twigs** purple-tinged. **Leaves** deciduous, alternate, oval or ovate, 3–6 cm long and 2–3 cm wide, bright green above, dull and paler below, tip of leaf with a small, sharp point; margins entire or with small scattered teeth, on purple-red stalks 1 cm long. **Flowers** very small, yellow-white, on threadlike stalks from leaf axils; male flowers usually in small groups, female flowers single. **Fruit** a purple-red berrylike drupe, 5–6 mm wide. May–June. ❀ Open bogs (especially near outer moat), swamps, thickets, wet depressions in forests, lakeshores. ⊕ ec Minn, all but sw Wisc, Mich, nw Ind. Nfld and Que to Minn, s to WVa and n Ind.

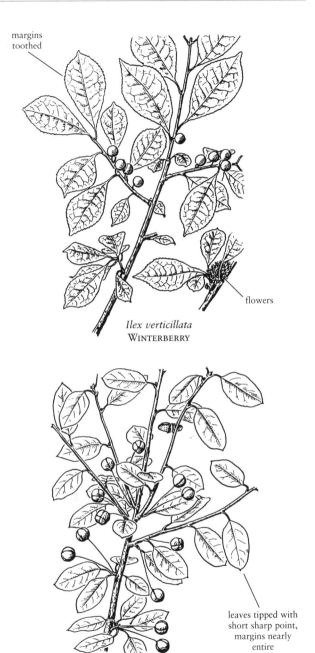

margins toothed

flowers

Ilex verticillata
WINTERBERRY

leaves tipped with short sharp point, margins nearly entire

Nemopanthus mucronata
MOUNTAIN-HOLLY; CATBERRY

Araliaceae
Ginseng Family

▶**Oplopanax** (T. & G.) Miq. / Devil's club

Oplopanax horridus (J. E. Smith) Miq.
Devil's club   FACW

⚠
STATUS
Michigan - T

Shrub 1–2 m tall, forming small colonies. **Stems** with dense covering of very sharp spines to 1 cm long. **Leaves** deciduous, alternate, 2–4 dm wide, palmately lobed, dark green and smooth above, paler below with spines on veins; petioles spine-covered. **Flowers** small, green-white, in a dense raceme 1–2 dm long; petals 5. **Fruit** a bright red, berrylike drupe, 4–6 mm long. July. 🌿 Moist ravines and mixed woods. ⊕ In Great Lakes region, known only from several islands in Lake Superior: Isle Royale and adjacent islands (Mich) and Porphyry Island (Ont). Disjunct from main range of Mont to Alaska, s to Ore; e Asia.

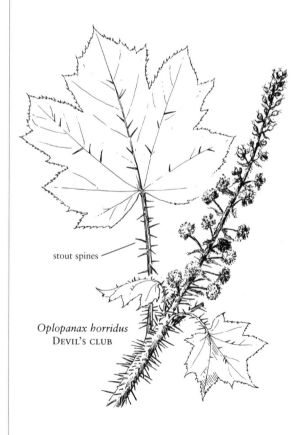

stout spines

Oplopanax horridus
Devil's club

Asclepiadaceae
Milkweed Family

▶**Asclepias** L. / Milkweed

Asclepias incarnata L.
Swamp-milkweed   OBL

☞ **Swamp-milkweed** is an important food for monarch butterfly caterpillars which feed on the leaves.

Perennial herb, from thick rhizomes; plants with milky juice. **Stems** stout, to 1.5 m long, branched above, smooth except for short, appressed hairs on upper stem. **Leaves** opposite, simple, mostly lance-shaped, 6–15 cm long and 1–5 cm wide, tapered to a sharp tip, margins entire, petioles short. **Flowers** pink to purple-red, numerous in umbels at ends of stems and from upper leaf axils, perfect, regular; sepals 5, spreading; petals 5, 4–6 mm long and curved downward; stamens 5; flowers with 5 petal-like "hoods," each with an awl-shaped "horn" projecting from the opening. **Fruit** a follicle (1-chambered and opening on 1 side only) with many seeds, the seeds having tufts of white hairs. June–Aug. ≢ Openings in conifer swamps, marshes, beaver ponds, streambanks, ditches, open bogs and fens; plants often in shallow water. ⊕ Minn, Wisc, Mich, ne Ill and nw Ind. NS to Sask, s to Fla, Tex and NM.

Asclepias incarnata
SWAMP-MILKWEED

Asteraceae
Aster Family

Annual, biennial or perennial herbs. **Leaves** simple or compound, opposite, alternate, or whorled. **Flowers** perfect (with both male and female parts) or single-sexed (sometimes sterile) and of 2 types: *ray* (or ligulate) and *disk* (or tubular). **Ray flowers** joined at base and with a long, flat, segment above (the ray); **disk flowers** tube-shaped with 5 lobes or teeth at tip. ▶ **Flowers** clustered in 1 of 3 types of heads which resemble a single flower and are attached to a common surface (the *receptacle*): ray flowers only (as in dandelion, *Taraxacum*); disk flowers only (discoid, as in tansy, *Tanacetum*); and heads with both ray and disk flowers (radiate), the ray flowers surrounding the disk flowers (as in sunflower, *Helianthus*). In addition to flowers, the receptacle may also have scales called chaff; if no scales are present, the receptacle is termed *naked*. ▶ Each head is surrounded by **involucral bracts** (sometimes called *phyllaries*); collectively, the bracts are termed the *involucre*, comparable to the group of sepals (*calyx*) subtending an individual flower. Fertile flowers have 1 pistil tipped by a 2-cleft style (undivided in sterile flowers); 5 stamens; the ovary (and achene) often topped by a pappus composed of several to many scales, awns or hairs. **Fruit** is a seedlike achene.

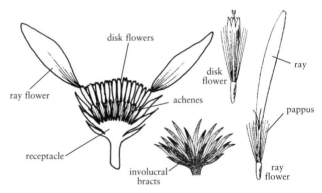

disk flowers

disk flower

ray

ray flower

achenes

pappus

receptacle

involucral bracts

ray flower

COMPOSITE FLOWER TERMINOLOGY

▶ **Climbing hempweed** [*Mikania scandens* (L.) Willd.] is a herbaceous vine (to 5 m long) known from several floodplain forests in ne Ill and nw Ind (⚠ state endangered), and was once known from wc LP of Mich. Its main range is along Atlantic coast from Maine to Fla and Tex, occasional inland in Ill, Ind and Ky (OBL; see illustration next page).

▶ **Camphor weed** [*Pluchea odorata* (L.) Cass.], known from only several locations in se Mich, ne Ill and nw Ind, is a large annual herb (to 1 m or more tall) of shores, ditches and salt marshes. Its main range is along Atlantic coast from Mass to Fla and Tex; occasional inland (OBL).

Mikania scandens
CLIMBING HEMPWEED

Pluchea odorata
CAMPHOR WEED

▶KEY TO ASTERACEAE

1 Plants aquatic, underwater leaves whorled and dissected into narrow segments . . . . *Megalodonta beckii*
. . . . WATER BEGGAR-TICKS; BECK'S WATER-MARIGOLD
1 Plants not aquatic (sometimes emergent); leaves not as above **2**

2 Plants with white milky juice; heads with ray flowers only **3**
2 Plants with watery juice; heads with both ray and disk flowers, or disk flowers only. **4**

3 Ray flowers yellow; leaves in a basal rosette. . . . .
. . . . *Crepis runcinata* / DANDELION HAWK'S BEARD
3 Ray flowers pink, purple, or rarely white; stems leafy. . . . .
. . . . *Prenanthes racemosa* / GLAUCOUS RATTLESNAKE-ROOT

4 Leaves with sharp spines . . . . *Cirsium* / THISTLE
4 Leaves without spines **5**

5 Leaves opposite or whorled **6**
5 Leaves at least in part alternate, or the leaves mostly all at base of plant. **10**

6 Receptacle (disk to which flowers are attached) not chaffy . . . .
. . . . *Eupatorium* / JOE-PYE-WEED
6 Receptacle chaffy **7**

7 Pappus (bristles or scales atop ovary/achene) of bristly hairs or bristle-tipped scales. **8**
7 Pappus absent. **9**

8 Involucral bracts in 2 series, the outer often leaflike and much larger than the inner; pappus of 2–4 awl-shaped bristles, the bristles with sharp, usually downward-pointing barbs . . . . *Bidens*
. . . . BEGGAR-TICKS; BUR-MARIGOLD
8 Involucral bracts in several series and overlapping, ± equal in size; pappus of 2 lance-shaped, unbarbed awns. *Helianthus* / SUNFLOWER

9 Rays yellow, 1 cm or more long; large perennial herb, 1–3 m tall . . . . *Silphium* / CUP-PLANT; ROSIN-WEED
9 Rays small, white; annual herb to 1 m tall . . . . . . *Eclipta prostrata* . . . . YERBA-DE-TAJO

10 Heads with both disk and ray flowers; the rays yellow **11**
10 Heads with disk flowers only; or with both disk and ray flowers, the rays not yellow **17**

11 Pappus of 2–several awns or scales. **12**
11 Pappus of many hairlike bristles **15**

12 Receptacle not chaffy; leaves tapered to a stalkless base, continuing downward as wings on the stem . . . . *Helenium autumnale* . . . . COMMON SNEEZEWEED
12 Receptacle chaffy; leaves short-stalked, not continuing downward on the stem **13**

13 Leaves all alternate . . . . *Rudbeckia* / CONEFLOWER
13 Lower leaves opposite, upper leaves alternate **14**

14 Stem not wing-margined; achenes of disk flowers compressed but not strongly flattened . . . . *Helianthus* / SUNFLOWER
14 At least upper stem wing-margined; achenes of disk flowers strongly flattened . . . . *Verbesina alternifolia* / WINGSTEM

15 Involucral bracts in 1 series, of similar length and not overlapping in rows. . . . . *Senecio* / GROUNDSEL
15 Involucral bracts in several series, of different lengths and overlapping **16**

16 Flowers in a corymblike (± flat-topped) head; leaves narrow, 2–10 mm wide, entire, dotted with glands . . . . *Euthamia* . . . . FLAT-TOPPED GOLDENROD
16 Flowers in a paniclelike head; leaves wider, 1–4 cm wide, toothed, not gland-dotted . . . . *Solidago* / GOLDENROD

17 Heads either male or female and of different shapes, the male flowers in small heads above the larger female heads; involucral bracts of the female heads with hooked spines, enclosing the flowers to form a bur . . . . *Xanthium strumarium* / COMMON COCKLEBUR
17 Heads with both male and female flowers, or rarely either male or female; involucral bracts neither spiny nor bur-like **18**

18 Main leaves large and at base of plant, arrowhead-shaped or palmately lobed, white-woolly at least on underside; plants flowering in spring to early summer before leaves develop. . . . . *Petasites* . . . . SWEET COLTSFOOT
18 Main leaves along stem, neither arrowhead-shaped nor palmately lobed; plants flowering late-summer or fall (except the earlier flowering *Erigeron philadelphicus*) **19**

19 Heads with disk flowers only **20**
19 Heads with both disk and ray flowers (the rays narrow and ± equal to the involucral bracts in *Erigeron lonchophyllus*, and therefore inconspicuous) **25**

20 Leaves pinnately dissected; pappus absent . . . . . . *Artemisia biennis*
. . . . Biennial wormwood
20 Leaves simple, entire or toothed; pappus of many hairlike bristles. .
. . . . **21**

21 Plants annual; leaves linear **22**
21 Plants perennial (sometimes biennial in *Erigeron lonchophyllus);*
leaves wider **23**

22 Stems with wool-like hairs. . . . . *Gnaphalium uliginosum*
. . . . Marsh cudweed
22 Stems without hairs . . . . *Aster brachyactis* / Rayless aster

23 Flowers white . . . . *Cacalia* / Indian plantain
23 Flowers purple or pink-purple **24**

24 Flowers in a long, spikelike head; leaves linear . . . . . *Liatris spicata*
. . . . Marsh blazing star; Gay feather
24 Flowers in an open corymb; leaves lance-shaped. . . . .
. . . . *Vernonia fasciculata* / Smooth ironweed

25 Pappus of 2 bristles about as long as achene and several very small
bristles . . . . *Boltonia asteroides* / White boltonia
25 Pappus of many hairlike bristles **26**

26 Rays wider than 0.5 mm . . . . *Aster* / Wild aster
26 Rays very narrow, to 0.5 mm wide. . . . *Erigeron* / Daisy; Fleabane

▶**Artemisia** L. / Wormwood; Sage

Artemisia biennis Willd.
Biennial wormwood   FACW-

Taprooted, annual or biennial herb. **Stems** erect, to 1 m
or more long, often branched, smooth, only faintly
scented. **Leaves** alternate, pinnately dissected nearly
to middle, 5–12 cm long and 2–5 cm wide, the segments linear and toothed. **Flowers** in stalkless
heads from upper leaf axils; the heads composed
of many small green disk flowers, grouped into
spikelike inflorescences, with leafy bracts much
longer than the clusters of heads; pappus absent.
Fruit a small oblong achene. Aug–Sept. ❦ Sandy
lakeshores, streambanks, ditches, mud flats, disturbed areas; often where seasonally flooded. ⊕
Minn, Wisc, Mich, ne Ill and nw Ind. Native to nw
USA, occasional in our region as a weed; Que to
BC, s to NJ, Ky, Mo and Calif.

▶**Aster** L. / Wild aster

Mostly perennial herbs (annual in *A. brachyactis* and *A. subulata*).
Leaves simple, alternate. **Flower heads** with both ray and disk flowers
(disk flowers only in *Aster brachyactis*); ray flowers white, pink, blue or
purple, usually more than 0.5 mm wide (in contrast to the **fleabanes**,

Erigeron); disk flowers red, purple or yellow; involucral bracts in 2 or more series, usually overlapping; receptacle naked (not chaffy), ± flat; pappus of numerous hairlike bristles.

▶**KEY TO ASTER**

1 Upper stem leaves stalkless, the base of leaf clasping stem; involucral bracts sometimes with gland-tipped hairs **2**
1 Upper stem leaves not clasping; involucral bracts without gland-tipped hairs. **4**

2 Leaf margins entire; involucral bracts and flower stalks with glands
 . . . . *A. novae-angliae* / NEW ENGLAND ASTER
2 Leaf margins usually with at least some teeth; involucral bracts without glands. **3**

3 Plants with long, creeping rhizomes; upper stems with lines of hairs, lower stems ± smooth; leaves appearing crowded in head . *A. firmus*
 . . . . SHINING ASTER
3 Plants from a short rhizome or crown; stems hairy, but the hairs not in uniform lines; leaves in heads not crowded . . . . *A. puniceus*
 . . . . BRISTLY ASTER; PURPLE-STEM ASTER

4 Plants annual; rays absent or less than 2 mm long **5**
4 Plants perennial; rays present and larger. **6**

5 Rays absent; leaves less than 4 mm wide, with small, rough prickles on margins. . . . . *A. brachyactis* / RAYLESS ASTER
5 Rays present but very small; leaves more than 6 mm wide; leaf margins smooth. . . . . *A. subulatus* / ANNUAL SALTMARSH ASTER

6 Heads in a ± flat-topped cluster; midrib of involucral bract ± same width its entire length **7**
6 Heads in elongate panicles; midvein of involucral bracts expanded to a ± diamond-shape above middle of bract **8**

7 Leaves linear, less than 7 mm wide; rays pink . . . . *A. nemoralis*
 . . . . LEAFY BOG-ASTER
7 Leaves broader, more than 9 mm wide; rays white . . . *A. umbellatus*
 . . . . TALL FLAT-TOPPED WHITE ASTER

8 Involucral bracts covered with hairs . . . . *A. ontarionis*
 . . . . LAKE ONTARIO ASTER; BOTTOMLAND-ASTER
8 Involucral bracts smooth, or only fringed with hairs on margins . . **9**

9 Involucral bracts tipped with a short sharp spine. . . . . . . *A. pilosus*
 . . . . FROST ASTER
9 Involucral bracts not spine-tipped **10**

10 Leaf undersides net-veined, the veins dark green, the spaces enclosed by the veins paler and not elongate; rays blue. . . . . *A. praealtus*
 . . . . VEINY LINED ASTER
10 Leaf undersides not distinctly net-veined with paler spaces, or if somewhat net-veined, the spaces elongate; rays mostly white to pink (blue in *Aster longifolius*). **11**

11 Leaves hairy, at least on underside midvein; disk flowers deeply lobed (to half or more the length of expanded portion of corolla above the tube). **12**

11 Leaf undersides ± smooth; disk flowers shallowly lobed (to 1/3 or less the length of expanded portion of corolla above tube) **13**

12 Leaf underside smooth except for hairs on midvein; stems in a clump from a crown . . . . . . *A. lateriflorus* / CALICO ASTER; GOBLET ASTER
12 Leaf underside covered with short hairs; stems single from slender rhizomes . . . . *A. ontarionis*
. . . . LAKE ONTARIO ASTER; BOTTOMLAND-ASTER

13 Flower heads less than 1.5 cm wide, on stalks 1–5 cm long. . . . . . .
. . . . *A. dumosus* / BUSHY ASTER
13 Flower heads 1.5–3 cm wide, on stalks less than 1 cm long. **14**

14 Stem leaves clasping at base of leaf; involucral bracts ± same length
. . . . . *A. longifolius* / NEW YORK ASTER; LONG-LEAVED BLUE ASTER
14 Stem leaves stalkless or only slightly clasping at base **15**

15 Stems less than 2 mm wide; leaves less than 6 mm wide, margins often rolled under; flowers in clusters of 1–15 heads, the flower stalks spreading. . . . . *A. borealis* / NORTHERN BOG-ASTER
15 Stem 3 mm or more wide; leaves more than 6 mm wide, margins flat; flowers in clusters of 20 heads or more, the flower stalks usually ascending. . . . . *A. lanceolatus* / EASTERN LINED ASTER

Aster borealis Prov.

Northern bog-aster   OBL

Perennial herb, from rhizomes 1–2 mm wide. **Stems** erect, slender, 3–8 dm tall and to 2 mm wide, unbranched below, usually branched in the head; smooth except for lines of short, appressed hairs below base of upper leaves. **Leaves** alternate, linear, 4–12 cm long and 2–6 mm wide, sometimes slightly clasping at base, margins rough-to-touch, petioles absent. **Flower heads** usually few to rarely many, in an open, broad inflorescence; the heads 1.5–2 cm wide; involucre 5–7 mm high, the involucral bracts overlapping, often purple at tips and on margins; ray flowers 20–50, white to light blue or lavender, 1–1.5 cm long. **Fruit** an achene; pappus of pale hairs. Aug–Sept. *A. junciformis*. ❦ Conifer swamps, calcareous fens, open bogs, wet meadows, shores and seeps. ⊕ Minn (all but extreme sw and se), Wisc, Mich (all, but local in w UP), ne Ill and nw Ind. Que to Alaska, s to NJ, Minn, Neb, Colo, Idaho and BC.

Aster brachyactis S. F. Blake

Rayless aster   FAC

Taprooted annual herb. **Stems** unbranched and erect, to branched and spreading, 2–6 dm long, smooth. **Leaves** alternate, linear, 2–10 cm long and mostly 2–5 mm wide, margins fringed with scattered hairs, petioles absent. **Flower heads** several to many, in an open inflorescence which forms much of plant; flower heads bell-shaped, 1–2 cm wide, involucre 5–10 mm high, the involucral bracts mostly green, linear, of equal length or slightly overlapping; ray flowers absent. **Fruit** a flattened achene, 1–2 mm long; pappus of many long, soft hairs. Aug–Sept. *Brachyactis ciliata, B. angusta*. ❦ Shores (including along Great Lakes), streambanks, wet meadows, roadside ditches, usually where brackish. ⊕ Introduced from w N Amer; mostly w Minn (local in n and sc), Wisc, Mich (s UP near Lake Mich, LP near Great Lakes), ne Ill and nw Ind. Minn to BC, s to Mo, Kans, Colo, Utah and Wash; Siberia.

Aster dumosus L.
Bushy aster   FAC+
Perennial herb, spreading by long or short rhizomes. **Stems** branched above, 3–10 dm long, smooth or with fine hairs on upper stem. **Leaves** alternate, all from stem, linear to narrowly lance-shaped, 3–10 cm long and to 1 cm wide, much smaller and bractlike on branches, upper surface usually rough-to-touch, underside smooth, margins rough-to-touch, petioles absent. **Flower heads** many in an open, branched inflorescence, on stalks 2 cm or more long; involucre 4–6 mm long, smooth, the involucral bracts broad and green at tip, overlapping; ray flowers 15–30, usually white, rarely blue to pale violet, 5–10 mm long. **Fruit** a hairy achene; pappus white. Aug–Oct. ⚘ Moist to wet sandy or mucky shores, interdunal swales, sedge meadows, sometimes where calcium-rich; also in drier oak and jack pine woods. ⊕ Mich LP and e UP, ne Ill and nw Ind. Maine to Mich and n Ill, s to Fla and Ark.

Aster firmus Nees.
Shining aster   FACW+

☞ Shining aster is similar to **bristly aster** (*Aster puniceus*) and sometimes considered a variety of it (*A. puniceus* var. *firmus*).

Perennial herb, from long creeping rhizomes. **Stems** stout, unbranched, or branched in head, 0.5–2 m long, lower stem mostly smooth or sparsely hairy, upper stem and branches with lines of fine hairs. **Leaves** alternate, crowded, especially on upper part of stem, often shiny, lance-shaped to oblong, 5–15 cm long and 1–4 cm wide, clasping at base, margins ± entire, petioles absent. **Flower heads** few to many in a leafy inflorescence; involucre 5–12 mm high, the involucral bracts tapered to a tip; ray flowers 20–60, pale blue or lavender (sometimes white), to 2 cm long. **Fruit** a smooth or finely hairy achene; pappus nearly white. Aug–Sept. *A. lucidulus.* ⚘ Swamps, streambanks, shores, sedge meadows, calcareous fens, marshes, thickets, and roadside ditches; sometimes forming large colonies. ⊕ Minn, Wisc, Mich, ne Ill and nw Ind. w NY to Minn and SD, s to WVa and s Mo.

Aster lanceolatus Willd.
Eastern lined aster   FACW

☞ **Eastern lined aster** is one of the region's most common asters, and found in a wide variety of habitats.

Perennial herb, forming colonies from long rhizomes. **Stems** 0.5–1.5 m long, upper stem with lines of hairs. **Leaves** alternate, all on stem, lance-shaped to linear, 8–15 cm long and 3–30 mm wide, upper surface smooth or slightly rough-to-touch, margins toothed or sometimes entire; petioles absent or blades tapered to petiolelike base, sometimes slightly clasping stem. **Flower heads** many in an elongate leafy inflorescence; the involucre 3–6 mm high, the involucral bracts tapered to a green tip, smooth or margins fringed with hairs, strongly overlapping; ray flowers 20–40, usually white, sometimes lavender or blue, 4–12 mm long. **Fruit** an achene; pappus white. Aug–Oct. *A. hesperius, A. interior, A. paniculatus, A. simplex.* ⚘ Marshes, wet meadows, fens, swamp openings, low prairie, streambanks and shores. ⊕ Minn, Wisc, Mich, ne Ill and nw Ind. NS to ND, s to Va and Tex.

Aster lateriflorus (L.) Britton
Calico aster; Goblet aster   FACW-
Perennial herb, from a branched base or short rhizome. **Stems** 3–14 dm long, smooth to finely hairy. **Leaves** from base of plant and along stem; basal leaves ovate, with a long petiole; stem leaves alternate, lance-shaped, 5–15 cm long and 0.5–3 cm wide, branch leaves much smaller; upper surface rough-to-touch or smooth, underside smooth except for finely hairy midvein; margins with forward-pointing teeth or sometimes entire; petioles short or absent; basal and lower stem leaves usually soon

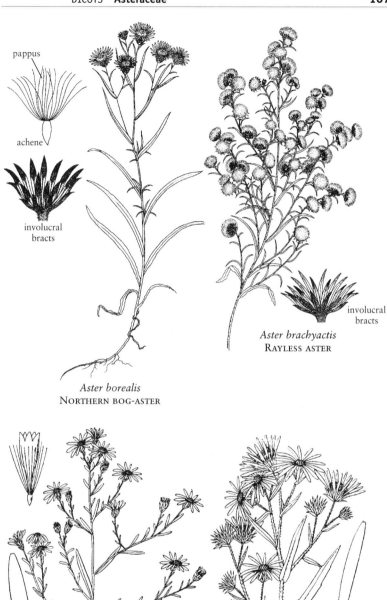

pappus

achene

involucral
bracts

Aster borealis
NORTHERN BOG-ASTER

involucral
bracts

Aster brachyactis
RAYLESS ASTER

ray flower

Aster dumosus
BUSHY ASTER

disk
flower

ray
flower

Aster firmus
SHINING ASTER

deciduous. **Flower heads** many, mostly on 1 side of inflorescence branches; involucre smooth, 4–6 mm long, the involucral bracts overlapping in 3–4 series, with a green-purple tip; ray flowers 9–15, white or pale purple, 4–7 mm long. Aug–Oct. *A. agrostifolius, A. hirsuticaulis.* ≽ Swamps, thickets, floodplain forests, shores, streambanks, roadsides, moist hardwood and mixed conifer-hardwood forests; often where shaded. ⊕ Minn (all but sw), Wisc, Mich, ne Ill and nw Ind. Que s to Fla, w to Minn, e SD, e Kans and Tex.

Aster longifolius Lam.
New York aster; Long-leaved blue aster   FACW

Perennial herb, from long creeping rhizomes. **Stems** 2–14 dm long, smooth or upper stems with lines of fine hairs. **Leaves** alternate, mostly on the stem, often thick and firm, lance-shaped to oval, 4–15 cm long and 5–25 mm wide, base of leaf narrowed and somewhat clasping; margins entire or with forward-pointing teeth, rough-to-touch; petioles absent. **Flower heads** several to many, 5–10 mm wide; involucre smooth, the involucral bracts overlapping, and some usually spreading at tip; rays 20–50, blue, violet or sometimes white, 5–15 mm long. **Fruit** a smooth achene; pappus whitish. Aug–Oct. *Aster novi-belgi.* ≽ Moist open areas, especially where sandy or gravelly, including shores, streambanks, rocky Lake Superior shoreline, seasonally wet meadows. ⊕ Local in n Wisc, UP and n LP of Mich. Nfld to SC along Atlantic coast where often in salt marshes, occasional inland to Wisc.

Aster nemoralis Aiton
Leafy bog-aster   OBL

Perennial herb, spreading by rhizomes. **Stems** 1–6 dm long, finely hairy, the hairs slightly sticky. **Leaves** alternate, all from the stem, firm, linear to oval or oblong, 1–5 cm long and to 1 cm wide, upper surface rough-to-touch, finely hairy below (at least along veins); margins often rolled under; petioles absent. **Flower heads** 1 to several, on slender stalks; involucre 5–7 mm high, the involucral bracts awl-shaped, overlapping, green-purple; ray flowers 15–25, pink or lilac-purple, 10–15 mm long. **Fruit** a glandular-hairy achene; pappus white. Aug–Sept. ≽ Fens (especially where sphagnum mosses are sparse), occasional on sandy shores; often with **sweet gale** (*Myrica gale*) and **twig-rush** (*Cladium mariscoides*). ⊕ UP of Mich. Nfld and Labr to James Bay, s to NJ, NY and n Mich.

Aster novae-angliae L.
New England aster   FACW

Perennial herb, from a short rhizome or crown. **Stems** stout, erect, 4–10 dm long, with stiff, spreading, sometimes gland-tipped hairs. **Leaves** alternate, lance-shaped, 3–7 cm long and 1–2.5 cm wide, upper surface rough-to-touch or with short hairs, underside soft hairy, base of leaf strongly clasping stem, margins entire, petioles absent. **Flower heads** several to many, in clusters at ends of branches, 1.5–3 cm wide; involucre 7–12 mm high, the involucral bracts awl-shaped, glandular-hairy, sometimes purple; ray flowers 40 or more, blue-violet to less often red or pink, 1–2 cm long. **Fruit** a hairy achene; pappus red-tinged. Aug–Oct. ≽ Wet meadows, low prairie, shores, thickets, calcareous fens, roadsides; usually in moist or wet open areas. ⊕ Mostly w and s Minn; Wisc, Mich (especially s LP), ne Ill and nw Ind. Mass to ND and Wyo, s to Ala, Okla and NM.

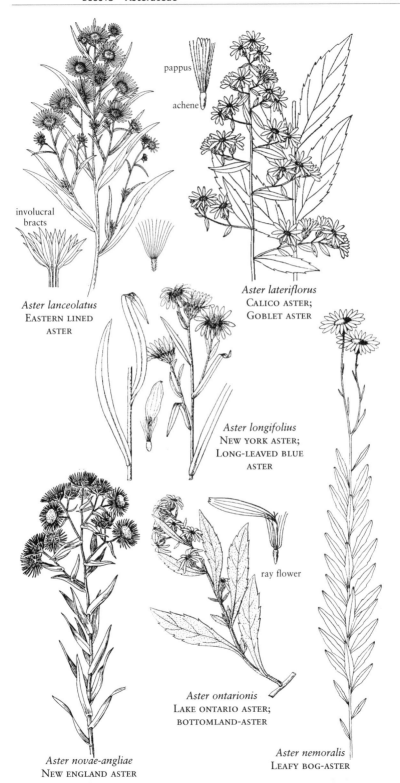

pappus

achene

involucral bracts

Aster lanceolatus
EASTERN LINED
ASTER

Aster lateriflorus
CALICO ASTER;
GOBLET ASTER

Aster longifolius
NEW YORK ASTER;
LONG-LEAVED BLUE
ASTER

ray flower

Aster ontarionis
LAKE ONTARIO ASTER;
BOTTOMLAND-ASTER

Aster nemoralis
LEAFY BOG-ASTER

Aster novae-angliae
NEW ENGLAND ASTER

Aster ontarionis Wieg.

Lake Ontario aster; Bottomland-aster   FAC

☞ Similar to **calico aster** (*A. lateriflorus*), but with long rhizomes rather than a crown or short rhizomes.

Perennial herb, from long creeping rhizomes. **Stems** branched, 3–8 dm long, upper stems with short spreading hairs. **Leaves** alternate, thin, oblong lance-shaped, 5–10 cm long and 1–3 cm wide (upper leaves smaller), upper surface rough-hairy to nearly smooth, underside finely to densely hairy; margins with sharp, forward-pointing teeth above middle of blade; petioles absent. **Flower heads** 1–2 cm wide, on short stalks from short leafy branches; involucre smooth to finely hairy, 5–7 mm high, the involucral bracts overlapping; ray flowers white, 9 or more. **Fruit** an achene; pappus white. Sept–Oct. ❦ Floodplain forests, river terraces, thickets. ⊕ s and c Minn, Wisc, Mich LP (local in c UP), ne Ill and nw Ind. NY to SD, s to Ky, Miss and Okla.

Aster pilosus Willd.

Frost aster   FACU+

Perennial herb, from a large crown. **Stems** to 1.5 m long, ± smooth (var. *pringlei*) or stems and leaves with spreading hairs (var. *pilosus*). **Leaves** alternate, lower leaves oblong lance-shaped, 5–10 cm long and 1–2 cm wide, stalked; upper leaves smaller, linear, stalkless; margins entire or slightly toothed; petioles fringed with hairs; basal leaves and lower stem leaves soon deciduous (or basal leaves persistent). **Flower heads** at ends of small branches, forming an open inflorescence; involucre urn-shaped, narrowed near middle and flared upward, 3–5 mm high, smooth, involucral bracts overlapping to nearly equal in length, green-tipped; ray flowers 15–35, white. **Fruit** an achene; pappus white. ❦ Sandy and gravelly shores, interdunal swales, wet meadows; often where calcium-rich; sometimes weedy in disturbed fields and roadsides. ⊕ se Minn, Wisc, Mich, ne Ill and nw Ind. NS to s Minn and Neb, s to N Fla, La and Kans.

Aster praealtus Poiret

Veiny lined aster   FACW

Perennial herb, spreading by rhizomes and forming colonies. **Stems** to 1 m long, with lines of hairs, especially in upper stem. **Leaves** alternate, firm, lance-shaped, 6–12 cm long and 1–2 cm wide, upper surface rough-to-touch to nearly smooth, underside smooth or finely hairy, with conspicuous netlike veins surrounding lighter colored areas (areole); margins ± entire; petioles absent, the base of leaves often slightly clasping. **Flower heads** at ends of short leafy branches; involucre 5–7 mm high, the involucral bracts overlapping; rays 5–15 mm long, blue-purple (rarely white). **Fruit** an achene; pappus white. Sept–Oct. *A. nebraskensis, A. woldeni.* ❦ Wet meadows, low prairie, moist fields, thickets. ⊕ s Wisc, local in s LP of Mich, ne Ill and nw Ind. Mich to Neb, s to Ga, Ariz and Mex; occasional e to Mass and MD.

Aster puniceus L.

Bristly aster; Purple-stem aster   OBL

Large perennial herb, from a short rhizome or crown, sometimes also with short stolons. **Stems** stout, red-purple, 0.5–2 m long, unbranched, or branched in head, with long stiff hairs or sometimes nearly smooth. **Leaves** alternate, lance-shaped to oblong lance-shaped, 6–18 cm long and 1–4 cm wide, rough-to-touch to nearly smooth above, underside smooth or with long hairs on midvein; margins with scattered sharp teeth or sometimes entire; petioles absent, base of leaf clasping. **Flower heads** numerous, 1.5–2.5 cm wide; involucre 6–10 mm high, involucral bracts about equal in length, smooth or fringed with hairs, green and spreading; ray flowers 20–50, blue (rarely white). **Fruit** a smooth achene;

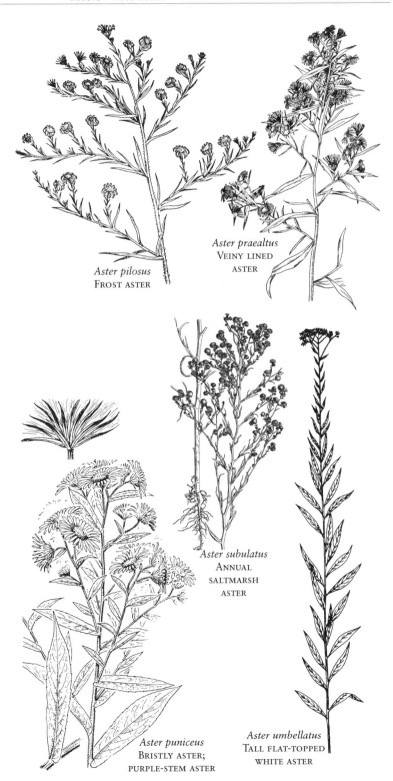

Aster pilosus
FROST ASTER

Aster praealtus
VEINY LINED
ASTER

Aster subulatus
ANNUAL
SALTMARSH
ASTER

Aster puniceus
BRISTLY ASTER;
PURPLE-STEM ASTER

Aster umbellatus
TALL FLAT-TOPPED
WHITE ASTER

pappus ± white. Aug–Sept. ❦ Swamps, sedge meadows, thickets, calcareous fens, streambanks, shores, springs. ⊕ Minn, Wisc, Mich, ne Ill and nw Ind. Newf to ND, s to Ga, Ala, Ill and Neb.

Aster subulatus Michx.
Annual saltmarsh aster   OBL
Annual herb, from a short taproot; plants smooth and fleshy. **Stems** to 1 m long. **Leaves** alternate, linear to lance-shaped, to 20 cm long and 1 cm wide; margins ± entire; petioles absent, base sometimes slightly clasping; bracts in head much smaller and awl-shaped. **Flower heads** usually many in an open inflorescence; involucre 5–8 mm high, the involucral bracts overlapping in 3–4 series, often purple-tinged at tips and margins; rays 20–30, small, blue-purple. **Fruit** a compressed achene; pappus white. Sept–Oct. ❦ Ditches along salted highways. ⊕ Local, but probably increasing in s LP of Mich, n Ind and n Ill. Salt marshes along Atlantic coast from NB to c Amer; occasional inland to NY, n Ill and Ark.

Aster umbellatus Miller
Tall flat-topped white aster   FACW
Perennial herb, from thick rhizomes. **Stems** 0.5–2 m long, upper stem with appressed, short hairs. **Leaves** alternate, lance-shaped to oblong lance-shaped, 4–15 cm long and 1–4 cm wide, rough-to-touch above, densely short-hairy below; margins entire; petioles short, or absent on upper leaves. **Flower heads** usually many, 1–1.5 cm wide, in a ± flat-topped inflorescence; involucre 3–5 mm high, the involucral bracts short-hairy and overlapping; rays 5–10, white, 5–8 mm long. **Fruit** a nerved achene; pappus nearly white. July–Sept. ❦ Openings in swamps and moist forests, thickets, streambanks, sedge meadows, calcareous fens, roadside ditches, rocky shores of Lake Superior. ⊕ Minn, Wisc, Mich, ne Ill and nw Ind. Nfld to Minn and Alberta, s to Va, n Ala, Ill and Neb. ☞ Two vars. in our region: *A. umbellatus* var. *pubens* (sometimes considered a separate species, *A pubentior*) with leaves hairy on underside, and *A. umbellatus* var. *umbellatus*, with leaves smooth on underside (apart from hairs on midvein).

▸Bidens L. / Beggar-ticks

☞ The perennial aquatic species formerly known as *Bidens beckii* is now classified as Megalodonta beckii.

Weedy annual or biennial herbs. Leaves opposite, simple, lobed, or pinnately divided. **Flower heads** with both disk and ray flowers, or with disk flowers only; ray flowers often about 8, yellow; involucral bracts in 2 series, the outer row leaflike and spreading, the inner row much shorter and erect; receptacle ± flat and chaffy. **Fruit** a flattened achene; pappus of 2–5 barbed awns which persist atop the achene; the body of achene barbed or with stiff hairs (at least on the angles), the "stick-tights" facilitating dispersal of seed by animals.

▸KEY TO BIDENS

1 Leaves simple and toothed, or rarely lobed; achenes 3–4-awned . . **2**
1 Leaves all (or mostly) pinnately divided or compound; achenes 2-awned **5**

2 Leaves mostly stalkless **3**
2 Leaves with a petiole 1–4 cm long **4**

3 Heads nodding when mature; outer involucral bracts widely spreading . . . . *B. cernua* / Nodding beggar-ticks

3 Heads mostly upright; outer involucral bracts ± erect . . . *B. comosa*
. . . . Strawstem beggar-ticks

4 Stems straw-colored; disk flowers 4-lobed, pale yellow; achenes mostly 3-awned . . . . *B. comosa* / Strawstem beggar-ticks
4 Stems green-purple; disk flowers 5-lobed, yellow-orange; achenes mostly 4-awned (sometimes 2-awned) . . . . *B. connata*
. . . . Purplestem beggar-ticks

5 Heads with disk flowers only, or with short rays less than 5 mm long
. . . . **6**
5 Heads with both disk and ray flowers, the rays over 10 mm long . **8**

6 Outer involucral bracts 2–5 (usually 4), not fringed with hairs . . . .
. . . . *B. discoidea* / Few-bracted beggar-ticks
6 Outer involucral bracts 6 or more, fringed with hairs (at least near base). **7**

7 Disk flowers orange; outer involucral bracts mostly 6–8 *B. frondosa*
. . . . Devil's beggar-ticks
7 Disk flowers yellow; outer involucral bracts 10 or more . *B. vulgata*
. . . . Tall beggar-ticks

8 Achenes broad and ovate, mostly more than 3 mm wide . *B. aristosa*
. . . . Bearded beggar-ticks
8 Achenes narrow and ± straight-sided, less than 3 mm wide . . . .
. . . . *B. coronata* / Northern tickseed-sunflower

Bidens aristosa (Michx.) Brit.
Bearded beggar-ticks   FACW
Annual or biennial herb. **Stems** 3–12 dm long, much-branched, ± smooth. **Leaves** pinnately divided, 5–15 cm long, the segments narrowly lance-shaped, hairy on underside; margins with coarse, forward-pointing teeth or shallow lobes; petioles 1–3 cm long. **Flower heads** 2–5 cm wide, numerous on leafless stalks; rays yellow, usually 8, 1–2.5 cm long; the outer involucral bracts 8–10, 5–10 mm long, margins smooth or fringed with hairs. **Fruit** a flattened achene, 5–7 mm long; pappus of 2 (rarely 4) barbed awns, or sometimes absent. Aug–Sept. ❦ Marshy areas, ditches, disturbed wetlands. ⊕ Minn, Wisc, se LP of Mich, ne Ill and nw Ind. Maine to Minn, s to Va and Tex.

Bidens cernua L.
Nodding beggar-ticks   OBL
Annual herb. **Stems** often branched, to 1 m long, smooth or with spreading hairs. **Leaves** opposite, smooth, lance-shaped to oblong lance-shaped, 3–16 cm long and 0.5–5 cm wide; margins with sharp, forward-pointing teeth and often rough-to-touch; petioles absent, the leaves usually clasping at base. **Flower heads** many, globe-shaped, 1.5–3 cm wide, usually nodding after flowering; rays yellow, 6–8, to 1.5 cm long, or absent; outer involucral bracts 4–8, unequal in length, the margins often fringed with hairs. **Fruit** a ± straight-sided achene, 5–7 mm long, with downward-pointing barbs on margins; pappus with 4 (sometimes 2) awns, the awns with downward-pointing barbs. July–Oct. *B. cernuus*. ❦ Exposed sandy or muddy shores, streambanks, marshes, forest depressions, wet meadows, ditches and other wet places. ⊕ Minn, Wisc, Mich, ne Ill and nw Ind. NB to BC, s to NC, Okla, NM and Calif; Eurasia.

Bidens comosa (A. Gray) Wieg.

Strawstem beggar-ticks   FACW

Annual herb. **Stems** yellow, 1–12 dm tall, branched, smooth. **Leaves** opposite, lance-shaped to oval, 3–15 cm long and 0.5–5 cm wide, margins with coarse, forward-pointing teeth, rough-to-touch; petioles absent, or leaves tapered to a short, winged petiole. **Flower heads** 1–2.5 cm wide, several to many, remaining erect after flowering; disk flowers yellow-green; rays absent; outer involucral bracts leaflike, 5–10 or more, 2–4x longer than head. **Fruit** an achene, 3–7 mm long, downwardly barbed on the margins; pappus of 3 downwardly barbed awns, the awns shorter than the achenes. Aug–Oct. *B. acuta*, *B. comosus*, *B. tripartita*. ❦ Exposed shores, streambanks, mudflats, forest depressions, pond, wet meadows, ditches and other wet places. ⊕ Minn, Mich (mostly s LP, uncommon in UP), ne Ill and nw Ind. Maine and Que to Mont, s to NC, Tenn, NM and Utah.

Bidens connata Muhl.

Purplestem beggar-ticks   OBL

Annual herb. **Stems** green-purple, to 2 m long, usually branched, smooth. **Leaves** opposite, smooth, the lower leaves sometimes deeply lobed, 3–15 cm long and 1–4 cm wide; margins with coarse, forward-pointing teeth; petioles present on lower leaves, upper leaves short-petioled or stalkless. **Flower heads** several to many, 1–2 cm wide, upright; disk flowers orange-yellow; rays absent, or few and 3–4 mm long; outer involucral bracts 4–9, usually not much longer than the head. **Fruit** an achene, 3–7 mm long; pappus of 2–4 downwardly barbed awns, about half as long as achene. Aug–Oct. *B. connatus*, *B. tripartita* (in part). ❦ Exposed muddy shores, streambanks, marshes, pond, forest depressions, wet meadows, ditches and other wet places. ⊕ c and s Minn, Wisc, Mich, ne Ill and nw Ind. NS and Que to Minn and se ND, s to NJ, Mo and Kans.

Bidens coronata (L.) Britton

Northern tickseed-sunflower   OBL

Annual or biennial herb. **Stems** branched, 3–15 dm tall, smooth, often purple. **Leaves** opposite, smooth, to 15 cm long, pinnately divided into 3–7 narrow leaflets; margins coarsely toothed or deeply lobed to sometimes entire; petioles 3–15 mm long. **Flower heads** with both disk and ray flowers, large and numerous on slender stalks; rays about 8, gold-yellow, 1–2.5 cm long; outer involucral bracts 6–10, to 1 cm long, short-hairy on margins, inner bracts shorter. **Fruit** a flattened achene, 5–9 mm long, with long, stiff hairs on margins; pappus of 2 short, scalelike awns, 1–2 mm long. July–Oct. *B. coronatus*. ❦ Open bogs, fens, tamarack swamps, shores, streambanks, marshes, sand bars. ⊕ ec and se Minn, Wisc, Mich (mostly s LP, uncommon in UP), ne Ill and nw Ind. Mass and s Ont to Minn and SD, s to Ga, Ky, Iowa and Neb.

Bidens discoidea (T. & G.) Britton

Few-bracted beggar-ticks   FACW

Annual herb. **Stems** smooth, 3–10 dm long. **Leaves** opposite, smooth, divided into 3-leaflets, the **leaflets** lance-shaped, the terminal leaflet largest, to 10 cm long and 4 cm wide; margins with coarse, forward-pointing teeth; petioles slender, 1–6 cm long. **Flower heads** many on slender stalks, the disk to 1 cm wide; rays absent; outer involucral bracts usually 4, leaflike, much longer than disk. **Fruit** a flattened achene, 3–6 mm long; pappus of 2 awns to 2 mm long, with short, upward pointing bristles. Aug–Sept. *B. discoideus*. ❦ Hummocks or logs in swamps, exposed muddy shores; usually where shaded. ⊕ Local in ne Minn; s LP of Mich,

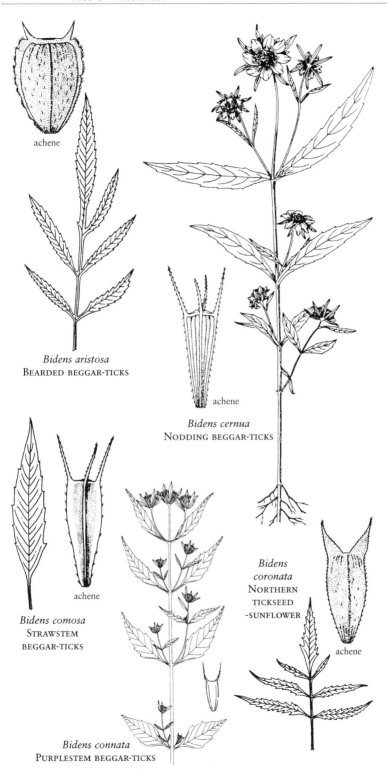

achene

Bidens aristosa
BEARDED BEGGAR-TICKS

achene

Bidens cernua
NODDING BEGGAR-TICKS

achene

Bidens comosa
STRAWSTEM
BEGGAR-TICKS

*Bidens
coronata*
NORTHERN
TICKSEED
-SUNFLOWER

achene

Bidens connata
PURPLESTEM BEGGAR-TICKS

local in ne Ill and nw Ind. NS to Que and Minn, s to Va, Ala, Okla, and Tex.

Bidens frondosa L.
Devil's beggar-ticks   FACW

Annual herb. **Stems** erect, 2–10 dm tall, branched, purple-tinged, ± smooth. **Leaves** pinnately divided into 3–5 segments, the segments lance-shaped, to 10 cm long and 3 cm wide, underside sometimes with short hairs; margins with coarse, forward-pointing teeth; petioles slender, 1–6 cm long. **Flower heads** many on long stalks; disk flowers orange, the disk to 1 cm wide; rays absent or very small; the outer involucral bracts usually 8, green and leaflike, longer than disk, fringed with hairs on margins. **Fruit** a flattened, nearly black achene, 5–10 mm long; pappus of 2 slender awns with downward-pointing barbs. July–Oct. *B. frondosus.* ❧ Wet, sandy or gravelly shores, forest depressions, streambanks, pond margins; weedy in wet disturbed areas. ⊕ Minn, Wisc, Mich, ne Ill and nw Ind. s Can, s to Ga, Tex and Calif.

Bidens vulgata Greene
Tall beggar-ticks   FACU

Annual herb. **Stems** to 2 m tall, smooth or upper stem and leaves short-hairy. **Leaves** opposite, pinnately divided into 3–5 segments, the segments lance-shaped, to 15 cm long and 5 cm wide, with prominent veins; margins with sharp, forward-pointing teeth; petioles present. **Flower heads** on stout, leafless stalks, disk flowers yellow; ray flowers usually present, small, yellow; outer involucral bracts about 13, leaflike. **Fruit** a flattened, olive-green or brown achene, 10–12 mm long; pappus of 2 awns with downward-pointing barbs. Aug–Oct. *B. puberula, B. vulgatus.* ❧ Streambanks, wet meadows, wet forests; weedy in moist disturbed areas. ⊕ Minn, Wisc, Mich, ne Ill and nw Ind. s Can and n USA, s to NC, Mo and Calif.

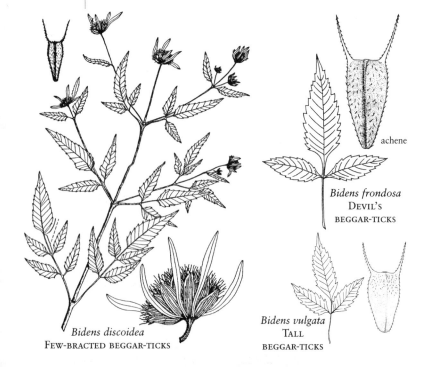

achene

Bidens frondosa
Devil's
beggar-ticks

Bidens discoidea
Few-bracted beggar-ticks

Bidens vulgata
Tall
beggar-ticks

▶**Boltonia** L'Her. / Boltonia

Boltonia asteroides (L.) L'Her.
White boltonia   FACW
Perennial herb, fibrous-rooted, sometimes with shallow rhizomes. **Stems** stout, erect, 3–15 dm long, smooth. **Leaves** alternate, lance-shaped or oval, 5–16 cm long and 0.5–2 cm wide, becoming smaller in the head, narrowed to stalkless or slightly clasping base; margins entire but rough-to-touch. **Flower heads** many, with both disk and ray flowers, 1.5–2.5 cm wide; disk flowers yellow; rays white, pink, or lavender, 5–15 mm long; involucres 2.5–5 mm high, the bracts overlapping, chaffy on outer margins, with a green midvein. **Fruit** a flattened, obovate achene, 1–2 mm long, with a winged margin; pappus of 2 awns and 2–4 shorter bristles. Aug–Sept. *B. latisquama.* ⚘ Seasonally flooded muddy shores, wet meadows, marshes, low prairie. ⊕ c and s Minn, s Wisc, extreme s LP of Mich, ne Ill and nw Ind. NJ to s Man, s to Fla and Tex; introduced in nw USA.

▶**Cacalia** L. / Indian plantain

Large perennial herbs with basal or alternate **leaves**. **Flower heads** with white disk flowers only, the ray flowers absent. **Fruit** an achene, tipped by a pappus of numerous, slender bristles.

▶KEY TO CACALIA

1 Leaves entire or with a few teeth; involucral bracts 10–15 . . . .
. . . . *C. plantaginea* / Tuberous Indian plantain
1 Leaves sharply toothed; involucral bracts 5 . . . . *C. suaveolens*
. . . . Sweet-scented Indian plantain

Cacalia plantaginea (Raf.) Shinners
Tuberous Indian plantain   OBL

⚠
STATUS
Minnesota - T
Wisconsin - T

Perennial herb, from a tuberous base and fleshy roots. **Stems** stout, smooth, 5–18 dm long, winged. **Leaves** alternate, mostly at base and lower stem of plant, thick, oval to ovate, strongly 5–9-veined, 5–20 cm long and 2–10 cm wide; margins entire or slightly wavy; petioles long on lower leaves, becoming short or absent on upper leaves. **Flower heads** many, of white disk flowers only, in a branched inflorescence at end of stem; involucral bracts 5, of equal length. **Fruit** a smooth achene; pappus of many, rough white bristles. June–Aug. *C. tuberosa, Arnoglossum plantagineum, Mesadenia tuberosa.* ⚘ Marshes, low prairie, fens, sedge meadows, calcareous shores. ⊕ se Minn, s Wisc, LP of Mich, ne Ill and nw Ind. Ohio and s Ont to Minn and SD, s to Ala and Tex.

Cacalia suaveolens L.
Sweet-scented Indian plantain   OBL

⚠
STATUS
Minnesota - E

Perennial herb, from fleshy roots. **Stems** ± smooth, grooved, 1–2.5 m tall, leafy to the inflorescence. **Leaves** alternate, smooth; lower leaves triangular with a pair of outward-pointing lobes at base, 5–20 cm long and nearly as wide; upper leaves smaller and often not lobed; margins sharply and irregularly toothed; petioles winged. **Flower heads** of disk flowers only, in a ± flat-topped inflorescence, the disk about 1 cm wide; disk flowers white or light pink; involucre 1 cm long, the main involucral bracts 10–15. **Fruit** an achene; pappus of many soft, white bristles.

July–Sept. *Hasteola suaveolens, Synosma suaveolens.* ❦ Riverbanks, shores, calcareous fens, wet low areas. ⊕ Rare and local in se Minn, s Wisc, uncommon in ne Ill and nw Ind. Conn to s Minn, s to Md, Tenn, n Ga and Ill.

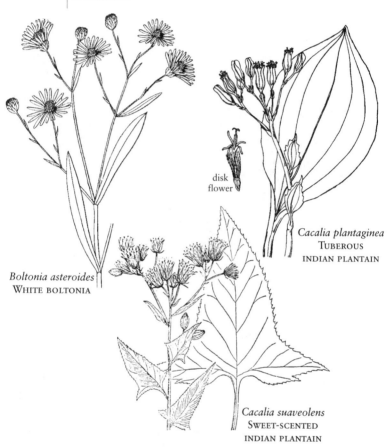

disk flower

Cacalia plantaginea
TUBEROUS
INDIAN PLANTAIN

Boltonia asteroides
WHITE BOLTONIA

Cacalia suaveolens
SWEET-SCENTED
INDIAN PLANTAIN

▶**Cirsium** Miller / Thistle

☞ Colonies of **Canada thistle** (*Cirsium arvense*) are sometimes found in on wetland margins, especially where disturbed. It is distinguished from other thistles by its rhizomatous habit and lack of a rosette of basal leaves.

Biennial or perennial herbs. **Stems** and leaves often spiny. **Leaves** from base of plant or alternate on stem. **Flower heads** of pink to purple disk flowers only; involucral bracts tipped with spines. **Fruit** a smooth achene; pappus of many slender bristles.

▶KEY TO CIRSIUM

1 Stem not winged; leaf undersides and involucral bracts often with cobwebby hairs; involucral bracts 2–3.5 cm long, flowers deep rose-purple; native and not weedy. . . . . *C. muticum* / SWAMP-THISTLE
1 Stem with spiny wings; leaf undersides and involucral bracts usually without cobwebby hairs; involucral bracts 1–2 cm long, flowers pale pink-purple; introduced and weedy . . . . *C. palustre* . . . . MARSH THISTLE; EUROPEAN SWAMP-THISTLE

Cirsium muticum Michx.
Swamp-thistle OBL
Stout biennial herb. **Stems** 0.5–2 m long, branched in head, with long, soft hairs when young, becoming ± smooth. **Leaves** deeply lobed into pinnate segments, 1–2 dm long, underside often with matted, cobwebby hairs, becoming ± smooth with age; margins toothed and often tipped with spines; petioles present on lower leaves, stem leaves stalkless. **Flower heads** of purple or pink disk flowers only, single on leafless stalks over 1 cm long at ends of stems; involucre 2–3.5 cm high; the involucral bracts overlapping, densely hairy with cottony hairs (especially on margins), sometimes tipped with a short spine 0.5 mm long. **Fruit** an achene, 5 mm long; pappus of long, slender bristles. Aug–Oct. ❦ Swamps, thickets, calcareous fens, sedge meadows, streambanks, shores. ⊕ Minn (all but far s), Wisc, Mich, ne Ill and nw Ind. Nfld to Sask, s to NC, Tenn, Mo and Tex.

Cirsium palustre (L.) Scop.
Marsh thistle; European Swamp-thistle (NI)
☞ **Marsh thistle** is an introduced species and aggressively spreading into wetlands of ne USA and s Canada.

Biennial herb. **Stems** 0.5–2 m tall, spiny. **Leaves** to 20 cm long, deeply lobed into pinnate segments, covered with loosely matted hairs or ± smooth, tapered at base and continued downward on stem as spiny wings; margin teeth spine-tipped. **Flower heads** of purple disk flowers only, on short stalks mostly less than 1 cm long; involucre 1–2 cm high; the involucral bracts overlapping, not spine-tipped. **Fruit** an achene, 3 mm long; pappus of slender bristles to 1 cm long. June–Aug. ❦ Roadside ditches and adjacent wetlands, including swamps, thickets and fens; resembling the native *C. muticum* in these habitats. ⊕ n Wisc, UP and n LP of Mich. ne USA and s Can.

Cirsium palustre
Marsh thistle;
European
swamp-thistle

Cirsium muticum
Swamp-thistle

▶**Crepis** L. / Hawk's beard

Crepis runcinata (James) T. & G.
Dandelion hawk's beard   FACW
Perennial herb with milky juice. **Stems** 2–6 dm long, smooth or sparsely
hairy, the stem leaves small and bractlike. **Leaves** in a rosette at base of
plant, oblong lance-shaped to oval, 5–20 cm long and 1–4 cm wide,
rounded at tip, tapered to a petiolelike base, margins entire or with widely spaced teeth. **Flower heads** 1–10, 1–2 cm wide, of yellow ray flowers
only; involucre 8–15 mm high, with gland-tipped hairs, the involucral
bracts in 2 series, the outer bracts shorter than inner. **Fruit** a brown achene, round in section, 4–5 mm long; pappus of many white slender bristles. June–July. *C. glaucella*. ☙ Wet meadows, low prairie, shores and
swales, especially where alkaline. ⊕ w Minn and Man to Wash, s to Neb,
NM, Calif and n Mex.

▶**Eclipta** L. / Yerba-de-tajo

Eclipta prostrata (L.) L.
Yerba-de-tajo   FACW
Annual herb. **Stems** spreading, branched, 5–8 dm long, with rough,
appressed hairs, often rooting at the nodes. **Leaves** opposite, lance-
shaped, 2–10 cm long and 0.5–2.5 cm wide, margins with shallow teeth;
petioles absent, or short on lower leaves. **Flower heads** with both disk
and ray flowers, in clusters of 1–3 at ends of stems or from leaf axils, on
stalks or nearly stalkless; the disk 4–6 mm wide; rays short, nearly white.
Fruit a flat-topped achene, 2–3 mm long; pappus a crown of very short
bristles. July–Oct. *E. alba*, *Verbesina alba*. ☙ Mud flats, muddy stream
banks and ditches, where somewhat weedy. ⊕ se LP of Mich, ne Ill and
nw Ind. Mass, s Ont to n Ill, s to c Amer.

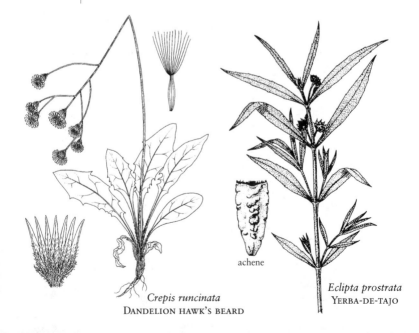

achene

Crepis runcinata
DANDELION HAWK'S BEARD

Eclipta prostrata
YERBA-DE-TAJO

▶**Erigeron** L. / Daisy; Fleabane

Biennial or perennial herbs with simple, alternate **leaves. Flower heads** with both disk and ray flowers; disk flowers yellow; rays white to pink, very narrow, only to about 0.5 mm wide; involucral bracts in 1–2 series, linear, about equal in length, green in middle and at base, translucent at tip and on upper margins. **Fruit** a flattened achene; pappus of 20–30 slender, rough bristles.

▶**KEY TO ERIGERON**

1 Leaves clasping stem; common and widespread. . . *E. philadelphicus*
. . . . PHILADELPHIA DAISY
1 Leaves not clasping stem; uncommon plants of w Minn or Mich UP
. . . . **2**

2 Leaves all ± same size; uncommon plant of Mich UP . . . .
. . . . *E. hyssopifolius* / HYSSOP-DAISY
2 Leaves becoming smaller upward on stem; uncommon plant of wc
Minn . . . . *E. lonchophyllus* / LOW MEADOW FLEABANE

Erigeron hyssopifolius Michx.
Hyssop-daisy   FACW

⚠
STATUS
Michigan - T

Perennial herb. **Stems** usually many, 1–4 dm long, smooth or sparsely hairy. **Leaves** thin, ± linear, 1–3 cm long and to 5 mm wide, smooth, lowest leaves scalelike; margins entire; petioles short. **Flower heads** 1–5, with both disk and ray flowers, on long, nearly leafless stalks; involucre 4–6 mm high; disk 5–12 mm wide; rays 20–50, white or sometimes pink-purple, to 8 mm long. **Fruit** an achene; pappus of long bristles, sometimes also with a ring of very short bristles. July–Aug. Ours are var. *hyssopifolius.* ❦ Calcareous fens and cedar swamps; also rocky Lake Superior shoreline in Ont. ⊕ e UP of Mich (and possibly Keweenaw Peninsula). New Eng to Yukon, s to n Mich.

Erigeron lonchophyllus Hook.
Low meadow fleabane   FACW-

Biennial or short-lived perennial herb. **Stems** 1–4 dm tall, with spreading hairs. **Leaves** alternate, lower leaves oblong lance-shaped, 5–15 cm long and 1–5 mm wide, tapered to a short petiolelike base, upper leaves linear and stalkless, not clasping, margins entire, fringed with hairs. **Flower heads** several to many, 1–1.5 cm wide; involucre 5–10 mm high, the involucral bracts coarsely hairy, the outer bracts shorter than inner; rays many, white, turning brown at tip, only to 0.2 mm wide. **Fruit** an achene; pappus of slender, rough bristles. July–Sept. ❦ Wet meadows, low prairie, seeps. ⊕ Uncommon in wc Minn. Que and Ont to Alaska, s to ND, NM, Utah and Calif.

Erigeron philadelphicus L.
Philadelphia daisy   FACW

Biennial or short-lived perennial herb. **Stems** 1 to several, branched in head, 2–7 dm long, usually long-hairy. **Leaves** alternate, lower leaves spatula-shaped, 5–15 cm long and 1–4 cm wide, tapered to a short petiole; upper leaves smaller, lance-shaped, clasping at base, hairy to nearly smooth, rounded at tip; margins entire or with rounded teeth. **Flower heads** few to many, with both disk and ray flowers, 1.5–2.5 cm wide; involucre 3–6 mm high, the involucral bracts hairy, of ± equal length; rays many, white to deep pink, 5–10 mm long and to 0.5 mm wide. **Fruit** a short-hairy achene; pappus of long rough bristles. May–Aug. ❦ Wet meadows, shores, streambanks, wet woods, floodplains, springs; also weedy in open disturbed areas and lawns. ⊕ Minn, Wisc, Mich, ne Ill and nw Ind. Newf to BC, s to Fla and Calif.

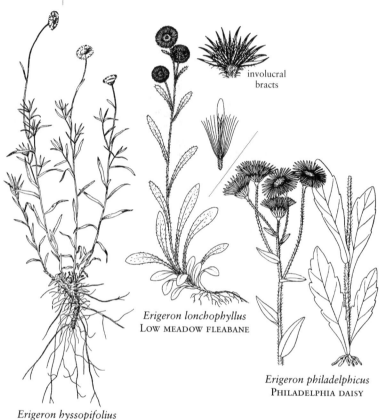

involucral bracts

Erigeron lonchophyllus
LOW MEADOW FLEABANE

Erigeron philadelphicus
PHILADELPHIA DAISY

Erigeron hyssopifolius
HYSSOP-DAISY

▶**Eupatorium** L. / Joe-pye-weed

☞ Eupatorium purpureum (Green-stemmed joe-pye-weed, FAC) is present on usually drier sites in s portions of the Great Lakes region. Its stem is purple only near the nodes, and with leaves in whorls of only 3-5.

Perennial herbs from a thick rhizome. **Stems** stout, erect. **Leaves** whorled, or opposite and joined at base, the stem passing through the joined leaves; lower leaves smaller; margins toothed. **Flower heads** of pink, purple or white disk flowers only, usually many in a ± flat-topped head at ends of stems; involucral bracts overlapping or nearly equal length. **Fruit** an angled achene; pappus of many slender bristles.

▶**KEY TO EUPATORIUM**

1 Leaves whorled 2
1 Leaves opposite 3

2 Stems waxy-coated; heads with less than 8 flowers; uncommon plant of s portion of the region . . . . *E. fistulosum*
   . . . . HOLLOW-STEMMED JOE-PYE-WEED
2 Stems not waxy-coated; heads with more than 8 flowers; common and widespread . . . . *E. maculatum* / SPOTTED JOE-PYE-WEED

3 Most leaves joined at base and perforated by the stem . . . .
. . . . *E. perfoliatum* / BONESET
3 Leaves on distinct stalks to 5 mm long . . . . *E. rugosum*
. . . . WHITE SNAKEROOT

Eupatorium fistulosum Barrat

Hollow-stemmed joe-pye-weed OBL

⚠
STATUS
Michigan - T

Perennial herb. **Stems** waxy, purple, hollow, to 3 m long. **Leaves** narrowly oval, in whorls of 4–7, 10–30 cm long and 3–15 cm wide; margins with small, rounded teeth; petioles short. **Flower heads** of pink-purple disk flowers only; involucre to 1 cm long, the involucral bracts overlapping. **Fruit** an achene; pappus of slender bristles. July–Sept. ✿ Indiana Dunes and vicinity in moist to wet swamp openings and marshy areas between dunes. ⊕ Uncommon in extreme sw Mich, nw Ind; reported from ne Ill. Maine to Iowa, s to Fla and Tex.

Eupatorium maculatum L.

Spotted joe-pye-weed OBL

Perennial herb. **Stems** 5–20 dm long, spotted or tinged with purple, short-hairy above, especially on branches of head. **Leaves** in whorls of mostly 4–5, lance-shaped to ovate, 5–20 cm long and 2–7 cm wide, upper surface with sparse short hairs, underside often densely short-hairy; margins with sharp, forward-pointing teeth; petioles to 2 cm long. **Flower heads** of light pink to purple disk flowers only, the inflorescence ± flat-topped; involucres 6–9 mm high, purple-tinged, the involucral bracts overlapping. **Fruit** a black, angled achene, 2–4 mm long; pappus of long, slender bristles. July–Sept. ✿ Wet meadows, marshes, low prairie, shores, streambanks, ditches, cedar swamps, open bogs, calcareous fens. ⊕ Common; Minn, Wisc, Mich, ne Ill and nw Ind. Newf to BC, s to Md, Ohio, Ill, NM and Utah.

Eupatorium perfoliatum L.

Boneset FACW+

Perennial herb. **Stems** 3–15 dm tall, with long, spreading hairs. **Leaves** opposite, mostly joined at the broad base and perforated by the stem (upper leaves sometimes separate), lance-shaped, 6–20 cm long and 1.5–5 cm wide, upper surface sparsely hairy, underside hairy, both sides dotted with yellow glands; margins finely toothed and rough-to-touch; petioles absent. **Flower heads** of dull white disk flowers only, in a flat-topped inflorescence; involucre 3–6 mm high, the involucral bracts green with white margins, hairy, overlapping in 3 series. **Fruit** a black achene, 1–2 mm long; pappus of long slender bristles. July–Sept. ✿ Marshes, wet meadows, low prairie, shores, streambanks, ditches, cedar swamps, thickets, calcareous fens. Often occurring with **spotted joe-pye-weed** (*Eupatorium maculatum*). ⊕ Common; Minn, Wisc, Mich, ne Ill and nw Ind. NS and Que to se Man, s to Fla and Tex.

Eupatorium rugosum Houttuyn

White snakeroot UPL

☠
CAUTION TOXIC!
Poisonous,
and the cause
of "milk
sickness" in
pioneers.

Perennial herb. **Stems** 1–3, 3–15 dm long, smooth or with short hairs. **Leaves** opposite, ovate, 5–16 cm long and 3–12 cm wide, smooth or hairy, especially on underside veins, margins coarsely sharp-toothed; petioles 1–3 cm long. **Flower heads** of bright white disk flowers only, in a flat-topped or rounded inflorescence; involucre 3–5 mm high, smooth or short-hairy, the involucral bracts linear, nearly equal, in 1–2 series. **Fruit** a ± smooth achene; pappus of long, slender bristles. July–Oct. *E.*

urticaefolium. ❧ Floodplain forests, cedar swamps, thickets, stream-banks, wooded ravines. ⊕ s Minn, Wisc, Mich, ne Ill and nw Ind. NS to Sask, s to Ga and Tex. ☞ Our plants are var. *rugosum*.

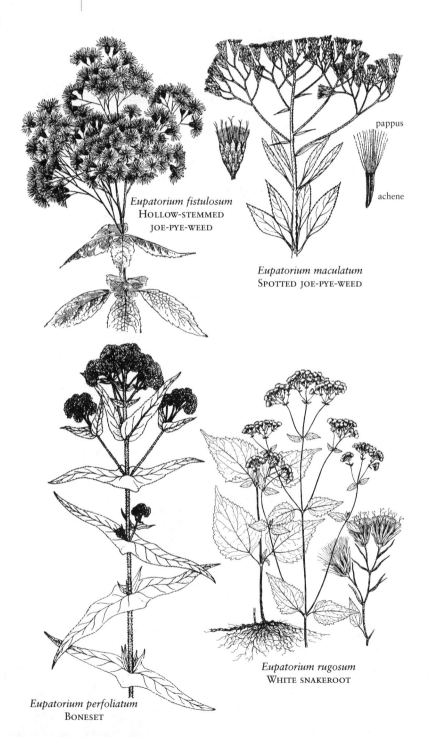

Eupatorium fistulosum
HOLLOW-STEMMED
JOE-PYE-WEED

Eupatorium maculatum
SPOTTED JOE-PYE-WEED

pappus

achene

Eupatorium rugosum
WHITE SNAKEROOT

Eupatorium perfoliatum
BONESET

▶**Euthamia** Nutt. / Flat-topped goldenrod

☞ Euthamia is typically included with **goldenrods** (*Solidago*) in older floras.

Perennial herbs, spreading by rhizomes. **Stems** leafy. **Leaves** alternate, covered with resinous dots; margins entire; petioles absent or very short. **Flower heads** small, of yellow disk and ray flowers, in a ± flat-topped cluster at ends of stems; involucre somewhat sticky. **Fruit** an achene; pappus of slender white bristles.

▶**KEY TO EUTHAMIA**

1 Largest stem leaves 4 mm or more wide, with 3 conspicuous longitudinal veins; leaves and upper stem short-hairy; upper leaves dull, glandular dots usually indistinct. . . . . *E. graminifolia* . . . . COMMON FLAT-TOPPED GOLDENROD
1 Largest stem leaves less than 3 mm wide, with single longitudinal vein (midrib) and sometimes with faint pair of longitudinal veins; leaves and upper stem smooth; upper leaves shiny, with conspicuous glandular dots . . . . *E. remota* / LAKES FLAT-TOPPED GOLDENROD

Euthamia graminifolia (L.) Nutt.
Common flat-topped goldenrod   FACW-
Perennial herb, spreading by rhizomes. **Stems** erect, 5–15 dm tall, smooth to hairy, usually branched in head. **Leaves** alternate, linear to narrowly lance-shaped or oval, 3–15 cm long and 3–10 mm wide, 3-veined, with small glandular dots; margins entire, smooth or rough-to-touch; petioles absent or very short. **Flower heads** small, in flat-topped clusters at ends of stems; with yellow disk and ray flowers, the rays small, to 1 mm long; involucre 3–5 mm high, somewhat sticky, the involucral bracts overlapping in several series, yellow or green-tipped. **Fruit** a finely hairy achene, 1 mm long; pappus of many white, slender bristles. Aug–Sept. *Solidago graminifolia.* ❀ Shores, wet meadows, low prairie, springs, fens, swamps, interdunal wetlands, streambanks, often where sandy or gravelly; also weedy in abandoned fields. ⊕ Common; Minn, Wisc, Mich, ne Ill and nw Ind. Newf and Que to BC, s to Va, Ala, Tex and NM.

Euthamia remota Greene
Lakes flat-topped goldenrod   FAC+
Perennial herb, spreading by rhizomes. **Stems** smooth, 3–8 dm long, branched in head. **Leaves** alternate, linear, 2–8 cm long and 2–3 mm wide, often with clusters of smaller leaves in axils of main leaves, 1-veined or with another pair of fainter veins, with glandular dots; margins entire, sometimes rough-to-touch; petioles absent. **Flower heads** of yellow disk and ray flowers, in flat-topped clusters at ends of stems; involucre sticky, 3–5 mm long; the involucral bracts overlapping. **Fruit** a short-hairy achene; pappus of slender white bristles. Includes plants sometimes called *Euthamia* or *Solidago gymnospermoides.* ❀ Sandy or mucky shores (especially on recently exposed lakeshores), interdunal swales. ⊕ s Wisc, Mich, ne Ill, n Ind and n Ohio (this is the total known range of the species).

▶**Gnaphalium** L. / Cudweed

Gnaphalium uliginosum L.
Marsh cudweed   FAC
Annual herb. **Stem** branched and spreading, 10–25 cm tall, covered with

white wool-like hairs. **Leaves** alternate, entire, linear or oblong lance-shaped, 2–4 cm long and to 5 mm wide, with sparse woolly hairs. **Flower heads** of whitish disk flowers only, the rays absent, in numerous clusters from leaf axils and at end of stem-branches, shorter than the subtending leaves. **Fruit** a smooth or bump-covered achene. *Filaginella uliginosa.* ⚜ Introduced from Europe and now weedy, especially on streambanks, and in wet to dry disturbed areas. ⊕ Minn, Wisc, Mich, Ill, Ind. Nfld to Alaska, s to Va, Ill, NM and Calif.

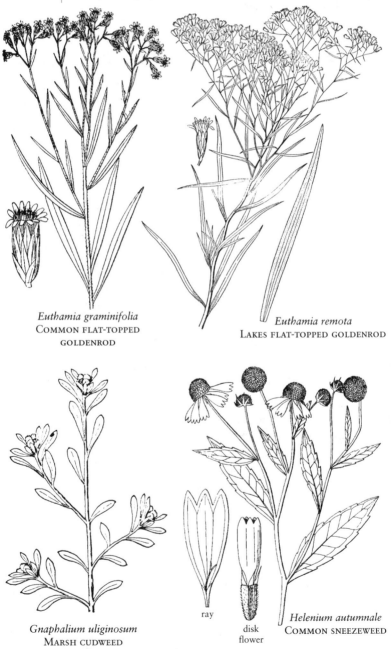

Euthamia graminifolia
COMMON FLAT-TOPPED
GOLDENROD

Euthamia remota
LAKES FLAT-TOPPED GOLDENROD

Gnaphalium uliginosum
MARSH CUDWEED

ray

disk
flower

Helenium autumnale
COMMON SNEEZEWEED

▶**Helenium** L. / Sneezeweed

Helenium autumnale L.
Common sneezeweed   FACW+

Perennial herb. **Stems** single or clustered, erect, 3–13 dm tall, smooth or finely hairy, branched in head. **Leaves** alternate, bright green, lance-shaped to oval, 4–12 cm long and 0.5–3.5 cm wide, usually short-hairy, glandular-dotted; margins entire to shallowly toothed; petioles absent, the blades tapered to a narrow base extending downward as wings on stem. **Flower heads** ± round, 1.5–4 cm wide; few to many on slender stalks in a leafy inflorescence, with both disk and ray flowers, the disk flowers yellow to brown, the rays yellow and drooping, 1.5–2.5 cm long; involucral bracts in 2–3 series, linear, short-hairy, bent downward with age. **Fruit** a finely hairy, 4–5-angled achene, 1–2 mm long; pappus of several translucent, awn-tipped scales. July–Sept. ✿ Wet meadows, shores, streambanks, marshes, fens, tamarack swamps. ⊕ All but ne Minn; Wisc, Mich, ne Ill and nw Ind. Que to BC, s to Fla and Ariz.

▶**Helianthus** L. / Sunflower

Large perennial herbs (those included here), with fibrous or fleshy roots and short to long rhizomes. **Stems** unbranched or branched above. **Leaves** usually opposite on lower part of stem and alternate above, lance-shaped, margins entire or with forward-pointing teeth; petioles present. **Flower heads** large, mostly 1 to several (rarely many), at ends of stems and branches, with yellow disk and ray flowers, the rays large and showy; involucre of several series of narrow, overlapping bracts; receptacle chaffy. **Fruit** a flattened achene; pappus of 2 deciduous, awn-tipped scales.

▶**KEY TO HELIANTHUS**

1 Upper side of leaf rough-to-touch; stems hairy . . . . *H. giganteus*
. . . . Swamp-sunflower
1 Upper side of leaf not (or only slightly) rough-to-touch; stems smooth, often waxy-coated, or sometimes with sparse hairs on upper stem . . . . *H. grosseserratus* / Sawtooth sunflower

---

Helianthus giganteus L.
Swamp-sunflower   FACW

⚠
STATUS
Illinois - E

Perennial herb, with short rhizomes and thick, fleshy roots. **Stems** 1–3 m long, often purple, with coarse hairs or sometimes nearly smooth, often branched in head. **Upper leaves** generally alternate, **lower leaves** opposite; lance-shaped, 6–20 cm long and 1–4 cm wide, base with 3 main veins, upper surface very rough-to-touch, underside with short, stiff hairs; margins toothed to ± entire; petiole short or absent. **Flower heads** 3–6 cm wide, several to many, on long stalks in an open inflorescence; with yellow disk and ray flowers, the rays 1.5–3 cm long; involucral bracts narrow, awl-shaped, green or dark near base, hairy or margins fringed with hairs. **Fruit** a smooth achene; pappus of 2 awl-shaped scales. July–Sept. *H. subtuberosus*. ✿ Wet meadows, low prairie, sedge meadows, fens, floodplain forests, streambanks. ⊕ Minn, Wisc, Mich (especially s LP), local in ne Ill, nw Ind. NB to s Alberta, s to SC, n Ga. and Neb.

Helianthus grosseserratus Martens
Sawtooth sunflower   FACW-

Perennial herb, with fleshy roots, spreading by rhizomes and forming colonies. **Stems** 1–3 m tall, short-hairy in head, smooth and often waxy below, purple or blue-green. **Upper leaves** alternate, **lower leaves** oppo-site; lance-shaped, 10–20 cm long and 2–5 cm wide, rough-to-touch on both sides, also densely short hairy on the paler underside; margins with coarse, forward-pointing teeth, upper leaves often entire; petioles 1–4 cm long. **Flower heads** 3–8 cm wide, several to many at ends of stems and branches; with yellow disk flowers and deep yellow ray flowers, the rays 2.5–4 cm long; involucral bracts narrowly lance-shaped, fringed with hairs and sometimes hairy on back. **Fruit** a smooth achene, 3–4 mm long; pappus of 2 lance-shaped scales. July–Oct. ❦ Wet meadows, low prairie, streambanks, swamps, ditches, roadsides. ⊕ Common; Minn, Wisc, mostly s LP of Mich, ne Ill and nw Ind. NY to Sask s to Ark and Tex.

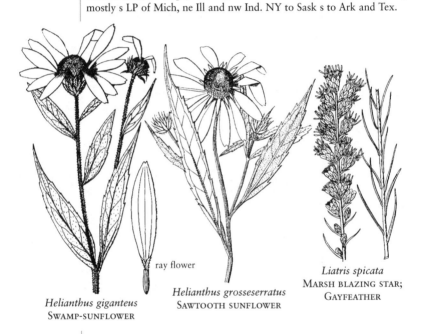

ray flower

Helianthus giganteus
SWAMP-SUNFLOWER

Helianthus grosseserratus
SAWTOOTH SUNFLOWER

Liatris spicata
MARSH BLAZING STAR;
GAYFEATHER

▶Liatris Schreb. / Blazing star

Liatris spicata (L.) Willd.
Marsh blazing star; gayfeather   FAC

Perennial herb. **Stems** smooth, upright, 5–20 dm tall. **Leaves** numerous, lower leaves linear, often ± blunt-tipped, 10–30 cm long; upper leaves smaller, linear to awl-shaped. **Flower heads** stalkless, of blue-purple (rarely white) disk flowers only, numerous in an elongated spike; involu-cral bracts appressed, overlapping in series of 4–6; pappus of barbed hairs. **Fruit** an achene. ❦ Low prairie, calcareous fens, wet meadows, wet, sandy flats, and conifer swamps. ⊕ se Wisc, Mich LP (especially s and c), n Ill and n Ind.NY to s Wisc, s to Fla and La; occasional in Great Plains. ☞ **Prairie blazing star** (*Liatris pycnostachya* Michx., FAC-) occurs in moist prairies and calcareous fens of Minn, s to Miss and westward, and occasionally as an escape from gardens in the east. Its involucral bracts spread outward at the tip in contrast to the appressed bracts of *L. spicata*.

▶**Megalodonta** Greene / Water beggar-ticks

Megalodonta beckii (Torr. ex Spreng.) Greene

Water beggar-ticks OBL

⚠ STATUS Illinois - E Indiana - E

Perennial aquatic herb. **Stems** 0.4–2 m long, little-branched. **Underwater leaves** opposite or whorled, dissected into threadlike segments; **emersed leaves** simple, opposite, lance-shaped to ovate, margins with forward-pointing teeth, petioles absent. **Flower heads** single or few at ends of stems; rays 6–10, gold-yellow, 1–1.5 cm long, notched at tip; involucral bracts smooth. **Fruit** an achene, ± round in section, 10–15 mm long; pappus of 3–6 slender awns, longer than achenes, the upper portion of awn with downward-pointing barbs. June–Sept. *Bidens beckii*. ❦ Quiet, shallow to deep water of lakes, ponds, rivers and streams. ⊕ n and c Minn, Wisc, Mich, uncommon in ne Ill and nw Ind. Que to Man, s to NJ and Mo; Pacific NW.

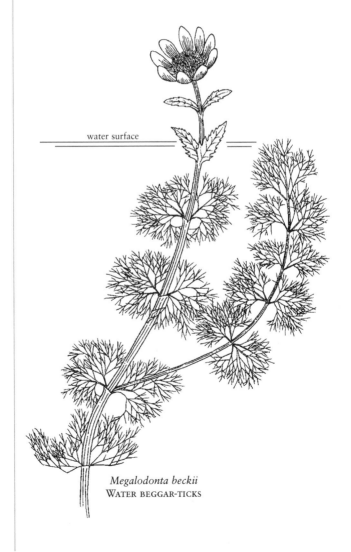

water surface

Megalodonta beckii
WATER BEGGAR-TICKS

▶**Petasites** Miller / Sweet coltsfoot

Perennial herbs, spreading by rhizomes. **Leaves** mostly from base of plant on long petioles, arrowhead-shaped or palmately lobed, with white woolly hairs on underside; stem leaves alternate, reduced to bracts. Flowering before or as leaves expand in spring, the heads white, the **flowers** mostly either male and female and on different plants; or the heads sometimes with both male and female flowers, the **male heads** usually with disk flowers only, the **female heads** with all disk flowers or sometimes with short rays; involucral bracts in a single series; receptacle not chaffy. **Fruit** a linear, ribbed achene; pappus of many white, slender bristles.

▶KEY TO PETASITES

1 Leaf blades palmately lobed; widespread in n portions of region . . . . *P. frigidus* / NORTHERN SWEET COLTSFOOT
1 Leaf blades arrowhead-shaped, toothed and not lobed; uncommon in Great Lakes region . . *P. sagittatus* / ARROWHEAD SWEET COLTSFOOT

Petasites frigidus (L.) Fries.
Northern sweet coltsfoot   FACW

☞ Hybrids with P. sagittatus sometimes occur (*Petasites x vitifolius*).

Perennial herb, spreading by rhizomes. **Stems** 1–6 dm long, smooth or short-hairy in the head. **Leaves** mostly from base of plant, triangular to nearly round in outline, palmately lobed, 5–30 cm wide, upper surface green and smooth, underside densely white-hairy, sometimes becoming smooth with age; margins coarsely toothed; petioles of basal leaves 1–3 dm long; stem leaves small and bractlike, 2–6 cm long. **Flower heads** nearly white, male and female flowers mostly on separate plants; rays of female heads to 7 mm long, involucre 4–9 mm high. **Fruit** a narrow achene; pappus of many slender bristles. May–June. Our plants are var. *palmatus*. *P. palmatus*. ❀ Wet conifer forests and swamps, wet trails and clearings, aspen woods. ⊕ nc and ne Minn, n Wisc, UP and n and c LP of Mich. Circumboreal, s to Mass, Mich, Minn, ND and Calif.

Petasites sagittatus (Banks) A. Gray
Arrowhead sweet coltsfoot   OBL

⚠ STATUS Michigan - T Wisconsin - T

Perennial herb. **Stems** 3–6 dm tall, sparsely covered with woolly white hairs. **Leaves** mostly from base of plant, arrowhead-shaped, 10–40 cm long and 3–30 cm wide, upper surface smooth to sparsely hairy, densely white hairy below; margins wavy with outward-pointing teeth; petioles 1–3 dm long; the stem leaves reduced in size. **Flower heads** ± white; rays of female heads 8–9 mm long. **Fruit** a linear achene; pappus of slender bristles. May–June. ❀ Wet meadows, marshes, sedge meadows, open swamps. ⊕ n and c Minn, far nw Wisc, c UP of Mich. Labr to Alaska, s to Minn, SD, Colo, Idaho and Wash.

▶**Prenanthes** L. / Rattlesnake-root

Prenanthes racemosa Michx.
Glaucous rattlesnake-root   FACW

Perennial herb. **Stems** slender, erect, ridged, 4–18 dm tall, smooth and somewhat waxy, hairy in the head. **Leaves** thick, smooth and waxy; lower leaves oval to obovate, 10–20 cm long and 2–10 cm wide; margins shallowly toothed; petioles long and winged; stem leaves becoming smaller upwards, stalkless and partly clasping the stem. **Flower heads** many in a narrow, elongate inflorescence, of ray flowers only, pink or purplish; involucre 9–14 mm high, purple-black, long-hairy. **Fruit** a linear achene; pappus of straw-colored bristles. Aug–Sept. ⚘ Sandy or gravelly shores, streambanks, wet meadows, low prairie, fens, rocky shores of Lake Superior. ⊕ Minn (all but ne), Wisc, e UP and LP of Mich (also Isle Royale and Keweenaw Peninsula), ne Ill and nw Ind. Que to Alberta, s to NJ, Ill, Mo and Colo. ☞ **White rattlesnake-root** (*Prenanthes alba*), typically found in deciduous woods, sometimes occurs in wet woods or along streams in the Great Lakes region. It differs from *Prenanthes racemosa* by its usually deeply lobed leaves and hairless involucre.

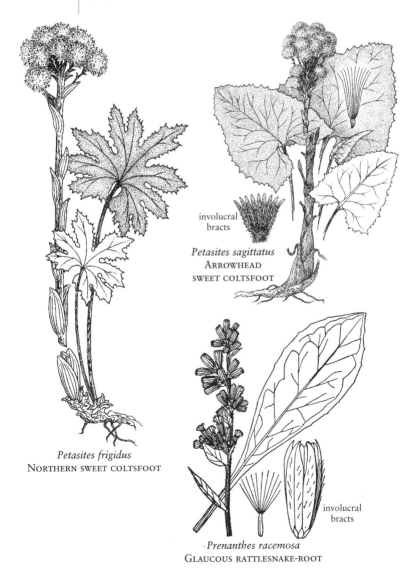

involucral bracts

Petasites sagittatus
ARROWHEAD
SWEET COLTSFOOT

Petasites frigidus
NORTHERN SWEET COLTSFOOT

involucral bracts

Prenanthes racemosa
GLAUCOUS RATTLESNAKE-ROOT

▶**Rudbeckia** L. / Coneflower

☞ The genus includes the well-known **black-eyed Susan** (*Rudbeckia hirta*), widespread on drier sites.

Perennial herbs. **Stems** and leaves rough-hairy. **Leaves** alternate, entire to deeply lobed. **Flower heads** with both disk and ray flowers, the rays yellow to orange; involucral bracts green, overlapping; receptacle rounded, chaffy. **Fruit** a smooth, 4-angled achene; pappus absent or a short crown.

▶**KEY TO RUDBECKIA**

1 Leaves simple, not lobed . . . . . . *R. fulgida* / EASTERN CONEFLOWER
1 Main leaves 3–7 lobed. **2**

2 Largest leaves 3 lobed; disk dark purple. . . . . *R. triloba*
. . . . BROWN-EYED SUSAN
2 Largest leaves 5–7 lobed; disk green-yellow. . . . . *R. laciniata*
. . . . TALL OR CUTLEAF CONEFLOWER

Rudbeckia fulgida Aiton
Eastern coneflower   OBL

Perennial herb, often spreading by stolons. **Stems** to 1 m long, hairy. **Leaves** alternate, the lower leaves lance-shaped to oblong, 5–10 cm long and 2–4 cm wide, hairy; margins entire or sparsely toothed; petioles long and winged; upper leaves smaller, stalkless. **Flower heads** several, 2–4 cm wide, at ends of long stalks, with both disk and ray flowers, the disk round, dark purple or brown,; the rays yellow to orange, notched at tip; involucre 1–2 cm high. **Fruit** an achene. Aug–Sept. *R. speciosa* var. *sullivantii*. ✹ Sedge meadows, calcareous fens, wet streambanks, low prairie. ⊕ s LP of Mich, occasional in ne Ill and nw Ind. Pa to Mich, Ill and Mo, s to Fla and Tex.

Rudbeckia laciniata L.
Tall or Cutleaf coneflower   FACW+

Perennial herb, from a woody base. **Stems** branched, 0.5–3 m long, smooth and often waxy. **Leaves** alternate, to 30 cm wide, deeply lobed, nearly smooth to hairy on underside; margins coarsely toothed as well as lobed, or entire on upper leaves; petioles long on lower leaves, becoming short above. **Flower heads** several to many at ends of stems, with both disk and ray flowers, disk flowers green-yellow, rays lemon-yellow, drooping, 3–6 cm long; involucral bracts of unequal lengths; receptacle round at first, becoming cylindric. **Fruit** a 4-angled achene. July–Sept. ✹ Floodplain forests, swamps, streambanks, thickets, ditches; usually in partial or full shade. ⊕ Common; Minn, Wisc, Mich, ne Ill and nw Ind. Que to Mont, s to Fla and Ariz.

Rudbeckia triloba L.
Brown-eyed Susan   FAC-

Perennial herb. **Stems** 0.5–1.5 m long, with coarse spreading hairs or sometimes nearly smooth. **Leaves** alternate, thin, coarsely hairy (or sometimes nearly hairless), the basal leaves broadly ovate to heart-shaped, with long petioles; the stem leaves narrower, with short petioles or the petioles absent, usually with some leaves deeply trilobed; margins sharp-toothed or nearly entire. **Flower heads** several to many at ends of stems, with both disk and ray flowers, the disk dark purple, rays 6–12, yellow but usually orange at base, 1–3 cm long; involucral bracts of unequal lengths, green and leaflike. **Fruit** a 4-angled achene. July–Sept. ✹ Edges of wet forests and marshes, wet praire, shorelines. ⊕ se Minn, s and c Wisc, s Mich, n Ill and n Ind. NY to Mich and Kans, s to Fla, La and Okla.

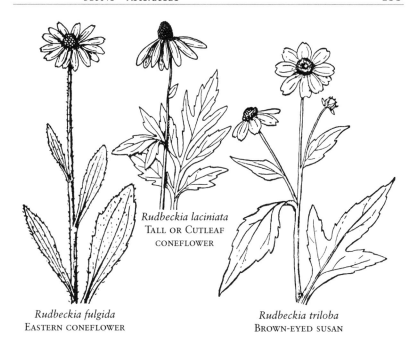

Rudbeckia laciniata
TALL OR CUTLEAF
CONEFLOWER

Rudbeckia fulgida
EASTERN CONEFLOWER

Rudbeckia triloba
BROWN-EYED SUSAN

▶**Senecio** L. / Groundsel

Erect perennial or annual herbs. **Leaves** alternate or from base of plant, stalked near base, stalkless and usually smaller upward. **Flower heads** with both disk and ray flowers, few to many in clusters at ends of stems; disk flowers perfect and yellow, the rays yellow; involucral bracts in 1 series and not overlapping, of equal lengths; receptacle flat or convex, not chaffy. **Fruit** an achene, nearly round in section; pappus of slender bristles.

▶**KEY TO SENECIO**

1 Plants annual or biennial, hollow-stemmed; basal rosette of leaves absent, leaves ± similar in size and shape . . . . *S. congestus*
. . . . NORTHERN SWAMP GROUNDSEL
1 Plants perennial, solid-stemmed; basal leaves crowded and larger than stem leaves **2**

2 Heads with disk flowers only. . . . . *S. indecorus*
. . . . TALLER DISCOID GROUNDSEL
2 Heads with both ray and disk flowers **3**

3 Basal leaves heart-shaped at base; widespread. . . . . *S. aureus*
. . . . HEART-LEAVED GROUNDSEL
3 Basal leaves ovate; w and s Minn only . . . . *S. pseudaureus*
. . . . WESTERN HEART-LEAVED GROUNDSEL

Senecio aureus L.
Heart-leaved groundsel   FACW
Perennial herb, from a spreading crown or rhizome. **Stems** single or clumped, 3–8 dm long, slightly hairy when young, soon becoming

smooth. **Basal leaves** heart-shaped, 5–10 cm long and to as wide, often purple-tinged, on long petioles, the margins with rounded teeth; **stem leaves** much smaller and ± pinnately lobed, becoming stalkless. **Flower heads** several to many, the disk 5–10 mm wide, rays gold-yellow, 6–13 mm long involucre 5–8 mm high, the involucral bracts often purple-tipped. **Fruit** a smooth achene; pappus of slender white bristles. May–July. *S. gracilis.* ❦ Floodplain forests, wet forest depressions, swamp openings and hummocks, sedge meadows, thickets, fens, ditches. ⊕ Minn, Wisc, Mich, ne Ill and nw Ind. Labr to Minn, s to Fla, Ga, and Ark.

Senecio congestus (R. Br.) DC.
Northern swamp groundsel   FACW+

Annual or biennial herb. **Stems** stout, single, 2–10 dm long, hollow near base, sparsely to densely hairy. **Leaves** lance-shaped to oblong or the lower spatula-shaped, 5–20 cm long and 0.5–5 cm wide, smooth or hairy, rounded at tip; margins entire to coarsely toothed or cleft; lower leaves stalked, upper leaves stalkless and clasping at base. **Flower heads** 1–1.5 cm wide, usually many in crowded clusters; with both disk and ray flowers, the rays pale yellow, 4–9 mm long; involucre 4–8 mm high, the involucral bracts chaffy near tip. **Fruit** a smooth achene, 1–3 mm long; pappus bristles white, very slender and numerous, lengthening after flowering. May–Aug. ❦ Shores and mud flats. ⊕ Minn and nw Wisc; once known from n LP of Mich. Circumboreal, s to Que, n Iowa, e SD and Alberta.

Senecio indecorus Greene
Taller discoid groundsel   FACW

⚠
STATUS
Michigan - T

Perennial herb. **Stems** 3–8 dm long, smooth apart from woolly hairs in leaf axils. Basal **leaves** ovate, 3–6 cm long and 2–4 cm wide, margins with coarse, forward-pointing teeth, the petioles longer than blades; **stem leaves** few, much smaller, deeply cleft, ± stalkless. **Flower heads** few to several on slender stalks and forming a rounded cluster; with yellow disk flowers only; involucre 6–10 mm high, the involucral bracts often purple-tipped. **Fruit** a smooth achene; pappus of long slender bristles. July–Aug. *S. discoideus.* ❦ Cedar swamps, moist conifer or mixed conifer and deciduous forests, rocky Lake Superior shores, streambanks. ⊕ Uncommon in extreme ne Minn, n Wisc, w UP of Mich. Que to Alaska, s to n Mich, Wyo, and n Calif.

Senecio pseudaureus Rydb.
Western heart-leaved groundsel   FACW

Perennial herb, from a crown or short rhizome. **Stems** single or few, solid, 2–5 dm long, smooth or with tufts of woolly hairs in leaf axils when young. **Basal leaves** ovate to oval, 2–4 cm long and 1–2 cm wide, underside often purple, margins with rounded teeth, petioles long and slender; **stem leaves** 2–6 cm long and 0.5–2 cm wide, pinnately cleft at least near base, stalkless and often clasping. **Flower heads** 1–1.5 cm wide, few to many in a single cluster; with both disk and ray flowers, the rays pale yellow, 6–10 mm long; involucre 4–7 mm high, the involucral bracts green. **Fruit** a smooth achene, 1–2 mm long; pappus of white bristles. May–July. ❦ Wet meadows, low prairie, fens. ⊕ w and s Minn, more common westward. Minn to Sask and BC, s to Mo, Kans, NM and Calif. ☞ Ours are var. *semicordatus.*

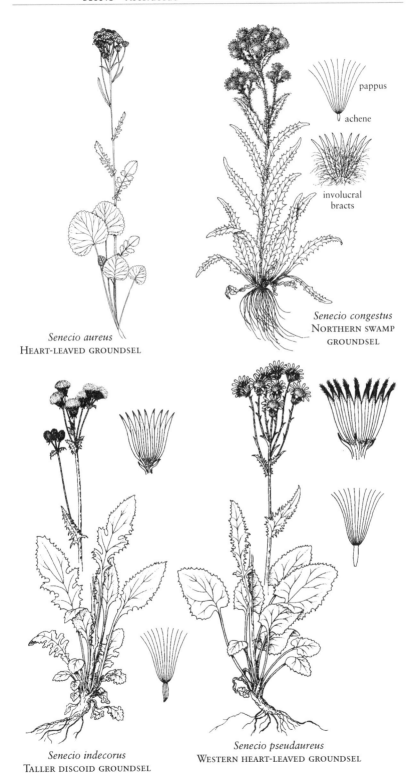

Senecio aureus
HEART-LEAVED GROUNDSEL

pappus
achene

involucral
bracts

Senecio congestus
NORTHERN SWAMP
GROUNDSEL

Senecio indecorus
TALLER DISCOID GROUNDSEL

Senecio pseudaureus
WESTERN HEART-LEAVED GROUNDSEL

▶**Silphium** L. / Cup-plant; Rosin-weed

Tall perennial herbs, with resinous juice. **Leaves** opposite or all from base of plant, broadly ovate. **Flower heads** with yellow disk and ray flowers, in clusters at ends of stems; involucral bracts overlapping, receptacle ± flat, chaffy. **Fruit** an achene; pappus absent or of 2 small scales from top of achene.

▶**KEY TO SILPHIUM**

1 Stems leafy and 4-angled . *S. perfoliatum* / Cup-plant; Indian-cup
1 Leaves all at base of plant; stems round . . . . . . *S. terebinthinaceum*
. . . . Rosin-weed; prairie-dock

Silphium perfoliatum L.

Cup-plant; Indian-cup   FACW-

⚠
STATUS
Michigan - T

Perennial herb, spreading by rhizomes. **Stems** erect, 4-angled, smooth, 1–2.5 m long. **Leaves** opposite, broadly ovate, 8–30 cm long and 4–15 cm wide, rough-to-touch, margins coarsely toothed, the lower leaves often short-stalked and joined by wings on the petioles; upper leaves joined at base, forming a cup around stem. **Flower heads** several to many in an open inflorescence, with both disk and ray flowers, the disk 1.5–2.5 cm wide, the rays yellow, 1.5–2.5 cm long; involucre 1–2.5 cm high, the involucral bracts ovate, nearly equal, fringed with hairs on margins; receptacle flat, chaffy. **Fruit** a flat, obovate achene, 8–10 mm long and 5–6 mm wide, the margins narrowly winged; pappus absent. July–Sept. ⚘ Floodplain forests, streambanks, springs. ⊕ s and ec Minn, s Wisc, s LP of Mich, ne Ill and nw Ind. s Ont to ND, s to Ga and La.

Silphium terebinthinaceum Jacq.

Rosin-weed; prairie-dock   FACU

Taprooted perennial herb. **Stems** 1–3 m long, branched above, ± leafless, smooth. Main **leaves** all from base of plant, ovate, leathery, 1–5 dm long and 1–3 dm wide, usually heart-shaped at base, usually rough-to-touch, margins sharply toothed, petioles long; stem leaves few and reduced to large bracts. **Flower heads** many in an open inflorescence, with yellow disk and ray flowers, the disk 1.5–3 cm wide, the rays 2–3 cm long; involucre 1–2.5 cm high, the involucral bracts smooth, loose and overlapping. **Fruit** an obovate, narrowly winged achene; pappus reduced to 2 small teeth at top of achene. July–Sept. *S. rumicifolium.* ⚘ Low prairie, fens; especially where calcium-rich. ⊕ Fairly common; s Wisc, s LP of Mich (local in c UP), ne Ill and nw Ind. s Ont and Ohio to Wisc, s to Ga and Miss.

▶**Solidago** L. / Goldenrod

Erect perennials, spreading by rhizomes or from a crown. **Leaves** alternate, margins entire or toothed. **Flower heads** small, many, in flat-topped (corymblike), rounded (paniclelike) or spikelike clusters at ends of stems; the flowers sometimes mostly on 1 side of inflorescence branches (secund) in species with paniclelike heads; the heads with yellow disk and ray flowers; involucral bracts in several overlapping series, papery at base and tipped with green; receptacle flat or convex, not chaffy. **Fruit** an achene, angled or nearly round in cross-section; pappus of many slender white bristles.

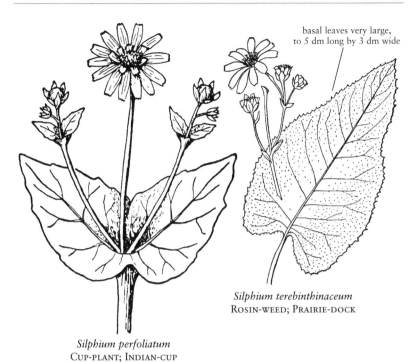

Silphium terebinthinaceum
ROSIN-WEED; PRAIRIE-DOCK

basal leaves very large,
to 5 dm long by 3 dm wide

Silphium perfoliatum
CUP-PLANT; INDIAN-CUP

▶**KEY TO SOLIDAGO**

1 Heads in a ± flat-topped cluster at end of stems **2**
1 Heads in an elongate or pyramid-shaped cluster **4**

2 Rare species near Michigan and Ontario Great Lakes shorelines; rays
3–5 mm long. . . . . *S. houghtonii*
. . . . HOUGHTON'S OR GREAT LAKES GOLDENROD
2 Widespread species; rays 1–3 mm long. **3**

3 Flower stalks rough-hairy; upper leaves folded inward along midrib,
with 3 or more veins at base . . *S. riddellii* / RIDDELL'S GOLDENROD
3 Flower stalks ± smooth; leaves flat, not 3-veined at base. . . . .
. . . . *S. ohioensis* / OHIO GOLDENROD

4 Flower heads spiraled around branches of inflorescence *S. uliginosa*
. . . . NORTHERN BOG GOLDENROD
4 Flower heads mostly on upper side of branches of inflorescence . . **5**

5 Stem leaves with 3 prominent veins . . . . *S. gigantea*
. . . . SMOOTH GOLDENROD
5 Stem leaves with strong midvein only, not 3-veined. **6**

6 Leaves smooth, lowest stem leaves clasping stem . . . . . . *S. uliginosa*
. . . . NORTHERN BOG GOLDENROD
6 Upper leaf surface rough-to-touch, lowest stem leaves not clasping
stem . . . . *S. patula* / ROUGH-LEAVED GOLDENROD

Solidago gigantea Aiton
Smooth goldenrod   FACW

Perennial herb, from stout rhizomes, often forming colonies. **Stems** 0.5–2 m long, mostly smooth, sometimes waxy, short-hairy on upper branches. **Leaves** alternate, lance-shaped to oval, 6–15 cm long and 1–4 cm wide, prominently 3-veined, tapered to an stalkless or short, petiolelike base, smooth, or sparsely hairy on underside veins; margins with sharp, forward-pointing teeth. **Flower heads** many, in large paniclelike clusters, on 1 side of the spreading branches, with yellow disk and ray flowers, the rays 2–3 mm long; involucre 2–5 mm high, the involucral bracts linear. **Fruit** a short-hairy achene, 1–2 mm long; pappus of slender white bristles. July–Sept. *S. serotina*. ❦ Wet meadows, streambanks, swamps, floodplain forests, thickets, marshes, calcareous fens, ditches; also in moist to dry open woods and roadsides. ⊕ Common; Minn, Wisc, Mich, ne Ill and nw Ind. NS and Que to BC, s to Ga, NM and Ore. ☞ **Canada goldenrod** (*Solidago canadensis* L.) is a common species that sometimes occurs in moist to wet open areas (as well as drier places). It is similar to smooth goldenrod but generally smaller and densely short-hairy on leaf undersides and upper stems.

Solidago houghtonii T. & G.
Houghton's or Great Lakes goldenrod   OBL

⚠
STATUS
Michigan - T
USA - T

flower head

Perennial herb, from a crown. **Stems** slender, 2–5 dm long, smooth below, short-hairy in the inflorescence. **Leaves** alternate, largest at base of plant, becoming smaller upward, linear, to 20 cm long and 1–2 cm wide; margins entire but rough-to-touch; lower leaves tapered to a petiolelike base, petioles absent on upper leaves. **Flower heads** often many, crowded in flat-topped to rounded clusters at ends of stems, with yellow disk and ray flowers; involucre 5–8 mm high, the involucral bracts rounded at tip. **Fruit** a smooth, angled achene; pappus of slender, sometimes feathery hairs. July–Sept. ❦ Moist flats and depressions between dunes near n shores of Lakes Huron and Michigan, also in nearby fens, limestone pavements on Drummond Island, Mich; usually where calcium-rich. ⊕ e UP and extreme n LP of Mich.

Solidago ohioensis Riddell
Ohio goldenrod   OBL

Perennial herb, from a crown. **Stems** 5–10 dm long, smooth. **Leaves** alternate, largest at base of plant and becoming smaller upward, lance-shaped to oblong lance-shaped, to 2 dm long and 1–5 cm wide, pinnately-veined, margins entire or slightly toothed near tip, rough-to-touch; tapered to a long petiole on lower leaves, upper leaves stalkless. **Flower heads** many in a branched, flat-topped to rounded inflorescence at ends of stems, with yellow disk and ray flowers; involucre smooth, 4–5 mm high, the involucral bracts rounded at tip. **Fruit** a smooth, angled achene; pappus of slender white bristles. July–Sept. ❦ Wet, sandy or gravelly shores, streambanks, sedge meadows, calcareous fens, low prairie; soils often calcium-rich. ⊕ Wisc, e UP and LP of Mich, ne Ill and nw Ind. NY and s Ont to Mich and Ill.

Solidago patula Muhl.
Rough-leaved goldenrod   OBL

Perennial herb, from a crown. **Stems** 5–20 dm long, lower stem smooth, strongly angled, upper stem short-hairy. **Leaves** alternate, largest at base of plant, 1–3 dm long and 4–10 cm wide, becoming smaller upward, oval to ovate, pinnately veined, upper surface rough-to-touch, underside smooth; margins with large, forward-pointing teeth; petioles long and winged on lower leaves, upper leaves stalkless. **Flower heads** in a pani-clelike head, the branches spreading and curved downward at tip, flower heads mostly on 1 side of branches, with yellow disk and ray flowers; involucre 3–4 mm high, the involucral bracts tapered to a sharp or rounded tip. **Fruit** a sparsely hairy achene; pappus of slender white bris-tles. Aug–Sept. *S. salicina*. ⚘ Swamps, thickets, calcareous fens, sedge meadows. ⊕ Wisc, sc UP and LP of Mich, ne Ill and nw Ind. Vt to Wisc, s to Ga and Tex.

Solidago riddellii Frank
Riddell's goldenrod   OBL

Perennial herb, from a crown and sometimes also with rhizomes. **Stems** 2–10 dm long, smooth but sometimes sparsely hairy in head. **Leaves** alternate, smooth, largest at base of plant, these often early-deciduous, lance-shaped to linear, 10–20 cm long and 5–30 mm wide, becoming smaller upward, the upper leaves sickle-shaped and folded along midrib; margins entire; petioles of lower leaves long and winged, upper leaves stalkless and clasping stem. **Flower heads** many, crowded in a branched, rounded to flat-topped inflorescence, the heads not confined to 1 side of the branches, with yellow disk and ray flowers, the rays 1–2 mm long; involucre 5–6 mm high, the involucral bracts rounded at tip. **Fruit** a smooth achene, 1–2 mm long; pappus of slender bristles. Aug–Oct. ⚘ Wet meadows, calcareous fens, low prairie, lakeshores, streambanks. ⊕ w and s Minn, c and s Wisc, c and s LP of Mich, ne Ill and nw Ind. Ont to e ND and SD, s to Ohio and Mo.

Solidago uliginosa Nutt.
Northern bog goldenrod   OBL

Perennial herb, from a branched crown. **Stems** stout, 5–15 dm long, smooth but finely hairy in the head. **Leaves** alternate, largest at base of plant, 5–35 cm long and 1–5 cm wide, becoming smaller upward, lance-shaped to oblong lance-shaped, smooth, margins finely toothed, or entire on upper leaves, rough-to-touch; lower leaves tapered to long petioles, somewhat clasping stem, upper leaves stalkless. **Flower heads** in a long, crowded spikelike inflorescence, the branches ascending, straight or curved downward at tip, the heads sometimes mostly on 1 side of branches, with yellow disk and ray flowers; involucre 3–5 mm high, the inner involucral bracts rounded at tip, the outer often acute. **Fruit** a ± smooth achene; pappus of slender bristles. Aug–Sept. ⚘ Conifer swamps, fens, open bogs, low prairie, wet meadows, interdunal wet-lands, Lake Superior rocky shore. ⊕ n and c Minn (but absent from far w), Wisc, Mich, ne Ill and nw Ind. Nfld and Que to Minn, s to NC, Tenn, and Ill.

▶**Verbesina** L. / Wingstem

Verbesina alternifolia (L.) Britton
Wingstem   FACW

Large perennial herb. **Stems** usually winged, sometimes round, 1–3 m long, finely hairy to nearly smooth. **Leaves** alternate, lance-shaped or oblong lance-shaped, 10–25 cm long and 2–8 cm wide, becoming small-er above, rough-to-touch; margins with forward-pointing teeth or near-ly entire; petioles short. **Flower heads** in open clusters at ends of stems and branches, with both disk and ray flowers, the disk globe-shaped, 1–1.5 cm wide; rays 2–10, yellow, 1–3 cm long; involucral bracts narrow,

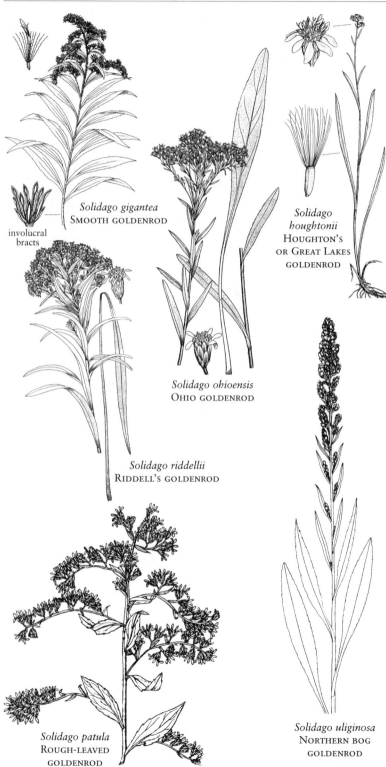

Solidago gigantea
SMOOTH GOLDENROD

involucral
bracts

Solidago houghtonii
HOUGHTON'S
OR GREAT LAKES
GOLDENROD

Solidago ohioensis
OHIO GOLDENROD

Solidago riddellii
RIDDELL'S GOLDENROD

Solidago patula
ROUGH-LEAVED
GOLDENROD

Solidago uliginosa
NORTHERN BOG
GOLDENROD

loosely spreading. **Fruit** a winged (or sometimes wingless) achene; pappus of 2 spreading awns. Aug–Oct. *Actinomeris alternifolia, Ridan alternifolia.* ❧ Floodplain forests, thickets, fens, streambanks. ⊕ s LP of Mich, ne Ill and nw Ind. NY and s Ont to Neb, s to Fla, La, and Okla.

▶**Vernonia** Schreber / Ironweed

Vernonia fasciculata Michx.
Smooth ironweed   FACW

Stout perennial herb, from a thick rootstock. **Stems** erect, single or clumped, 5–12 dm long, red or purple, smooth but short-hairy on branches of the head. **Leaves** alternate, lance-shaped, 5–15 cm long and 1–4 cm wide, smooth above, underside finely pitted, margins sharp-toothed, petioles short. **Flower heads** usually many, crowded in flat-topped clusters to 10 cm wide, with purple disk flowers only; involucre 6–9 mm high, the involucral bracts overlapping, green with purple tips; receptacle flat, not chaffy. **Fruit** a ribbed achene, 3–4 mm long; pappus of purple to brown, slender bristles. July–Sept. ☞ Plants of our region are mostly var. *fasciculata.* ❧ Marshes, low prairie, streambanks. ⊕ Minn (all but ne), Wisc, ne Ill and nw Ind. Ohio to Man and Sask, s to Mo and n Tex.

▶**Xanthium** L. / Cocklebur

Xanthium strumarium L.
Common cocklebur   FAC

Weedy taprooted annual herb; plants variable in size and habit, rough-to-touch or sometimes nearly smooth. **Stems** 2–15 dm long, often brown-spotted. **Leaves** alternate, ovate to nearly round, sometimes with 3–5 shallow lobes, 3–15 cm long and 2–20 cm wide, margins with blunt teeth; petioles 3–10 cm long. **Flower heads** either male or female, the male flowers brown, in clusters of small round heads at ends of stems above the larger female heads; female heads in several to many clusters from leaf axils, each head with 2 flowers, with a spiny involucre enclosing the head; petals absent. **Fruit** a brown bur formed by the involucre, 1.5–3 cm long, covered with hooked prickles; **achenes** thick, 1 in each of the 2 chambers of the bur. Aug–Sept. ❧ Shores, streambanks, wet meadows, sand bars, dried depressions, often where disturbed; also in cultivated and abandoned fields, roadsides and waste places. ⊕ Introduced and common; Minn (but local in ne), Wisc, c UP and LP of Mich, ne Ill and nw Ind.

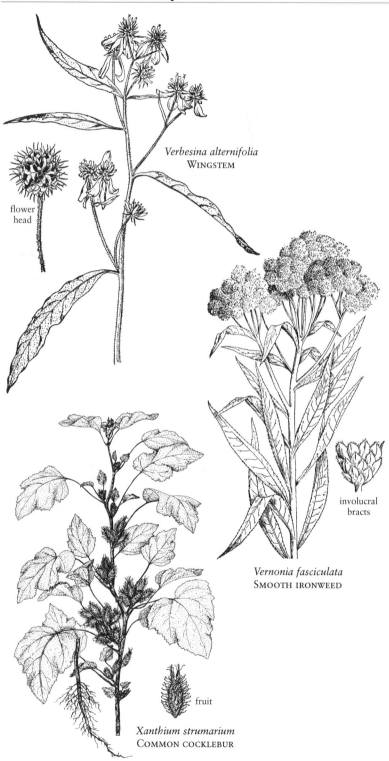

Verbesina alternifolia
WINGSTEM

flower
head

Vernonia fasciculata
SMOOTH IRONWEED

involucral
bracts

fruit

Xanthium strumarium
COMMON COCKLEBUR

Balsaminaceae
Touch-Me-Not Family

▶**Impatiens** L. / Touch-me-not

Smooth annual herbs with hollow, succulent **stems** and shallow, weak roots. **Leaves** simple, alternate, the blades shallowly toothed. **Flowers** with both male and female parts, irregular, yellow to orange-yellow, pouchlike and spurred, hanging from the petioles in few-flowered racemes from upper leaf axils; sepals 3, petal-like; petals 3; stamens 5. **Fruit** a 5-valved capsule; the mature capsules splitting when jarred or touched, scattering the seeds away from parent plants. ☞ Small, cleistogamous (self-fertile) flowers lacking petals are sometimes produced in summer and are often the only flowers found on plants growing in shaded situations.

▶**KEY TO IMPATIENS**

1 Flowers orange-yellow, usually with red-brown spots . . . *I. capensis*
. . . . ORANGE TOUCH-ME-NOT; JEWEL-WEED
1 Flowers pale yellow, spots faint or absent . . . . *I. pallida*
. . . . YELLOW TOUCH-ME-NOT

Impatiens capensis Meerb.
   Orange touch-me-not; Jewel-weed   FACW
Annual herb. **Stems** 3–10 dm long, usually branched above. **Leaves** ovate to oval, 3–9 cm long and 1.5–4 cm wide, tapered to tip or rounded and tipped with a short slender point, margins shallowly and irregularly toothed; petioles longest on lower leaves, shorter upward, 0.5–5 cm long. **Flowers** orange-yellow, 1.5–3 cm long, usually mottled with red-brown spots, with a spur recurved parallel to the sac and to half its length. **Fruit** a capsule about 2 cm long, splitting when mature to forcefully eject the seeds. July–Sept. ❋ Swamps, low areas in woods, floodplain forests, thickets, streambanks, shores, marshes, fens, springs; often where disturbed. ⊕ Common; Minn, Wisc, Mich, ne Ill and nw Ind. Newf and Que to Sask, s to Fla, Ala, and Tex.

Impatiens pallida Nutt.
   Yellow touch-me-not   FACW
Annual herb, similar to **orange touch-me-not** (*I. capensis*) but much less common. *I. pallida* is typically larger, the **leaves** to 12 cm long and 8 cm wide, and more finely toothed than those of *I. capensis*. **Flowers** pale yellow, unspotted or with faint red-brown spots, 2–4 cm long, the spur recurved at a right angle to sac, and to 1/4 length of sac. July–Sept. ❋ Floodplain forests, low spots in woods, swamps, streambanks, shores; often where somewhat disturbed. ⊕ s Minn, s Wisc, Mich LP (especially s), ne Ill and nw Ind. Que and NS to Sask, s to NC, Tenn, Mo and Okla.

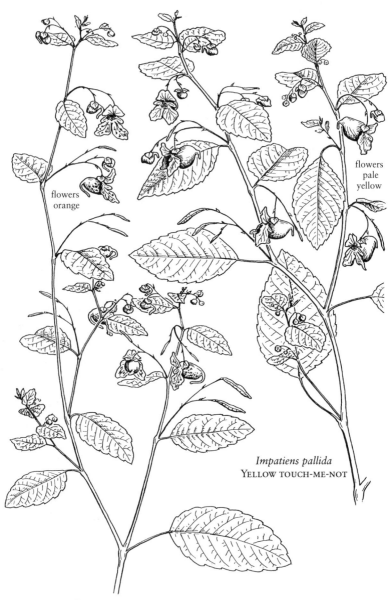

flowers orange

flowers pale yellow

Impatiens pallida
Yellow touch-me-not

Impatiens capensis
Orange touch-me-not; Jewel-weed

Betulaceae
Birch Family

Trees or shrubs. **Leaves** deciduous, simple, alternate, with toothed margins and pinnate veins. **Flowers** small, male and female flowers separate on same plant, crowded into catkins (aments) that open in spring before leaves fully open; male catkins hang downward; conelike female catkins erect or drooping. **Fruit** a small, 1-seeded, winged nutlet.

▸**KEY TO BETULACEAE**

1 Female catkins in loose clusters of several catkins; scales of female catkins persistent, becoming hard and stiff . . . . *Alnus* / ALDER
1 Female catkins single; scales of female catkins soon deciduous . . . .
. . . . *Betula* / BIRCH

▸**Alnus** Miller / Alder

Thicket-forming shrubs, or an introduced tree (*Alnus glutinosa*). **Leaves** deciduous, ovate, toothed on margins. Male and female **flowers** separate on same plant, male flowers in long, drooping catkins which fall after shedding pollen; female flowers in short, persistent conelike clusters. **Fruit** a flattened achene with winged or thin margins.

▸**KEY TO ALNUS**

1 Introduced tree uncommon in s part of Gt Lakes region; leaves broadly rounded, tip rounded to blunt or notched. . . . . *A. glutinosa*
. . . . BLACK ALDER
1 Shrubs; leaves ovate to oval, tapered to a sharp tip. **2**

2 Twigs and young leaves sticky, leaves with small, sharp teeth; catkins on long stalks; winter buds not stalked; fruit broadly winged; n portion of region only . . . . . . *A. viridis* / GREEN OR MOUNTAIN ALDER
2 Twigs and young leaves not sticky, leaves unevenly double-toothed; catkins stalkless or on short stalks; winter bud stalked, blunt at tip; fruit narrowly winged; widespread in n and c areas of region . . . . .
. . . . *A. incana* / SPECKLED ALDER; TAG ALDER

Alnus glutinosa (L.) Gaertner
Black alder   FACW-

Tree to 20 m tall; twigs, young leaves and fruits sticky-to-touch. **Leaves** oval to nearly round, tip rounded or with a small notch, veins 5–8 on each side of midvein, dark green and ± shiny above, paler below, margins finely toothed. Male and female **flowers** separate on same tree; female catkins drooping from leaf axils, 1.5–2.5 cm long and 10–12 mm wide. April–May. *A. alnus, A. vulgaris.* ❦ Floodplain forests, riverbanks; also in drier places. ⊕ Occasional in s Wisc, c and s LP of Mich, ne Ill and nw Ind. Introduced from Eurasia and planted as an ornamental; occasionally escaping and naturalized from Mass to Ill and s Wisc.

Alnus incana (L.) Moench
Speckled alder; Tag alder   OBL

⚠
STATUS
Illinois - E

Thicket-forming shrub to 5 m tall; **twigs** red-brown, waxy, with conspicuous pale lenticels. **Leaves** ovate to oval, broadest near or below middle, 6–14 cm long and 4–7 cm wide, dark green and smooth above, paler and hairy below; margins sharply toothed and shallowly lobed; petioles 1–2.5 cm long. **Flowers** in catkins clustered at ends of branches; male catkins developing in late summer, short-stalked, elongate, 4–9 cm long; female catkins appear in late summer, stalkless, rounded, 1–2 cm long and to 1 cm wide, the scales unlobed, becoming conelike, persistent. **Fruit** a flat nutlet, narrowly winged on margin, 2–4 mm long. April–June. *A. rugosa.* ❀ Swamps, thickets, bog margins, shores and streambanks. ⊕ n, ec and se Minn, Wisc (but local in sw), Mich (but local in se), ne Ill and nw Ind. Newf to Alaska, s to Md, Ohio, n Ind, Minn, ND, NM, Ariz and Calif; Eurasia.

female
catkin

Alnus viridis (Villars) Lam.
Green or Mountain alder   FAC

Thicket-forming shrub to 4 m tall; **bark** red-brown to gray; **twigs** brown, sticky, somewhat hairy, lenticels pale and scattered. **Leaves** round-oval, bright green above, slightly paler and shiny below, sticky when young, margins wavy with small, sharp teeth; petioles 6–12 mm long. **Flowers** in catkins; male catkins stalked, slender, developing in late summer and expanding in spring; female catkins appear in spring, becoming long-stalked, blunt and conelike, persistent, 1–2 cm long. **Fruit** a nutlet, 2–3 mm long, with a pale, thin wing. *A. crispa, A. mollis.* ❀ Lakeshores, wet depressions in woods, rock outcrops, beaches along Lake Superior. ⊕ ne and nc Minn, nw and nc Wisc, UP of Mich. ± circumboreal, s to Mass, NY, Minn, Idaho and Calif.

▶Betula L. / Birch

☞ **Paper
birch** (*Betula
papyrifera*) a
common tree
across most of
the Great Lakes
region, is
sometimes
found on
hummocks in
swamps and on
wetland
margins. It
is identified
by its
characteristic
white papery
bark marked
by horizontal
lenticels.

Trees or shrubs (often with many stems from base); bark sometimes peeling in thin layers. **Leaves** deciduous, alternate, sharply toothed. Male and female **flowers** separate on same plant, catkins appearing in fall, opening the following spring, male flowers in drooping slender catkins; female flowers in erect conelike catkins. **Fruit** an achene with a winged margin.

▶KEY TO BETULA

1 Shrub to 2 m tall; bark not shredding; leaves to 5 cm long *B. pumila*
. . . . Bog birch
1 Small to large trees; bark shredding with age 2

2 Bark yellow-gray; leaves rounded at base, margins not wavy-toothed; widespread . . . . *B. alleghaniensis* / Yellow birch
2 Bark red-brown; leaves wedge-shaped at base, margins wavy-toothed; absent from Mich . . . . *B. nigra* / River birch

Betula alleghaniensis Britton
Yellow birch   FAC

⚠
STATUS
Illinois - E

Medium to large tree to 25 m tall; **bark** on young trees thin and smooth with conspicuous horizontal lenticels, becoming yellow-gray and shredding into thin, shaggy horizontal strips; bark of old trees breaking into large plates; **twigs** hairy when young, becoming smooth and shiny, wintergreen-scented when crushed. **Leaves** alternate, simple, ovate, tapered

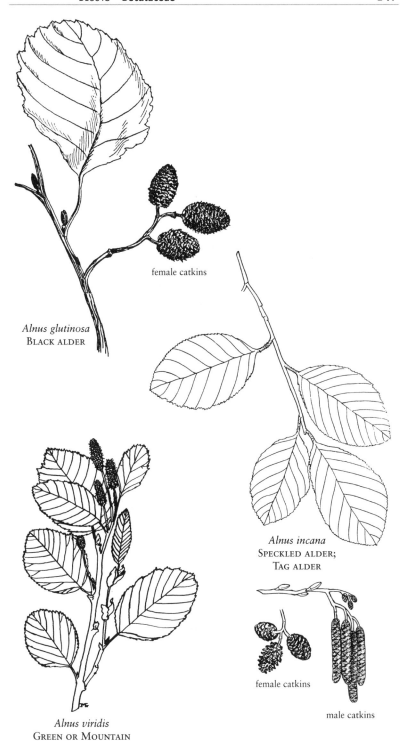

Alnus glutinosa
Black alder

female catkins

Alnus incana
Speckled alder;
Tag alder

Alnus viridis
Green or Mountain
alder

female catkins

male catkins

to a short, sharp tip, dark green above, paler yellow-green below, 6–12 cm long, margins coarsely double-toothed, petioles grooved and hairy. Male and female **flowers** in catkins, separate on same tree, appearing before leaves in spring; male catkins drooping, yellow-purple, 7–10 cm long; female catkins erect, green, 2–4 cm long, ± stalkless. **Fruit** a winged nutlet, 3–5 mm wide. April–May. *B. lutea.* ❦ North in our region, occasional in swamps, thickets, streambanks and forest depressions with **red maple** (*Acer rubrum*), **black ash** (*Fraxinus nigra*), **black spruce** (*Picea mariana*), **eastern hemlock** (*Tsuga canadensis*) and **speckled alder** (*Alnus incana*); more common in moist forests with **sugar maple** (*Acer saccharum*) and **American beech** (*Fagus grandifolia*). Southward, mostly confined to deciduous swamps with **red maple, black ash** and **tamarack** (*Larix laricina*). ⊕ e Minn, Wisc, Mich, ne Ill and nw Ind. Nfld to se Man, s to Pa, Ohio, n Ill, and Iowa, s in mts to Ga.

Betula nigra L.
River birch   FACW

Small or medium tree to 20 m tall, trunk to 6 dm wide, crown rounded; **bark** red-brown, shredding and curly; **twigs** slender, red-brown; buds pointed, hairy. **Leaves** alternate, simple, ovate, 4–8 cm long, upper surface smooth, lower surface paler and densely hairy; margins coarsely double-toothed, except untoothed near base; petioles with woolly hairs. Male and female **flowers** small, separate but on same tree; male flowers in slender drooping clusters; female flowers in short, woolly clusters. **Fruit** a small hairy nutlet with a 3-lobed, winged margin, crowded in a cylindrical cone 1.5–3 cm long. May. ❦ Floodplain forests, riverbanks, swamps. ⊕ se along Miss R in Minn, c and s Wisc, ne Ill and nw Ind. NH to Ohio and s Minn, s to Fla and Tex.

Betula pumila L.
Bog birch   OBL

☞ Hybrids between *Betula pumila* and *B. papyrifera* (*B. xsandbergii*) have been reported.

Shrub 1–3 m tall; **bark** dull gray or brown; **twigs** gray, short-hairy and dotted with resin glands, becoming red-brown and waxy with age. **Leaves** leathery, rounded to obovate, 2–4 cm long and 1–3 cm wide, dark green above, paler and often waxy below; margins coarsely toothed, the teeth blunt or sharp; petioles 3–6 mm long. **Flowers** in catkins; male catkins stalkless, cylindric, 15–20 mm long and 2–3 mm wide; female catkins stalked, cylindric, 1–2 cm long and 5 mm wide; scales 3-lobed. **Fruit** a flat, winged, rounded nutlet, 2–3 mm long and 2–4 mm wide. May. *B. glandulosa* var. *glandulifera.* ❦ Swamps, bogs, fens, seeps; often where calcium-rich. ⊕ Minn (all but sw), Wisc (but rare in driftless area), Mich, ne Ill and nw Ind. Newf to Alaska, s to Maine, n NY, Ind, Ont, Minn, SD, Wyo, Idaho and Calif.

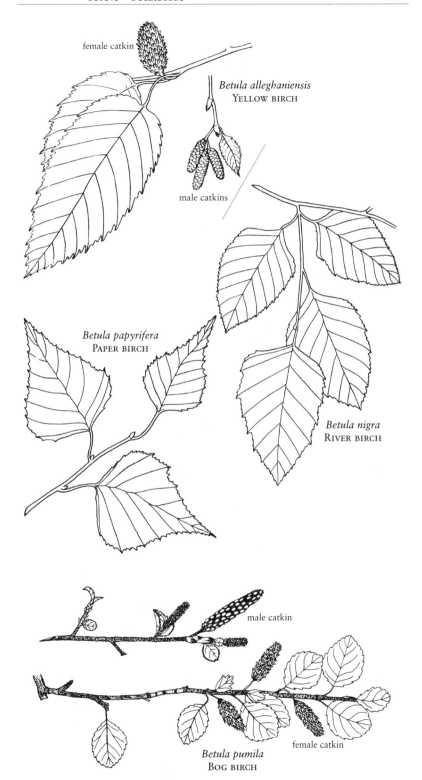

female catkin

Betula alleghaniensis
YELLOW BIRCH

male catkins

Betula papyrifera
PAPER BIRCH

Betula nigra
RIVER BIRCH

male catkin

female catkin

Betula pumila
BOG BIRCH

Boraginaceae
Borage Family

Annual or perennial herbs with usually bristly **stems** and alternate, bristly **leaves**. **Flowers** typically in a spirally coiled, spikelike head that uncurls as flowers mature; flowers perfect (with both male and female parts), with 5 petals, 4–5 sepals, and 5 stamens. **Fruit** a dry capsule with 4 nutlets.

▸**KEY TO BORAGINACEAE**

1 Flowers tubelike, the petal lobes erect or slightly spreading. . . . . . .
. . . . *Mertensia* / Bluebell
1 Flowers tubelike, but petal lobes abruptly flared and flattened . . . .
. . . . *Myosotis* / Forget-me-not; Scorpion-grass

▸**Mertensia** Roth / Bluebell

Perennial herbs; plants smooth or hairy. **Leaves** alternate and entire. **Flowers** usually blue (pink in bud), tube-, funnel- or bell-shaped, petals widened and shallowly lobed at tip; in small clusters at ends of stems and branches. **Fruit** a smooth or wrinkled nutlet.

▸**KEY TO MERTENSIA**

1 Leaves and sepals hairy . . . . *M. paniculata* / Northern bluebells
1 Leaves and sepals without hairs . *M. virginica* / Eastern bluebells

Mertensia paniculata (Aiton) G. Don.
Northern bluebells   FAC
Perennial herb. **Stems** erect, 3–10 dm long, branched above, smooth or with sparse hairs. **Basal leaves** ovate, rounded at base; **stem leaves** lance-shaped to ovate, 5–15 cm long, tapered to a tip, hairy, entire; petioles short on lower leaves, upper leaves ± stalkless. **Flowers** blue-purple, narrowly bell-shaped, 10–15 mm long, on slender stalks, in few-flowered racemes at ends of stems and branches; sepal lobes lance-shaped, 3–6 mm long, with dense, short hairs. **Fruit** a nutlet. June–July. ≋ Conifer swamps, streambanks, seeps. ⊕ n and se Minn, n Wisc, w UP of Mich. Hudson Bay to n Mich, n Wisc and n Minn, w to Alaska and Ore; disjunct in se Minn and ne Iowa.

Mertensia virginica (L.) Pers.
Eastern bluebells   FACW
Perennial herb; plants smooth. **Stems** upright, 3–7 dm long. **Leaves** oval to obovate, entire, 5–15 cm long, rounded or blunt at the tip; upper leaves stalkless, lower leaves with winged petioles. **Flowers** showy, blue-purple, trumpet-shaped, 5-lobed at tip, 2–3 cm long, stalked, in a cluster at end of stem; sepals rounded at tip, 3 mm long. **Fruit** a nutlet. April–May. ≋ Floodplain forests, moist deciduous forests, streambanks; sometimes escaping from gardens where grown as an ornamental. ⊕ se Minn, local in wc and s Wisc along river bottoms, s LP of Mich, ne Ill and nw Ind. NY to Iowa, Kans, s to Mo and Ala.

☞ Native populations of eastern bluebells are listed as threatened in Michigan.

▶**Myosotis** L. / Forget-me-not; Scorpion-grass

Perennial (sometimes annual) herbs; plants with short, appressed hairs. **Leaves** alternate and entire. **Flowers** blue, tube-shaped and abruptly flared outward at tip, in a 1-sided raceme. **Fruit** a nutlet.

▶**KEY TO MYOSOTIS**

1 Plants without stolons; lobes of sepals as long or longer than corolla tube; flowers up to 6 mm wide; nutlets longer than style . . . *M. laxa* . . . . Smaller forget-me-not
1 Plants creeping and spreading by stolons; lobes of sepals shorter than corolla tube; flowers mostly 6 mm or more wide; nutlets shorter than style . . . . *M. scorpioides* / Water scorpion-grass

Myosotis laxa Lehm.
Smaller forget-me-not   OBL

⚠
STATUS
Indiana - E

Short-lived perennial (sometimes annual) herb. **Stems** slender, 1–4 dm long, often lying on ground at base, but not creeping, with fine, short, appressed hairs. **Leaves** oblong or spatula-shaped, 2–6 cm long. **Flowers** blue, on stalks usually much longer than the flower, in 1-sided clusters at ends of stems; sepals covered with short hairs, sepal lobes shorter than the tube; petal lobes shorter or slightly longer than the tube. **Fruit** a nutlet distinctly longer than the style. June–Sept. ⚘ Cedar swamps, wet shores and streambanks. ⊕ s Minn, Wisc, UP and n and c LP of Mich, uncommon in nw Ind. ± circumboreal, s to ne and c USA.

Myosotis scorpioides L.
Water scorpion-grass   OBL
Colony-forming perennial herb. **Stems** 2–6 dm long, with short, appressed hairs, often creeping at base and producing stolons. **Leaves** 3–8 cm long and 0.5–2 cm wide, lower leaves oblong lance-shaped, upper leaves oblong or oval; stalkless or the lower leaves on short petioles. **Flowers** blue with a yellow center, tube-shaped, abruptly flared at tip, in a 1-sided raceme at ends of stems; flower stalks spreading in fruit; sepals with short, appressed hairs, sepal lobes equal or shorter than the tube. **Fruit** a nutlet shorter than the style. May–Sept. *M. palustris*. ⚘ Streambanks, shores, ditches, swamps, wet depressions in forests. ⊕ Local in e Minn; Wisc, Mich, ne Ill and nw Ind. ☞ Introduced and naturalized throughout ne and c USA and s Canada.

Mertensia paniculata
NORTHERN BLUEBELLS

flower

Mertensia virginica
EASTERN BLUEBELLS

Myosotis laxa
SMALLER FORGET-ME-NOT

Myosotis scorpioides
WATER SCORPION-GRASS

Brassicaceae
Mustard Family

Alliaria
petiolata
GARLIC-
MUSTARD

Annual, biennial or perennial herbs. **Leaves** simple or compound, alternate on stems or basal, smooth or hairy, some species with branched hairs. **Flowers** in terminal or lateral clusters (racemes), the lower portion often fruiting while tip in flower, the stalks elongating in fruit. **Flowers** perfect, cross-shaped, with 4 sepals and 4 yellow, white, pink or purple petals; stamens 6, the outer 2 stamens shorter than the inner 4; pistil 1, style 1, ovary superior. **Fruit** a cylindrical (*silique*) or round (*silicle*) pod with 2 chambers and 1 to many seeds in 1 or 2 rows in each chamber. ☞ **Garlic-mustard** (*Alliaria petiolata*) is a highly invasive, garlic-scented European biennial herb found mostly in s and c portions of the region. It occupies a wide range of habitats, especially where shaded. In wetlands, garlic-mustard occurs in floodplain forests, where it may be found to the exclusion of native herbaceous species.

▶**KEY TO BRASSICACEAE**

1 Flowers yellow **2**
1 Flowers white, pink, or purple **3**

2 Leaf segments rounded or broadly oval in outline, the terminal segment much larger than lateral segments; plants without hairs . . . . *Barbarea orthoceras* / NORTHERN WINTER-CRESS
2 Leaf segments tapered to a tip, the terminal segments about same size as lateral segments; plants hairy or smooth   *Rorippa* / WATER-CRESS

3 Petals pink or purple **4**
3 Petals white or green **5**

4 Plants smooth throughout; uncommon in our region in se Minn and n Ill . . . . *Iodanthus pinnatifidus* / PURPLE ROCKET
4 Plants hairy, at least on lower stems or leaves . . . . *Cardamine* . . . . BITTER-CRESS; TOOTHWORT

5 Leaves all basal, linear and entire, plants usually flowering and fruiting underwater; uncommon aquatic plant of ne Minn, Isle Royale, and e UP of Mich . . . . *Subularia aquatica* / WATER AWLWORT
5 Leaves basal and on stems, pinnately divided; widespread **6**

6 Plants aquatic; underwater leaves divided into many linear, threadlike segments, the segments easily detaching from stem . . . . *Armoracia lacustris* / LAKE-CRESS
6 Plants on land or in water; leaves broader, not threadlike **7**

7 Plants rooting only at base, basal rosette usually present on young plants; fruit straight and erect on upright stalks; seeds smooth . . . . *Cardamine* / BITTER-CRESS; TOOTHWORT
7 Plants rooting along underwater nodes of stem; basal rosette absent; fruit often curved, on spreading stalks; seeds netlike on surface. . . . . *Rorippa nasturtium-officinale* / WATER-CRESS

▶**Armoracia** Gaertn., Meyer, & Scherb. / Cress

Armoracia lacustris (A. Gray) Al-Shehbaz & V. Bates
  Lake-cress   OBL

⚠
STATUS
Indiana - E
Michigan - T
Wisconsin - T

Perennial, fibrous-rooted herb; **stems** and leaves smooth, usually under-water. Underwater **leaves** pinnately dissected into many threadlike segments; emersed leaves, if present, lance-shaped, 3–7 cm long, coarsely toothed. **Flowers** on spreading stalks to 1 cm long; sepals turning upright; petals white, 6–8 mm long. **Fruit** oval, 5–8 mm long, 1-chambered, tipped by a persistent slender style 2–4 mm long, but apparently rarely maturing. June–Aug. *Armoracia aquatica.* 🌿 Quiet water in lakes (including Lake Superior), rivers and streams, muddy shores. ⊕ Uncommon in extreme se Minn, n and ec Wisc, c and e UP, far n LP of Mich ; ne Ill and nw Ind. Que to Minn, s to Fla and Tex.

▶**Barbarea** R. Br. / Winter-cress

Barbarea orthoceras Ledeb.
  Northern winter-cress   OBL
Biennial herb; plants smooth or with sparse covering of unbranched hairs. **Stems** 3–8 dm long, unbranched, or branched above. **Leaves** simple or with 1–4 pairs of lateral lobes, the middle and upper leaves deeply lobed. **Flowers** in racemes; on short stalks to 1 mm long, the stalks club-like at tip; petals yellow, 3–5 mm long. **Fruit** upright, 2–4 cm long, with a beak 0.5–2 mm long. June–July. 🌿 Rocky shores, swamps and wet woods. ⊕ Local in ne and ec Minn, Wisc, and e UP and far n LP of Mich. Circumboreal; s to New Eng, n Great Lakes and Calif.

Armoracia lacustris
Lake-cress

Barbarea orthoceras
Northern winter-cress

▶**Cardamine** L. / Bitter-cress; Toothwort

Annual, biennial or perennial herbs, smooth or with short hairs near base of stem. **Leaves** simple to pinnately divided, the basal leaves often different in shape than stem leaves. **Flowers** in racemes or umbel-like clusters; sepals green to yellow, early deciduous; petals white. **Fruit** a 2-chambered, linear pod (silique), the seeds in a single row in each chamber.

▶**KEY TO CARDAMINE**

1 Stem leaves simple or with 1–2 small lobes only **2**
1 Stem leaves pinnately dissected, with 2 or more deep lobes **3**

2 Petals pink to purple (rarely white); sepals purple, turning brown with age . . . . *C. douglassii* / PINK SPRING-CRESS
2 Petals white (rarely pink); sepals green, turning yellow with age . . . . *C. rhomboidea* / SPRING-CRESS

3 Plants annual or biennial; petals 2–4 mm long . . . . *C. pensylvanica* . . . . PENNSYLVANIA BITTER-CRESS
3 Plants perennial; petals 5 mm or more long . . . . *C. pratensis* . . . . CUCKOO-FLOWER

Cardamine douglassii Britton
Pink spring-cress   FACW
Perennial herb, spreading by shallow rhizomes; plants with dense to sparse hairs. **Stems** to 6 dm long **Leaves** simple, basal leaves round or heart-shaped, deciduous before plants in full flower; stem leaves 3–5, narrowly oblong to ovate; petioles long on lower leaves, becoming shorter above. **Flowers** in a raceme; sepals purple, turning brown with age; petals pink, purple, or rarely white. **Fruit** an upright silique, 2–3 cm long and 2–3 mm wide, on a stalk 1–2 cm long. April–May. ✿ Floodplain forests and low deciduous woods, often in shade. ⊕ e Wisc, s LP of Mich, ne Ill and nw Ind. NH to s Wisc, s to Va, Tenn and Mo.

Cardamine pensylvanica Muhl.
Pennsylvania bitter-cress   FACW+
Annual or biennial herb. **Stems** erect or spreading, to 6 dm long, usually hairy on lower stem. **Leaves** pinnately divided into 2–5 pairs of lateral leaflets and a single terminal segment, 4–8 cm long and 1–4 cm wide, the leaflets entire or with a few teeth or lobes, the terminal leaflet largest, 1–4 cm long and 1–2 cm wide; petioles shorter than blades, becoming shorter upward. **Flowers** in a raceme; sepals 1–2 mm long; petals white, 2–4 mm long. **Fruit** an upright silique, 2–3 cm long and to 1 mm wide, with a style-beak to 2 mm long, on stalks 5–15 mm long. May–Sept. *C. parviflora.* ✿ Streambanks, swamps, and wet forests (often where seasonally flooded); wet, disturbed areas. ⊕ Common; Minn, Wisc, Mich, ne Ill and nw Ind. Labr to BC, s to Fla, Ala, Ark, Okla and n Calif.

Cardamine pratensis L.
Cuckoo-flower   OBL

STATUS
Illinois - E
Perennial upright herb. **Stems** 2–5 dm long. **Basal leaves** on long petioles, divided into 3–8 broad leaflets, 5–20 mm long, the terminal segment largest and ± entire; lower stem leaves similar to basal ones, becoming shorter and with shorter petioles upward on stem; **stem leaves** with 7–17 oval to linear leaflets. **Flowers** in a crowded raceme; petals white, 8–15

mm long. **Fruit** an upright silique, 2.5–4 cm long, with a style-beak 1–2 mm long, on stalks 8–15 mm long. May–June. Ours are the native *C. pratensis* var. *palustris*. *C. palustris*. ❧ Peatlands, tamarack and cedar swamps, wet depressions in forests. ⊕ Minn, uncommon in ec and se Wisc, Mich, ne Ill. Circumboreal, s to NJ, Ohio, n Ind, Minn.

Cardamine douglassii
PINK SPRING-CRESS

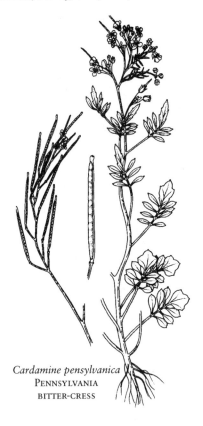

Cardamine pensylvanica
PENNSYLVANIA
BITTER-CRESS

Cardamine pratensis
CUCKOO-FLOWER

Cardamine rhomboidea (Pers.) DC.

Spring-cress   OBL

Perennial herb. **Stems** 1 to several from a short thick tuber, unbranched or with a few branches above, 2–6 dm long, smooth or with short hairs on lower stems. **Leaves** simple, sparsely to densely covered with short hairs; basal leaves round or heart-shaped, on long petioles, withering before plants in full flower; stem leaves 4–8, oblong to oval, 2–7 cm long and 0.5–2.5 cm wide; petioles shorter upward on stem. **Flowers** in racemes; sepals green, turning yellow after flowering, 2–4 mm long; petals white (rarely pink), 6–15 mm long. **Fruit** a silique, 1–2.5 cm long and 1–2 mm wide, with a style beak 2–4 mm long, on spreading stalks 1–3 cm long, the pod often falling before mature. May–June. *C. bulbosa*. ❧ Wet forest depressions, floodplain forests, streambanks, wet meadows, swamps, calcareous fens. ⊕ Minn (all but ne), c and s Wisc, c and s LP of Mich, ne Ill and nw Ind. Que to se ND, s to Fla and e Tex.

▶**Iodanthus** T. & G. / Purple rocket

Iodanthus pinnatifidus (Michx.) Steudel
Purple rocket   FACW

⚠ STATUS
Minnesota - E

Perennial herb; plants smooth. **Stems** to 1 m long, unbranched except in head. **Leaves** lance-shaped to oval or oblong, leaf base often with lobes which clasp stem; lower leaves often divided at base into 1–4 pairs of small segments; margins deep-toothed; petioles short. **Flowers** in a branched raceme, on stalks 5–10 mm long, pale violet to white; sepals rounded at tip, 3–5 mm long; petals 10–13 mm long. **Fruit** a linear, cylindric silique, 2–4 cm long and 1–2 mm wide, on spreading stalks. June–July. ❧ Wet or moist floodplain forests. ⊕ Uncommon in se Minn; ne Ill. w Pa to Ill and Minn, s to WVa, Ark and Okla.

Iodanthus pinnatifidus PURPLE-ROCKET

Cardamine rhomboidea SPRING-CRESS

▶**Rorippa** Scop. / Yellow-cress

Annual, biennial or perennial herbs; plants smooth or with unbranched hairs. **Leaves** sometimes in a basal rosette in young plants, toothed to pinnately divided, petioles short or absent. **Flowers** small, in racemes at ends of stems or from lateral branches; sepals green to yellow, deciduous by fruiting time; petals yellow or white, shorter to longer than sepals. **Fruit** a short-cylindric to linear pod (silique), mostly 2-chambered, the seeds in 2 rows.

▶**KEY TO RORIPPA**

1 Petals white; plants rooting from lower nodes of stem . . . .
. . . . *R. nasturtium-officinale* / WATER-CRESS
1 Petals yellow; plants usually not rooting at lower nodes **2**

2 Plants annual or biennial, taprooted; petals shorter or equal to sepals
. . . . **3**
2 Plants perennial, roots creeping; petals longer than sepals **4**

3 Stalks of fruit 3 mm or more long; fruit to 1.5x longer than its stalk
. . . . *R. palustris* / COMMON YELLOW-CRESS
3 Stalks of fruit 1–2 mm long; fruit more than 1.5x longer than its stalk
. . . . *R. sessiliflora* / SOUTHERN YELLOW-CRESS

4 Stems sprawling or spreading; lateral leaf segments entire or with few
shallow teeth; beak of fruit 1–2 mm long . . . . *R. sinuata*
. . . . WESTERN YELLOW-CRESS
4 Stems ± erect; lateral leaf segments with sharp teeth; beak of fruit
0.5–1 mm long . . . . *R. sylvestris* / CREEPING YELLOW-CRESS

Rorippa nasturtium-officinale (L.) Hayek
Water-cress   OBL

☞ **Water-cress** is the edible salad herb, introduced from Eurasia and now naturalized throughout most of USA and Canada.

Perennial herb; plants smooth. **Stems** underwater, floating, or trailing on mud; rooting from lower nodes. **Leaves** 4–12 cm long and 2–5 cm wide, pinnately divided into 3–9 segments, the lateral segments round to ovate in outline, the terminal segment largest; margins entire or with a few shallow rounded teeth; petioles present. **Flowers** in 1 to several racemes per stem, flat-topped and elongating in fruit; flowers 5 mm wide, sepals green-white, oblong, 1–3 mm long; petals white, sometimes purple-tinged, obovate, 4–5 mm long. **Fruit** a linear, often curved pod (silique), 1–2.5 cm long and 2 mm wide, tipped with a short style beak to 1 mm long. May–Sept. *Nasturtium officinale*. ❦ Springs, slow-moving streams, ditches. ⊕ ec and se Minn, Wisc (especially s), LP of Mich (local in UP), ne Ill and nw Ind.

Rorippa palustris (L.) Besser
Common yellow-cress   OBL

Annual or biennial herb. **Stems** erect, usually 1, to 1 m long, unbranched or branched upward. **Leaves** lance-shaped to obovate, mostly pinnately divided; the blades oblong to oblong lance-shaped, 5–30 cm long and 2–6 cm wide, middle stem leaves usually with basal lobes and clasping stem, smooth to densely hairy on lower surface; margins deeply lobed and slightly wavy; petioles short or absent. **Flowers** in racemes at ends of stems and from leaf axils, the terminal raceme flowering and fruiting first, the oldest siliques on lowest portions of raceme; sepals green, 1–3 mm long, early deciduous; petals yellow, drying white, 2–3 mm long. **Fruit** a round to short-cylindric pod, 3–10 mm long and 1–3 mm wide, straight-sided or slightly tapered to tip, on stalks 3–10 mm long. June–Sept. *R. islandica*. ❦ Marshes, wet meadows, shores, streambanks, ditches and other wet places. ⊕ Minn, Wisc, Mich, ne Ill (⚠ var. *hispida* is state endangered) and nw Ind. Labr to Alaska, s to n S Amer.

Rorippa sessiliflora (Nutt.) A. S. Hitchc.
Southern yellow-cress   OBL

Annual (sometimes biennial) herb. **Stems** erect, 2–4 dm long, branched, smooth. Lower **leaves** oblong, coarsely round-toothed, lower part of blade usually deeply cleft; upper leaves smaller, ovate, entire or toothed. **Flowers** in racemes from ends of branches and upper leaf axils; sepals yellow, petals absent; stamens 3–6. **Fruit** a pod (silique), 6–10 mm long and 3–4 mm wide, often somewhat sickle-shaped, on short, spreading or ascending stalks 1–2 mm long, the style beak very short. June–July.

Radicula sessiliflora. ❧ Muddy shores and streambanks. ⊕ ne Ill and nw Ind. Va to Ohio, and Ill, s to Fla and Tex.

Rorippa sinuata (Nutt.) A. S. Hitchc.
Western yellow-cress   FACW

Perennial herb, spreading by rhizomes. **Stems** usually several, sprawling, 1–4 dm long, sparsely to densely covered with blunt-tipped hairs. **Leaves** all from stem (basal leaves absent), 2–8 cm long and 0.5–2 cm wide, oblong, pinnately divided into 5–7 pairs, sometimes with basal lobes clasping stem, margins entire or with a few teeth. **Flowers** in racemes at ends of stems and from upper leaf axils, all flowering at about same time or flowers from axils first; sepals yellow-green, 3–5 mm long, early deciduous; petals yellow, 4–6 mm long, longer than sepals. **Fruit** a linear pod (silique), 5–12 mm long and 1–2 mm wide, tapered to the style beak, on upright to spreading stalks, 4–10 mm long. June–Aug. *Radicula sinuata.* ❧ Stream and riverbanks, ditches, and other low places, especially where sandy. ⊕ s Minn, ne Ill. n Ill to s Sask and Wash, s to Ark, Okla, n Tex, NM, Ariz and Calif.

Rorippa sylvestris (L.) Besser
Creeping yellow-cress   OBL

Perennial herb, spreading by rhizomes and sometimes stolons. **Stems** erect, branched above, 2–6 dm long, smooth or sparsely hairy on lower stem; basal rosettes present on young plants. Stem **leaves** pinnately divided, oblong in outline, 3–15 cm long and 2.5 cm wide, gradually reduced in size upward on stem, margins usually toothed; petioles present on lower leaves, petioles absent on upper leaves. **Flowers** in racemes at ends of stems and from upper leaf axils, all flowering at about same time or the oldest siliques on lower portion of terminal racemes; sepals yellow-green, 2–3 mm long; petals yellow, 3–5 mm long, to 2 mm longer than the sepals. **Fruit** a linear pod (silique), 4–10 mm long and to 1 mm wide, usually upright on spreading stalks 5–10 mm long. June–Aug. *Radicula sylvestris.* ❧ Wet forests, lakeshores, muddy streambanks and ditches; sometimes weedy. ⊕ c and s Wisc, c UP and s LP of Mich, ne Ill and nw Ind. Introduced to N Amer from Europe, now from Newf to BC, s to NC, La, Kans, Colo and Ore.

▶ Subularia L. / Awlwort

Subularia aquatica L.
Water awlwort   OBL

⚠
STATUS
Michigan - E
Minnesota - T

Small, annual aquatic herb; plants underwater or sometimes on muddy shores. **Stems** 3–10 cm long. **Leaves** all basal, awl-shaped or linear, 1–5 cm long. **Flowers** small, 2–10, widely separated in a raceme; sepals persistent, petals white. **Fruit** a short, oval or oblong pod (silicle), 2–4 mm long. June–Aug. Our plants are var. *americana.* ❧ Cold lakes in shallow water to 1 m deep. ⊕ Rare in ne Minn and Isle Royale and e UP of Mich. Circumboreal, s to New Eng, Minn, Wyo and Calif.

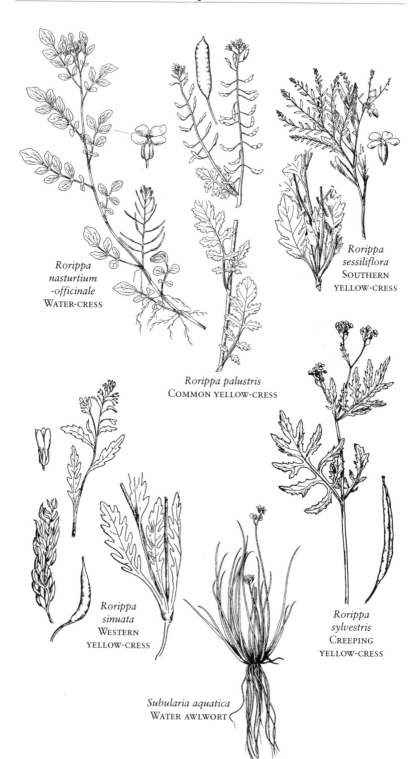

*Rorippa
nasturtium
-officinale*
WATER-CRESS

*Rorippa
sessiliflora*
SOUTHERN
YELLOW-CRESS

Rorippa palustris
COMMON YELLOW-CRESS

*Rorippa
sinuata*
WESTERN
YELLOW-CRESS

Subularia aquatica
WATER AWLWORT

*Rorippa
sylvestris*
CREEPING
YELLOW-CRESS

Cabombaceae
Water-Shield Family

Aquatic perennial herbs with floating and/or underwater leaves. **Flowers** perfect (with both male and female parts), white (*Cabomba*), or purple (*Brasenia*), emergent on long stalks from upper nodes, sepals 3–4, petal-like, petals 3–4. **Fruit** a capsule of 3 to many segments.

▶**KEY TO CABOMBACEAE**

1 Leaves floating, alternate and entire; flowers purple, stamens 12–18; widespread . . . . *Brasenia schreberi* / WATER-SHIELD

1 Leaves mostly underwater, opposite and dissected; flowers white, stamens 6; sw Mich only . . . . *Cabomba caroliniana* / FANWORT

▶**Brasenia** Schreber / Water-shield

Brasenia schreberi J. F. Gmelin
Water-shield   OBL

☞ The gelatinous coating on the stems, petioles, and leaf undersides of **water-shield** is distinctive.

Perennial aquatic herb; underwater portions of plant with a slippery jelly-like coating. **Stems** to 2 m long. **Leaf blades** floating, oval, 4–12 cm long and half as wide; petiole attached to center of blade underside. **Flowers** dull-purple, on stalks to 15 cm long from leaf axils; sepals 3, petals 3, 12–15 mm long. **Fruit** oblong, 3–5 mm long. July. ⚘ Quiet ponds and lakes; water usually acid. ⊕ ne and c Minn, Wisc, Mich, ne Ill and nw Ind. NS and Que to Minn, s to Fla and Tex; Mont and BC to Wash and Calif.

▶**Cabomba** Aublet / Fanwort

Cabomba caroliniana A. Gray
Fanwort   OBL

☞ **Fanwort** is our only aquatic vascular species with opposite, highly dissected leaves on distinct petioles.

Perennial aquatic herb. **Stems** branched, to 2 m long. **Leaves** all underwater or with a few small floating leaves; underwater leaves opposite, 2–5 cm wide, palmately dissected into narrow segments, on petioles 1–3 cm long; floating leaves small, oblong, 6–20 mm long, often lobed at ends, petiole attached at center of blade underside. **Flowers** white with yellow base, on stalks 3–10 cm long from upper leaf axils; sepals and petals 3 each, 6–12 mm long, obovate stamens 6. **Fruit** with 3 segments. ⚘ Lakes and streams. ⊕ Local in sw Mich. NJ, Ohio, s Mich and Mo, s to Fla and Tex. ☞ Possibly introduced in our region from s USA as fanwort is often used as a plant in aquariums.

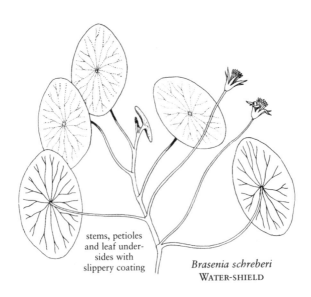

stems, petioles
and leaf under-
sides with
slippery coating

Brasenia schreberi
WATER-SHIELD

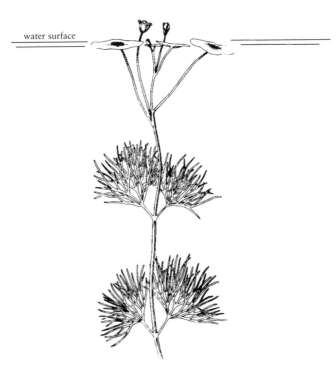

water surface

Cabomba caroliniana
FANWORT

Caesalpiniaceae
Caesalpinia Family

▶**Senna** Miller / Wild senna

Senna hebecarpa (Fern.) Irwin & Barneby
Northern wild senna   FACW

☞ **Northern wild senna** is sometimes included within the Pea Family (Fabaceae).

Perennial herb. **Stems** erect, mostly unbranched, 1–2 m long, smooth or with scattered hairs on upper stem. **Leaves** compound, divided into 6–10 pairs of leaflets, the leaflets oblong or oval, 2–5 cm long and 1–2 cm wide, rounded at end but with a small, sharp tip; margins fringed with hairs; leaf petioles short. **Flowers** perfect, yellow, 1–2 cm long, in many-flowered, crowded racemes from upper leaf axils; sepals unequal; petals nearly alike, 10–15 mm long. **Fruit** a pod, 6–10 cm long and 5–8 mm wide, sparsely hairy; seeds flat, oval, longer than wide. July–Aug. *Cassia hebecarpa, C. marilandica.* ≋ Floodplain forests, streambanks, fens. ⊕ s LP of Mich, ne Ill and nw Ind. s NH and Mass to s Mich, s to NC, Tenn and Ill.

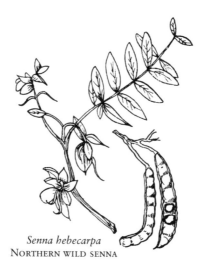

Senna hebecarpa
NORTHERN WILD SENNA

Callitrichaceae
Water-starwort Family

▶**Callitriche** L. / Water-starwort

Small, annual aquatic herbs with weak, slender **stems** and fibrous roots.
Leaves simple, opposite, all underwater or upper leaves floating; underwater leaves linear, 1-nerved, entire except for shallowly notched tip;
floating leaves mostly in clusters at ends of stems, obovate to spatula-
shaped, 3–5-nerved, rounded at tip. **Flowers** tiny, male and female flowers usually separate on same plant, each flower with 1 stamen or 1 pistil; single and stalkless in middle and upper leaf axils, or 1 male and 1
female flower in each axil, subtended by a pair of thin, translucent,
deciduous bracts, or the bracts absent; styles 2, ovary flattened, oval to
round, 4-chambered, separating when mature into 4 nutlets.

▶**KEY TO CALLITRICHE**

1 Leaves all underwater, 1-veined, linear . . . . *C. hermaphroditica*
. . . . AUTUMNAL WATER-STARWORT
1 Leaves both underwater and floating; floating leaves 3-veined, spatula-shaped or obovate **2**

2 Fruit as long as wide, rounded at base, pits on fruit not in rows . . .
. . . . *C. heterophylla* / LARGER WATER-STARWORT
2 Fruit slightly longer (0.2 mm) than wide, narrowed at base, pitted in
rows . . . . *C. palustris* / SPINY WATER-STARWORT

Callitriche hermaphroditica L.
Autumnal water-starwort   OBL
Annual herb. **Stems** 10–30 cm long. **Leaves** all underwater, alike, linear,
1-nerved, 3–12 mm long and to 1.5 mm wide, shallowly notched at tip,
clasping at base, the opposite leaf bases not connected; darker green than
our other species. **Flowers** either male or female; single in leaf axils, not
subtended by translucent bracts. **Fruit** flattened, rounded, 1–2 mm long,
deeply divided into 4 segments. June–Sept. *C. autumnalis.* ❦ Shallow to
deep water of lakes, ponds, marshes, ditches and slow-moving streams.
⊕ n Minn, n Wisc, UP of Mich. Circumboreal, s to Maine, NY, Mich,
Minn, n Neb, NM and Calif.

Callitriche heterophylla Pursh
Larger water-starwort   OBL

⚠
STATUS
Michigan - T

Annual herb. **Stems** 10–20 cm long. **Leaves** of 2 types; **underwater leaves**
linear, 1–2 cm long and to 1.5 mm wide, 1-nerved, notched at tip, the
leaf pairs connected at base by a narrow wing; **floating leaves** in clusters
at ends of stems or opposite along upper stems, 3–5-nerved, obovate to
spatula-shaped, rounded at tip, 6–15 mm long and 3–7 mm wide; leaves
intermediate between underwater and floating leaves often present.
Flowers either male or female; usually 1 male and 1 female flower
together in leaf axils, subtended by a pair of translucent, deciduous
bracts. **Fruit** about 1 mm long and not more than 0.1 mm longer than
wide, often broadest above middle, not wing-margined, pits on surface

not in rows. May–Aug. ☙ Shallow water or mud of springs, stream
pools, ponds and wet depressions. ⊕ Uncommon in n and sw Minn,
Wisc, LP of Mich, ne Ill and nw Ind. NS to s Minn and w SD, s to Fla
and Tex; also w Mont to Wash, s to Calif and central Amer. ☞ Similar
to **spiny water-starwort** (*C. palustris,* below) but less common, differing
mainly in the fruits.

Callitriche palustris L.

Spiny water-starwort   OBL

Annual herb. **Stems** 10–20 cm long. Leaves of 2 types; **underwater leaves**
mostly linear, 1–2 cm long and to 1 mm wide, shallowly notched at tip,
the leaf pairs connected at base by a narrow wing; **floating leaves** in clusters at ends of stems or opposite along upper stems, 3–5–nerved, obovate
to spatula-shaped, rounded at tip, 5–15 mm long and 2–5 mm wide;
leaves intermediate between underwater and floating leaves usually present. **Flowers** either male or female; usually 1 male and 1 female flower
together in leaf axils, subtended by a pair of translucent bracts, these
soon deciduous. **Fruit** 1–1.5 mm long and about 0.2 mm longer than
wide, broadest above middle, narrowly winged near tip, pitted in vertical rows. June–Sept. *C. verna.* ☙ Shallow water of lakes, ponds, streams;
exposed mudflats. ⊕ Minn, Wisc, UP of Mich (occasional in LP), uncommon in ne Ill. Circumboreal, s to WVa, Ohio, n Ill, Iowa, Kans, NM and
Calif.

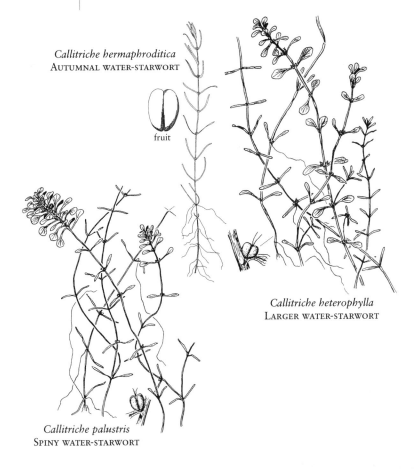

Callitriche hermaphroditica
AUTUMNAL WATER-STARWORT

fruit

Callitriche heterophylla
LARGER WATER-STARWORT

Callitriche palustris
SPINY WATER-STARWORT

Campanulaceae
Bellflower Family

☞ The genus Lobelia is sometimes placed in the Lobelia Family (Lobeliaceae).

Perennial herbs. **Stems** usually with milky sap. **Leaves** simple, alternate. **Flowers** in racemes at ends of stems or single from upper leaf axils, perfect (with both male and female parts), 5-parted, regular and funnel-shaped (*Campanula*) or irregular (*Lobelia*); petals blue, white or scarlet; stamens separate or joined into a tube around style. **Fruit** a many-seeded capsule.

▶**KEY TO CAMPANULACEAE**

1 Flowers regular, stamens separate; plants weak and reclining on surrounding plants ... *Campanula aparinoides* / MARSH-BELLFLOWER
1 Flowers irregular, stamens united to form a tube around the style; plants with upright stems .... *Lobelia* / LOBELIA

▶**Campanula** L. / Bellflower

Campanula aparinoides Pursh
Marsh-bellflower   OBL

Perennial herb, spreading by slender rhizomes. **Stems** slender, weak, usually reclining on other plants, 2–6 dm long, 3-angled, rough-to-touch. **Leaves** linear or narrowly lance-shaped, larger below and smaller upward on stem, 2–8 cm long and 2–8 mm wide, tapered to a sharp tip; margins and midvein on leaf underside often rough; petioles absent. **Flowers** single on long slender stalks from upper leaf axils, funnel-shaped, sepals triangular to lance-shaped, 2–5 mm long; petals pale blue to white, 5–12 mm long. **Fruit** a capsule, opening near its base to release seeds. July–Sept. ❦ Sedge meadows, marshes, calcareous fens, conifer swamps (cedar, tamarack), thickets, open bogs; soils often calcium-rich. ⊕ Minn (all but far sw), Wisc, Mich, ne Ill and nw Ind. NS and Que to s Sask, s to Ga, Ky, Mo and Neb.

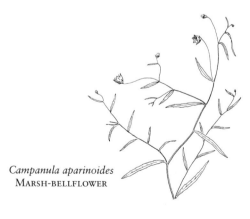

Campanula aparinoides
MARSH-BELLFLOWER

▶**Lobelia** L. / Lobelia

Perennial herbs. **Stems** single, usually with milky juice. **Leaves** alternate. **Flowers** irregular, in racemes at ends of stems; white, bright red, or pale to dark blue, often with white or yellow markings; 2-lipped, the 3 lobes of lower lip spreading, the 2 lobes of upper lip erect or pointing forward, divided to base, the anthers projecting through the split; stamens 5, joined to form a tube around style, the lower 2 anthers hairy at tip and shorter than other 3. **Fruit** a capsule.

▶**KEY TO LOBELIA**

1 Stem leaves narrow, to 4 mm wide, margins entire or with a few small teeth; or leaves all from base of plant **2**
1 Stem leaves broader, 1–5 cm wide, margins toothed **3**

2 Leaves all from base of plant, usually underwater; n portion of region . . . . *L. dortmanna* / WATER-LOBELIA
2 Leaves all from stem; widespread . . . . . *L. kalmii* / BROOK LOBELIA

3 Flowers small, to 1.5 cm long, lateral slits near base of flower absent . . . . *L. spicata* / SPIKED LOBELIA
3 Flowers larger, 2–4 cm long, base of flower with lateral slits **4**

4 Flowers bright red (rarely white), 3 cm or more long . . . . *L. cardinalis* / CARDINAL-FLOWER
4 Flowers blue with white stripes on lower lip (rarely all white), less than 2.5 cm long . . . . *L. siphilitica* / GREAT BLUE LOBELIA

Lobelia cardinalis L.
Cardinal-flower   OBL

Perennial herb. **Stems** erect, usually unbranched, 5–15 dm long, hairy to smooth. **Leaves** lance-shaped to oblong, 10–15 cm long and 3–5 cm wide, tapered to a point, margins toothed; lower leaves on short petioles, upper leaves ± stalkless. **Flowers** bright scarlet (rarely white), in racemes 1–4 dm long, the racemes with small, leafy, linear bracts; flowers 2–4 cm long, on hairy stalks 5–15 mm long. July–Sept. ❦ Floodplain forests, swamps, thickets, streambanks, shores and ditches; sometimes in shallow water. ⊕ ec and se Minn along Miss River; Wisc, s UP and LP of Mich, ne Ill and nw Ind. NB to Minn, s to Fla and Tex.

Lobelia dortmanna L.
Water-lobelia   OBL

Perennial herb; plants usually underwater or sometimes on exposed sandy shores. **Stems** upright, hollow, smooth, with milky juice. **Leaves** in dense rosettes at base of plants, fleshy, hollow, linear, 3–8 cm long, rounded at tip; stem leaves tiny. **Flowers** pale blue or white, 1–2 cm long, in a few-flowered raceme; sepals 2 mm long. July–Sept. ❦ Shallow water of acid lakes and ponds; wet, sandy shores. ⊕ ne Minn, n Wisc, UP of Mich. Nfld to NJ, w to Minn; Pacific coast; Europe.

Lobelia kalmii L.
Brook lobelia   OBL

Small perennial herb. **Stems** erect, smooth, 1–4 dm long, unbranched or with a few branches above, sometimes with a rosette of small, obovate leaves at base of plant. Stem **leaves** linear, 1–5 cm long and 1–5 mm wide, blunt to sharp-tipped, margins with a few small teeth. **Flowers** blue with a white center, 6–10 mm long, in an open raceme, the flowers on stalks 4–10 mm long. July–Oct. *L. strictiflora.* ❦ Wet, sandy or gravelly shores, wet meadows, interdunal wetlands, conifer swamps (cedar, tamarack), rock ledges and crevices; usually where calcium-rich. ⊕ Minn, Wisc, Mich, ne Ill and nw Ind. Newf to BC, s to Pa, Ohio, Ill, Minn, ND, Mont and Wash.

Lobelia siphilitica L.
Great blue lobelia   FACW+
Perennial herb. **Stems** stout, erect, 3–12 dm long. **Leaves** oblong or oval, smaller upward, 6–12 cm long and 1–3 cm wide, tip sharp or blunt, margins irregularly toothed, petioles absent. **Flowers** dark blue, in crowded racemes 1–3 dm long; the lower lip blue and white-striped, 1.5–2.5 cm long, on ascending stalks 4–10 mm long; sepals triangular to lance-shaped, 5–20 mm long, usually with narrow lobes near base; petals absent. Aug–Sept. ❦ Swamps, floodplain forests, thickets, streambanks, calcareous fens, wet meadows. ⊕ Common; Minn, Wisc, Mich (but local in e UP), ne Ill and nw Ind. Maine to Man, s to NC, Tex and Colo.

Lobelia spicata Lam.
Spiked lobelia   FAC
Perennial herb. **Stems** unbranched, 3–10 dm long, hairy toward base. **Leaves** obovate to lance-shaped, 5–10 cm long, hairy, becoming smaller above. **Flowers** pale blue to white, 6–10 mm long, on stalks 2–4 mm long, in a slender, crowded raceme; base of sepals often with distinct, curved lobes (auricles), 1–2 mm long. May–Aug. ❦ Moist to wet prairie (sometimes where disturbed), wet meadows, swamp margins. ⊕ Minn (all, but local in ne), Wisc, Mich LP (occasional in c and e UP), ne Ill and nw Ind. Que and NS to Minn, s to Ga and Ark.

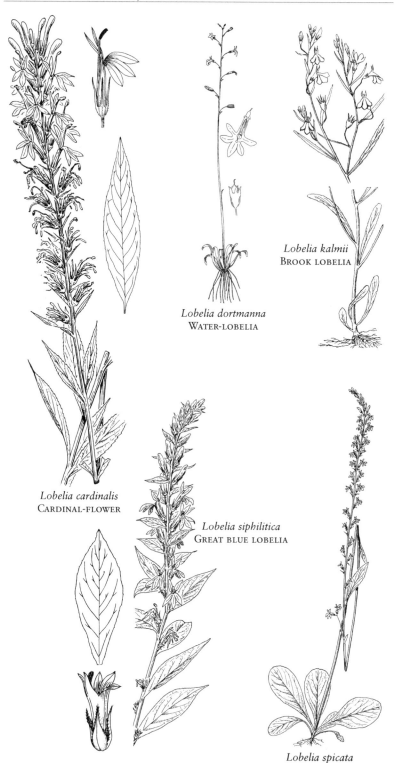

Lobelia dortmanna
WATER-LOBELIA

Lobelia kalmii
BROOK LOBELIA

Lobelia cardinalis
CARDINAL-FLOWER

Lobelia siphilitica
GREAT BLUE LOBELIA

Lobelia spicata
SPIKED LOBELIA

Caprifoliaceae
Honeysuckle Family

Shrubs or vines, with opposite, mostly simple **leaves** (compound in *Sambucus*). **Flowers** perfect (with both male and female parts), mostly 5-parted. **Fruit** a fleshy berry or dry capsule.

▸KEY TO CAPRIFOLIACEAE

1 Leaves pinnately divided . . . . *Sambucus* / ELDER
1 Leaves simple **2**

2 Plants small, creeping, evergreen; flowers paired and nodding at tips
of slender stalks . . . . *Linnaea borealis* / TWINFLOWER
2 Plants larger shrubs, upright, deciduous **3**

3 Leaf margins lobed and usually toothed. . . . *Viburnum* / VIBURNUM
3 Leaf margins entire **4**

4 Flowers in pairs from leaf axils . . . . *Lonicera* / HONEYSUCKLE
4 Flowers in clusters at ends of stems . . . . *Viburnum* / VIBURNUM

▸Linnaea L. / Twinflower

Linnaea borealis L.
Twinflower   FAC
Evergreen, trailing vine. **Stems** slightly woody, to 1–2 m long, with numerous short, erect, leafy branches to 10 cm long; **branches** green to red-brown, finely hairy; older stems woody, 2–4 mm wide. **Leaves** opposite, simple, evergreen, oval to round, 1–2 cm long, blunt at tip, upper surface and margins with short, straight hairs; margins rolled under, with a few rounded teeth near tip; petiole short, short-hairy. **Flowers** small, pink to white, bell-shaped, shallowly 5-lobed, slightly fragrant, in nodding pairs atop a Y-shaped stalk to 10 cm long, the stalk with gland-tipped hairs and 2 small bracts at the fork and a pair of smaller bracts at base of each flower. **Fruit** a small, dry, 1-seeded capsule. June–Aug. Our plants are var. *longiflora. L. americana.* ❧ Hummocks in cedar swamps and thickets, moist conifer woods, on rotten logs and mossy boulders. ⊕ Common in n portions of our region, becoming local southward. n and ec Minn, Wisc, Mich, uncommon in ne Ill and nw Ind. Circumpolar, s to NJ, WVa, n Ind, ne Ill, Minn, NM, Ariz and Calif.

Linnaea borealis
TWINFLOWER

▶**Lonicera** L. / Honeysuckle

Shrubs (those included here) or vines. **Leaves** opposite, simple, entire. **Flowers** long and tubular or funnel-shaped, in pairs from leaf axils. **Fruit** a few-seeded, blue or red berry.

▶KEY TO LONICERA

1 Flowers and fruits on short stalks (1 cm or less), fruit blue; bark red-brown and peeling in papery layers. . . . . *L. caerulea* / WATERBERRY
1 Flowers and fruits on longer stalks (1 cm or more), fruit red; bark gray-brown and shredding. *L. oblongifolia*
. . . . SWAMP FLY-HONEYSUCKLE

Lonicera caerulea L.
Waterberry   FACW

Shrub to 1 m tall; **branches** upright, red-brown to gray, outer thin layers soon peeling to expose red-brown inner layers; **twigs** purple-red, with long, soft hairs. **Leaves** opposite, oval to oblong, 2–6 cm long and 1–3 cm wide, blunt or rounded at tip, upper surface dark green, underside paler and hairy, especially on veins; margins fringed with hairs and often rolled under; petioles absent or to 1–2 mm long. **Flowers** yellow, tubular to funnel-shaped, 10–15 mm long, in pairs on short hairy stalks from axils of lower leaves. **Fruit** an edible dark blue berry consisting of the 2 joined ovaries. May–July. *L. villosa*. ❦ Cedar and tamarack swamps, thickets, fens, shores. ⊕ n and ec Minn, n and c Wisc, Mich UP and occasional in n and c LP. ± circumboreal, Labr to NW Terr, s to Pa, the Great Lakes and Calif.

Lonicera oblongifolia (Goldie) Hook.
Swamp fly-honeysuckle   OBL

Thicket-forming shrub 1–1.5 m tall; **branches** upright, with shredding bark and solid pith; **twigs** green to purple, smooth. **Leaves** opposite, oblong or oval, 3–8 cm long and 1–4 cm wide, rounded or blunt at tip, underside hairy when young, becoming smooth; margins entire, not fringed with hairs; petioles absent or to 1–2 mm long. **Flowers** yellow-white, tube-shaped with 2 spreading lips, 10–15 mm long, in pairs at ends of slender stalks up to 4 cm long from leaf axils. **Fruit** an orange-red to red (or sometimes purple), few-seeded berry composed of the 2 joined ovaries. May–June. *Xylosteon oblongifolia*. ❦ Cedar and tamarack swamps, fens, open bogs, wet streambanks and shores; often over limestone. ⊕ n and ec Minn, uncommon in nc and e Wisc, Mich. NB to Man, s to Pa, Ohio, s Wisc and Minn.

▶**Sambucus** L. / Elder

Shrubs or small trees. **Stems** pithy, the bark with wartlike lenticels. **Leaves** pinnately divided. **Flowers** small, white, perfect, 5-lobed; in large, rounded clusters at ends of stems. **Fruit** a red or dark purple, berrylike drupe.

▶KEY TO SAMBUCUS

1 Flowers opening in summer after leaves developed, in broad, ± flat clusters; fruit purple-black, edible; leaflets usually 7 . . *S. canadensis*
. . . . COMMON ELDER
1 Flowers opening in late spring with unfolding leaves, in pyramid-

shaped or rounded clusters; fruit red, inedible; leaflets usually 5 . . .
. . . . *S. racemosa* / RED-BERRIED ELDER

Sambucus canadensis L.

Common elder   FACW-

Shrub to 3 m tall; spreading underground and forming thickets. **Young
stems** soft or barely woody, smooth; **older stems** with warty gray-brown
bark; inner pith white. **Leaves** large, opposite, pinnately divided into
5–11 (usually 7) leaflets, the lower pair of leaflets sometimes divided into
2–3 segments; leaflets lance-shaped to oval, tapered to a long sharp tip,
base often asymmetrical, smooth or hairy on underside, especially along
veins; margins with sharp, forward-pointing teeth. **Flowers** small, white,
5-parted, 3–5 mm wide, numerous, in flat or slightly rounded clusters
10–15 cm wide at ends of stems. **Fruit** a round, purple-black, berrylike
drupe, edible. July–Aug (blooming when fruit of *Sambucus racemosa* is
about ripe). ❦ Floodplain forests, swamps, wet forest depressions, thickets, shores, meadows, roadsides, fencerows. ⊕ c and s Minn, Wisc, Mich,
ne Ill and nw Ind. NS and Que to Man and SD, s to W Indies and Mex.

Sambucus racemosa L.

Red-berried elder   FACU+

⚠
STATUS
Illinois - E

Shrub to 3 m tall. **Stems** soft or barely woody; **twigs** yellow-brown and
hairy, **branches** with warty gray-brown bark; inner pith red-brown.
Leaves large, opposite, pinnately divided into 5–7 (usually 5) leaflets, the
leaflets lance-shaped to ovate, tapered to a long sharp tip, smooth or
hairy on underside; margins with small, sharp, forward-pointing teeth.
Flowers small, white, 5-parted, 3–4 mm wide, many, in elongate, pyram-
idal clusters at ends of stems, the clusters 5–12 cm long and usually
longer than wide. **Fruit** a round, red, berrylike drupe, inedible.
May–June (flowers opening with developing leaves). *S. pubens.* ❦
Occasional in swamps and thickets; more common in moist deciduous
forests, roadsides and fencerows. ⊕ Minn, Wisc, Mich, ne Ill and nw Ind.
Circumboreal, Nfld to BC, s to Pa, NC, Ind, Ill and Minn.

▶Viburnum L. / Viburnum

Shrubs or small trees. **Leaves** simple, entire or toothed, often palmately
lobed. **Flowers** white or pink, in rounded clusters at ends of stems, sometimes outer florets larger and sterile. **Fruit** a drupe with a large seed;
white, yellow, pink, or orange at first, maturing to orange, red, or blue-
black.

▶KEY TO VIBURNUM

1 Leaves not lobed; pinnately veined . . . . *V. nudum*
. . . . WITHE-ROD; WILD RAISIN
1 Leaves 3-lobed; palmately veined from base of leaf. **2**

2 Flowers on leafy shoots at ends of stems, of 2 types; outer flowers
large and showy, inner flowers smaller. . . . . *V. opulus*
. . . . HIGH-BUSH CRANBERRY
2 Flowers few, all alike, on short branches from lateral buds . *V. edule*
. . . . SQUASHBERRY; LOW-BUSH CRANBERRY

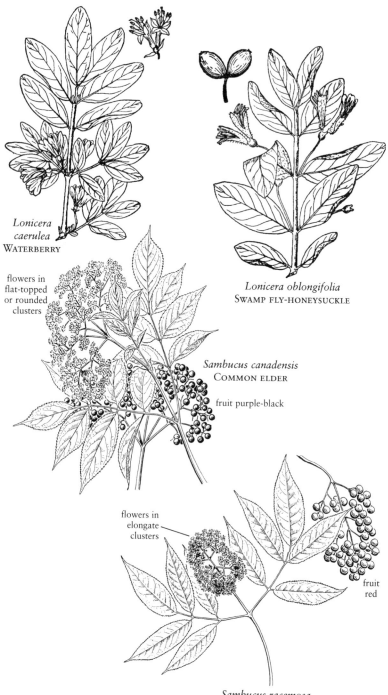

Lonicera caerulea
WATERBERRY

Lonicera oblongifolia
SWAMP FLY-HONEYSUCKLE

flowers in flat-topped or rounded clusters

Sambucus canadensis
COMMON ELDER

fruit purple-black

flowers in elongate clusters

fruit red

Sambucus racemosa
RED-BERRIED ELDER

Viburnum edule (Michx.) Raf.

Squashberry; Low-bush cranberry   FACW

STATUS
Michigan - T
Wisconsin - E

Shrub 1–2 m tall. **Stems** upright or spreading; **twigs** brown-purple, smooth, often angled or ridged. **Leaves** opposite, mostly shallowly 3-lobed and palmately veined (leaves at ends of stems often unlobed), 5–12 cm long and 3–12 cm wide, tapered to a sharp tip; underside veins hairy; margins coarsely toothed; petioles 1–3 cm long, **Flowers** creamy-white, small, in few-flowered, stalked clusters 1–3 cm wide, on short, 2-leaved branches from lateral buds on last year's shoots. **Fruit** a round, berrylike drupe 6–10 mm long, yellow at first, becoming orange or red. June–July. *V. pauciflorum, V. eradiatum.* ❦ Moist conifer forests, thickets, forest openings, talus slopes. ⊕ ne Minn, uncommon in nw Wisc and Mich (Isle Royale only). Labr to Alaska, s to Pa, n Minn, Colo and Ore.

Viburnum nudum L.

Withe-rod; Wild raisin   FACW

STATUS
Indiana - E

Shrub to 4 m tall. Young **stems** brown-scurfy at first, becoming smooth; winter buds gold-brown. **Leaves** opposite, oval to oblong, 5–10 cm long and 3–5 cm wide, tapered to an abrupt, blunt tip, main vein on under-side brown-hairy; margins entire or shallowly toothed; petioles grooved, 5–15 mm long. **Flowers** creamy-white, unpleasantly scented, all-alike, in ± flat-topped clusters 5–10 cm wide at ends of stems. **Fruit** a round to oval drupe, 6–10 mm long, yellow-white at first, then pink, ripening to blue or blue-black and covered with a waxy bloom. May–July. *V. cassinoides.* ❦ Cedar swamps, open bogs, fens, floodplain forests, wetland margins; occasional in drier woods. ⊕ Local in ne Wisc; Mich (all, but uncommon in w UP), reported from nw Ind. Nfld to Man, s to Fla and Tex.

Viburnum opulus L.

High-bush cranberry   FACW

STATUS
Indiana - E

Shrub, 3–4 m tall. Young **stems** smooth. **Leaves** opposite, maple-like, sharply 3-lobed and palmately veined, 5–10 cm long and about as wide, the lobes tapered to sharp tips; smooth or hairy beneath, especially on the veins; margins entire or coarsely toothed, petioles grooved, 1–3 cm long, with several club-shaped glands present near base of blade. **Flowers** white, in large, flat-topped clusters 5–15 cm wide at ends of stems; outer flowers sterile with large petals, surrounding the inner, smaller fertile flowers. **Fruit** an orange to red, round or oval drupe, 10–15 mm long. June. Our native plants are var. *americanum* (sometimes considered a separate species—*V. trilobum*). ❦ Swamps, fens, streambanks, shores, ditches. ⊕ Introduced (in part). Minn (all but sw), Wisc, Mich, ne Ill and nw Ind. Nfld to BC, s to Pa, n Ohio, Ind, Ill, Iowa and Wash.

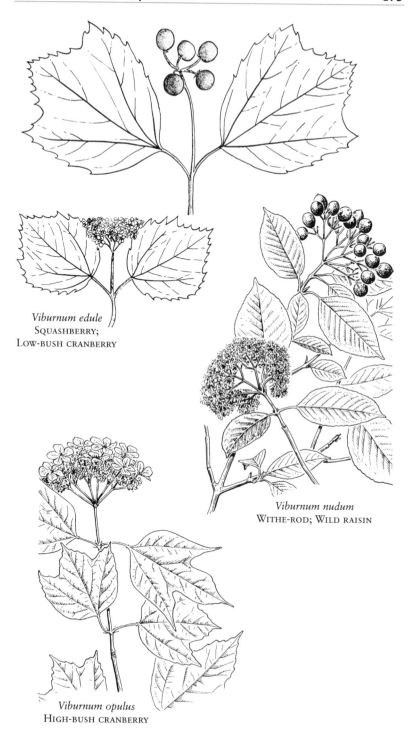

Viburnum edule
SQUASHBERRY;
LOW-BUSH CRANBERRY

Viburnum nudum
WITHE-ROD; WILD RAISIN

Viburnum opulus
HIGH-BUSH CRANBERRY

Caryophyllaceae
Pink Family

Annual or perennial herbs. **Leaves** simple, entire, mostly opposite but sometimes alternate or whorled. **Stems** often swollen at nodes. **Flowers** perfect (with both male and female parts) or imperfect, in open or compact heads at ends of stems or from leaf axils; sepals usually 5, separate or joined into a tube; petals 5 (sometimes 4), separate, often lobed or toothed, sometimes absent; stamens 3–10, anthers often distinctly colored. **Fruit** a few- to many-seeded capsule.

▶**KEY TO CARYOPHYLLACEAE**

1 Leaves succulent; stipules present . . . . . *Spergularia* / SAND-SPURREY
1 Leaves not succulent; stipules absent **2**

2 Sepals joined to form a toothed or lobed tube . . . . *Silene nivea* . . . . SNOWY CAMPION
2 Sepals free or joined only at base . . . . *Stellaria* / STITCHWORT

▶**Silene** L. / Catchfly; Campion

Silene nivea (Nutt.) Otth
Snowy campion   FACW

STATUS
Minnesota - T

Perennial herb, spreading by rhizomes; plants smooth or with a few short hairs. **Stems** 2–3 dm long. **Leaves** mostly on stem, opposite, lance-shaped or oblong, 5–10 cm long and 1–3 cm wide, stalkless or on short petioles. **Flowers** few, mostly in leaf axils; sepals joined to form a tubelike flower 1.5 cm long; petals white, stamens 10, styles 3. **Fruit** a 1-chambered capsule. June–July. *S. alba.* ❦ Streambanks, wooded ravines, calcareous fens. ⊕ se Minn, s Wisc, ne Ill. NJ and Pa to Ill, s Minn, SD and Neb, s to Va, Tenn and Mo.

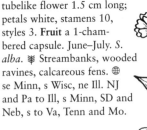

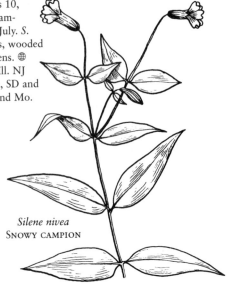

Silene nivea
SNOWY CAMPION

▶**Spergularia** (Pers.) J.&K. Presl. / Sand-spurrey

☞ In the Great Lakes region, Spergularia is an introduced species occasionally found in moist ditches along highways where salt is applied in winter.

Low, succulent herbs. **Leaves** opposite, linear or reduced to bristles. **Flowers** in branched clusters at ends of stems; sepals and petals each 5. **Fruit** a capsule.

▶**KEY TO SPERGULARIA**

1 Sepals less than 4 mm long, stamens 2–5, seeds wingless . *S. marina*
. . . . LESSER SALT SPURREY
1 Sepals more than 4 mm long, stamens 9–10, seeds thin-winged. . . .
. . . . *S. media* / SALT SPURREY

Spergularia marina (L.) Griseb.

Lesser salt spurrey   (FAC)
Annual herb. **Stems** upright, or sprawling, to 30 cm long, smooth or with gland-tipped hairs. **Leaves** fleshy, 5–40 mm long and to 1.5 mm wide, tipped with a short spine. **Flowers** pink or white; stamens 2–5; seeds less than 1 mm wide, usually without a wing. Summer. *S. salina* var. *salina*. ❦ Highway ditches where salted. ⊕ Introduced. s Wisc, s Mich, ne Ill and nw Ind; also NY and Ohio.

Spergularia media (L.) C. Presl.

Salt spurrey   (FAC)
Annual or perennial herb; plants smooth or with a few gland-tipped hairs. **Stems** upright or sprawling, to 40 cm long. **Leaves** fleshy, 1–5 cm long and to 2 mm wide, usually tipped with a short spine. **Flowers** white; stamens 9–10; seeds about 1 mm wide, with a wing 0.1–0.3 mm wide. Summer. *S. maritima*. ❦ Highway ditches where salted. ⊕ Introduced. se Mich, ne Ill. ne USA; Calif.

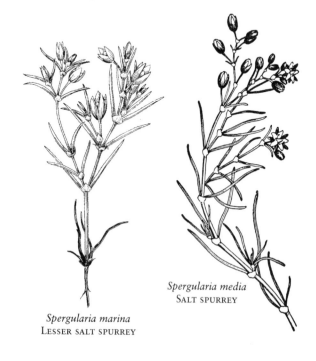

Spergularia media
SALT SPURREY

Spergularia marina
LESSER SALT SPURREY

▶Stellaria L. / Stitchwort

Low, spreading or erect perennials (ours), mostly without hairs. **Stems** slender, 4-angled. **Flowers** single in forks of stems or in few-flowered clusters at ends of stems; sepals green with translucent margins; petals white, lobed or deeply cleft (sometimes absent in *S. borealis*); stamens 10 or less; styles 3. **Fruit** an ovate or oblong capsule.

▶KEY TO STELLARIA

1 Plants large, stems to 8 dm long; styles 5 . . . . *S. aquatica*
. . . . GIANT CHICKWEED
1 Plants smaller; styles 3–4 . . . . **2**

2 Flowers single in forks of stems, not subtended by membranous
bracts **3**
2 Flowers in branched terminal clusters, subtended by small membranous bracts **4**

3 Stems 25 cm or more long; seeds smooth . . . . *S. borealis*
. . . . NORTHERN STITCHWORT
3 Stems to 20 cm long; seeds rough . . . . *S. crassifolia*
. . . . FLESHY STITCHWORT

4 Petals shorter than sepals **5**
4 Petals much longer than sepals **6**

5 Flowers mostly in clusters from leaf axils; seeds covered with small
bumps; se Minn only . . . . *S. alsine* / BOG-STITCHWORT
5 Flowers in clusters at ends of stems; seeds smooth; n portions of
region . . . . *S. borealis* / NORTHERN STITCHWORT

6 Heads open and widely branched, the stalks spreading; leaves spreading to ascending, widest at or above middle . . . . *S. longifolia*
. . . . LONG-LEAVED STITCHWORT
6 Head narrow, the stalks erect to ascending; leaves upright, widest
near base . . . . *S. longipes* / LONG-STALKED STITCHWORT

Stellaria alsine Grimm
Bog-stitchwort   (FACW)
Annual herb. **Stems** sprawling, smooth, angled, rooting at nodes. **Leaves** oval to oblong, 1.5–3 cm long and to 1 cm wide; lower leaves on petioles, upper leaves stalkless. **Flowers** in few-flowered clusters from leaf axils, sepals 3–4 mm long, petals white, shorter than sepals. **Fruit** a capsule, longer than the sepals; seeds 0.5 mm long, covered with small bumps. May–Aug. *Alsine uliginosa.* ❦ Marshes, streambanks, seeps. ⊕ Introduced. Uncommon in se Minn near Miss River. Nfld and Que s to Md and WVa, occasional westward; BC; Eurasia.

Stellaria aquatica (L.) Scop.
Giant chickweed   FAC+
Perennial herb, spreading by rhizomes. **Stems** sprawling and matted, to 8 dm long, rooting at nodes, covered with gland-tipped hairs. **Leaves** ovate to lance-shaped, 2–8 cm long and 1–4 cm wide, petioles short or absent. **Flowers** in open, leafy clusters at ends of stems; sepals 5–9 mm long; petals white, much longer than sepals. **Fruit** a capsule; seeds 0.8 mm long, covered with small bumps. June–Oct. *Alsine aquatica,*

Myosoton aquaticum. ☙ Streambanks, ponds, wet or moist disturbed areas, often in partial shade. ⊕ Introduced. e Minn, Wisc, Mich, ne Ill and nw Ind. Que and Ont to e Minn, s to NC, Mo and Kans.

Stellaria borealis Bigelow
Northern stitchwort   OBL
Perennial herb, spreading by rhizomes. **Stems** sprawling, to 5 dm long, branched, angled. **Leaves** lance-shaped, narrowed at base, 1–5 cm long and 2–8 mm wide, margins hairy. **Flowers** in clusters at ends of stems; sepals 2–4 mm long; petals usually absent. **Fruit** a dark capsule, longer than sepals; seeds to 1 mm long, nearly smooth. June–Aug. *Alsine borealis*, *S. calycantha.* ☙ Openings and hollows in conifer forests, margins of ponds and marshes. ⊕ ne Minn, local in n Wisc, UP and n LP of Mich. Labr to Alaska, s to NY, WVa, Great Lakes, Colo and Ore.

Stellaria crassifolia Ehrh.
Fleshy stitchwort   (FACW, OBL)
Perennial herb. **Stems** sprawling and matted to erect, freely branched, 8–30 cm long, fleshy, smooth. **Leaves** soft, oval to lance-shaped, narrowed at base, 1–3 cm long and 1–3 mm wide. **Flowers** single in forks of stem, nodding on stalks 1–3 cm long; sepals 2–4 mm long; petals longer than sepals. **Fruit** an ovate capsule, to 5 mm long and longer than the sepals; seeds red-brown, to 1 mm long. June–July. ☙ Streambanks and wet shores. ⊕ c Minn, Wisc, sw LP of Mich, uncommon in e UP. Circumboreal, Newf to Alaska, s to NY, Minn, SD, Ariz and Calif.

⚠
STATUS
Michigan - T

Stellaria longifolia Muhl.
Long-leaved stitchwort   FACW+
Perennial herb. **Stems** sprawling, prominently 4-angled, usually freely branched, 1–5 dm long. **Leaves** spreading to ascending, linear to lance-shaped, 2–5 cm long and 1–6 mm wide, widest at or above middle, tapered at both ends. **Flowers** in branched clusters at ends of stems; sepals 3–5 mm long; petals longer than sepals. **Fruit** a green-yellow to brown capsule, usually longer than the sepals; seeds light brown, about 1 mm long. May–July. ☙ Wet meadows and marshes, shrub thickets, swamps, streambanks, pond margins. ⊕ Minn, Wisc, Mich, ne Ill and nw Ind. Circumboreal, s to SC, La, Ariz and Calif.

Stellaria longipes Goldie
Long-stalked stitchwort   OBL
Perennial herb, spreading by rhizomes. **Stems** erect, or sprawling and matted, 5–30 cm long. **Leaves** upright, stiff and shiny-waxy, linear or lance-shaped, 1–4 cm long and 1–4 mm wide, widest near base, tapered to tip. **Flowers** in branched clusters at ends of stems or appearing lateral from stem; sepals 4–5 mm long; petals slightly longer than sepals. **Fruit** a straw-colored to shiny purple capsule, longer than the sepals; seeds red-brown, oblong to oval, about 1 mm long. May–July. ☙ Wet meadows, ditches and thickets; in Michigan, sand dunes near Lakes Michigan and Superior. ⊕ Uncommon in nw Minn; nc Wisc, e UP of Mich. Circumpolar, Newf to Alaska, s to NY, Minn, SD, Ariz and Calif.

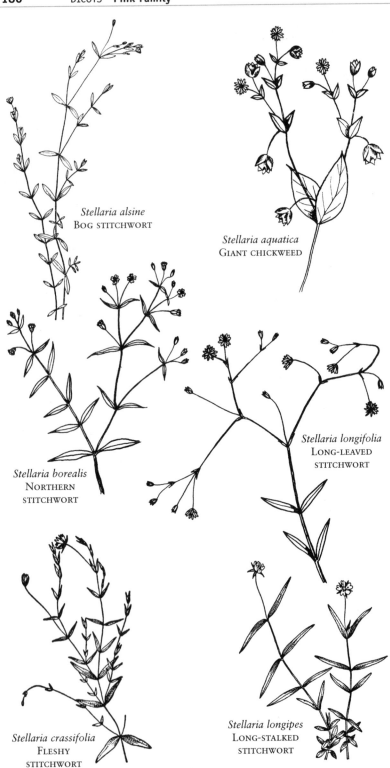

Stellaria alsine
BOG STITCHWORT

Stellaria aquatica
GIANT CHICKWEED

Stellaria borealis
NORTHERN
STITCHWORT

Stellaria longifolia
LONG-LEAVED
STITCHWORT

Stellaria crassifolia
FLESHY
STITCHWORT

Stellaria longipes
LONG-STALKED
STITCHWORT

Ceratophyllaceae
Hornwort Family

▶**Ceratophyllum** L. / Coontail; Hornwort

☞
Ceratophyllum
is our only
genus of
aquatic
vascular
plant with
whorled,
forked
leaves.

Aquatic perennial herbs, often forming large patches; roots absent, but plants usually anchored to substrate by pale, modified leaves. **Stems** slender, branched. **Leaves** in whorls, with more than 4 leaves per node, whorls crowded at ends of stems (hence the common name of coontail), dissected 2–3x into narrow segments. **Flowers** small, inconspicuous in leaf axils, male and female flowers separate on same plant, male usually above female on stems.

▶**KEY TO CERATOPHYLLUM**

1 Leaves usually stiff, forked 1–2 times, margins coarsely toothed; achenes with 2 spines near base . *C. demersum* / COMMON HORNWORT
1 Leaves limp, some larger leaves forked 3–4 times, margins not toothed; achenes with several spines along each margin . . . .
. . . . *C. echinatum* / PRICKLY HORNWORT

Ceratophyllum demersum L.
Common hornwort   OBL
Aquatic herb. **Stems** long, branched. **Leaves** in whorls of 5–12 at each node, stiff, 1–3 cm long, 1–2-forked; leaf segments linear, 0.5–1 mm wide, coarsely toothed. **Fruit** an oval achene, 4–6 mm long, with 2 spines at base. ❧ Shallow to deep water of lakes, ponds, backwater areas, ditches, and may form dense masses; water typically neutral or alkaline. ⊕ Common; Minn, Wisc, Mich, ne Ill and nw Ind. Cosmopolitan; s Can to S Amer; Eurasia.

Ceratophyllum echinatum A. Gray
Prickly hornwort   OBL
Aquatic herb. Similar to *C. demersum*, but **leaves** usually limp, larger leaves usually 3- or sometimes 4-forked, the segments narrower and mostly without teeth. **Fruit** an achene with 2 spines at base and several unequal spines on achene body. *C. muricatum.* ❧ Lakes, ponds and quiet water of rivers and streams; water acidic. ⊕ Uncommon in nc and ec Minn; local in n Wisc and Mich. NS and NB to BC, s to Fla and c Amer.

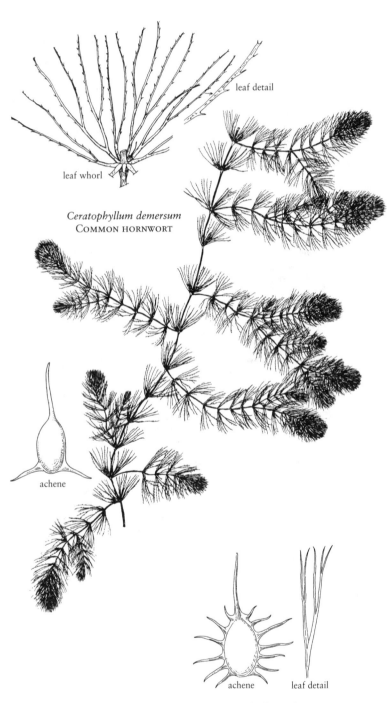

leaf detail

leaf whorl

Ceratophyllum demersum
COMMON HORNWORT

achene

achene   leaf detail

Ceratophyllum echinatum
PRICKLY HORNWORT
(achene and leaf detail only)

Chenopodiaceae
Goosefoot Family

Annual or perennial herbs, often in alkaline soil. **Stems** often angled or jointed, succulent in *Salicornia*. **Leaves** simple, alternate, or occasionally opposite (*Salicornia*), sometimes covered with thin, flaky scales giving a mealy appearance. **Flowers** 1 to many, small, green or red-tinged, clustered in leaf axils or at ends of stems; perfect, or male and female flowers separate; sepals usually 5; petals absent; ovary superior, 1-chambered. **Fruit** a 1-seeded utricle.

▶KEY TO CHENOPODIACEAE

1 Leaves reduced to scales, opposite; stems succulent; w Minn only . . . . *Salicornia rubra* / WESTERN GLASSWORT
1 Leaves not scalelike, mostly alternate; stems not succulent; more widespread in region **2**

2 Leaves without petioles, linear, round in cross-section . . . . *Suaeda calceoliformis* / PLAINS SEA-BLITE
2 Leaves mostly with petioles, blades broader **3**

3 Male and female flowers separate, in spikelike heads without leafy bracts or with only a few bracts low on spike; sepals and petals absent in female flowers, fruit enclosed by a pair of sepal-like small bracts . . . . *Atriplex patula* / HALBERD-LEAF SALTBUSH; SPEARSCALE
3 Flowers perfect (with both male and female parts), in spikes which have small leafy bracts throughout; fruit surrounded by the persistent sepals and petals . . . . *Chenopodium* / GOOSEFOOT

▶**Atriplex** L. / Saltbush

Atriplex patula L.
Halberd-leaf saltbush; Spearscale   FACW-
Taprooted annual herb. **Stems** erect to sprawling, usually branched, 2–10 dm long. **Leaves** alternate (or the lowest opposite), lance-shaped or triangular, 2–8 cm long and 1–6 cm wide, with outward pointing basal lobes, gray and mealy when young, becoming dull green and smooth with age; petioles present, or absent on upper leaves. **Flowers** tiny, green; either male or female but on same plant, usually intermixed in crowded spikes from leaf axils and at ends of stems, the spikes simple or branched, without bracts or with a few small bracts near base of spikes; **male flowers** with a 5-lobed group of sepals, stamens 5; **female flowers** without sepals or petals, surrounded by 2 sepal-like, small bracts, these expanding and enclosing fruit when mature. **Fruit** lens-shaped, dark brown to black, 1–3 mm wide. Aug–Sept. *A. acadiensis, A. hastata.* ❧ Shores, streambanks and mud flats, usually where brackish; disturbed places. ⊕ Introduced. w and s Minn, Wisc, mostly s Mich, ne Ill and nw Ind. Newf to BC, s to NC, Ohio, Ind, Mo, Tex, Ariz and Calif.

▶Chenopodium L. / Goosefoot

Taprooted annual herbs. **Stems** erect to spreading. **Leaves** alternate, mostly lance-shaped to broadly triangular, somewhat fleshy and often mealy on lower surface. **Flowers** perfect, small and numerous, green or red-tinged, in dense spikelike clusters from leaf axils or at ends of stems, the spikes with small leafy bracts; sepals often curved over the fruit; petals absent; stamens 1–5; styles 2–3. **Fruit** a 1-seeded utricle.

▶KEY TO CHENOPODIUM

1 Leaves persistently white-mealy on underside, dull green above . . .
. . . . *C. glaucum* / Oak-leaved goosefoot
1 Leaves not white-mealy when mature, green on upper and lower sides, often red-tinged . . . . *C. rubrum* / Alkali-blite

---

Chenopodium glaucum L.
Oak-leaved goosefoot   FACW

Annual herb. **Stems** upright to sprawling, 1–6 dm long, usually branched from base, sometimes red-tinged. **Leaves** lance-shaped to ovate, 1–4 cm long and to 2 cm wide, dull green above, densely white-mealy on underside (especially when young); margins entire, wavy, or with few rounded teeth; petioles slender, shorter on upper leaves. **Flowers** in small, often branched, spikelike clusters from leaf axils, the spikes often shorter than leaves; sepals mostly 3; petals absent. **Seeds** dark brown, shiny, 1 mm wide. Aug–Oct. *C. salinum.* ❀ Shores, streambanks, and disturbed areas such as railroad ballast and barnyards; soils often brackish. ⊕ w Minn, Wisc, mostly LP of Mich, ne Ill and nw Ind. Introduced from Eurasia and naturalized across much of USA and Can. NB to Alberta, s to Va, Mo, Tex, NM, Ariz and Ore; Africa and Australia.

Chenopodium rubrum L.
Alkali-blite   OBL

Annual herb. **Stems** usually erect, sometimes sprawling, 1–8 dm long, often branched from base. **Leaves** lance-shaped to broadly triangular, 2–10 cm long and 1–8 cm wide, green and often red-tinged on both surfaces, smooth, not mealy; margins wavy-toothed or lobed; petioles present. **Flowers** small, in upright, branched spikes from leaf axils and at ends of stems, the spikes often longer than leaves; sepals 3, red; petals absent. **Seeds** dark brown, shiny, to 1 mm wide. Aug–Oct. ❀ Lakeshores, streambanks, disturbed areas. ⊕ Probably introduced in our area from w USA. Minn (mostly w), Wisc, local in c and s LP of Mich, uncommon in ne Ill. Newf to BC, s to NJ, Mo, Neb, n NM and Calif; Eurasia.

▶Salicornia L. / Glasswort

Salicornia rubra A. Nels.
Western glasswort   OBL

STATUS
Minnesota - T

Taprooted annual herb; plants succulent, green to bright red. **Stems** 0.5–2 dm long; **branches** opposite, fleshy, jointed at nodes, breaking apart when plants are trampled. **Leaves** opposite, small and scalelike, 1–2 mm long. **Flowers** in spikes 1–5 cm long at ends of stems; perfect, or some flowers female only; sepals enclosing flower except for a small opening from which stamens and style branches protrude; petals absent. **Seeds** 1 mm long. Aug–Oct. ❀ Shores, seeps and ditches; soils brackish.

⊕ Local in extreme nw and wc Minn. w Minn to s BC and e Wash, s to Kans, NM, and Nev. ☞ **Slender glasswort** (*Salicornia europaea* L.), an obligate wetland species, has been collected from several salty, disturbed locations in s Wisc, s Mich and n Ill. This species is more common in salt marshes along the Atlantic coast. It is distinguished from western glasswort by having the joints of the spike mostly longer than wide (in western glasswort, the joints of the spike are about as wide or wider than long).

▶**Suaeda** Forsskål / Sea-blite

Suaeda calceoliformis (Hook.) Moq.
  Plains sea-blite   FACW
Annual taprooted herb. **Stems** upright to sprawling, usually branched, 0.5–6 dm long. **Leaves** alternate, linear, flat on 1 side and convex on other, green, succulent, 5–30 mm long and 1 mm wide, reduced to wider bracts 1–5 mm long in the head; petioles absent. **Flowers** small, perfect, or male or female flowers separate, green or sometimes red-tinged, in dense clusters of 3–7 flowers in bract axils; sepals joined, deeply 5-lobed, the lobes unequal and hooded; stamens 5. **Fruit** a utricle enclosed by the sepals; seeds black, shiny, about 1 mm wide. July–Sept. *S. depressa.* ≋ Brackish wetlands, and along salted highways. ⊕ nw and wc Minn, s Wisc, occasional in s Mich, ne Ill and nw Ind. s Mich to BC, s to n Ill, Mo, Tex, Ariz and Calif.

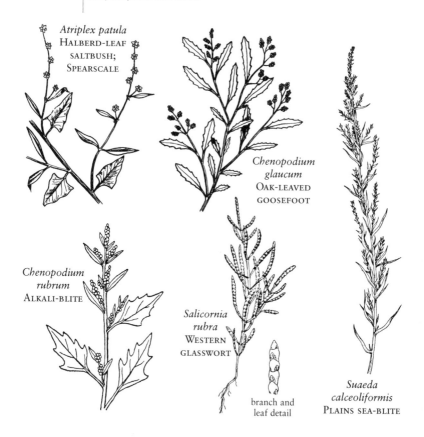

Atriplex patula
HALBERD-LEAF
SALTBUSH;
SPEARSCALE

Chenopodium glaucum
OAK-LEAVED
GOOSEFOOT

Chenopodium rubrum
ALKALI-BLITE

Salicornia rubra
WESTERN
GLASSWORT

branch and
leaf detail

Suaeda calceoliformis
PLAINS SEA-BLITE

Clusiaceae
St. John's-Wort Family

Smooth annual or perennial herbs (shrubby in *Hypericum kalmianum*). **Stems** usually unbranched below, branched in head. **Leaves** simple, opposite, dotted with dark or translucent glands (visible when held to a light), especially on underside; margins entire; petioles absent. **Flowers** few to many in clusters at ends of stems or from upper leaf axils, perfect, regular, sepals 5, petals 5, yellow or pink to green or purple; stamens 9–35, separate or joined near base into 3 or more groups; styles 3, ovary superior. **Fruit** a 3-chambered, many-seeded capsule.

▸**KEY TO CLUSIACEAE**

1 Petals yellow; stamens 15–many . . . . *Hypericum* / St. John's-wort
1 Petals pink or purple; stamens 9 . . . . *Triadenum*
. . . . Marsh St. John's-wort

▸Hypericum L. / St. John's-wort

Hypericum gymnanthum Shore St. John's-wort

Shrubs or herbs. **Leaves** opposite, sometimes dotted with black and/or small transparent glands; margins entire. **Flowers** in clusters at ends of stems and upper leaf axils, yellow, perfect, regular, sepals 5, petals 5, stamens 5–many, separate or joined into 3 or 5 bundles. Fruit a capsule. ☞ **Clasping St. John's-wort** (*Hypericum gymnanthum*), an annual herb, is known from a sandy wetland in nw Ind (⚠ state endangered). Plants are 2–6 dm tall, with stalkless, ± triangular leaves 1.5–3 cm long.

▸**KEY TO HYPERICUM**

1 Shrub to 1 m tall . . . . . . *H. kalmianum* / Kalm's St. John's-wort
1 Herbs **2**

2 Plants 1–2 m tall; flowers 4 cm or more wide; styles 5 . . . .
. . . . *H. pyramidatum* / Giant St. John's-wort
2 Plants smaller; flowers less than 3 cm wide; styles 3 . . . . **3**

3 Stamens 20 or more; styles joined, persisting on capsule as a straight beak **4**
3 Stamens less than 20; styles separate to base and often spreading, capsules not beaked **5**

4 Leaves 4–6x longer than wide, margins rolled under; n Ill and n Ind only . . . . *H. adpressum* / Shore St. John's-wort
4 Leaves 2–3x longer than wide, margins flat; n portions of region . .
. . . . *H. ellipticum* / Pale St. John's-wort

5 Sepals broadest above middle; fruit rounded at tip **6**
5 Sepals lance-shaped, broadest below middle; fruit tapered to tip . . **7**

6 Bracts leafy and oval, uppermost 0.5–2 mm wide; sepals much shorter than fruit . . . . *H. boreale* / Northern St. John's-wort

6 Bracts narrow and awl-shaped, uppermost to 0.2 mm wide; sepals same length as fruit . . . . . *H. mutilum* / SLENDER ST. JOHN'S-WORT

7 Leaves 1-nerved (sometimes 3-nerved), tapered to base; sepals 2–4 mm long . . . . *H. canadense* / CANADIAN ST. JOHN'S-WORT

7 Leaves 5–7-nerved, rounded at base and broadest below middle; sepals 5–6 mm long . . . . . . *H. majus* / LARGE CANADIAN ST. JOHN'S-WORT

Hypericum adpressum Barton
Shore St. John's-wort OBL

⚠
STATUS
Illinois - E
Indiana - E

Perennial herb, spreading by rhizomes. **Stems** 3–8 dm long, sometimes spongy at base. **Leaves** numerous, ascending on stem, narrowly oblong, 3–6 cm long and 5–10 mm wide, tapered to a rounded tip; margins entire, rolled under; petioles absent. **Flowers** in ± flat-topped clusters at end of stems; sepals lance-shaped to ovate, 2–6 mm long; petals yellow, 6–8 mm long, stigmas 3 (sometimes 4). **Fruit** an ovate capsule, 4–6 mm long, gradually tapered to a beak formed by the persistent styles. July–Aug. ❦ Marsh borders, sandy low prairie, ditches. ⊕ Mass, s to Tenn and Ga, occasional inland to nw Ind and ne Ill.

Hypericum boreale (Britton) E. Bickn.
Northern St. John's-wort OBL
Perennial herb, from slender rhizomes. **Stems** 1–4 dm long, round or slightly 4-angled, branched above. **Leaves** oval or oblong, rounded at ends and nearly clasping stem, 3–5-nerved, larger leaves 1–2 cm long and 0.5–1 cm wide; petioles absent. **Flowers** in clusters at ends of stems and from upper leaf axils; sepals blunt-tipped; petals yellow, 3 mm long; stamens 8–15; styles 3 (sometimes 4), less than 1 mm long. **Fruit** a 1-chambered purple capsule, 3–5 mm long. July–Sept. ❦ Pond and marsh margins, low areas between dunes, open bogs. ⊕ ne and ec Minn, Wisc, UP and most of LP of Mich, ne Ill and nw Ind. Nfld and Que to w Ont, s to Va, Ohio, n Ill and Minn.

Hypericum canadense L.
Canadian St. John's-wort FACW
Annual or perennial herb, with short leafy stolons from base of plant. **Stems** upright, branched, 1–6 dm long. **Leaves** linear, 1–4 cm long and 1–4 mm wide, blunt-tipped, mostly 1-nerved, bracts much smaller; petioles absent. **Flowers** in open clusters at ends of stems and from upper leaf axils; sepals lance-shaped, 3–5 mm long; petals yellow, 2–3 mm long; stamens 12–22; styles 3 (sometimes 4), less than 1 mm long. **Fruit** a purple capsule 4–6 mm long. July–Sept. ❦ Sandy shores, wetland margins, ditches. ⊕ Wisc, Mich, ne Ill and nw Ind. Nfld and Que to Wisc, s to Ga and Ala.

Hypericum ellipticum Hook.
Pale St. John's-wort OBL
Perennial herb, spreading by rhizomes. **Stems** 2–5 dm long, branched only in head. **Leaves** oval, 1–4 cm long and 1–1.5 cm wide, rounded at tip, narrowed at base and sometimes clasping stem; petioles absent. **Flowers** few to many, in clusters at ends of stems; sepals to 6 mm long; petals pale yellow, 6–7 mm long; stigmas 3 (sometimes 4), small. **Fruit** a 1-chambered capsule, 5–6 mm long, rounded to a short beak formed by the persistent styles. July–Aug. ❦ Streambanks, sandy shores and flats, thickets, bogs. ⊕ ne Minn, n Wisc, Mich UP. Nfld and NS to n Minn, s to Conn, NY and n Ind.

Hypericum kalmianum L.

Kalm's St. John's-wort   FACW-

Branched shrub to 1 m tall; **branches** 4-angled, **twigs** flattened. **Leaves** linear, 2–4 cm long and 3–8 mm wide, often waxy on underside; margins sometimes rolled under; petioles absent. **Flowers** in clusters of 3–7 at ends of stems, yellow, 2–3.5 cm wide; stamens many, not joined; styles 5. **Fruit** a 5-chambered, ovate capsule, 7–10 mm long, beaked by the persistent style base. June–Sept. ⚘ Dunes (especially wet areas between dunes) and rocky lakeshores, mostly near Great Lakes, often on limestone or where calcium-rich. ⊕ s Wisc, Mich (c and e UP, LP), ne Ill and nw Ind. Que and Ont, s to NY, Mich and Ill.

Hypericum majus (A. Gray) Britton

Large Canadian St. John's-wort   FACW

Perennial herb, spreading from rhizomes or stolons. **Stems** upright, unbranched or branched above, 1–6 dm long. **Leaves** lance-shaped, 2–4 cm long and 3-10 mm wide, dotted with brown sunken glands, 5–7-nerved from base; leaf tip rounded, leaf base rounded or heart-shaped and weakly clasping; petioles absent. **Flowers** few to many in clusters at ends of stems and from upper leaf axils; sepals lance-shaped, 4–6 mm long; petals yellow, equal to sepals but then shriveling to half the length of sepals; stamens 14–21, not joined; styles to 1 mm long. **Fruit** a red-purple ovate capsule, 5–7 mm long. July–Sept. ⚘ Streambanks, sandy, mucky or calcareous shores, low areas between dunes, marshes, wetland margins. ⊕ Minn (but local in sw), Wisc, Mich, ne Ill and nw Ind. Newf and Que to BC, s to NJ, Pa, Ill, Iowa, Kans and Colo.

Hypericum mutilum L.

Slender St. John's-wort   FACW

Annual or perennial herb. **Stems** 1–8 dm long, branched above. **Leaves** lance-shaped to oval, 1–4 cm long, 3–5 nerved from base, petioles absent. **Flowers** in branched, leafy clusters at ends of stems and from upper leaf axils, upper leaves bractlike and 1–4 mm long; sepals linear and pointed at tip; petals pale orange-yellow, 2–3 mm long; stamens 5–16; styles 3, less than 1 mm long. **Fruit** a green capsule, 2–4 mm long. July–Sept. *H. parviflorum.* ⚘ Streambanks, wet meadows, marshes, ditches; usually where sandy. ⊕ s Wisc, c and s LP of Mich, ne Ill and nw Ind. Nfld and Que to Man, occasional s to Fla and Tex.

Hypericum pyramidatum Aiton

Giant St. John's-wort   FAC+

Perennial herb. **Stems** upright, branched, 6–20 dm long. **Leaves** lance-shaped to oval, 4–10 cm long and 1–4 cm wide, base often clasping stem; petioles absent. **Flowers** few, 4–6 cm wide, mostly single on stalks from upper leaf axils; stamens numerous, joined at base into 5 bundles; petals bright yellow; styles 5, not persisting. **Fruit** an ovate, 5-chambered capsule, 15–30 mm long. July–Aug. *H. ascyron.* ⚘ Streambanks, ditches, fen and marsh margins. ⊕ e Minn, Wisc, Mich, uncommon in ne Ill and nw Ind. Que to Minn, s to NJ, Pa, Ind, Ill and Kans.

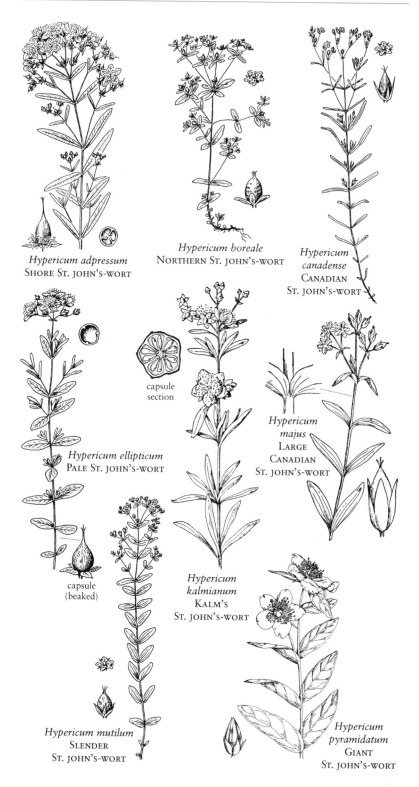

Hypericum adpressum
SHORE ST. JOHN'S-WORT

Hypericum boreale
NORTHERN ST. JOHN'S-WORT

Hypericum canadense
CANADIAN
ST. JOHN'S-WORT

Hypericum ellipticum
PALE ST. JOHN'S-WORT

capsule
section

Hypericum majus
LARGE
CANADIAN
ST. JOHN'S-WORT

capsule
(beaked)

Hypericum kalmianum
KALM'S
ST. JOHN'S-WORT

Hypericum mutilum
SLENDER
ST. JOHN'S-WORT

Hypericum pyramidatum
GIANT
ST. JOHN'S-WORT

▶**Triadenum** Raf. / Marsh St. John's-wort

Smooth perennial herbs. **Leaves** opposite, entire and oval-shaped, ours dotted with small dark and transparent glands. **Flowers** pink to green-purple, in clusters at ends of stems and from leaf axils; stamens 9, in 3 groups of 3; sepals 5; petals 5; styles 3. **Fruit** a cylindric capsule.

▶**KEY TO TRIADENUM**

1 Sepals 3–4 mm long, oval and rounded at tip; styles mostly less than 1 mm long; widespread in region   *T. fraseri* / MARSH ST. JOHN'S-WORT
1 Sepals 5–8 mm long, lance-shaped and tapered to a tip; styles 2–3 mm long; uncommon in IL, IN, sw MI . . . . *T. virginicum* . . . . MARSH ST. JOHN'S-WORT

Triadenum fraseri (Spach) Gleason

  Marsh St. John's-wort   OBL

Perennial herb, with creeping rhizomes. **Stems** upright, mostly unbranched, red, smooth, 3–6 dm long. **Leaves** oval or ovate, 3–6 cm long and 1–3 cm wide, pinnately veined, rounded at tip, rounded or heart-shaped and clasping at the base, with dark dots and transparent glands on underside. **Flowers** in clusters at ends of stems and from leaf axils, often remaining closed; sepals 3–5 mm long, rounded at tip; petals pink to green-purple, 5–8 mm long; stamens 9, joined at base into 3 bundles, the bundles alternating with orange glands; styles 1–2 mm long. **Fruit** a purple, cylindric capsule, 7–12 mm long, abruptly narrowed to the 1 mm long persistent style beak. July–Aug. *Hypericum virginicum* var. *fraseri, Triadenum virginicum* subsp. *fraseri.* ✺ Marshes, sedge meadows, open bogs, fens, sandy and calcium-rich shores. ⊕ nw and e Minn, Wisc, Mich, ne Ill and nw Ind. Newf and Que to Minn, s to WVa, Ind and Neb.

Triadenum virginicum (L.) Raf.

  Marsh St. John's-wort   OBL

⚠
STATUS
Illinois - E

Perennial herb spreading by rhizomes, similar to *T. fraseri* but with larger flowers. **Stems** upright, mostly unbranched, red, smooth, 3–6 dm long. **Leaves** oblong, oval or ovate, 3–6 cm long and 1–3 cm wide, pinnately veined, rounded at tip, ± heart-shaped and clasping at base, with dark dots and transparent glands on leaf underside. **Flowers** in clusters at ends of stems and from leaf axils; sepals 5–8 mm long, lance-shaped; petals pink to green-purple, 8–10 mm long; stamens 9, joined at base into 3 bundles; styles 1–2 mm long. **Fruit** a red-purple cylindric capsule, 8–12 mm long, gradually tapered to the 2–3 mm long persistent style beak. July–Aug. *Hypericum virginicum.* ✺ Sphagnum bogs, wet meadows, shores. ⊕ Atlantic coastal disjunct in ne Ill, nw Ind and sw Mich. NS s to Fla and Miss, inland in NY, s Ont, Mich and n Ind.

Cornaceae
Dogwood Family

☞ Nyssa is
sometimes
placed in a
separate
family—
Nyssaceae or
the Tupelo
Family.

Trees (*Nyssa*), shrubs or semi-shrubs (*Cornus*). **Leaves** simple, entire, alternate (*Nyssa*), opposite or whorled (*Cornus*). **Flowers** either male or female (*Nyssa*) or perfect (*Cornus*), in a rounded or flat-topped cluster. **Fruit** a drupe, blue-black in *Nyssa*, red or white in *Cornus*. The shrubby dogwoods are preferred deer foods and are often reduced in size due to repeated browsing.

▶ **KEY TO CORNACEAE**

1 Shrubs (or herbaceous stems from woody rhizomes in *C. canadensis*); leaves opposite or whorled (alternate in *C. alternifolia*); flowers perfect . . . . *Cornus* / Bunchberry; Dogwood
1 Tree of s portion of region; leaves alternate; flowers either male or female . . . . *Nyssa sylvatica* / Black tupelo; Black gum

▶ **Cornus** L. / Bunchberry; Dogwood

Shrubs, or herbaceous shoots from a woody rhizome in **bunchberry** (*Cornus canadensis*). **Leaves** opposite, simple, entire. **Flowers** 4-parted, sepals and petals small. **Fruit** a berrylike drupe with 1–2 hard seeds.

▶ **KEY TO CORNUS**

1 Plants herbaceous from a woody rhizome, less than 3 dm tall; leaves whorled . . . . *C. canadensis* / Bunchberry; Dwarf cornel
1 Taller shrubs, 5 dm or more tall; leaves opposite or alternate **2**

2 Leaves alternate on stems . . . . *C. alternifolia*
. . . . Pagoda dogwood; Alternate-leaved dogwood
2 Leaves opposite **3**

3 Leaves with stiff, rough hairs on upper surface; s portion of our region . . . . *C. drummondii* / Rough-leaved Dogwood
3 Leaves smooth, not rough-hairy above; widespread **4**

4 Fruit white; young twigs densely short-hairy . . . . *C. amomum*
. . . . Silky dogwood
4 Fruit blue; young twigs ± smooth **5**

5 Twigs gray; leaves with fewer than 5 pairs of lateral veins . . . .
. . . . *C. racemosa* / Northern swamp dogwood
5 Twigs red; leaves with 5 or more pairs of lateral veins . . . .
. . . . *C. sericea* / Red-osier Dogwood

Cornus alternifolia L. f.

Pagoda dogwood; Alternate-leaved dogwood (FAC-)
Shrub, to 5 m tall; **twigs** red-green or brown, somewhat shiny, alternate on stems, pith white. **Leaves** alternate, sometimes crowded and appear-

ing whorled near ends of stems, oval to ovate, 5–12 cm long and 3–7 cm wide, tapered to a sharp tip, underside finely hairy; lateral veins 4–5 pairs, these curving toward tip of blade; margins entire; petioles to 5 cm long. **Flowers** small, creamy-white, in crowded, flat-topped or rounded clusters at ends of stems. **Fruit** a round, blue, berrylike drupe, 6 mm wide, atop a red stalk. May–July. *Svida alternifolia.* ≋ Swamps, thickets, streambanks and springs; also in drier deciduous and mixed forests. ⊕ Minn, Wisc, Mich, ne Ill and nw Ind. Nfld and NS to Minn, s to Fla, Ga, Ala and Ark.

Cornus amomum Miller
Silky dogwood   FACW+

Shrub, 1–3 m tall; older **branches** red and gray-streaked, young **twigs** gray, finely hairy; pith brown. **Leaves** opposite, oval to ovate, 5–12 cm long and 2–5 cm wide, usually less than half as wide as long, tapered to a sharp tip, lateral veins 4–6 on each side, underside finely hairy; margins entire; petioles 1–2 cm long, often curved and causing the leaves to droop. **Flowers** small, creamy-white, in flat-topped or slightly rounded, hairy clusters. **Fruit** a round, blue or blue-white, berrylike drupe, 8 mm wide, atop a long stalk. June–July (our latest flowering dogwood). *C. obliqua.* ≋ Conifer swamps, marshes, open bogs, calcareous fens, lakeshores, streambanks, wet dunes. ⊕ Common; se Minn, c and s Wisc, LP of Mich (occasional in s UP), ne Ill and nw Ind. Maine and Que to Minn, s to Ga, Ala, Ark and Okla.

Cornus canadensis L.
Bunchberry; Dwarf cornel   FACW-

⚠
STATUS
Illinois - E
Indiana - E

Perennial from horizontal, woody rhizomes, often forming large colonies. **Stems** erect, green, 1–2 dm tall, with a pair of small bracts on lower stem, topped with a whorl-like cluster of 4–6 leaves. **Leaves** oval to obovate, 4–7 cm long, tapered at both ends; lateral veins 2–3 pairs, arising from midvein below middle of blade; margins entire; petioles short or absent. **Flowers** small, yellow-green or creamy-white in a single cluster at end of a stalk 1–3 cm long; flowers surrounded by 4 white or pinkish, petal-like showy bracts, 1–2 cm long, these soon deciduous. **Fruit** a cluster of round, bright red berrylike drupes, the drupes 6–8 mm wide. June–July. ≋ Cedar swamps, thickets and moist conifer forests, often on hummocks or rotting logs; also in drier, mixed conifer-decidu-ous forests. ⊕ Common in n portion of our area, occasional to rare southward. n, c and se Minn, n and c Wisc, Mich, ne Ill and nw Ind. Greenland to Alaska, s to NJ, Pa, Va, WVa, n Ind, N Ill and Minn; Rocky Mts, Calif; e Asia.

Cornus drummondii C. A. Meyer.
Rough-leaved Dogwood   FACW-

Shrub, 2–4 m tall, sometimes forming thickets; **twigs** red and finely hairy when young, becoming gray-brown and smooth; pith brown. **Leaves** opposite, lance-shaped to ovate, 5–8 cm long and 3–5 cm wide, abrupt-ly tapered to a rounded tip, rough-to-touch on upper surface, underside finely hairy; lateral veins 3 or 4 on each side of midvein; margins entire; petioles finely hairy, to 2 cm long. **Flowers** small, creamy-white, many, in loose ± flat-topped clusters. **Fruit** a white, round, berrylike drupe, 6 mm wide, on a red-purple stalk. May–June. ≋ Streambanks, thickets. ⊕ s Wisc, se LP of Mich, nw Ind, ne Ill. Ohio to s Wisc, Iowa and Neb, s to Ga and Tex.

Cornus racemosa Lam.

Northern swamp dogwood   FACW-

Shrub, 1–3 m tall, often forming dense thickets; **twigs** red, becoming gray or light brown; pith usually brown. **Leaves** opposite, lance-shaped to oval, 4–9 cm long and 2–4 cm wide, abruptly tapered to a rounded tip, underside with short hairs; lateral veins 3 or 4 on each side of midvein; margins entire; petioles to 1 cm long. **Flowers** small, creamy-white, ill-scented, in numerous, open, elongated clusters. **Fruit** a round, berrylike drupe, at first lead-colored, becoming white, 5 mm wide, on red stalks. June–July. *C. foemina.* ❦ Lakeshores, streambanks, swamps, thickets, marshes, moist woods, low prairie. ⊕ Common; Minn (all but far ne), Wisc (but local in nc), Mich LP (occasional in c and e UP), ne Ill and nw Ind. Maine and s Que to s Man, s to Va, s Ill and Mo.

Cornus sericea L.

Red-osier dogwood   FACW

Many-stemmed shrub, 1–3 m tall, forming thickets; **branches** upright or prostrate and rooting; **twigs** and young branches red; pith white. **Leaves** opposite, green, ovate to oval, mostly 5–15 cm long and 2–7 cm wide, tapered to a tip, soft hairy on underside; margins entire; petioles to 2.5 cm long. **Flowers** small, white, many in flat-topped or slightly rounded clusters. **Fruit** a round, white or blue-tinged, berrylike drupe, 6–9 mm wide. May–Aug. *C. stolonifera.* ❦ Swamps, marshes, shores, streambanks, floodplain forests, shrub thickets, calcareous fens; also on sand dunes. ⊕ Common (but plants reduced in size and abundance where deer numbers are high). Minn, Wisc, Mich, ne Ill and nw Ind. Newf to Alaska, s to Pa, Ill, Neb and n Mex.

▶ Nyssa L. / Sour gum

Nyssa sylvatica Marshall

Black tupelo; Black gum   (FACW+, OBL)

Small to medium tree, to 15 m tall; trunk 2–4 dm wide; **bark** dark gray to red-brown, deeply furrowed into blocky plates; **twigs** red-brown. **Leaves** alternate, thick and firm, oval to obovate, 4–12 cm long and half as wide, usually abruptly tapered to a rounded tip, dark green, smooth and shiny on upper surface, turning bright scarlet in fall, paler and often hairy below; margins entire; petioles short. **Flowers** greenish, on thin, finely hairy stalks; the male and female flowers on separate trees or sometimes the flowers perfect; **male flowers** on slender, finely hairy stalks in a many-flowered head, stamens 5–10; **female flowers** 2–8, at end of a stalk 3–5 cm long, petals 5. **Fruit** a sour, blue-black, oval drupe, 1–1.5 cm long, in clusters of 1–3. May–June. ❦ Swamp margins, shores, wet depressions in forests. ⊕ Local in extreme se Wisc; c and s LP of Mich, ne Ill and nw Ind. s Maine to se Wisc, e and s Ill, s to Fla, Mo and Tex.

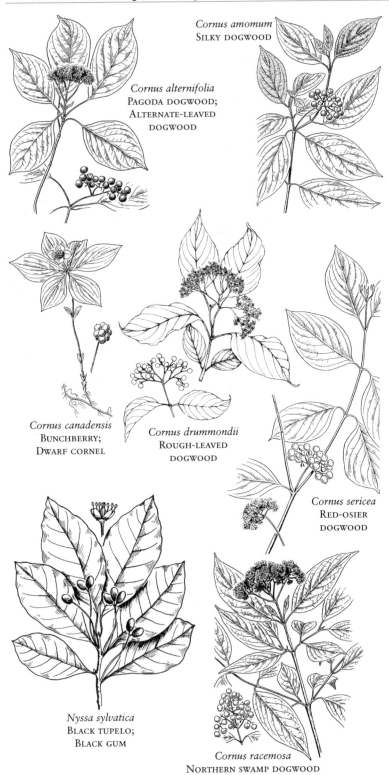

Cornus amomum
SILKY DOGWOOD

Cornus alternifolia
PAGODA DOGWOOD;
ALTERNATE-LEAVED
DOGWOOD

Cornus canadensis
BUNCHBERRY;
DWARF CORNEL

Cornus drummondii
ROUGH-LEAVED
DOGWOOD

Cornus sericea
RED-OSIER
DOGWOOD

Nyssa sylvatica
BLACK TUPELO;
BLACK GUM

Cornus racemosa
NORTHERN SWAMP DOGWOOD

Crassulaceae
Stonecrop Family

▶**Crassula** L. / Pygmy-weed

Crassula aquatica (L.) Schönl
Pygmy-weed   OBL

⚠
STATUS
Minnesota - T

Small annual herb. **Stems** branched, 2–10 cm long. **Leaves** opposite, linear, succulent, 3–6 mm long, spreading, margins entire, petioles absent. **Flowers** small, 1 mm long, single in leaf axils; petals white or green-white, 4, erect or slightly spreading; stamens 4, alternate with petals; pistils 3–4, with a short style. Aug–Sept. *Tillaea aquatica.* ❦ Muddy shores and shallow water. ⊕ Rare in ne and far sw Minn. Nfld and Que s to Md, La, Tex; Eurasia.

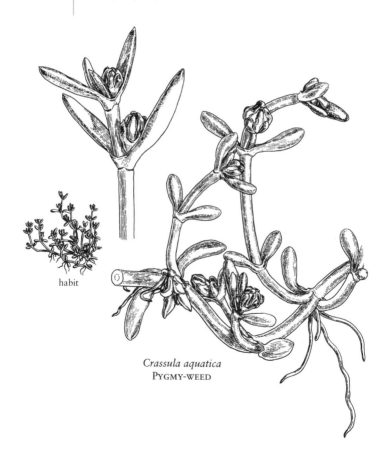

habit

Crassula aquatica
Pygmy-weed

Curcurbitaceae
Gourd Family

Annual herbaceous vines (our species). **Flowers** green or white, either male or female and on same plants (ours). **Fruit** a dry or fleshy, cucumber- or squash-like fruit (*pepo*).

▶KEY TO CURCURBITACEAE

1   Male flowers 6-lobed; fruit inflated, 3–5 cm long, 4-seeded. . . . . . .
. . . . *Echinocystis lobata* / WILD CUCUMBER; BALSAM-APPLE

1   Male flowers 5-lobed; fruit not inflated, to 1.5 cm long, 1-seeded . .
. . . . *Sicyos angulatus* / BUR-CUCUMBER

▶Echinocystis T. & G. / Wild cucumber

Echinocystis lobata (Michx.) T. & G.
Wild cucumber; Balsam-apple   FACW-

Annual vining herb, to 5 m or more long. **Leaves** round in outline, with 3–7 (usually 5) sharp, triangular lobes; petioles 3–8 cm long. **Flowers** white; **male flowers** 8–10 mm wide, with lance-shaped lobes, in long, upright racemes; **female flowers** 1 to several on short stalks from leaf axils. **Fruit** green, ovate, inflated, 3–5 cm long, with soft prickles. Aug–Sept. ✤ Floodplain forests, wet deciduous forests, streambanks, thickets, and waste ground. ⊕ Minn, Wisc, Mich, ne Ill and nw Ind. New Eng, s to Fla and Tex.

▶Sicyos L. / Bur-cucumber

Sicyos angulatus L.
Bur-cucumber   FACW-

Annual vining herb, to 2 m long. **Stems** angled, sticky-hairy, with branched tendrils. **Leaves** round in outline, with 3–5 shallow, toothed lobes, rough on both sides; petioles hairy, 3–10 cm long. **Flowers** green or white; **male flowers** 8–10 mm wide, 5-lobed, on stalks 10 cm or more long; **female flowers** on stalks to 8 cm long. **Fruit** yellow, ovate, 1.5 cm long, hairy and spine-covered. Aug–Sept. ✤ Floodplain forests, wet deciduous forests, streambanks, thickets and waste ground. ⊕ s Minn, Wisc, Mich, ne Ill and nw Ind. Que and Maine to Minn, s to Fla and Ariz.

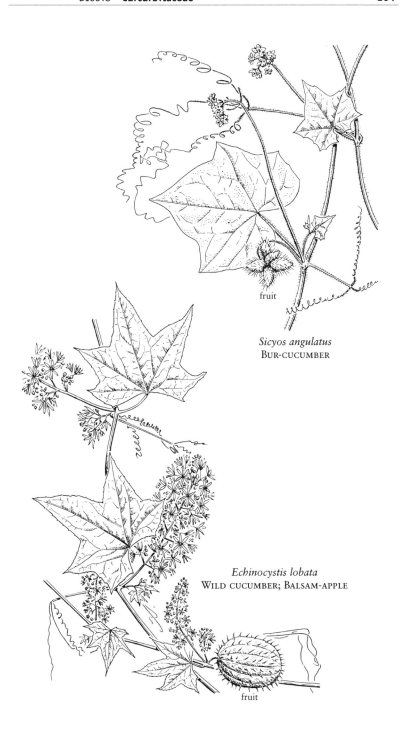

Sicyos angulatus
Bur-cucumber

fruit

Echinocystis lobata
Wild cucumber; Balsam-apple

fruit

Droseraceae
Sundew Family

▶Drosera L. / Sundew

☞ The insectivorous habit of Drosera is an adaptation to the nutrient-poor habitats occupied by these plants –the digested insects provide nitrogen.

Perennial herbs. **Leaves** all from base of plant, covered with stalked, sticky glands that trap and digest insects. **Flowers** white, several, on 1 side of erect, leafless stalks, the stalks nodding at tip; with 5 petals and 5 sepals; stamens mostly 5, styles 3. **Fruit** a dry, many-seeded capsule.

▶**KEY TO DROSERA**

1 Leaves widely spreading, blades round, wider than long . . . .
. . . . *D. rotundifolia* / Round-leaved sundew
1 Leaves upright, blades linear or broad at tip and tapered to base, longer than wide **2**

2 Leaf blades linear, 10–20x longer than wide; young petals pink . . .
. . . . *D. linearis* / Linear-leaved sundew
2 Leaf blades broad near tip and narrowed to base, 2–7x as long as wide; young petals white **3**

3 Blades 2–3x as long as wide, petioles without hairs; flower stalks from side of plant base and curving upward . . . . *D. intermedia*
. . . . Spoon-leaved sundew
3 Blades 5–7x as long as wide, petioles with some hairs; flower stalks erect from center of plant base . . . . *D. anglica*
. . . . English or Great sundew

Drosera anglica Hudson
English or Great sundew   (OBL)

⚠ STATUS Wisconsin - T

Perennial insectivorous herb. **Leaf blades** obovate to spatula-shaped, 15–35 mm long and 3–4 mm wide, upper surface covered with gland-tipped hairs; petioles 3–6 cm long, smooth or with few glandular hairs. **Flowers** 1–9 in a racemelike cluster atop a stalk 6–25 cm tall; flowers 6–7 mm wide; sepals 5–6 mm long; petals white, 6 mm long, spatula-shaped. **Seeds** black, 1 mm long, with fine lines. June–Aug. ❀ Floating sphagnum mats, calcareous fens, wet areas between dunes. ⊕ nc Minn, nw Wisc, n LP of Mich, local in UP. Circumboreal, s to Que, Maine, s Ont, n Minn, Mont and Calif. ☞ Similar to **spoon-leaved sundew** (*D. intermedia*) but rarely occurring together. Plants of *D. anglica* are generally larger, with shorter petioles (1–3x as long as leaf blades vs. 2.5–3.5x as long in *D. intermedia*).

Drosera intermedia Hayne
Spoon-leaved sundew   OBL

⚠ STATUS Illinois - T

Perennial insectivorous herb. **Leaves** in a basal rosette and also usually along lower stem; spatula-shaped, 2–4 mm wide, upper surface covered with long, gland-tipped hairs; petioles smooth, 2–5 cm long. **Flowers** on stalks to 20 cm tall; sepals 3–4 mm long; petals white, 4–5 mm long. **Seeds** red-brown, to 1 mm long, covered with small bumps. July–Sept. ❀ Low spots in open bogs, sandy shores, often in shallow water. ⊕ nc, ne and ec Minn, Wisc, Mich, ne Ill and nw Ind. ± circumboreal, Nfld to, s to Fla and Tex; Idaho.

Drosera linearis Goldie
Linear-leaved sundew   OBL

Perennial insectivorous herb. **Leaf blades** linear, 2–5 cm long and 2 mm wide; petioles smooth, 3–7 cm long. **Flowers** 1–4 atop stalks 6–15 cm tall; flowers 6–8 mm wide; sepals 4–5 mm long; petals obovate, 6 mm long, white. **Seeds** black, less than 1 mm long, with small craterlike pits on surface. June–Aug. ☙ Calcareous fens, wet areas between dunes near Great Lakes; rarely in sphagnum moss. ⊕ nc and ec Minn, uncommon in nw and se Wisc, Mich UP (especially e), n and se LP. Occasional across s Can, s to Maine, Great Lakes, Tenn and Tex; nw Mont.

Drosera rotundifolia L.
Round-leaved sundew   OBL

⚠
STATUS
Illinois - E

Small, perennial insectivorous herb. **Leaf blades** ± round, wider than long, 2–10 mm long and as wide or wider, covered with long, red, gland-tipped hairs; abruptly tapered to a petiole longer than blade; petioles 2–5 cm long covered with gland-tipped hairs. **Flowers** 2–15 in a ± 1-sided, racemelike cluster, on a leafless stalk 10-30 cm tall; flowers 4–7 mm wide, sepals 5, 4–5 mm long; petals white to pink, longer than sepals; stamens 5, shorter than petals. **Seeds** light brown, shiny and with fine lines, 1–1.5 mm long. July–Aug. ☙ Swamps and open bogs, usually in sphagnum; wet sandy shores and openings. ⊕ n and c Minn (not w), Wisc, Mich, ne Ill and nw Ind. Circumboreal, s to Ga, Tenn, Ill, Minn, ND, Idaho, and Calif.

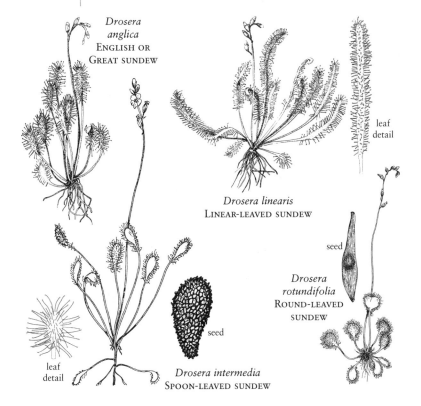

Drosera anglica ENGLISH OR GREAT SUNDEW

Drosera linearis LINEAR-LEAVED SUNDEW

leaf detail

seed

Drosera rotundifolia ROUND-LEAVED SUNDEW

seed

leaf detail

Drosera intermedia SPOON-LEAVED SUNDEW

Round-leaved sundew (Drosera rotundifolia)**.** The region's most common sundew is typically found in wet, sphagnum moss peatlands. The gland-tipped hairs on the leaf blade exude a sticky substance which attracts flying insects. The insects are then held and the leaf blade slowly curls around the insect to begin the digestive process.

Elatinaceae
Waterwort Family

▶**Elatine** L. / Waterwort

Small, branched, annual herbs of shallow water, shores and mud flats. **Leaves** simple, opposite, entire or toothed, with small membranous stipules. **Flowers** small, single from leaf axils, perfect; sepals, petals and stamens 2–3 (ours); styles 3; ovary superior, 3–4-chambered. **Fruit** a capsule with numerous small seeds.

▶**KEY TO ELATINE**

1 Flowers with 2 sepals and 2 petals, seeds all at base of fruit . . . . . .
. . . . *E. minima* / SMALL WATERWORT
1 Flowers with 3 sepals and 3 petals; seeds at differing levels in fruit
. . . . *E. triandra* / LONG-STEMMED WATERWORT

Elatine minima (Nutt.) Fischer & C. A. Meyer
Small Waterwort   OBL

☞ Elatine minima is typically a smaller plant than the otherwise similar *E. triandra*.

Annual herb, forming small mosslike mats on mud; plants smooth, with branches to 5 cm long. **Leaves** opposite, oblong to obovate, rounded at tip, to 4 mm long, petioles absent. **Flowers** small, single and stalkless in leaf axils, sepals 2, petals 2. **Fruit** a round capsule; seeds with rows of small, rounded pits. ❧ Shallow water and wet shores along lakes and ponds, usually where sandy or mucky. ⊕ ne and ec Minn, n Wisc, w and c UP, sw LP of Mich. Nfld to Ont and Minn, s to Md and Va.

Elatine triandra Schk.
Long-stemmed Waterwort   OBL

Annual herb; plants small, matted, to 15 cm long, somewhat fleshy, smooth, branched from base, the branches sprawling or floating, often rooting at nodes. **Leaves** opposite, linear to obovate, 3–10 mm long and 1–3 mm wide, margins entire, petioles absent; stipules very small. **Flowers** small, single and stalkless in leaf axils, 1.5–2 mm wide, sepals 3, petals 3. **Fruit** a round capsule, 1–2 mm wide; seeds 0.5 mm long, ridged and with tiny, angled pits. July–Sept. *E. americana*, *E. brachysperma*. ❧ Mud flats or in shallow water of lakes and ponds. ⊕ ne and sw Minn, sw Wisc. Wisc to Alberta and Wash, s to Tex, n Mex and Calif; Eurasia.

Empetraceae
Crowberry Family

▶**Empetrum** L. / Crowberry

Empetrum nigrum L.
Black crowberry   FACW-

⚠
STATUS
Michigan - T
Minnesota - E

Much-branched low shrub to 3 dm tall; sometimes forming mats 1–2 m wide. **Leaves** evergreen and needlelike, dark green and leathery, linear-oblong, only 4–8 mm long, rounded or blunt at tip, narrowed at base to a short stalk, margins rolled under. **Flowers** small, pink to purple, single in axils of upper leaves, either male or female or perfect. **Fruit** purple-black to black, berrylike, 4–6 mm wide, somewhat juicy, with 6–9 hard nutlets. July–Aug. ❦ Cedar and black spruce swamps, rocky shorelines; also on drier, sandy, pine-covered ridges. ⊕ Uncommon in extreme ne Minn and UP of Mich, mostly near Lake Superior. Circumboreal, s to New Eng, NY, Mich and Minn.

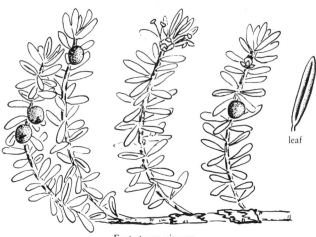

leaf

Empetrum nigrum
BLACK CROWBERRY

Ericaceae
Heath Family

Shrubs or scarcely woody shrubs. **Leaves** evergreen or deciduous, mostly alternate, simple, with entire or toothed margins. **Flowers** usually perfect (with both male and female parts), urn- or vase-shaped, white, pink, or cream-colored; stamens as many (or 2x as many) as petals. **Fruit** a berry or dry capsule.

▶**KEY TO ERICACEAE**

1 Leaves deciduous. **2**
1 Leaves evergreen **3**

2 Leaves with shiny, orange-yellow resinous dots (especially on underside). . . . . *Gaylussacia baccata* / BLACK HUCKLEBERRY
2 Leaves without resinous dots . . . . *Vaccinium* (BLUEBERRIES)

3 Plants creeping on ground surface **4**
3 Plants upright **5**

4 Stems covered with brown hairs; fruit a white berry . . . .
. . . . *Gaultheria hispidula* / CREEPING SNOWBERRY
4 Stems not covered with brown hairs; fruit a red berry. . . . .
. . . . *Vaccinium* (CRANBERRIES)

5 Leaf margins distinctly rolled under **6**
5 Leaf margins not rolled under **8**

6 Leaf underside densely covered with woolly hairs. . . . .
. . . . *Ledum groenlandicum* / LABRADOR-TEA
6 Leaf underside white; woolly hairs absent **7**

7 Leaves alternate . . . . . . *Andromeda glaucophylla* / BOG-ROSEMARY
7 Leaves opposite . . . . *Kalmia polifolia* / BOG-LAUREL

8 Leaves alternate . . . . *Chamaedaphne calyculata* / LEATHERLEAF
8 Leaves opposite . . . . *Kalmia angustifolia* / SHEEP-LAUREL

▶**Andromeda** L. / Bog-rosemary

Andromeda glaucophylla Link
Bog-rosemary   OBL
Low upright or trailing shrub, 3–6 dm tall. **Stems** gray to blackish; **twigs** brown, with hairs in lines running down stems, or sometimes smooth. **Leaves** evergreen and leathery, often blue-green, linear or narrowly oval, 2–5 cm long and 3–10 mm wide, the tip sharp-pointed and tipped with a small spine, the base tapered to the stem or a short petiole, dark green above and whitened below by short stiff hairs; margins entire and distinctly rolled under. **Flowers** in drooping clusters at ends of branches, white or often pink, urn-shaped, 5-parted, 5–6 mm long, on curved

stalks to 8 mm long. **Fruit** a rounded capsule to 5 mm wide, the style persistent from indented top of capsule; fruit drooping at first, but erect when mature. May–June. ☙ Sphagnum bogs, black spruce and tamarack swamps. ⊕ n and c Minn, Wisc (all but sw), Mich (but rare in se), uncommon in ne Ill and nw Ind. Nfld and Labr to Sask, s to NJ, WVa, n Ind, n Ill and Minn.

▶**Chamaedaphne** Moench / Leatherleaf

Chamaedaphne calyculata (L.) Moench
Leatherleaf   OBL

⚠
STATUS
Illinois - T

Upright shrub to 1 m tall. Older **stems** gray, the outer bark shredding to expose the smooth, red inner bark; **twigs** brown, with fine hairs and covered with small, round scales. **Leaves** evergreen and leathery, becoming smaller toward ends of flowering branches, oval, 1–5 cm long and 3–15 mm wide, the tip rounded or pointed, brown-green and smooth above, pale brown with a covering of small, round scales below; margins entire or with small rounded teeth; petioles short. **Flowers** white, urn-shaped or cylindric, in 1-sided, leafy racemes, hanging from axils of reduced leaves near ends of branches; 5-parted, 5–7 mm long, on stalks 2–5 mm long. **Fruit** a brown, rounded capsule to 6 mm wide, the hairlike style persistent from indented top of capsule; capsules persisting on branches for several years. May–June. ☙ Open bogs, black spruce and tamarack swamps, peaty lakeshores and streambanks, often forming low, dense thickets. ⊕ Common in n portions of region, occasional in s. n and c Minn, Wisc (all but driftless area), Mich, ne Ill and nw Ind. Circumboreal, s to NJ, NC, Ohio, n Ill and Minn.

Andromeda glaucophylla
Bog-rosemary

*Chamaedaphne
calyculata*
Leatherleaf

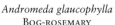

capsule

▶**Gaultheria** L. / Wintergreen

Gaultheria hispidula (L.) Muhl.
Creeping snowberry   FACW
Low, creeping, matted shrub. **Stems** 2–4 dm long, covered with brown
hairs. **Leaves** crowded, evergreen, oval to nearly round, 4–10 mm long
and to 5 mm wide, abruptly tapered to tip, green above, underside paler,
with brown, bristly hairs; margins rolled under; petioles short. **Flowers**
few, single in leaf axils, white, bell-shaped, 4-parted, 2–4 mm long, on
curved stalks 1 mm long. **Fruit** a translucent, juicy, white berry 5–10 mm
wide, slightly wintergreen-flavored. May–June. *Chiogenes hispidula*. ❦
Open bogs, swamps, wet conifer woods, often in moss on hummocks or
downed logs. ⊕ nc and ne Minn, n and c Wisc (rare in se), Mich. Nfld
and Labr to BC, s to NJ, NC, Pa, and Great Lakes.

▶**Gaylussacia** HBK. / Huckleberry

Gaylussacia baccata (Wangenh.) K. Koch.
Black huckleberry   FACU
Medium shrub. **Stems** upright, much-branched, 3–10 dm long; **branches**
brown, finely hairy when young, dark and smooth with age. **Leaves**
alternate, deciduous, leathery, oval, 2–5 cm long and 1–2.5 cm wide;
dark green above, paler below, both sides with shiny, orange-yellow
resinous dots; margins entire, often fringed with small hairs; petioles 2–4
mm long. **Flowers** yellow-orange or red-tinged, cylindric, 5-lobed, 4–6
mm long, in ± 1-sided racemes from lateral branches, the flowers on
short, gland-dotted stalks 4–5 mm long. **Fruit** a red-purple to black,
berrylike drupe, 6–8 mm long, with 10 nutlets; edible but seedy.
May–June. ❦ Open bogs, usually with **tamarack** and **leatherleaf**
(*Chamaedaphne calyculata*); more common in dry, acid, sandy or rocky
habitats. ⊕ se Minn, Wisc (mostly s and c), Mich. Nfld and Que to Man,
s to Ga and La.

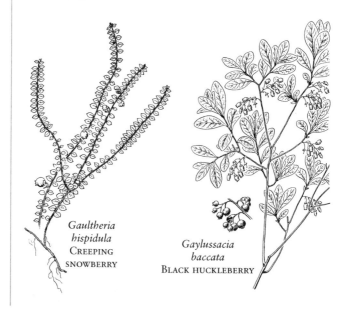

*Gaultheria
hispidula*
Creeping
snowberry

*Gaylussacia
baccata*
Black huckleberry

▶**Kalmia** L. / Laurel

Evergreen shrubs. **Leaves** opposite entire and leathery (ours). **Flowers** showy, 5-parted, in lateral or terminal clusters. **Fruit** a rounded capsule.

▶**KEY TO KALMIA**

1 Stems round; leaves oval, stalked; flowers in spreading or drooping clusters from leaf axils; e UP and n LP of Mich only. *K. angustifolia* . . . . Sheep-laurel

1 Stems flattened; leaves narrower, stalkless; flowers in upright terminal clusters; widespread in n portions of region. . . . . *K. polifolia* . . . . Bog-laurel

Kalmia angustifolia L.
Sheep-laurel   FAC

Medium shrub, 6–10 dm tall. Older **stems** smooth and gray; **twigs** round in section, brown and finely hairy when young. **Leaves** opposite or in whorls of 3, evergreen and leathery, oval to oval, 2–5 cm long and 5–20 mm wide, tip blunt or rounded; dark green above, paler and smooth or with scattered stalked glands below; margins entire and somewhat rolled under; petioles 3–10 mm long. **Flowers** showy, deep pink, several to many in lateral clusters from axils of previous year's leaves, saucer-shaped, 5-parted, 9–12 mm wide, on stalks to 2 cm long. **Fruit** a round capsule to 5 mm wide, the style persistent. Clusters of capsules may persist for several years. June–July. ❦ Open bogs and wet conifer forests; sometimes in dry jack pine forests. ⊕ e UP and n LP of Mich. Newf and Labr, s to Va, w to s Ont and Mich.

Kalmia polifolia Wangenh.
Bog-laurel   OBL

Low shrub, to 6 dm tall. Older **stems** dark; **twigs** swollen at nodes, flattened and 2-edged in section, smooth, pale brown when young. **Leaves** opposite, evergreen and leathery, linear to narrowly oval, 1–4 cm long and 6–12 mm wide, tip blunt or narrowed to an abrupt point; dark green and smooth above, white below with a covering of short, white hairs, midrib on underside with large purple, stalked glands; margins entire and rolled under; petioles absent. **Flowers** showy, pale to rose-pink, in terminal clusters at ends of current year's branches, saucer-shaped, 5-parted, 8–11 mm wide, on stalks to 3 cm long. **Fruit** a round capsule to 6 mm wide, tipped by the persistent style, the capsules in upright clusters. May–June. ❦ Sphagnum peatlands, black spruce and tamarack swamps. ⊕ nc and ne Minn, n and c Wisc, UP and n and c LP of Mich. Labr to Alaska, s to NJ, Great Lakes and Calif.

▶**Ledum** L. / Labrador-tea

Ledum groenlandicum Oeder
Labrador-tea   OBL

Medium shrub, to 1 m tall. Older **stems** gray or red-brown; **twigs** covered with woolly, curly brown hairs. **Leaves** alternate, evergreen and leathery, fragrant when rubbed, narrowly oval to oblong, 2.5–5 cm long and 5–20 mm wide, rounded at tip; dark green and smooth above, the midvein sunken; underside covered with tan to rust-colored curly hairs; margins entire and rolled under; petioles short. **Flowers** creamy-white, in rounded clusters at ends of branches, 5-parted, to 1 cm wide, on finely hairy stalks 1–2 cm long. **Fruit** a lance-shaped capsule 5–6 mm long, the style persistent and hairlike; capsules splitting at base to release numerous small seeds, the empty capsules persistent on stems for several years. May–June. ⚘ Sphagnum bogs, swamps and wet conifer forests. ⊕ n and ec Minn, n and c Wisc, UP and n LP of Mich. Greenland to Alaska, s to Mass, NJ, Pa, and Great Lakes.

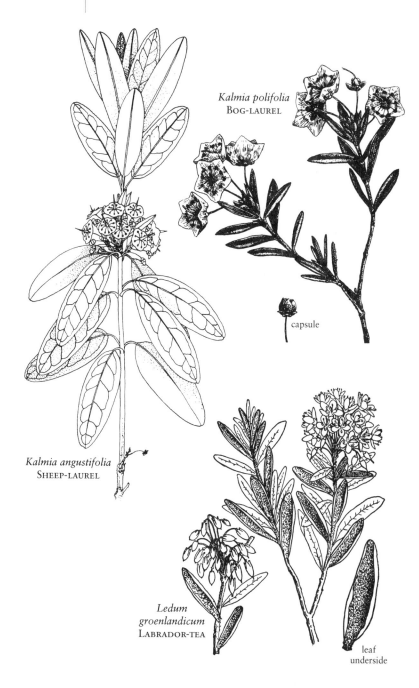

Kalmia polifolia
Bog-laurel

capsule

Kalmia angustifolia
Sheep-laurel

Ledum groenlandicum
Labrador-tea

leaf underside

▶**Vaccinium** L. / Blueberry; Cranberry

Deciduous or evergreen shrubs. **Leaves** alternate, simple. **Flowers** 4- or 5-parted, single in leaf axils or in clusters in axils or at ends of branches; ovary inferior. **Fruit** a many-seeded, red, blue, or black berry. ☞ The genus may be divided into subgroups, 2 of which occur in wetlands of the Great Lakes region (see key below):
- BLUEBERRIES (*V. angustifolium, V. corymbosum, V. myrtilloides*)
- CRANBERRIES (*V. macrocarpon, V. oxycoccos, V. vitis-idaea*).

▶**KEY TO VACCINIUM**

1 Plants low and trailing; leaves evergreen, less than 5 mm wide; mature fruit a red berry (CRANBERRIES) **2**
1 Plants upright and bushy; leaves deciduous, more than 5 mm wide; mature fruit a blue to black berry (BLUEBERRIES) **4**

2 Leaf underside with black, bristly glands; ne Minn, nw Wisc and Isle Royale, Mich . . . . *V. vitis-idaea* / MOUNTAIN CRANBERRY
2 Leaf underside without black glands; widespread, especially in n portions of region. **3**

3 Leaves blunt or rounded at tip (and sometimes notched), pale below; bracts on flower stalk green and leaflike (more than 1 mm wide) . . . . *V. macrocarpon* / CRANBERRY
3 Leaves tapered to pointed tip, white below; bracts on flower stalk red and narrow (less than 1 mm wide) *V. oxycoccos* / SMALL CRANBERRY

4 Tall shrubs (usually 1–2 m tall) . . . . *V. corymbosum* . . . . HIGHBUSH BLUEBERRY
4 Low shrubs (usually less than 0.5 m tall) **5**

5 Leaf underside hairy; margins with small, bristle-tipped teeth . . . . *V. angustifolium* / LOWBUSH BLUEBERRY
5 Leaf underside without hairs or only sparsely hairy; margins entire, usually fringed with fine hairs . . . . *V. myrtilloides* . . . . VELVETLEAF-BLUEBERRY

Vaccinium angustifolium Aiton
Lowbush blueberry   FACU

Low shrub 1–6 dm tall, forming colonies from surface runners. Older **stems** red-brown to black; **twigs** green-brown, with hairs in lines down stems, or sometimes smooth. **Leaves** deciduous, bright green oval, 2–5 cm long and 5–15 mm wide, smooth on both sides or sparsely hairy on veins; margins finely toothed with bristle-tipped teeth; petioles very short. **Flowers** in clusters, opening before or with leaves, white or pale pink, narrowly bell-shaped, 5-parted, 4–6 mm long. **Fruit** blue and wax-covered, 5–12 mm wide, edible and sweet. Flowering April–June, fruit ripening July–Aug. ❦ Sphagnum peatlands and wetland margins; also in dry, sandy openings and forests. ⊕ n and ec Minn, n, c and se Wisc, Mich, ne Ill and nw Ind. Labr and Nfld to Man, s to NJ, NC, Pa, Ill and Minn.

Vaccinium corymbosum L.
Highbush blueberry   FACW

⚠
STATUS
Illinois - E

Shrub, 1–3 m tall. Older **stems** red-brown to black; **twigs** green-brown, with small hairs in lines down stems. **Leaves** deciduous, dark green, oval to ovate, 3–8 cm long and 1.5–3 cm wide, tapered to an often bristle-pointed tip; smooth above or sometimes finely hairy along veins, green or paler below, hairy at least on veins; margins entire with a fringe of hairs, or with small, gland-tipped teeth; petioles very short. **Flowers** in clusters at ends of branches, opening with leaves, white or pink, urn-shaped or cylindric, 5-parted, 6–10 mm long (our largest flowered blueberry). **Fruit** blue or blue-black, wax-covered, 7–12 mm wide, edible, sweet and juicy. Flowering May–June, fruit ripening July–Aug. ⚘ Moist, low forests and swamps, shrubby peatlands and wetland margins. ⊕ c and s LP of Mich, ne Ill and nw Ind. NS and Maine to Mich, n Ill, Ark and e Okla, s to Fla and e Tex.

Vaccinium macrocarpon Aiton
Cranberry OBL

Evergreen trailing shrub. **Stems** slender, to 1 m or more long, with **branches** to 2 dm tall. **Leaves** leathery, oblong-oval, 5–15 mm long and 2–5 mm wide, rounded or blunt at tip, pale on underside; margins flat or slightly rolled under; petioles absent or very short. **Flowers** white to pink, 1 cm wide, 4-lobed, the lobes turned back at tips, single or in clusters of 2–6, on stalks 1–3 cm long, the stalks with 2 bracts above middle of stalk, the bracts green, 2–4 mm long and 1–2 mm wide. **Fruit** red, 1–1.5 cm wide, edible but tart, often persisting over-winter. Flowering June–July, fruit ripening Aug–Sept. *Oxycoccus macrocarpon*. ⚘ Sphagnum bogs, swamps and peaty pond margins. ⊕ ne and c Minn, mostly n Wisc (also c to se; cultivated in n and c), Mich, ne Ill and nw Ind. Nfld to Man, s to Va, NC, Ohio, Tenn, n Ill and Minn.

⚠ STATUS
Illinois - E

☞ Vaccinium macrocarpon is the cultivated cranberry.

Vaccinium myrtilloides Michx.
Velvetleaf-blueberry FACW-

⚠ STATUS
Indiana - E

Low shrub, often forming colonies. **Stems** 3–6 dm long, red-brown to black with numerous wartlike lenticels; young **twigs** green-brown, densely velvety white-hairy. **Leaves** deciduous, thin and soft, oval, 2–5 cm long and 1–2.5 cm wide, dark green above, paler and soft hairy below, not waxy; margins entire and finely hairy; petioles very short. **Flowers** in clusters at ends of short, leafy branches, opening with leaves, creamy or green-white, tinged with pink, bell-shaped or short-cylindric, 5-parted, 4–5 mm long. **Fruit** blue, wax-covered, 6–9 mm wide; edible but tart. Flowering May–July, fruit ripening July–Sept. ⚘ Sphagnum bogs and swamps; also in dry to moist woods and clearings. ⊕ ne, nc, ec and se Minn, n and c Wisc (and uncommon in se), Mich, rare in ne Ill and Ind. Labr to BC, s to Va, WVa, Pa, n Ill and ne Iowa.

Vaccinium oxycoccos L.
Small cranberry OBL

⚠ STATUS
Illinois - E
Indiana - T

Evergreen trailing shrub. **Stems** slender, 0.5 m or more long, with upright **branches** 1–2 dm tall. **Leaves** leathery, ovate to oval or narrowly triangular, 2–10 mm long and 1–3 mm wide, pointed or rounded at tip, strongly whitened on underside; margins flat or strongly rolled under; petioles absent or very short. **Flowers** pale pink, 1 cm wide, 4-lobed, the lobes turned back at tips, single or in clusters of 2–4, on stalks 1–3 cm long, the stalks with 2 bracts at or below middle of stalk, the bracts red, scalelike, to 2 mm long and less than 1 mm wide. **Fruit** pale and red-speckled when young, becoming red, 6–12 mm wide, edible but tart. Flowering June–July, fruit ripening Aug–Sept. *Oxycoccus oxycoccos*. ⚘ Wet, acid, sphagnum bogs. ⊕ Common in n portion of region, local southward. n and ec Minn, n and ec Wisc (and local in se), Mich, ne Ill and nw Ind. Circumboreal, s to NJ, Pa, Ohio, n Ind, n Ill and Minn.

Vaccinium vitis-idaea L.
Mountain cranberry
FAC

☞ **Mountain cranberry** can be distinguished from the more common cranberries (*V. macrocarpon* and *V. oxycoccos*) by the black, bristly, glandular dots on the leaf underside.

Low evergreen, trailing shrub. Older **stems** brown-black with peeling bark, branching, the **branches** upright, slender, 1–2 dm long, often forming mats; **twigs** green-brown to red, ± smooth. **Leaves** alternate, leathery, oval to oval, 0.5–2 cm long and 4–15 mm wide, rounded or slightly indented at tip; upper surface dark green, shiny and smooth, paler and with dark bristly glands below; margins entire and rolled under; petioles hairy, 1–2 mm long. **Flowers** white to pink, bell-shaped and 4-lobed, style longer than petals, several in 1-sided clusters at ends of branches, the flowers on short glandular stalks, the stalks with 2 small bracts at base. **Fruit** a dark red berry, to 1 cm wide, persisting over winter, tart but edible, especially the following spring. June–July. ❦ Sphagnum bogs; also in drier, sandy or rocky places. ⊕ ne Minn, nw Wisc and on Isle Royale, Mich. Circumboreal, Greenland to Alaska, s to New Eng, Great Lakes and BC. ☞ Gathered in Europe (where known as **lingen** or **red whortleberry**) and N Amer (where available) and cooked and eaten like commercial cranberries.

Cranberry (Vaccinium macrocarpon**).** Cranberry, shown here in flower, is a common species in sphagnum moss peatlands in northern portions of the Great Lakes region. The species extends southward into northeastern Illinois where it is listed as endangered due to its rarity and the scarcity of suitable habitat. The trailing plants produce tart, purple-red berries sometimes gathered in the wild, or grown commercially across large acreages as in central Wisconsin.

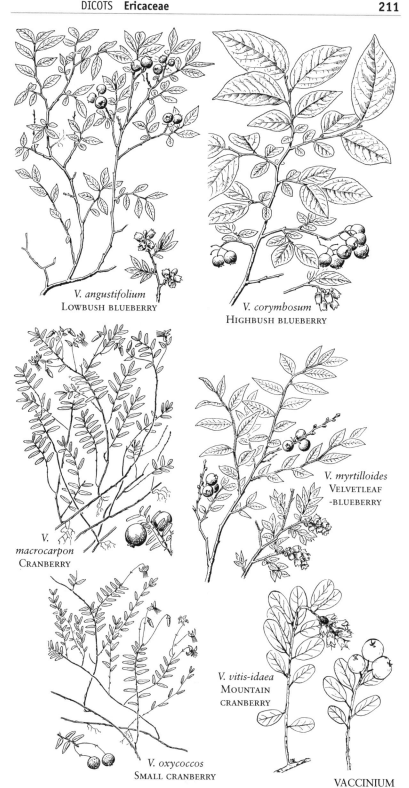

V. angustifolium
LOWBUSH BLUEBERRY

V. corymbosum
HIGHBUSH BLUEBERRY

V. macrocarpon
CRANBERRY

V. myrtilloides
VELVETLEAF
-BLUEBERRY

V. oxycoccos
SMALL CRANBERRY

V. vitis-idaea
MOUNTAIN
CRANBERRY

VACCINIUM

Fabaceae
Pea or Bean Family

Perennial shrubs (*Amorpha*) and herbs. **Leaves** alternate, pinnately divided, the terminal leaflet sometimes modified as a tendril (*Lathyrus*). **Flowers** in simple or branched racemes, perfect (with both male and female parts), irregular, 5-lobed (only 1 lobe in *Amorpha*), the upper lobe (banner) larger than the other lobes, with 2 outer lateral petals (wings), and 2 inner petals which are partly joined (the keel), and enclosing the 10 stamens and style; pistil 1, ovary 1-chambered, maturing into a pod.

▶**KEY TO FABACEAE**

1 Shrub; flowers 1-lobed, only the banner present . *Amorpha fruticosa*
. . . . FALSE INDIGO
1 Herbs; flowers 5-lobed **2**

2 Leaves with tendrils . . . . *Lathyrus palustris* / MARSH-PEA
2 Leaves without tendrils **3**

3 Plants vinelike and sprawling . . . . *Apios americana*
. . . . COMMON GROUND-NUT; WILD-BEAN; INDIAN-POTATO
3 Plants upright, not vinelike . *Astragalus agrestis* / FIELD MILKVETCH

▶**Amorpha** L. / False indigo; Lead-plant

Amorpha fruticosa L.
   False indigo   FACW+
Much-branched shrub, mostly 1–3 m tall; **twigs** tan to gray. **Leaves** pinnately divided, 5–15 cm long; **leaflets** 9–27, oval to obovate, 1–4 cm long and 0.5–3 cm wide, upper surface smooth, underside short-hairy, margins entire, petioles 2–5 cm long, stipules absent. **Flowers** dark purple, in dense spikelike racemes 2–15 cm long at ends of stems; petals 1-lobed, only the banner present, 3–5 mm long, folded to enclose the 10 stamens. **Fruit** an oblong pod, curved near tip, 5–7 mm long, spotted with glands, with 1–2 seeds. June–July. ✿ Wet meadows, streambanks, shores, ditches. ⊕ nw, c and s Minn; wc and sw Wisc along St. Croix, Wisc and Miss Rivers; local in s LP of Mich; ne Ill and nw Ind. Pa to Sask, s to Ala and n Mex.

▶**Apios** Fabr. / Ground-nut

Apios americana Medic.
   Common ground-nut; Wild-bean; Indian-potato   FACW
Perennial herbaceous vine, rhizomes with a necklace-like series of 2 or more tubers; plants with milky juice. **Stems** to 1 m long, climbing over other plants. **Leaves** pinnately divided; main leaves with 5–7 leaflets; **leaflets** ovate, 4–6 cm long, tapered to a point, smooth to short-hairy

beneath, margins entire. **Flowers** brown-purple, 10–13 mm long, single or paired, in crowded racemes from leaf axils. **Fruit** a linear pod, 5–10 cm long. July–Aug. ❧ Floodplain forests, thickets, shores, wet meadows, low prairie. ⊕ c and s Minn, c and s Wisc, Mich LP (and uncommon in c and e UP), ne Ill and nw Ind. Que to Minn and SD, s to Fla and Tex.

▶**Astragalus** L. / Milkvetch

Astragalus agrestis Douglas
Field milkvetch   FACW-

Perennial herb, from slender rhizomes. **Stems** slender, 1–3 dm tall, smooth or sparsely hairy. **Leaves** pinnately divided; **leaflets** 13–21, oblong to lance-shaped, sparsely hairy on both sides, margins entire. **Flowers** purple, upright, 15–20 mm long, in crowded, long-stalked racemes, 2–4 cm long; sepals covered with mix of black and white hairs. **Fruit** an erect, ovate pod, 7–9 mm long, covered with stiff hairs. May. *A. goniatus.* ❧ Wet meadows and low prairie. ⊕ w and sc Minn. Minn and Iowa to Yukon, s to Kans, NM and Calif; Eurasia. ☞ **Alpine milk-vetch** (*Astragalus alpinus* L.) is rare on moist, sandy or gravelly shores in n Minn and nw Wisc, disjunct from its main range further north (⚠ state endangered, Minn and Wisc; FAC). The violet flowers open in spring and continue to flower through the summer.

Astragalus alpinus ALPINE MILKVETCH

▶**Lathyrus** L. / Vetchling; Wild pea

Lathyrus palustris L.
Marsh-pea   FACW

Perennial vining herb, spreading by rhizomes. **Stems** to 1 m long, strongly winged, climbing and clinging to surrounding plants by tendrils. **Leaves** pinnately divided, with 4–8 leaflets and a terminal leaflet modified into a tendril; **leaflets** linear to lance-shaped, 2–7 cm long and 3–20 mm wide; stipules prominent, ± arrowhead-shaped, 1–3 cm long; margins entire; petioles absent. **Flowers** in racemes from leaf axils, 2–6 flowers per raceme, red-purple, drying blue to blue-violet; sepals irregular, 7–10 mm long, the lowest lobe longest; petals 12–20 mm long. **Fruit** a flat, many-seeded pod, 3–5 cm long. June–Aug. ❧ Conifer swamps, thickets, wet meadows, marshes, streambanks, calcareous fens, low prairie. ⊕ Minn (all but far ne), se Wisc (local elsewhere), Mich (but local in w UP), ne Ill and nw Ind. Circumboreal, s to NJ, Ohio, Ind, Mo, Neb, Colo and Calif.

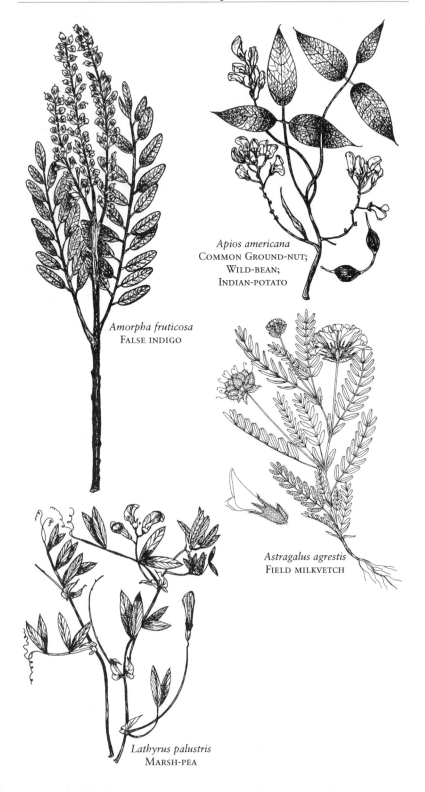

Apios americana
COMMON GROUND-NUT;
WILD-BEAN;
INDIAN-POTATO

Amorpha fruticosa
FALSE INDIGO

Astragalus agrestis
FIELD MILKVETCH

Lathyrus palustris
MARSH-PEA

Fagaceae
Beech Family

▶**Quercus** L. / Oak

Deciduous trees (our species). **Leaves** alternate, simple, lobed, pinnately veined. Male and female **flowers** separate but on same tree. **Fruit** a nut (acorn) partially enclosed by a cuplike structure (cupule).

▶**KEY TO QUERCUS**

1 Leaf margins with coarse, rounded teeth. . . . . *Q. bicolor*
. . . . SWAMP WHITE OAK
1 Leaf margins tipped with sharp bristles . . . . *Q. palustris* / PIN-OAK

Quercus bicolor Willd.

Swamp white oak   FACW+

Medium tree to 20 m tall; trunk to 1 m wide; crown broad and rounded; **bark** gray-brown, deeply furrowed, becoming flaky; **twigs** gray to yellow-brown; **buds** clustered at branch tips, yellow-brown, smooth or sparsely hairy. **Leaves** alternate, broadest above middle, to 15 cm long and 10 cm wide, smooth or hairy on upper surface, white and soft hairy on underside; margins with coarse, rounded teeth or shallow lobes; petioles 2–3 cm long. Male and female **flowers** separate but on same tree, appearing with leaves in spring; male flowers in slender, drooping catkins, female flowers in groups of 2–4. **Fruit** a pair of acorns, on stalks 2–3 cm long, the acorns ovate, pale brown, 2.5–4 cm long, the cup rough and hairy, covering about 1/3 of acorn. May. ❦ Floodplain forests, low woods and swamps. ⊕ se and sc Minn, c and s Wisc, s LP of Mich, ne Ill and nw Ind. Que and Maine to c Minn, s to NC, Tenn and n Ark.

Quercus palustris Muenchh.

Pin-oak   FACW

Medium tree to 25 m tall; trunk less than 1 m wide; crown narrowly rounded; lower branches drooping; **bark** light or dark brown, only shallowly furrowed; **twigs** red-brown to dark gray; **buds** clustered at branch tips, red-brown to dark gray, smooth. **Leaves** alternate, to 15 cm long and 10 cm wide, divided more than halfway to middle into 5–7 bristle-tipped lobes, upper surface dark green and shiny, lower surface paler and with hairs on veins; petioles 3–4 cm long. Male and female **flowers** separate but on same tree, appearing with leaves in spring; male flowers in slender, drooping catkins, female flowers in groups of 1–3. **Fruit** an acorn, in groups of 1–4, with or without stalks, the acorns hemisphere-shaped, pale brown, 10–14 mm long, the cup thin, finely hairy, covering less than 1/4 of acorn. May. ❦ Floodplain forests, low wet woods, swamps; tolerant of periodic flooding. ⊕ s LP of Mich, ne Ill and nw Ind. Vt to s Mich, n Ill, Iowa and Kans, s to NC, Tenn and Okla.

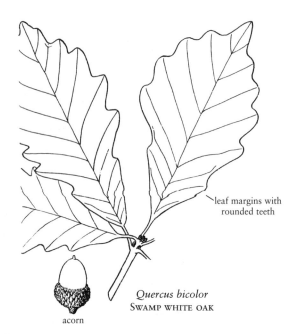

leaf margins with
rounded teeth

Quercus bicolor
SWAMP WHITE OAK

acorn

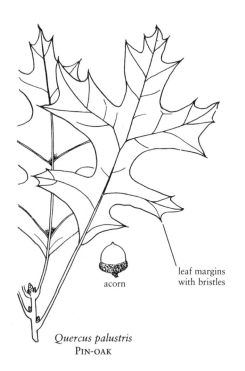

leaf margins
with bristles

acorn

Quercus palustris
PIN-OAK

Gentianaceae
Gentian Family

Annual, biennial or perennial herbs; plants usually smooth. **Leaves** simple, entire, opposite or whorled, stem leaves without petioles. **Flowers** often showy, perfect (with both male and female parts), regular, single at end of stems or in clusters; petals 4-5, blue, purple, white or green, joined for at least part of their length; stamens 4 or 5. **Fruit** a 2-chambered, many-seeded capsule enclosed by the withered, persistent petals.

▶**KEY TO GENTIANACEAE**

1 Leaves reduced to small, narrow scales less than 3 mm long . . . . *Bartonia* / SCREW-STEM
1 Leaves well-developed, not scalelike **2**

2 Flowers pink . . . . *Sabatia angularis* / COMMON MARSH-PINK
2 Flowers blue, purple-green, or white **3**

3 Petals 4, spurred at base; flowers green, tinged with purple . . . . *Halenia deflexa* / SPURRED GENTIAN
3 Petals 4, with fringed lobes; or petals 5 and not spurred; blue, purple or white **4**

4 Petals 4, fringed; flowers on stalks longer than the flowers; seeds covered with small bumps . . . . *Gentianopsis* / FRINGED GENTIAN
4 Petals 5, not fringed; flower stalks short or absent; seeds smooth . **5**

5 Flowers 2.5–4 cm long, on short stalks; seeds flattened and winged. . . . . *Gentiana* / GENTIAN
5 Flowers 1–2 cm long, stalkless; seeds round . *Gentianella* / GENTIAN

▶**Bartonia** Muhl. / Screw-stem

Slender annual or biennial herbs. **Stems** pale green to yellow or purple. **Leaves** reduced to small opposite or alternate scales. **Flowers** small, 4-parted, green-white to green-yellow, bell-shaped, in slender panicles or racemes at ends of stems.

▶**KEY TO BARTONIA**

1 Leaf-scales mostly alternate, or the lower opposite . . *B. paniculata* / . . . . SCREW-STEM
1 Leaf-scales mostly opposite . . . . *B. virginica* / YELLOW SCREW-STEM

Bartonia paniculata (Michx.) Muhl.
⚠ Screw-stem   OBL
STATUS Annual or biennial herb. **Stems** slender, 2–4 dm long, upright or lax.
Illinois - E **Leaves** small and scalelike, 1–2 mm long, mostly alternate, or the lower
Michigan - T

leaves opposite. **Flowers** yellow-white or greenish, 2–4 mm long, in panicles 5–20 cm long; the flowers on slender, arched and spreading stalks; sepals awl-shaped, 2 mm long; petals lance-shaped; anthers yellow. **Fruit** a capsule. Aug–Sept. *B. lanceolata.* ❦ Tamarack swamps, fens, sphagnum bogs, open wetlands. ✺ Rare in e UP and sw LP of Mich. Atlantic coast from Nfld to Fla and Miss, n inland to Ky, Mo, and Okla; disjunct in Mich and s Ont.

Bartonia virginica (L.) BSP.

Yellow screw-stem   FACW+

⚠
STATUS
Minnesota - E

Annual or biennial herb. **Stems** slender, erect, yellow-green, 1–4 dm long. **Leaves** mostly opposite, small and scalelike, 1–2 mm long. **Flowers** green-yellow or green-white, 3–4 mm long, in a slender raceme or panicle, the branches and flower stalks opposite and upright; sepals awl-shaped; petals oblong, tapered to a rounded tip. **Fruit** a capsule 2–3 mm long. Aug–Sept. ❦ Swamps (often in sphagnum moss), open bogs, wet woods and depressions, sandy shores and ditches. ✺ Rare in se Minn; Wisc, e UP and LP of Mich, ne Ill and nw Ind. NS and Que to Minn, s to Fla and La.

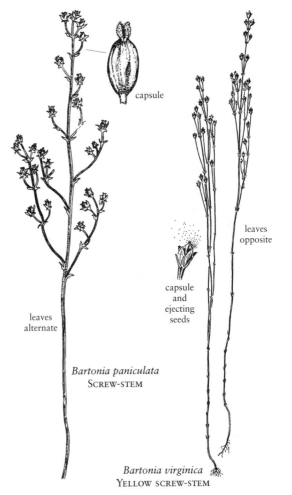

capsule

leaves
opposite

capsule
and
ejecting
seeds

leaves
alternate

Bartonia paniculata
SCREW-STEM

Bartonia virginica
YELLOW SCREW-STEM

▶**Gentiana** L. / Gentian

Perennial herbs, with thick, fibrous roots. **Leaves** opposite or whorled, simple, margins entire, petioles absent. **Flowers** large, blue, green-white or yellow, 5-parted, in clusters near ends of stems; petals forming a tube-like, shallowly lobed flower, the lobes alternating with a folded membrane as long or longer than petal lobes; stamens 5. **Fruit** a 2-chambered capsule.

▶**KEY TO GENTIANA**

1 Leaves and petal lobes fringed with tiny hairs (under 10x magnification); widespread . . . . *G. andrewsii* / BOTTLE GENTIAN
1 Leaves and petal lobes smooth; plants of n portions of region **2**

2 Leaves dark green, linear, less than 1 cm wide; Mich UP only . . . . .
. . . . *G. linearis* / NARROW-LEAVED GENTIAN
2 Leaves light green, lance-shaped to ovate, larger leaves more than 1 cm wide; n portions of region . . . . *G. rubricaulis*
. . . . GREAT LAKES GENTIAN

Gentiana andrewsii Griseb.
Bottle gentian   FACW
Perennial herb. **Stems** erect, single or few together, 2–8 dm long, unbranched, smooth. **Leaves** opposite, lance-shaped, 4–12 cm long and 1–3 cm wide, margins fringed with hairs. **Flowers** 1 to many, stalkless in upper leaf axils, 3–5 cm long; sepals forming a tube around petals, the sepal lobes unequal, fringed with hairs; petals forming a tubelike flower, usually remaining closed, the folds between petal lobes finely fringed (use hand lens to see this) and longer than the petal lobes. **Fruit** a capsule; seeds winged. Aug–Sept. ❀ Wet meadows, swamps and wet woods, thickets, low prairie, shores, ditches. ⊕ Minn, Wisc, Mich, ne Ill and nw Ind. Que to Man, s to NJ, NC, Ohio, Mo and Neb.

Gentiana linearis Froelich
Narrow-leaved gentian   FACW
⚠
STATUS
Michigan - T
Perennial herb. **Stems** smooth, 2–8 dm long. **Leaves** dark green, linear to narrowly lance-shaped, 4–9 cm long and less than 1 cm wide, margins entire. **Flowers** opening slightly, several in a cluster at end of stem and upper leaf axils; sepal lobes green, linear, 4–10 mm long; petals blue (sometimes white), 3–5 cm long, the lobes ovate, rounded, not fringed. **Fruit** a capsule; seeds winged. Aug–Sept. ❀ Wet meadows, shores, streambanks, thickets. ⊕ Uncommon in w and c UP of Mich. Que, Labr, NB and Mich, s to NJ, Pa, s Ont, locally s to Tenn.

Gentiana rubricaulis Schwein.
Great Lakes gentian   OBL
Perennial herb. **Stems** smooth, 3–7 dm long. **Leaves** pale green, lance-shaped, 4–8 cm long and 2–3 cm wide, margins entire. **Flowers** 3–5 cm long, green-blue below, blue above, narrowly open, in a cluster at end of stem; sepal lobes oblong, 4–12 mm long, chaffy and translucent near base. **Fruit** a capsule; seeds winged. *G. linearis* var. *latifolia*. ❀ Wet meadows, peatlands, streambanks, thickets, conifer swamps, Lake Superior rocky shores; soils usually calcium-rich. ⊕ nc, ne and ec Minn, n Wisc, UP and n LP of Mich. s and w Ont to s Sask, s to n Mich, Wisc and Minn; disjunct in NB and Maine.

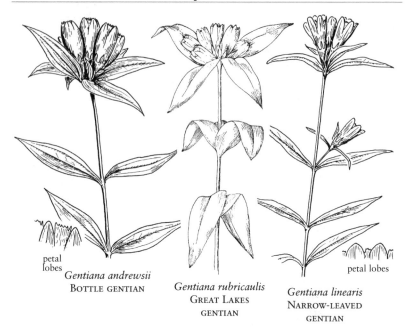

petal lobes
Gentiana andrewsii
BOTTLE GENTIAN

Gentiana rubricaulis
GREAT LAKES
GENTIAN

Gentiana linearis
NARROW-LEAVED
GENTIAN

petal lobes

▶**Gentianella** Moench / Gentian

Annual or biennial herbs. **Leaves** opposite, stalkless, margins entire. **Flowers** 4–5-parted, blue to white, funnel-shaped or tubular; in clusters from ends of stems or upper leaf axils; petals withering and persistent around capsule.

▶KEY TO GENTIANELLA

1 Petal lobes with fringe of hairs at base; nw Minn only . *G. amarella*
. . . . NORTHERN GENTIAN; FELWORT
1 Petal lobes not fringed with hairs at base; s portions of region . . . .
. . . . *G. quinquefolia* / STIFF GENTIAN

Gentianella amarella (L.) Boerner
Northern gentian; Felwort   OBL

Annual or biennial herb. **Stems** unbranched, 1–6 dm long. **Leaves** lance-shaped, 2–6 cm long; margins entire. **Flowers** blue, 10–15 mm long, 5-parted (rarely 4-parted); single from middle leaf axils, several in a cluster from upper axils, on stalks less than 1 cm long; sepal lobes linear, 3–5 mm long; petals forming a tubelike to flared, funnel-like flower, petal lobes 3–5 mm long, the base of lobe fringed with hairs 2 mm long. **Fruit** a capsule. July–Aug. *Gentianella acuta, Gentiana amarella*. ẅ Low prairie, wet or moist sandy or gravelly soil. ⊕ Local in nw Minn. ± circumboreal, s to New Eng, Minn and w SD; Mex.

Gentianella quinquefolia (L.) Small
Stiff gentian   FAC

⚠
STATUS
Michigan - T

Annual or biennial herb. **Stems** 4-angled, 2–8 dm long, usually branched. **Leaves** at base spatula-shaped, upper leaves lance-ovate, 2–7 cm long; margins entire. **Flowers** blue (rarely white), 15–25 mm long, in clusters of 1–7 flowers at ends of stems or upper leaf axils, on stalks to 1 cm long;

sepal lobes lance-shaped; petals forming a narrowly funnel-shaped flower, petal lobes 4–6 mm long, not fringed with hairs at base. **Fruit** a capsule; seeds round. Aug–Sept. *Gentianella occidentalis, Amarella occidentalis.* 🌿 Wet meadows, streambanks, moist woods; often where calcium-rich. ⊕ se Minn, s Wisc, s LP of Mich, ne Ill and nw Ind. Ohio and s Ont to Minn, s to Ky, Ark and e Kans.

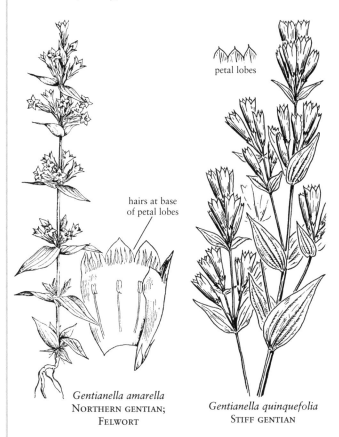

petal lobes

hairs at base
of petal lobes

Gentianella amarella
NORTHERN GENTIAN;
FELWORT

Gentianella quinquefolia
STIFF GENTIAN

▶**Gentianopsis** Ma / Fringed gentian

Smooth, taprooted, annual or biennial herbs. **Leaves** opposite, stalkless, margins entire. **Flowers** 1 to several, showy, blue, sometimes tinged with white on outside, long-stalked, at ends of stems and branches, 4-parted; sepals oblong cone-shaped; petals deeply lobed, forming a tubular or bell-shaped flower, the lobes ragged or fringed at tips and sometimes on sides, without a folded membrane between the lobes (present in *Gentiana*); stamens 4. **Fruit** a capsule; seeds covered with bumps.

▶KEY TO GENTIANOPSIS

1 Upper leaves lance-shaped to ovate; petal lobes long-fringed across tip and sides, the fringes 2–5 mm long . . *G. crinita* / FRINGED GENTIAN
1 Upper leaves linear; tips of petal lobes ragged with short, fine teeth, often fringed on sides . . . . . *G. procera* / LESSER FRINGED GENTIAN

Gentianopsis crinita (Froelich) Ma
Fringed gentian   FACW+

Annual or biennial herb. **Stems** erect, 2–7 dm long, usually branched above. **Basal leaves** spatula-shaped, smaller than stem leaves; **stem leaves** ovate, 2–6 cm long and 1–2.5 cm wide, the base usually clasping stem; margins entire. **Flowers** bright blue, 3–6 cm long, 4-parted, single at ends of main stems and branches, on stalks 5–20 cm long; sepals forming a tube, 1–2 cm long; petals joined to form a funnel-like to bell-shaped flower, the petal lobes fringed across tip and part way down sides with linear fringes 2–6 mm long. **Fruit** a capsule, broadest at middle. Aug–Oct. *Gentiana crinita*. ❦ Wet meadows, streambanks, ditches, wet woods; soils usually calcium-rich and sandy or gravelly. ⊕ nw, c and se Minn, c and s Wisc, LP of Mich, ne Ill and nw Ind. Maine to Man, s to Md, NC, Ohio, Iowa and SD.

Gentianopsis procera (Holm) Ma
Lesser fringed gentian   OBL

Annual herb, similar to *Gentianopsis crinita* but smaller. **Stems** simple or few-branched, 1–5 dm long. **Basal leaves** spatula-shaped; **stem leaves** linear to linear lance-shaped, 2–5 cm long and 2–7 mm wide, tapered to a blunt tip, the base not clasping stem; margins entire. **Flowers** bright blue, 2–5 cm long, mostly 4-parted, single on stalks at ends of stems; sepal tube 6–15 mm long; petals forming a tubelike flower, flared toward tip, petal lobes ragged toothed across tips, often fringed on sides. **Fruit** a capsule. Sept–Oct. *Gentiana procera*. ❦ Sandy and gravelly shores, wet meadows, calcareous fens, wetlands between dunes near Great Lakes; soils usually calcium-rich. ⊕ w and se Minn, e UP and LP of Mich, ne Ill and nw Ind. NY and Ont to Alberta, s to Ohio, Ill, Iowa, ND and Mont.

Gentianopsis crinita   *Gentianopsis procera*
FRINGED GENTIAN   LESSER FRINGED GENTIAN

▶**Halenia** Borkh. / Spurred gentian

Halenia deflexa (J. E. Smith) Griseb.
Spurred gentian   FAC
Annual herb. **Stems** erect, simple or few-branched, rounded 4-angled,
15–40 cm long. **Leaves** opposite, lower leaves spatula-shaped, narrowed
to a petiole; stem leaves lance-shaped to ovate, 2–5 cm long and 1–2.5
cm wide, stalkless; margins entire. **Flowers** green, tinged with purple,
10–12 mm long, 4-parted, on stalks to 4 cm long, in loose clusters of 5–9
flowers at ends of stems; petals lance-shaped, usually with downward-
pointing spurs at base, the spurs to 5 mm long. **Fruit** an oblong capsule.
July–Aug. ❧ Cedar swamps, moist conifer woods (especially along
shores), old logging roads. ⊕ n Minn (especially ne), n Wisc, UP and n
LP of Mich. Labr to BC, s to Mass, NY, Minn and Mont.

▶**Sabatia** Adans. / Marsh-pink; Sea-pink

Sabatia angularis (L.) Pursh
Common marsh-pink   FAC+

⚠
STATUS
Michigan - T

Biennial herb. **Stems** stout, 2–8 dm tall, sharply 4-angled, branches opposite, or alternate near base. **Leaves** opposite, ovate, 1–4 cm long, 3–7-
nerved, clasping at base, margins entire. **Flowers** showy, rose-pink with
a greenish center, single at ends of numerous branches, on stalks 1–3 cm
long; sepal lobes linear, half as long as petals; petal lobes 1–2 cm long,
obovate; style 2-parted. **Fruit** an oblong capsule. Aug–Sept. ❧ Sandy
shores, wet areas between dunes. ⊕ s Mich, ne Ill and nw Ind. Conn to
s Mich, n Ind and Kans, s to Fla and Tex.

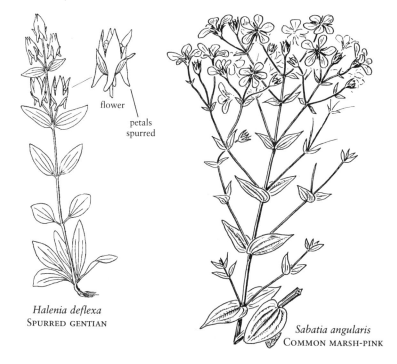

flower

petals
spurred

Halenia deflexa
SPURRED GENTIAN

Sabatia angularis
COMMON MARSH-PINK

Grossulariaceae
Gooseberry Family

▶**Ribes** L. / Gooseberry; Currant

☞ *Ribes* are of two types, **currants** and **gooseberries**. Currants lack spines and bristles (except in *Ribes lacustre*) and the stalk of the berry is jointed at its tip so that the berries detach from the stalk. Gooseberries have spines and bristles and the berry stalk is not jointed.

Small to medium shrubs with upright to spreading stems, the **stems** smooth or with spines at nodes and sometimes also with bristles between the nodes. **Leaves** alternate, palmately 3–5-lobed; margins toothed. **Flowers** 1–several in clusters or few to many in racemes; perfect, regular, ovary inferior; sepals 5; petals 5, green to white or yellow, shorter than the sepals; stamens 5, alternate with the petals; styles 2. **Fruit** a many-seeded berry, usually topped by persistent, dry flower parts.

▶**KEY TO RIBES**

1 Stems with spines or bristles, at least at nodes **2**
1 Stems without spines **5**

2 Spines and bristles persistent; berries with gland-tipped hairs or bristles
. . . . **3**
2 Spines and bristles deciduous during summer; berries without glands
or bristles **4**

3 Stems bristly between nodes; leaves with disagreeable scent when
rubbed; berries purple-black, with gland-tipped hairs . . . *R. lacustre*
. . . . PRICKLY CURRANT
3 Bristles between nodes usually absent; leaves not ill-scented; berries
wine-red and spiny . . . . *R. cynosbati* / PRICKLY GOOSEBERRY

4 Spines and bristles soft; leaves without glands on underside; bracts
below flowers with long hairs; widespread . . . . *R. hirtellum*
. . . . NORTHERN GOOSEBERRY
4 Spines and bristles firm; leaves with scattered glands on underside (at
least on veins); bracts below flowers with gland-tipped hairs; n Wisc
and w UP of Mich only . . . . *R. oxyacanthoides*
. . . . NORTHERN OR BRISTLY GOOSEBERRY

5 Stems upright; leaves dotted with resinous glands (at least on under-
side); berries black **6**
5 Stems spreading and reclining; leaves not resin-dotted; berries red   **7**

6 Leaves dotted on both sides with yellow to brown resinous glands;
flowers in drooping clusters . . . . *R. americanum*
. . . . EASTERN BLACK CURRANT
6 Leaves resin-dotted only on underside; flowers in upright clusters . .
. . . . *R. hudsonianum* / HUDSON BAY CURRANT

7 Plants with skunklike odor when rubbed; berries with gland-tipped
hairs . . . . *R. glandulosum* / SKUNK-CURRANT
7 Plants without skunklike odor; berries smooth . . . . *R. triste*
. . . . SWAMP RED CURRANT

Ribes americanum Miller
Eastern black currant   FACW

Shrub, 1–1.2 m tall. **Stems** without spines or bristles, young stems finely hairy; **branches** upright to spreading; **twigs** gray-brown and smooth, black with age. **Leaves** 3–8 cm long and 3–10 cm wide, 3-lobed and usually with 2 additional shallow lobes at base, dotted with shiny, yellow to brown resinous glands, especially on underside, smooth or short-hairy above, hairy below; margins coarsely toothed; petioles hairy and resin-dotted, 3–6 cm long. **Flowers** creamy-white to yellow, bell-shaped, 8–12 mm long; 6–15 in drooping racemes 3–8 cm long; each flower with a linear bract longer than the flower stalk, the stalks 2–3 mm long; sepals 4–5 mm long, rounded; petals blunt, 2–3 mm long; stamens about equaling petals. **Fruit** an edible, smooth, black berry, 6–10 mm wide. April–June. *R. floridanum.* ⚘ Moist to wet forests, swamps, marsh and lake borders, streambanks. ⊕ Minn, Wisc, Mich, ne Ill and nw Ind. NB to Alberta, s to Del, WVa, Ind, Neb and NM.

Ribes cynosbati L.
Prickly gooseberry   UPL

Shrub to 6–9 dm tall, branches upright to spreading. **Stems** and branches with 1–3 spines at nodes, outer bark peeling off, inner bark brown-purple to black; young stems brown-gray, finely hairy. **Leaves** 3–8 cm long and 3–7 cm wide, 3–5-lobed, the lobes rounded at tips; upper surface dark green, sparsely hairy, underside paler, finely hairy and with gland-tipped hairs along veins; margins with coarse, round teeth; petioles 2.5–4 cm long, finely hairy and with scattered gland-tipped hairs. **Flowers** green-yellow, bell-shaped, 6–9 mm long, in clusters of 2–3 from spurs on old wood, on stalks with gland-tipped hairs. **Fruit** a red-purple berry, 8–12 mm wide, covered with stiff, brown spines. May–June. ⚘ Occasional in wet woods, swamps, thickets and streambanks; more typical of moist hardwood forests (where our most common gooseberry). ⊕ Minn (but local in far n), Wisc, Mich, ne Ill and nw Ind. NB to Minn, s to Ala and Mo.

Ribes glandulosum Grauer
Skunk-currant   FACW

Shrub to 8 dm tall. **Stems** sprawling, spines and bristles absent; stems and leaves with skunklike odor when crushed; older stems smooth and dark as outer bark peels off; young stems smooth to finely hairy, brown-gray. **Leaves** 2–8 cm long and 4–8 cm wide, 3–5-lobed, smooth above, paler and finely glandular hairy below (at least along veins); margins toothed or double-toothed; petioles 3–6 cm long, finely hairy. **Flowers** yellow-green to purple, saucer-shaped, in loose upright clusters 3–6 cm long, on slender stalks; bracts very small, the stalks and bracts with gland-tipped hairs; sepals 2 mm long; petals 1–2 mm long. **Fruit** a dark red berry with bristles and gland-tipped hairs, 6 mm wide. June. *R. prostratum.* ⚘ Cedar and tamarack swamps, cool wet woods, thickets and streambanks. ⊕ n and ec Minn, n and c Wisc, UP and n LP of Mich. Nfld to BC, s to New Eng, NC and Great Lakes.

Ribes hirtellum Michx.
Northern gooseberry   FACW

STATUS
Illinois - E

Shrub to 9 dm tall. **Stems** upright, outer bark pale, soon peeling to expose dark inner layer; young stems gray and smooth, or with 1–3 slender spines at nodes and scattered bristles between nodes. **Leaves** 2.5–5 cm long and 2–5 cm wide, with 3 or 5 pointed lobes, upper surface dark

green, smooth to sparsely hairy, lower surface paler, hairy at least along
veins, without glands; margins coarsely toothed and fringed with hairs;
petioles 1–3 cm long, hairy, some of which are gland-tipped. **Flowers**
green-yellow to purple, bell-shaped, 6–9 mm long, in clusters of 2–3 on
short, smooth stalks; stamens as long or longer than sepals, the bracts
fringed with long hairs. **Fruit** an edible, smooth, dark blue–black berry,
8–12 mm wide. June. *R. huronense.* 🌿 Cedar and tamarack swamps,
thickets, shores, rocky openings. ⊕ n and c Minn; Wisc, Mich, ne Ill and
nw Ind. Nfld and Que to Alberta, s to NY, Pa, n Ill and Neb.

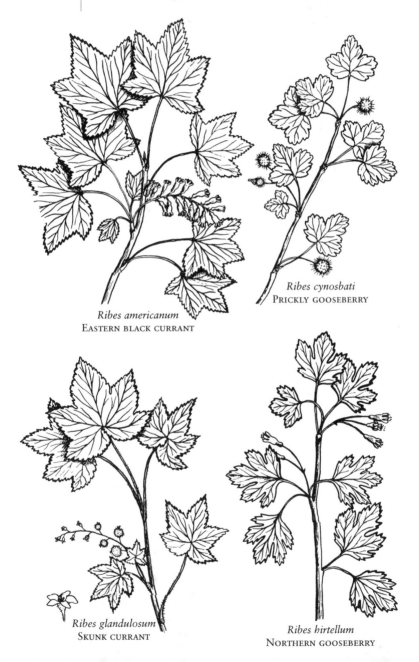

Ribes cynosbati
PRICKLY GOOSEBERRY

Ribes americanum
EASTERN BLACK CURRANT

Ribes glandulosum
SKUNK CURRANT

Ribes hirtellum
NORTHERN GOOSEBERRY

Ribes hudsonianum Richards.
Hudson Bay currant   OBL

Shrub, 6–9 dm tall. **Stems** upright, spines and bristles absent; bark gray, with scattered yellow resin dots, peeling to expose inner purple-black bark. **Leaves** 5–9 cm long and 6–13 cm wide, 3–5-lobed, with unpleasant odor when rubbed, upper surface dark green and mostly hairless, underside paler, smooth to hairy and with yellow resin dots; margins coarsely toothed, the teeth with a hard tip; petioles 2.5–8 cm long, with fine hairs and resin dots. **Flowers** white, bell-shaped, 4–5 mm long, in small clusters on threadlike stalks. **Fruit** a smooth, blue-black berry, 8–10 mm wide, barely edible. June. ❧ Cedar swamps, wet conifer woods and streambanks. ⊕ n Minn, local in far n Wisc, UP and n LP of Mich. n Ont to BC and Alaska, s to Mich and Minn; Wyo.

Ribes lacustre (Pers.) Poiret
Prickly currant   FACW

Shrub to 1 m tall. **Stems** upright or spreading, densely bristly, long-spiny at nodes; older bark gray, peeling to expose dark inner bark. **Leaves** 4–8 cm long and 4–7 cm wide, with 3–5 deeply parted, pointed lobes, upper surface dark green and mostly smooth, underside paler with scattered gland-tipped hairs; margins cleft into rounded teeth; petioles 2.5–4 cm long, with gland-tipped hairs. **Flowers** yellow-green to pinkish, saucer-shaped, 4–5 mm wide, on stalks with dark, gland-tipped hairs, in arching or drooping clusters. **Fruit** a purple-black berry covered with gland-tipped hairs, 9–12 mm wide. May–June. ❧ Moist conifer woods, swamps, thickets, and rock outcrops. ⊕ nc and ne Minn, nc and ne Wisc, UP and n LP of Mich. Labr to Alaska, s to Mass, Pa, Great Lakes; Rocky Mts.

Ribes oxyacanthoides L.
Northern or Bristly gooseberry   (FACW)

⚠
STATUS
Wisconsin - T

Shrub to 1 m tall. **Stems** upright with 1–3 spines to 1 cm long at nodes and smaller spines scattered between nodes; young stems gray-brown and finely hairy. **Leaves** 2.5–5 cm long and 2–5 cm wide, with 3–5 blunt or rounded lobes, upper surface sparsely hairy, some hairs tipped with glands, underside resin-dotted, hairy, some gland-tipped, especially along veins; margins coarsely toothed and hairy, some hairs gland-tipped; petioles 0.5–3 cm long, with short hairs and scattered glands. **Flowers** green-yellow, bell-shaped, 6–9 mm long, in clusters of 2–3 on short stalks; stamens shorter than petals. **Fruit** a smooth, edible, blue-black berry, 9–12 mm wide. June. *R. setosum.* ❧ Rocky and sandy shores, rocky openings, stabilized dunes, and moist, cold woods. ⊕ Uncommon in nw and ne Wisc, w UP of Mich. Hudson Bay to Alaska, s to n Wisc, Wyo and Nev.

Ribes triste Pallas
Swamp red currant   OBL

Low shrub, 0.4–1 m tall. **Stems** spreading or lying on ground and rooting at nodes, spines and bristles absent; older stems smooth, purple–black, young stems short-hairy. **Leaves** 4–10 cm long and 4–10 cm wide, with 3–5 broad lobes, dark green and mostly smooth above, paler and usually finely hairy below; margins with both rounded and sharp teeth, the teeth with a hard tip; petioles 2.5–6 cm long, with scattered gland-tipped hairs. **Flowers** green-purple, 4–5 mm wide, on stalks 1–4 mm long, in drooping clusters of 5–12. **Fruit** a smooth, red berry, 6–9 mm wide. May–June. ❧ Wet woods and swamps, alder thickets, seeps. ⊕ n and c Minn, all but sw Wisc, all but sw Mich; rare in ne Ill. Labr to Alaska, s to NJ, Mich, Minn, ND, and Ore; n Asia.

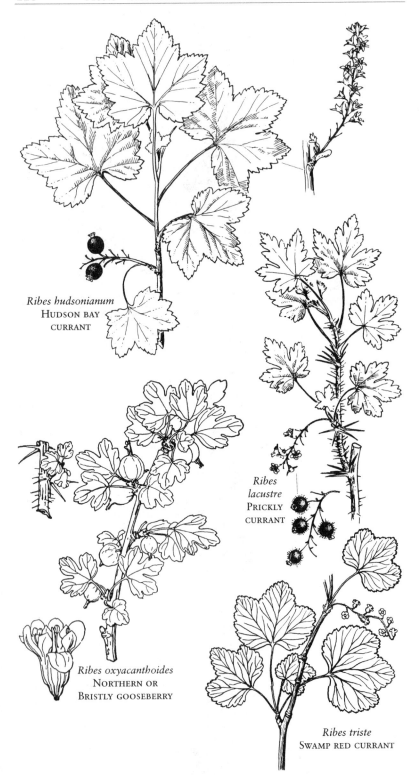

Ribes hudsonianum
HUDSON BAY
CURRANT

Ribes lacustre
PRICKLY
CURRANT

Ribes oxyacanthoides
NORTHERN OR
BRISTLY GOOSEBERRY

Ribes triste
SWAMP RED CURRANT

Haloragaceae
Water-Milfoil Family

Perennial aquatic herbs. **Leaves** alternate or whorled, finely dissected. **Flowers** small, stalkless in axils of leaves or bracts, 3- or 4-parted, regular, perfect (with both male and female parts) or imperfect, petals small or absent. **Fruit** small and nutlike, dividing into 3 or 4 segments.

▶**KEY TO HALORAGACEAE**

1 Flowers 4-parted; leaves mostly whorled, emersed leaves reduced to small bracts . . . . *Myriophyllum* / WATER-MILFOIL
1 Flowers 3-parted; leaves alternate, emersed leaves not bractlike. . . .
. . . . *Proserpinaca* / MERMAID-WEED

▶**Myriophyllum** L. / Water-milfoil

Perennial aquatic herbs. **Stems** submerged, sparsely branched, freely rooting at lower nodes. **Leaves** mostly whorled (alternate in *M. farwellii*), pinnately divided into threadlike segments, upper leaves often reduced to bracts. **Flowers** small, mostly imperfect, stalkless in axils of upper emersed leaves (the floral bracts) or axils of underwater leaves; male flowers above female flowers; perfect flowers (if present) in middle portion of spike; sepals inconspicuous; petals 4 or absent; stamens 4 or 8; pistil 4-chambered. **Fruit** nutlike, 4-lobed, each lobe (mericarp) with 1 seed, rounded on back or with a ridge or row of small bumps.

▶**KEY TO MYRIOPHYLLUM**

1 Leaves simple, reduced to small, blunt-tipped scales; stems erect from creeping rhizomes . . . . *M. tenellum* / SLENDER WATER-MILFOIL
1 Leaves dissected into narrow segments **2**

2 Leaves alternate, ± opposite, or scattered on stem . . . . . *M. farwellii*
. . . . FARWELL'S WATER-MILFOIL
2 Foliage leaves all whorled **3**

3 Flowers and bracts below flowers alternate on stem . . . .
. . . . *M. alterniflorum* / ALTERNATE-FLOWER WATER-MILFOIL
3 Flowers and bracts below flowers whorled **4**

4 Bracts surrounding male flowers deeply cleft . . . . . *M. verticillatum*
. . . . WHORLED WATER-MILFOIL
4 Bracts surrounding male flowers sharply toothed or entire **5**

5 Bracts sharply toothed and much longer than flowers . . . .
. . . . *M. heterophyllum* / TWO-LEAF WATER-MILFOIL
5 Bracts surrounding male flowers entire and not longer than flowers
. . . . **6**

6 Leaf segments mostly 5–12 on each side of midrib; small bulbs (turions) produced at ends of stems and in upper leaf axils . . . .
. . . . *M. sibiricum* / COMMON WATER-MILFOIL

6 Leaf segments many, 12–20 on each side of midrib; turions absent
. . . . *M. spicatum* / Eurasian water-milfoil

leaf

Myriophyllum alterniflorum DC.
Alternate-flower water-milfoil   OBL

Perennial herb. **Stems** very slender. **Leaves** in whorls of 3–5, usually less than 1 cm long and shorter than the stem internodes, pinnately divided. **Flower spikes** raised above water surface, 2–5 cm long; bracts mostly alternate, linear, shorter than the flowers; male flowers with 4 pink petals; stamens 8. **Fruit** segments 1–2 mm long, rounded on back and base. ❀ Acidic lakes, Lake Superior shoreline. ⊕ ne Minn, n Wisc, uncommon in Mich UP. Greenland to Nfld, Ont and Minn, s to Mass and NY.

⚠
STATUS
Michigan - T

leaf

Myriophyllum farwellii Morong
Farwell's water-milfoil   OBL

Perennial herb; plants entirely underwater, turions present at ends of stems. **Leaves** 1–3 cm long, dissected into threadlike segments, all or most leaves alternate, or ± opposite, or irregularly scattered on stems. **Flowers** underwater, single in axils of foliage leaves; female flowers with 4 purple petals; stamens 4, tiny. **Fruit** 2 mm long, each fruit segment with 2 small, bumpy, longitudinal ridges. ❀ Ponds and small lakes. ⊕ nc and ne Minn, n Wisc, rare in Mich UP. NS and Que to NY and Minn.

leaf

Myriophyllum heterophyllum Michx.
Two-leaf water-milfoil   OBL

Perennial herb. **Stems** stout, to 3 mm wide, often red-tinged, to 1 m or more long. **Leaves** whorled, 1.5–4 cm long, divided into threadlike segments. **Flowers** in spikes raised above water surface, 5–30 cm long; floral bracts whorled, smaller than foliage leaves, ovate, sharply toothed, spreading or curved downward. Flowers both perfect and imperfect; petals of male and perfect flowers 1–3 mm long; stamens 4. **Fruit** olive, ± round, 2 mm long; fruit segments rounded or with 2 small ridges, beaked by the curved stigma. June–Aug. ❀ Lakes, ponds and pools in streams; sometimes where calcium-rich. ⊕ Wisc, Mich, ne Ill and nw Ind. Que and Maine to SD, s to Fla, Tex and NM.

Myriophyllum sibiricum Komarov
Common water-milfoil   OBL

Perennial herb; plants often whitish when dried. **Stems** to 1 m or more long. **Leaves** in whorls of 3–4, 1–4 cm long, with mostly 5–10 threadlike segments on each side of midrib; internodes between whorls about 1 cm long. **Flowers** in spikes with whorled flowers and bracts, raised above water surface, red, clearly different than underwater stems, 4–10 cm long; flowers imperfect, the upper male, the lower female; floral bracts much smaller than the leaves, oblong to obovate; male flowers with pinkish petals (absent in female flowers), 2–3 mm long; stamens 8, the yellow-green anthers conspicuous when flowering. **Fruit** ± round, 2–3 mm long, the segments rounded on back. June–Sept. *M. exalbescens.* ❀ Shallow to deep water of lakes, ponds, marshes, ditches and slow-moving streams; sometimes where calcium-rich. ⊕ Common; w Minn, Wisc, Mich, ne Ill and nw Ind. Boreal N Amer, s to Md, Ohio, Ind, Tex, NM and Calif. ☞ Eurasian water-milfoil (*M. spicatum*), introduced from Eurasia, is similar to *M. sibiricum* but has more finely divided leaves (12–24 threadlike segments on each side of midrib) and larger floral bracts.

leaf

☞ When flowering, the numerous emersed red spikes of **common water-milfoil** are distinctive.

☞ **Eurasion water-milfoil** is an introduced species, spreading and becoming a serious nuisance in lakes throughout the e USA.

Myriophyllum spicatum L.
Eurasian water-milfoil   OBL

Perennial herb, similar to *M. sibiricum*. **Stems** widening below head and curved to a horizontal position, usually many-branched near water surface, internodes between leaves mostly 1–3 cm long, turions absent. **Leaves** with more leaf segments per side (mostly 12–20) than in *M. sibiricum*; lower flower bracts often divided into comblike segments and often longer than the flowers. **Fruit segments** 2–3 mm long. Aug–Sept. ❀ Lakes and ponds, where it may form large, dense mats, hindering boating, swimming, and fishing. ⊕ Minn, Wisc, LP of Mich, ne Ill and nw Ind.

leaves

Myriophyllum tenellum Bigelow
Slender water-milfoil   OBL

Perennial herb. **Stems** slender, 10–30 cm long, mostly upright and unbranched. **Leaves** absent or reduced to a few spaced scales. **Flowers** in spikes raised above water surface, 2–5 cm long; flower bracts mostly alternate, oblong to obovate, entire, shorter to slightly longer than the flowers. **Fruit segments** rounded on back and at base, 1 mm long. ❀ Acidic lakes; often forming large colonies, especially in deep water. ⊕ ne Minn, n Wisc, UP and mostly w LP of Mich. Nfld and Que to Minn, s to NJ.

stem detail

Myriophyllum verticillatum L.
Whorled water-milfoil   OBL

⚠ STATUS Indiana - T

Perennial herb, similar to *M. sibiricum*, but plants often larger. **Stems** 5–25 dm long. **Leaves** in whorls of 4–5, with 9–17 threadlike segments along each side of midrib, 1–5 cm long; lower and middle internodes between whorls mostly less than 1 cm long. **Flowers** perfect, or the lower female and upper male; in spikes 4–12 cm long, the floral bracts much smaller than the leaves, with comblike segments, mostly longer than the flowers; petals blunt-tipped, 2–3 mm long, smaller in female flowers; stamens 8. **Fruit** ± round, 2–3 mm long, the segments rounded on back. July–Sept. ❀ Lakes, ponds and quiet places in rivers. ⊕ n and c Minn; Wisc, Mich, uncommon in ne Ill and nw Ind. Circumboreal, s to Mass, NY, Ind, ne Tex, Neb, Utah and BC.

leaf

▶Proserpinaca L. / Mermaid-weed

Perennial aquatic herbs. **Stems** creeping, simple or with few branches. **Leaves** alternate, pinnately divided, or emersed leaves lance-shaped and sharply toothed. **Flowers** small, perfect, green or purple-tinged, 1–3 in axils of emersed leaves, stalkless; sepals triangle-shaped, persistent; petals absent, stamens 3, stigmas 3. **Fruit** nutlike, 3-angled, with 3 seeds.

▶**KEY TO PROSERPINACA**

1 Upper leaves unlike lower leaves; upper leaves lance-shaped, margins sharply toothed; widespread, but absent from Minn . . . .
. . . . *P. palustris* / Marsh mermaid-weed
1 Upper and lower leaves alike, pinnately divided; rare, s Mich only .
. . . . *P. pectinata* / Comb-leaf mermaid-weed

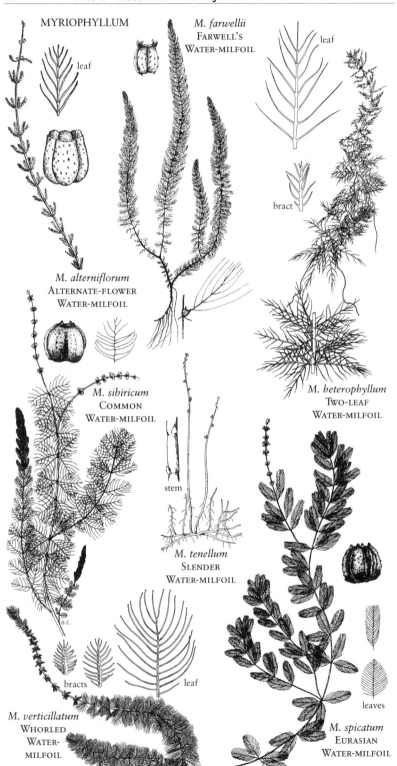

MYRIOPHYLLUM

leaf

M. farwellii
FARWELL'S
WATER-MILFOIL

leaf

bract

M. alterniflorum
ALTERNATE-FLOWER
WATER-MILFOIL

M. sibiricum
COMMON
WATER-MILFOIL

M. heterophyllum
TWO-LEAF
WATER-MILFOIL

stem

M. tenellum
SLENDER
WATER-MILFOIL

o.c.

bracts

leaf

M. verticillatum
WHORLED
WATER-
MILFOIL

leaves

M. spicatum
EURASIAN
WATER-MILFOIL

Proserpinaca palustris L.

Marsh mermaid-weed   OBL

Perennial aquatic herb, often forming large colonies. **Stems** horizontal at base and often rooting; the flower-bearing branches erect, 1–4 dm tall. **Underwater leaves**, if present, ovate in outline, 2–4 cm long, deeply divided into linear segments; **emersed leaves** narrowly lance-shaped, 2–6 cm long, margins with sharp, forward-pointing teeth. **Fruit** 2–5 mm long and as wide. June–Aug. ⚘ Shallow water of ponds, streambanks and ditches, muddy shores, sedge meadows; usually where seasonally flooded. ⊕ Wisc, LP and e UP of Mich, ne Ill and nw Ind. NS and Que to Ont and Wisc, s to Cuba and c Amer.

Proserpinaca pectinata Lam.

Comb-leaf mermaid-weed   (OBL)

⚠
STATUS
Michigan - E

Perennial aquatic herb. **Underwater leaves** similar to those of *P. palustris*; **emersed leaves** ovate in outline, 1.5–3 cm long, deeply divided into 6–12 pairs of narrow segments. **Fruit** 2–4 mm long and as wide. July–Aug. ⚘ Sandy ditches. ⊕ Atlantic coastal disjunct; rare in wc LP of Mich. NS to Fla and La.

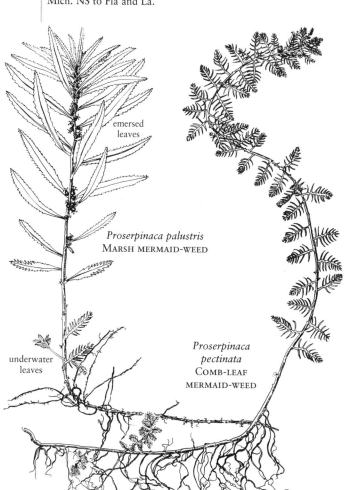

emersed leaves

Proserpinaca palustris
MARSH MERMAID-WEED

underwater leaves

Proserpinaca pectinata
COMB-LEAF
MERMAID-WEED

Hippocastanaceae
Horse-Chestnut Family

▶**Aesculus** L. / Buckeye

Aesculus glabra Willd.

Ohio-buckeye   (FACU-)

☞ **Ohio-buckeye** reaches its northern range limit in the southern portion of the Great Lakes region.

Small to medium tree, 10–12 m tall; trunk 15–30 cm wide; **bark** thin, yellow-brown, smooth to scaly, dark brown and deeply furrowed with age, bark and leaves foul-smelling when bruised and possibly poisonous; **twigs** red-brown, becoming light gray. **Leaves** appearing early in spring, turning yellow in fall, opposite, smooth, palmately compound into usually 5 (rarely 7) leaflets, the **leaflets** obovate, 7–15 cm long and 3–6 cm wide, tapered at both ends, margins finely toothed, petioles 10–15 cm long. **Flowers** perfect, or either male or female on same tree, numerous, yellow-green, appearing after leaves unfold in spring, in panicles 1–1.5 dm long and 6 cm wide at ends of branches; petals 4, pale yellow, hairy, 2 cm long, stamens 7, longer than the petals. **Fruit** a prickly, red-brown capsule, 2–3 cm wide, with 1 smooth, satiny brown seed. April–May. ❦ Floodplain forests, streambanks, thickets. ⊕ Local in sw Wisc, s LP of Mich, ne Ill and nw Ind. w Pa and s Ont to s Wisc, Iowa and Kans, s to Tenn, n Ala, Ark and Tex.

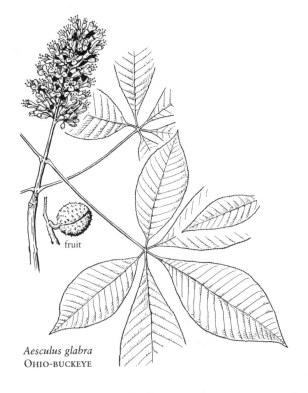

fruit

Aesculus glabra
OHIO-BUCKEYE

Hippuridaceae
Mare's-Tail Family

▶**Hippuris** L. / Mare's-tail

Hippuris vulgaris L.
  Mare's-tail   OBL
Perennial herb, from large, spongy rhizomes. **Stems** 2–6 dm long,
unbranched, underwater and lax, or emersed and upright, densely covered by the closely spaced whorls of leaves. **Leaves** numerous, in whorls
of 6–12, linear, 1–2.5 cm long and 1–3 mm wide, stalkless. **Flowers** very
small, perfect, stalkless and single in upper leaf axils, or often absent;
sepals and petals lacking; stamen 1, style 1, ovary 1-chambered. **Fruit**
nutlike, oval, 2 mm long. June–Aug. ⚘ Shallow water or mud of marshes, lakes, streams and ditches. ⊕ Minn (but local in se), Wisc, UP and n
LP of Mich, uncommon in ne Ill. Circumboreal, s to Maine, NY, n Ill,
Iowa, Neb, NM and Ariz.

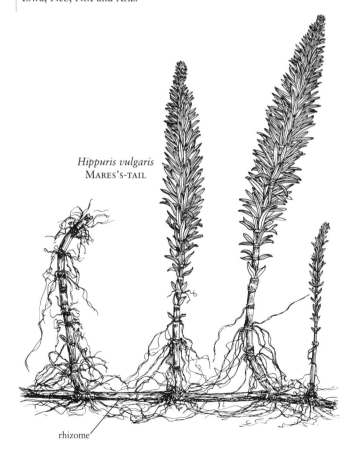

Hippuris vulgaris
Mares's-tail

rhizome

Juglandaceae
Walnut Family

▶**Carya** Nutt. / Hickory

Carya laciniosa (Michx.) Loudon
  Shellbark-hickory   FACW

Large tree to 30 m, trunk to 1 m wide; lower branches drooping; **bark** light gray, separating into long, vertical plates which curve away from trunk at tips; **twigs** stout, gray or brown, dotted with orange lenticels; **buds** dark brown, hairy, the outer bud scales tipped with a long, stiff point. **Leaves** alternate, pinnately divided into 5–9 leaflets; the **leaflets** lance-shaped to ovate, pointed at tip, rounded and unequal at base; upper surface dark green and smooth, underside paler and with soft hairs; margins finely toothed. **Flowers** tiny, male and female flowers separate but borne on same tree, appearing after leaves begin to unfold in spring; male flowers in drooping catkins, female flowers in clusters of 2–5. **Fruit** round but depressed at top, 3–5 cm wide, with an outer covering (husk) splitting into 4 sections; the nut compressed, ridged, sweet-tasting. ❦ Floodplain forests. ⊕ s LP of Mich, ne Ill and nw Ind. s Ont and NY to n Ill, Iowa and e Kans, s to NC, Ga and e Okla.

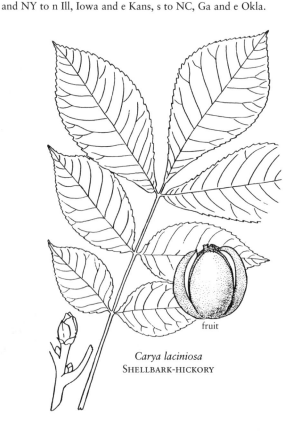

fruit

Carya laciniosa
SHELLBARK-HICKORY

Lamiaceae
Mint Family

Perennial, often aromatic, herbs. **Stems** usually 4-angled. **Leaves** simple, opposite, sharply toothed or deeply lobed. **Flowers** in leaf axils or in heads or spikes at ends of stems, perfect (with both male and female parts), nearly regular to irregular; sepals 5-toothed or sometimes 2-lipped; petals white, pink, blue or purple, often 2-lipped; stamens 2 or 4; ovary 4-lobed, splitting into 4, 1-seeded nutlets when mature.

▶**KEY TO LAMIACEAE**

1 Corolla regular or nearly so, with 4–5 lobes of equal length **2**
1 Corolla irregular, 1- or 2-lipped **3**

2 Stamens 2; plants not strongly scented . . . . *Lycopus*
. . . . WATER-HOREHOUND
2 Stamens 4; plants strongly mint-scented . . . . *Mentha arvensis*
. . . . FIELD-MINT

3 Upper lip of corolla absent, lower lip large. . . . *Teucrium canadense*
. . . . AMERICAN GERMANDER
3 Upper and lower corolla lips well-developed. **4**

4 Calyx with a rounded bump on upper side; petals blue . . *Scutellaria*
. . . . SKULLCAP
4 Calyx without bump on upper side; petal colors vary **5**

5 Flowers in stalked clusters at branch ends, the clusters forming a flat-topped or rounded inflorescence . . . . . *Pycnanthemum virginianum*
. . . . VIRGINIA MOUNTAIN-MINT
5 Flowers ± stalkless, in spikes or crowded heads **6**

6 Leaf margins ± entire. **7**
6 Leaf margins regularly toothed **8**

7 Leaves linear . . . . *Stachys hyssopifolia* / HYSSOP HEDGE-NETTLE
7 Leaves broader, less than 4x longer than wide . . . . *Prunella vulgaris*
. . . . SELF-HEAL

8 Flowers paired in slender spikes; leaves and stems smooth . . . .
. . . . *Physostegia virginiana* / OBEDIENCE; FALSE DRAGON-HEAD
8 Flowers 3 or more at each node; leaves and stems usually hairy . . .
. . . . *Stachys* / HEDGE-NETTLE

▶**Lycopus** L. / Water-horehound

Perennial, ± unscented herbs. **Stems** erect, 4-angled. **Leaves** opposite, coarsely toothed or deeply lobed, smaller on upper stems; petioles short or absent. **Flowers** small, in clusters in middle and upper leaf axils, often appearing whorled; white to pink, the sepals and petals often dotted on outer surface, 4-lobed, stamens 2. **Fruit** a nutlet.

▶**KEY TO LYCOPUS**

1 Sepal lobes broad, triangular to ovate, to 1 mm long, shorter than or nearly as long as nutlets, midvein not prominent **2**
1 Sepal lobes slender, 1–3 mm long, longer than nutlets, midvein prominent **3**

2 Leaves mostly less than 3 cm wide; stamens and styles visible, longer than petals; outer rim of nutlets taller than the inner rim . . . .
. . . . *L. uniflorus* / Northern water-horehound
2 Larger leaves 3 cm or more wide; stamens and styles hidden by petals; inner and outer rim of nutlets same height, the 4 nutlets appearing flat-topped across tops. . . . *L. virginicus* / Virginia water-horehound

3 Main leaves stalkless **4**
3 Leaves stalked **5**

4 Stems stout, coarsely hairy; leaves rough-to-touch, margins with mostly more than 6 pairs of teeth; widespread . . . . *L. asper*
. . . . Western water-horehound
4 Stems slender, smooth or finely hairy; leaves ± smooth, with up to 6 pairs of teeth; nw Ind only . . . . *L. amplectens*
. . . . Sessile water-horehound

5 Upper surface of leaves with appressed hairs . . . . *L. europaeus*
. . . . European water-horehound
5 Upper surface of leaves ± smooth **6**

6 Plants spreading by rhizomes; lower and middle stem leaves pinnately parted at least near base; leaf undersides smooth, or with appressed hairs on midvein. . . *L. americanus* / American water-horehound
6 Plants spreading by surface stolons; leaf margins sharp-toothed, not deeply parted; leaf undersides finely hairy . . . . *L. rubellus*
. . . . Stalked water-horehound

Lycopus americanus Muhl.
American water-horehound   OBL

☞ **American water-horehound** is the region's most common species of *Lycopus*.

Perennial herb, spreading by rhizomes, tubers absent. **Stems** erect, often branched, 2–8 dm long, upper stems smooth or short-hairy. **Leaves** opposite, lance-shaped, 3–8 cm long and 1–4 cm wide, with glandular dots, smooth or rough on upper surface, underside veins short-hairy; margins coarsely and irregularly deeply toothed or lobed, the lowest teeth largest; nearly stalkless or on short petioles. **Flowers** in dense, whorled clusters in leaf axils; sepal lobes narrow, sharp-tipped, 1–3 mm long, longer than fruits; petals white, sometimes pink to purple-dotted, 4-lobed, the upper lobe wider and notched. **Fruit** a nutlet, 1–2 mm long. July–Sept. ॐ Marshes, wet meadows, shores, streambanks, ditches, calcareous fens, wetland margins. ⊕ Minn, Wisc, Mich, ne Ill and nw Ind. Newf to BC, s to Fla, Tex and Calif.

Lycopus amplectens Raf.
Sessile water-horehound   (OBL)

⚠ STATUS Indiana - E

Perennial herb, similar to **stalked water-horehound** (*Lycopus rubellus*). **Leaves** narrowly ovate, 3–10 cm long and 1–3 cm wide, rounded to base, stalkless; margins with 4–6 teeth on each side. **Flowers** white, in dense clusters in leaf axils. **Fruit** a nutlet. ॐ Marshes and sandy shores. ⊕ Uncommon disjunct in nw Ind. Atlantic coast from Mass to Fla; nw Ind.

Lycopus asper Greene
Western water-horehound   OBL
Perennial emergent herb, spreading by rhizomes (tubers present) and also usually stolons. **Stems** erect, 2–8 dm long, simple or sometimes branched, hairy, at least on stem angles. **Leaves** opposite, oval to oblong lance-shaped, 3–10 cm long and 0.5–3 cm wide, smooth or rough; margins coarsely toothed; stalkless. **Flowers** in dense, whorled clusters in leaf axils; sepal lobes narrow, firm, sharp-tipped, 1–3 mm long, longer than nutlets; petals white, 4-lobed, only slightly longer than sepals. **Fruit** a nutlet, 1–2 mm long. July–Sept. ❦ Shores and ditches, especially where disturbed, often with **American water-horehound** (*L. americanus*). ⊕ Common to occasional. w and sc Minn, Wisc, LP of Mich (mostly near Great Lakes), ne Ill and nw Ind. Ont and Mich to BC, s to Ill, Iowa, Kans, NM and Calif.

Lycopus europaeus L.
European water-horehound   OBL
Perennial herb, similar to **American water-horehound** (*L. americanus*) and hybridizing with it, but often with slender stolons as well as rhizomes; plants more hairy, the hairs along veins of lower leaf-surface to 2 mm long. **Leaves** opposite, mostly wider and more bluntly toothed than in *L. americanus*, upper surface usually with appressed hairs. **Flowers** white, in dense, whorled clusters in leaf axils; sepals sharp-tipped, 3–5 mm long. **Fruit** a nutlet, 1–2 mm long. July–Aug. ❦ Moist to wet areas, often where disturbed. ⊕ Introduced. Minn, s Wisc, se LP of Mich, ne Ill and nw Ind. Atlantic coast from Mass to NC; s Great Lakes region.

Lycopus rubellus Moench
Stalked water-horehound   OBL
Perennial herb, spreading by stolons, each stolon ending in a slender tuber, producing a single stem the following year; plants smooth to densely hairy. **Leaves** opposite, lance-shaped to oval, 5–10 cm long and 1–3 cm wide; margins entire to sharply toothed; petioles present or blades below lowest tooth concave and petiolelike. **Flowers** crowded in whorled clusters in leaf axils; sepal lobes 5, tapered to a tip but not awl-like; petals white, 5-lobed, 2x longer than sepals. **Fruit** a nutlet to 1.5 mm long and 1 mm wide, flat across the top. Aug–Sept. ❦ Floodplain forests, wet woods and wet forest openings. ⊕ s Mich, ne Ill and nw Ind. Atlantic coast from Maine to Fla and Tex, local w to Mich, n Ill, Mo and Ark.

Lycopus uniflorus Michx.
Northern water-horehound   OBL
Perennial herb, similar to **western water-horehound** (*L. asper*). **Stems** smooth or short-hairy, 1–5 dm long. **Leaves** opposite, lance-shaped to oblong, 3–6 cm long and 1–3 cm wide, margins with a few outward-pointing teeth, petioles short or nearly absent. **Flowers** in dense, whorled clusters in leaf axils; sepal lobes broad, triangular to ovate, soft, rounded at tip, to 1 mm long, shorter to as long as nutlets; petals white or pink, 2–3 mm long, 5-lobed, longer than sepals. **Fruit** a nutlet 1–1.5 mm long. Aug–Sept. ❦ Swamps, streambanks, thickets, wet meadows, open bogs, calcareous fens, ditches; often with **American water-horehound** (*L. americanus*). ⊕ Common; Minn, Wisc, Mich, ne Ill and nw Ind. Newf to Alaska, s to NC, Ohio, Ill, Okla, Mont and Ore.

Lycopus virginicus L.
Virginia water-horehound   OBL
Perennial herb, spreading by stolons (tubers usually absent). **Stems** 2–6 dm long, with dense covering of appressed hairs. **Leaves** opposite, lance-

shaped to oval, 5–10 cm long and 1.5–5 cm wide, long-hairy, lower surface usually also with short, feltlike hairs; margins coarsely toothed, the
lowest tooth just below middle of blade, the margin below tooth concave
and petiolelike. **Flowers** in whorled clusters from leaf axils; sepals shorter than nutlets; petals white, 4-lobed, (upper lobe often notched). **Fruit** a
nutlet, 1–2 mm long, the group of 4 nutlets ± flat across tips. July–Sept.
L. membranaceus. ❦ Floodplain forests. ⊕ Local in ec and se Minn; s
Wisc, s LP of Mich, ne Ill and nw Ind. Mass, NY, Pa, to Great Lakes,
Okla and e Tex, s to n Fla. ☞ Probably hybridizes with **northern water-
horehound** (*L. uniflorus*) where their ranges overlap, producing a hybrid
swarm called *Lycopus sherardii.*

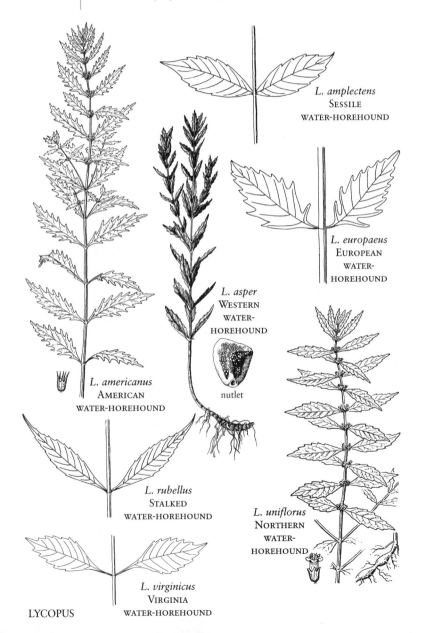

L. amplectens
SESSILE
WATER-HOREHOUND

L. europaeus
EUROPEAN
WATER-
HOREHOUND

L. asper
WESTERN
WATER-
HOREHOUND

nutlet

L. americanus
AMERICAN
WATER-HOREHOUND

L. rubellus
STALKED
WATER-HOREHOUND

L. uniflorus
NORTHERN
WATER-
HOREHOUND

L. virginicus
VIRGINIA
WATER-HOREHOUND

LYCOPUS

▶**Mentha** L. / Mint

Mentha arvensis L.
Field-mint   FACW

☞ Several
cultivated
mints, such
as **spearmint**
(*Mentha
spicata*) and
various hybrids
with *Mentha
arvensis*, may
occasionally
escape and
form colonies
in wetlands
of our region.
Perennial herb, strongly mint-scented, spreading by rhizomes and often also by stolons. **Stems** 2–8 dm long, 4-angled, hairy at least on stem angles. **Leaves** opposite, ovate to lance-shaped or oval–lance-shaped, 2–7 cm long and 0.5–3 cm wide, smooth or hairy; margins with sharp, forward-pointing teeth; petioles short. **Flowers** small, white or light pink to lavender, hairy, crowded in whorled clusters in middle and upper leaf axils; sepals 2–3 mm long, hairy and glandular; petals ± regular to slightly 2-lipped, 4–6 mm long, glandular on outside, 4- or 5-lobed; stamens and style longer than petals. **Fruit** a smooth nutlet to 1 mm long, enclosed by the persistent sepals. July–Sept. ❦ Wet meadows, marshes, swamps, thickets, streambanks, ditches, springs and other wet places. ⊕ Common; Minn, Wisc, Mich, ne Ill and nw Ind. Circumboreal, s to Va, Mo, n Tex, NM and Calif.

▶**Physostegia** Benth. / Obedience

Physostegia virginiana (L.) Benth.
Obedience; False dragon-head   FACW

☞ **Obedience**
is sometimes
cultivated for
its attractive
flowers.
Perennial herb, spreading by rhizomes. **Stems** erect, 5–15 dm long, often branched near top, 4-angled. **Leaves** opposite, oval to oblong lance-shaped, 2–15 cm long and 1–4 cm wide, sometimes smaller upward; margins with sharp teeth; stalkless, not clasping. **Flowers** in several racemes 5–20 cm long, the stalks short-hairy; sepals 4–8 mm long, often with some gland-tipped hairs; petals pink-purple or white with purple spots, 1.5–3 cm long, short-hairy to smooth. **Fruit** a nutlet, 2–3 mm long. July–Sept. *Dracocephalum virginianum.* ❦ Sedge meadows, low prairie, shores, swamps, floodplain forests, thickets and ditches. ⊕ Minn, Wisc, Mich, ne Ill and nw Ind. Que to Man, s to Va, Tenn, Ill, Mo and ne Kans.

▶**Prunella** L. / Self-heal

Prunella vulgaris L.
Self-heal   FAC

Perennial herb. **Stems** upright or sometimes spreading, 1–5 dm long, 4-angled. **Leaves** opposite, lance-shaped to oval or ovate, 2–8 cm long and 1–4 cm wide; lower leaves wider than upper; margins entire or with a few small teeth; petioles present. **Flowers** in dense spikes 2–5 cm long and 1–2 cm wide, with obvious bracts; sepals to 1 cm long, green or purple, with spine-tipped teeth; corolla 2-lipped, the upper lip hoodlike and entire, lower lip shorter and 3-lobed; petals blue-violet (rarely pink or white), 1–2 cm long; stamens 4, about as long as petals. **Fruit** a smooth nutlet. ☞ Var. *vulgaris*, introduced from Europe and found in mostly disturbed places, has broad leaves half as wide as long. The native var. *lanceolata* has narrower leaves, 1/3 as wide as long. June–Oct. ❦ Common in many types of wetlands (especially where disturbed): swamps, wet forest depressions, wet trails, streambanks, ditches; also in drier forests, fields and lawns. ⊕ Minn, Wisc, Mich, ne Ill and nw Ind. Throughout most of ne and c USA.

▶**Pycnanthemum** Michx. / Mountain-mint

Pycnanthemum virginianum (L.) Durand & B. D. Jackson
Virginia mountain-mint   FACW+
Perennial, strongly scented herb. **Stems** to 1 m long, branched above, 4-angled, angles short-hairy. **Leaves** numerous, opposite, narrowly lance-shaped, 3–4 cm long and to 1 cm wide (leaves in heads much smaller), upper surface smooth, with 3–4 pairs of lateral veins, undersides often finely hairy on midvein; margins entire but fringed with short, rough hairs; ± stalkless. **Flowers** small, 2-lipped, in branched, crowded clusters at ends of stems and branches from upper leaf axils; sepals short wool-ly-hairy; petals white, purple-spotted. **Fruit** a 4-parted nutlet. July–Sept.
☙ Wet meadows, marshes, tamarack swamps, calcareous fens, low prairie. ⊕ nw, c and s Minn; Wisc, c and s LP of Mich, ne Ill and nw Ind. Maine to ND, s to Ga and Okla. ☞ P. muticum (Michx.) Pers., FAC, is known from wet meadows in extreme sw Mich (⚠ state T). Its main leaves are ovate. Other species of *Pycnanthemum* in our region typically occur on dry uplands.

P. muticum

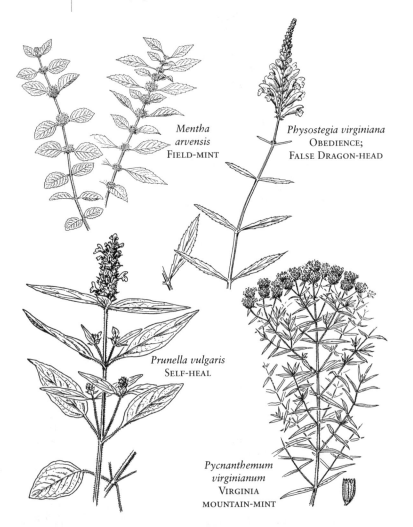

Mentha arvensis
FIELD-MINT

Physostegia virginiana
OBEDIENCE;
FALSE DRAGON-HEAD

Prunella vulgaris
SELF-HEAL

Pycnanthemum virginianum
VIRGINIA
MOUNTAIN-MINT

▶**Scutellaria** L. / Skullcap

Perennial herbs, spreading by rhizomes. **Stems** erect or spreading, 4-angled. **Leaves** opposite, ovate to lance-shaped, margins toothed, stalked or ± stalkless. **Flowers** blue or blue with white markings, single on short stalks in axils of middle and upper leaves, or in racemes from leaf axils; calyx 2-lipped, with a rounded bump on upper side; corolla 2-lipped, pubescent on outer surface, upper lip hoodlike, lower lip ± flat, 3-lobed; stamens 4, ascending into the upper corolla lip. **Fruit** a 4-parted nutlet.

KEY TO SCUTELLARIA

1 Flowers single in leaf axils; flowers more than 15 mm long. . . . . . .
. . . . *S. galericulata* / MARSH OR HOODED SKULLCAP
1 Flowers in racemes from leaf axils; flowers to 8 mm long . . . .
. . . . *S. lateriflora* / BLUE SKULLCAP

Scutellaria galericulata L.
Marsh or Hooded skullcap   OBL

Perennial herb, from slender rhizomes. **Stems** erect or spreading, 2–8 dm long, unbranched or branched, 4-angled, short-hairy at least on angles of upper stem. **Leaves** opposite, lance-shaped to narrowly ovate, 2–6 cm long and 0.5–2.5 cm wide, upper surface smooth, underside short-hairy, tapered to a blunt tip; margins with low, rounded, forward-pointing teeth; petioles very short. **Flowers** 2-lipped, single in leaf axils (and paired at nodes), on stalks 1–3 mm long; sepals 3–6 mm long; petals blue, marked with white, 15–25 mm long. **Fruit** a nutlet. June–Sept. *S. epilobiifolia.* ❧ Shores, streambanks, marshes, wet meadows, swamps, thickets, bogs, ditches. ⊕ Common; Minn, Wisc, Mich, ne Ill and nw Ind. Circumboreal, s to Del, Ohio, Ill, Mo, n Tex, Ariz and Calif.

Scutellaria lateriflora L.
Blue skullcap   OBL

Perennial herb. **Stems** 2–6 dm long, usually branched, 4-angled, short-hairy on upper stem angles or smooth. **Leaves** opposite, ovate to lance-shaped, 3–8 cm long and 1.5–5 cm wide, smooth; margins coarsely toothed; petioles 0.5–2 cm long. **Flowers** 2-lipped, in elongate racemes from leaf axils; sepals 2–4 mm long; petals blue (rarely pink or white), 5–8 mm long. **Fruit** a nutlet. July–Sept. ❧ Shores, streambanks, wet meadows, marshes, swamps, shaded wet areas. ⊕ Common; Minn, Wisc, Mich, ne Ill and nw Ind. Newf to BC, s to Ga, Tex and Calif.

▶**Stachys** L. / Hedge-nettle

Erect, perennial herbs, spreading by rhizomes; plants usually hairy. **Stems** 4-angled. **Leaves** opposite, margins entire or toothed, stalkless or with short petioles. **Flowers** in interrupted spikes at ends of stems, appearing whorled in ± evenly spaced clusters; sepals ± regular, with 5 equal teeth; corolla 2-lipped, petals pink, often with purple spots or mottles, upper lip concave, entire, lower lip spreading, 3-lobed; stamens 4, ascending under the upper lip. **Fruit** a dark brown, 4-lobed nutlet, loosely enclosed by the persistent sepals.

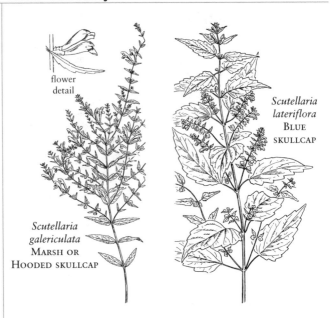

flower
detail

*Scutellaria
lateriflora*
BLUE
SKULLCAP

*Scutellaria
galericulata*
MARSH OR
HOODED SKULLCAP

▶**KEY TO STACHYS**

1 Stems smooth; leaves entire, ± stalkless, linear, less than 1 cm wide .
. . . . *S. hyssopifolia* / HYSSOP HEDGE-NETTLE
1 Stems hairy, at least on stem angles; leaves with sharp, forward-pointing teeth, stalkless or stalked, larger leaves more than 1 cm wide . **2**

2 Stems hairy on angles and sides *S. palustris* / MARSH HEDGE-NETTLE
2 Stems hairy only on stem angles. **3**

3 Sepals coarsely hairy, sepal lobes fringed with hairs . . . . . *S. hispida*
. . . . HISPID HEDGE-NETTLE
3 Sepals hairy only on the angles; sepal lobes smooth and entire . . . .
. . . . *S. tenuifolia* / SMOOTH HEDGE-NETTLE

Stachys hispida Pursh
Hispid hedge-nettle   FACW+
Perennial herb. **Stems** erect, 5–10 dm long, 4-angled, angles with bristly
hairs to 2 mm long. **Leaves** opposite, narrowly oblong or lance-shaped,
4–10 cm long and 1–4 cm wide, upper surface usually hairy; margins
with forward-pointing teeth; petioles to 1 cm long or absent. **Flowers**
pink, in evenly spaced clusters along a spike at end of stems; sepals 3–5
mm long, with short stiff hairs, the lobes narrowly lance-shaped. **Fruit** a
nutlet. July–Sept. *S. tenuifolia* var. *hispida*. ❧ Marshes, wet meadows,
floodplain forests, thickets, shores and streambanks. ⊕ n and e Minn,
Wisc, Mich, ne Ill and nw Ind. Vt to Ont and Man, s to Md, Ky and Ark.

Stachys hyssopifolia Michx.
Hyssop hedge-nettle   FACW+
Perennial herb. **Stems** 3–5 dm long, often branched from base, 4-angled,
smooth, or sometimes with fine hairs at nodes and on stem angles.
Leaves opposite, smooth, linear, 2–6 cm long and 3–10 mm wide, uppermost leaves reduced to short bracts; margins entire or with a few low
teeth; ± stalkless. **Flowers** in spaced, several-flowered clusters at ends of

stems and on branches from leaf axils; sepals smooth or with a few hairs; petals light purple, smooth. **Fruit** a nutlet. July–Sept. *S. atlantica.* ❦ Sandy shores and wet dune areas, wet meadows, low prairie. ⊕ sc UP and w LP of Mich and n Ind. Atlantic coast from Mass to Ga, disjunct in Mich and n Ind.

Stachys palustris L.
Marsh hedge-nettle   OBL

Perennial herb. **Stems** 3–8 dm long, unbranched or branched, 4-angled, stiffly hairy on angles and with short, gland-tipped hairs on sides. **Leaves** opposite, lance-shaped to oblong, 4–12 cm long and 2–5 cm wide, softly hairy on both sides; margins with rounded, forward-pointing teeth; stalkless or with short petioles. **Flowers** in clusters of 6–10 in an interrupted spike at end of stem (sometimes also clustered in upper leaf axils); sepals 5–8 mm long, with long, glandless hairs and shorter gland-tipped hairs; petals purple to pale red with purple spots, 9–13 mm long. **Fruit** a nutlet. June–Aug. ❦ Marshes, wet meadows, ditches, thickets, shores, streambanks, openings in swamps. ⊕ Native and introduced, fairly common; Minn, Wisc, Mich, ne Ill and nw Ind (especially near Great Lakes). Circumboreal; s in N Amer to NY, Ill, Mo, Okla, NM and Ariz.

Stachys tenuifolia Willd.
Smooth hedge-nettle   OBL

Perennial herb. **Stems** 4–10 dm long, 4-angled, smooth, or with downward-pointing, bristly hairs on stem angles. **Leaves** opposite, lance-shaped to ovate, 6–14 cm long and 2–6 cm wide, ± smooth; margins with sharp, forward-pointing teeth; petioles slender, 1–2 cm long or absent. **Flowers** in interrupted spikes at ends of stems or also in upper leaf axils; sepals 5–7 mm long, smooth; petals pale red to purple, 1.5–2.5 cm long. **Fruit** a nutlet. July–Sept. ❦ Floodplain forests, shores, streambanks, thickets, wet meadows. ⊕ n and e Minn, Wisc, Mich, ne Ill and nw Ind. NY to Man, s to SC, Tenn, La and Tex.

▶Teucrium L. / Germander; Wood-sage

Teucrium canadense L.
American germander   FACW-

Perennial herb, spreading by rhizomes. **Stems** 3–10 dm long, mostly unbranched, 4-angled, long-hairy. **Leaves** opposite, lance-shaped or oblong, 4–12 cm long and 1.5–5 cm wide, upper surface smooth or sparsely hairy, underside with dense, matted hairs, margins irregularly finely toothed, petioles 5–15 mm long. **Flowers** in a dense spikelike raceme, 5–20 cm long; bracts present and narrowly lance-shaped; flowers on stalks 1–3 mm long; sepals ± regular, purple or green, 4–7 mm long, covered with long silky hairs and very short glandular ones; corolla irregular, 10–16 mm long, with short gland-tipped hairs, upper lip absent, lower lip large; petals pink to purple; stamens 4, arched over the corolla. **Fruit** a golden nutlet. July–Sept. ❦ Marshes, wet meadows, shores, streambanks, thickets, floodplain forests, ditches. ⊕ ne, wc and s Minn, Wisc, Mich, ne Ill and nw Ind. Circumboreal; across s Can, throughout USA and into Mex.

Stachys hispida
HISPID
HEDGE-NETTLE

Teucrium canadense
AMERICAN
GERMANDER

Stachys tenuifolia
SMOOTH HEDGE-
NETTLE

Stachys palustris
MARSH HEDGE-NETTLE

Stachys hyssopifolia
HYSSOP HEDGE-NETTLE

Lauraceae
Laurel Family

▶**Lindera** Thunb. / Spicebush

Lindera benzoin (L.) Blume
  Northern spicebush   FACW-
Much-branched shrub to 4 m tall; **bark** gray-brown and rough with age.
Leaves alternate, aromatic, oval to obovate, 6–12 cm long and to 6 cm
wide, broadest at or above middle, larger leaves abruptly tapered to tip,
smaller leaves with rounded tips; margins entire; petioles 7–10 mm long.
Flowers yellow, 6 mm wide, in clusters of 4–6 at nodes of previous year
stems, appearing before leaves in spring, the male and female flowers
separate and on different plants. **Fruit** aromatic, bright red and shiny,
6–10 mm long, berrylike on a short stalk. April–May. ᭰ Moist to wet
deciduous forests and swamps, streambanks, occasionally in cedar
swamps; usually in shade. ⊕ c and s Mich, n Ill and n Ind. s Maine to n
Ill, s to Fla and Tex.

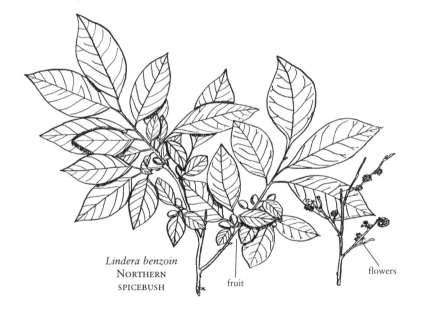

Lindera benzoin
NORTHERN
SPICEBUSH

fruit

flowers

Lentibulariaceae
Bladderwort Family

Insectivorous herbs. **Leaves** in a basal rosette (*Pinguicula*), or floating, or in peat, muck, or wet soil (*Utricularia*). **Flowers** perfect (with both male and female parts), irregular, 2-lipped, sometimes with a spur, 1 to several on an erect stem; stamens 2. **Fruit** a capsule.

▶KEY TO LENTIBULARIACEAE

1 Leaves ovate or oval, in a basal rosette; flowers single on a bractless stalk . . . . *Pinguicula* / BUTTERWORT
1 Leaves linear or dissected into narrow segments; flowers 1, or several in a raceme, each flower subtended by a bract . . . . *Utricularia*
. . . . BLADDERWORT

▶Pinguicula L. / Butterwort

Pinguicula vulgaris L.
Common or Violet butterwort; Bog violet   OBL

⚠ STATUS
Wisconsin - E

☞ Small insects are trapped by the sticky, slimy surface of the yellow-green leaves.

Perennial herb. **Leaves** 3–6 in a basal rosette, ovate or oval, 2–5 cm long, blunt-tipped, narrowed to base, upper surface sticky; margins inrolled. **Flowers** single atop a leafless stalk (scape) 5–15 cm long; corolla violet-purple, spurred, 2-lipped, the upper lip 3-lobed, the lower lip 2-lobed, 1.5–2 cm long (including spur). **Fruit** a 2-chambered capsule. June–July. ❦ Rock crevices in sandstone cliffs along Lake Superior, wet areas between dunes, marl flats and calcareous fens; usually found with **Mistassini primrose** (*Primula mistassinica*). ⊕ ne Minn along Lake Superior shoreline, nw Wisc (Ashland Co.), UP and extreme n LP of Mich. Labr to Alaska, s to New Eng, NY, Mich, Minn and Ore.

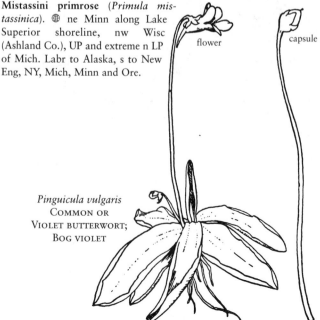

flower   capsule

Pinguicula vulgaris
COMMON OR
VIOLET BUTTERWORT;
BOG VIOLET

▶**Utricularia** L. / Bladderwort

Aquatic or wetland, annual or perennial herbs. **Leaves** underwater, alternate, entire or dissected into many linear segments, some with bladders which trap tiny aquatic invertebrates; or leaves in wet soil and rootlike or absent. **Flowers** perfect, irregular, 1 to several in a raceme atop stalks raised above water or soil surface, each flower subtended by a small bract; corolla yellow or purple, similar to a snapdragon flower, 2-lipped, the upper lip erect, entire or slightly 2-lobed, lower lip entire or 3-lobed, the corolla tube extended backward into a sac or spur, stamens 2. **Fruit** a many-seeded capsule.

▶**KEY TO UTRICULARIA**

1 Flowers purple or pink **2**
1 Flowers yellow **3**

2 Flowers 2–5 atop a stout stalk; plants floating in water, masses of leaves present. . . *U. purpurea* / SPOTTED OR PURPLE BLADDERWORT
2 Flowers single atop a slender stalk; plants not free-floating, rooted in peat or muck, appearing leafless . . . . *U. resupinata* . . . . LAVENDER BLADDERWORT

3 Scapes appearing leafless; leaves simple or absent; plants of peat, moist sand, or marl **4**
3 Scapes with leaves at base, the leaves dissected and with bladderlike traps; plants mostly floating in water **5**

4 Flowers single on a threadlike stalk, the bracts attached to the stalk from their middle; normal flowers rare, cleistogamous flowers typical (that is, flowers which do not open before fertilization and are instead self-fertilized), ... *U. subulata* / SLENDER BLADDERWORT
4 Flowers 1–6 on a slender stalk; normal flowers typical, cleistogamous flowers absent; bracts attached to stalk from their base . *U. cornuta* . . . . LEAFLESS BLADDERWORT

5 Scapes with a whorl of emersed leaves near the middle . . *U. radiata* . . . . FLOATING BLADDERWORT
5 Scapes leafless **6**

6 Leaf divisions flat in section. **7**
6 Leaf divisions round or threadlike **8**

7 Bladders borne on leaves; smallest leaf divisions entire (visible with a 10x hand lens); flower with a sac or spur much shorter than lower lip . . . . *U. minor* / LESSER BLADDERWORT
7 Bladders on branches separate from leaves; smallest leaf divisions finely toothed, the teeth spine-tipped; flower with a spur as long as lower lip . . . . *U. intermedia* / NORTHERN BLADDERWORT

8 Plants large; leaves floating; scapes 1 mm or more wide; flowers 13 mm or more long, 5 or more per head; larger bladders more than 2 mm wide . . . . *U. vulgaris* / COMMON BLADDERWORT
8 Plants smaller; leaves floating or creeping on lake bottom or wet shores; scapes threadlike; flowers to 12 mm long, 1–3 per head; larger bladders mostly less than 2 mm wide **9**

9 Plants forming tangled masses, creeping on bottom in shallow water

or on muck or drying pond edges; often with emergent scapes with at least 1 normal flower; cleistogamous flowers absent . . . . . *U. gibba*
. . . . CREEPING BLADDERWORT

9 Plants forming a delicate mass of floating leaves; emergent scapes with normal flowers rare; cleistogamous flowers common, on stalks 4–8 mm long. . . . . *U. geminiscapa* / MIXED BLADDERWORT

Utricularia cornuta Michx.
Leafless bladderwort   OBL

Annual or perennial herb. **Stems** and leaves underground, roots with tiny bladders. **Flowers** yellow, with a downward-pointing spur 6–15 mm long, on stalks 1–2 mm long, 1–6 atop an erect stalk 10–25 cm long; bracts ovate, 1–2 mm long. **Fruit** a rounded capsule. June–Sept. ☙ Acid lakes, shores, peatlands, calcareous pools between dunes, borrow pits. ⊕ n Minn, Wisc, Mich, rare in ne Ill and nw Ind. Nfld and Que to Mich and Minn, s to Fla and Tex; W Indies.

Utricularia geminiscapa Benj.
Mixed bladderwort   OBL

Annual or perennial herb, similar to **common bladderwort** (*U. vulgaris*) but smaller. **Stems** floating below water surface, sparsely branched. **Leaves** alternate, 1–2 cm long, branched into 4–7 segments and without bladders, or unbranched with bladders. **Flowers** yellow, 2–5 atop a slender stalk, 5–15 cm long, bracts below flowers 2–3 mm long; individual flower stalks 4–8 mm long, these arched when plants fruiting; cleistogamous flowers without petals more commonly produced, these single on leafless stalks 5–15 mm long along stems and often 1 at base of scape. July–Aug. *U. clandestina*. ☙ Acid lakes, pools in open bogs. ⊕ Occasional in n Wisc, Mich and nw Ind. Nfld and Que to Mich and n Wisc, s to Va and n Ind.

Utricularia gibba L.
Creeping bladderwort   OBL

Annual or perennial herb. **Stems** creeping on bottom in shallow water, mostly less than 10 cm long, radiating from base of flower stalk (scape) and forming mats. **Leaves** alternate, scattered, to 5 mm long, 1–2-forked into threadlike segments; bladders present. **Flowers** 1–3, yellow, 5–6 mm long, with a thick, blunt spur shorter than lower lip, atop a single stalk 5–10 cm long. **Fruit** a rounded capsule. July–Sept. ☙ Exposed shores, lakes, ponds, marshes, fens. ⊕ nc Minn, Wisc, Mich, local in ne Ill and nw Ind. Que to Wisc and Minn, s to Fla and La; Pacific states, c Amer, W Indies.

Utricularia intermedia Hayne
Northern bladderwort   OBL

Annual herb. **Stems** very slender, creeping along bottom in shallow water. **Leaves** alternate, 0.5–2 cm long, mostly 3-parted near base, then again divided 1–3x, the segments linear and flat, margins with small, bristly teeth; bladders 2–4 mm wide, borne on branches separate from leaves. **Flowers** yellow, 2–4 atop an emergent stalk 5–20 cm long; individual flower stalks to 15 mm long, remaining erect in fruit; spur nearly as long as lower lip. **Fruit** a capsule. June–Aug. ☙ Shallow water (usually alkaline), marly pools between dunes, calcareous fens, marshes, ponds and rivers. ⊕ n and Minn, Wisc, Mich, ne Ill and nw Ind. Circumboreal, s to Del, Ind, Iowa, ND and Calif.

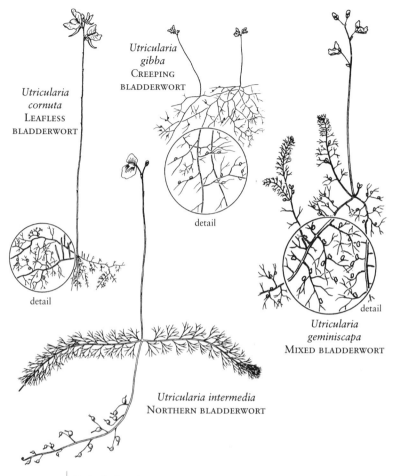

Utricularia gibba
CREEPING BLADDERWORT

detail

Utricularia cornuta
LEAFLESS BLADDERWORT

detail

detail

Utricularia geminiscapa
MIXED BLADDERWORT

detail

Utricularia intermedia
NORTHERN BLADDERWORT

Utricularia minor L.
Lesser bladderwort   OBL

⚠
STATUS
Illinois - E
Indiana - E

Perennial herb. **Stems** few-branched, 10–30 cm long, creeping on bottom in shallow water or on wet soil. **Leaves** alternate, to 1 cm long, with few divisions, the segments slender, flat, the smallest segments strongly tapered to tip, margins entire; bladders 1–2 mm wide, 1–5 on leaves. **Flowers** pale yellow, 2–8 atop a threadlike stalk 4–15 cm long; individual flower stalks to 1 cm long, curved downward in fruit; lower lip of flower 4–8 mm long, 2x longer than upper lip; spur small, to half length of lower lip. **Fruit** a capsule. June–Aug. ❦ Fens, open bogs, sedge meadows and marshes; often in shallow water and where calcium-rich. ⊕ n and ec Minn, Wisc, Mich, rare in ne Ill and n Ind. Circumboreal, s to NJ, Ind, ND and Calif.

Utricularia purpurea Walter
Spotted or Purple bladderwort   OBL

⚠
STATUS
Indiana - E

Annual or perennial herb. **Stems** underwater, to 1 m long. **Leaves** in whorls of 5–7, branched into threadlike segments, many segments tipped by a bladder. **Flowers** red-purple, 1–4 atop a stalk 3–15 cm long; corolla 1 cm long, lower lip 3-lobed, with a yellow spot near base; spur short and appressed to lower lip. **Fruit** a capsule. July–Sept. *Vesiculina pur-*

purea. ※ Acid lakes and ponds in water to 1 m deep, peatlands, marshes. ⊕ Minn, Wisc, e UP and LP of Mich, nw Ind. NS and Que to Minn and n Ind, s near Atlantic coast to Fla and La; W Indies.

Utricularia radiata Small
Floating bladderwort   OBL

Annual or perennial herb. **Stems** long, floating below water surface. **Lower leaves** alternate, 2–3 cm long, divided into threadlike, bladder-bearing segments; **uppermost leaves** below the flower stalk in whorls of 4–7, with petioles 1–4 cm long and inflated, tipped by finely dissected branches. **Flowers** yellow, mostly 3–5 atop a stalk 3–5 cm long, bracts 2–3 mm long; individual flowers on stalks 1–2 cm long; lower lip of flower shallowly 3-lobed, 8–10 mm long; spur short and appressed to lower lip. **Fruit** a capsule. July–Sept. *U. inflata* var. *minor.* ※ Pools between dunes. ⊕ Atlantic coastal plain, rarely inland to extreme sw Mich and nw Indiana.

Utricularia resupinata B. D. Greene
Lavender bladderwort   OBL

Annual or perennial herb. **Stems** delicate, on water surface in shallow water or creeping just below soil surface. **Leaves** alternate, 3-parted from base, the middle segment erect and linear, to 3 cm long; the 2 lateral segments slender, rootlike, with bladders. **Flowers** purple, 1 cm long, single atop an erect stalk 2–10 cm long; bract tubelike, surrounding the stem, its margin notched; flower tipped backward on stalk and facing upward; lower lip 3-lobed; spur ± horizontal. **Fruit** a rounded capsule. July–Aug. *Lecticula resupinata.* ※ Shallow to deep water, wet lake and pond shores where sandy or mucky. ⊕ Uncommon in ne Minn and n Mich. NS to n NY, n Minn and sw Ont, locally s to Fla and Ga.

Utricularia subulata L.
Slender bladderwort   OBL

Annual or perennial herb, with short, rootlike branches from base of flower stalk (these underground and rarely collected), with small bladders 0.5 mm long. Aboveground **leaves** short-lived, linear, to 1 cm long. **Flowers** yellow, 1–10, atop a very slender, erect stalk 3–20 cm long; bracts ovate or oval, 1–2 mm long, attached to flower stalk at or below their middle; individual flowers on stalks 5–15 mm long; lower flower lip 4–7 mm long; spur ± equal to lower lip and appressed to its underside. **Fruit** a round capsule. July–Sept. *U. cleistogama, Setiscapella cleistogama.* ※ Wet places between dunes, wet prairie. ⊕ sw LP of Mich near Lake Mich and nw Ind. NS to Fla and Tex, inland to Mich and n Ind.

Utricularia vulgaris L.
Common bladderwort   OBL

Perennial herb. **Stems** floating below water surface, sparsely branched, often forming large mats. **Leaves** alternate, 1–5 cm long, 2-forked at base and repeatedly 2-forked into segments of unequal length, the segments ± round in section, becoming smaller with each branching, the final segments threadlike; bladders 1–4 mm wide, borne on leaf segments. **Flowers** yellow, 6–20 atop a stout stalk 6–25 cm long; lower flower lip 1–2 cm long, sometimes much smaller on late-season flowers, upper lip ± equal to lower lip; spur about 2/3 as long as lower lip; stalks bearing individual flowers curved downward in fruit. **Fruit** a capsule. June–Aug. *U. macrorhiza.* ※ Shallow water of lakes, ponds, peatlands, marshes and rivers. ⊕ Minn, Wisc, Mich, ne Ill and nw Ind. Circumboreal, s to Fla, Tex, Ariz and Calif.

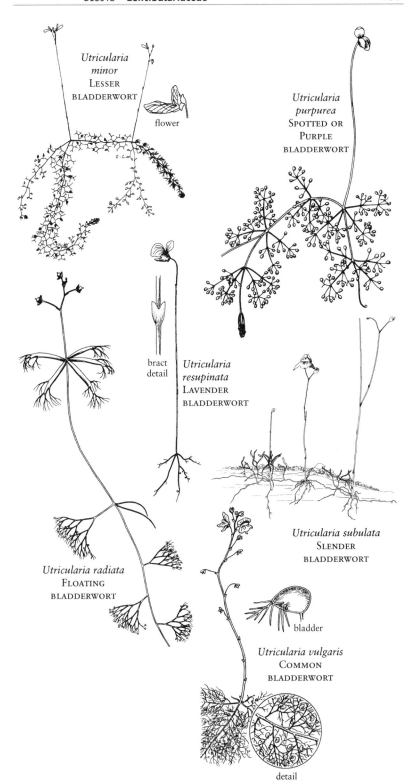

Utricularia minor
LESSER BLADDERWORT

flower

Utricularia purpurea
SPOTTED OR PURPLE BLADDERWORT

bract detail

Utricularia resupinata
LAVENDER BLADDERWORT

Utricularia subulata
SLENDER BLADDERWORT

Utricularia radiata
FLOATING BLADDERWORT

bladder

Utricularia vulgaris
COMMON BLADDERWORT

detail

Linaceae
Flax Family

▶Linum L. / Flax

Perennial herbs (those included here). **Leaves** simple, alternate or opposite, narrow, margins entire, petioles absent. **Flowers** regular, perfect, 5-
parted; petals yellow (ours) or blue. **Fruit** a 10-chambered capsule. ☞
Southern yellow flax (*L. intercursum* E. Bickn.) is rare in wet, sandy soil
in nw Ind (⚠ state endangered), disjunct from Atlantic coast (OBL). The
capsules of this yellow-flowered species are cone-shaped above the middle vs. ± round in the species below.

▶KEY TO LINUM

1 Stems not angled; branches of head stiffly ascending . . . *L. medium*
. . . . COMMON YELLOW FLAX
1 Stems sharply angled and winged; branches of head spreading . . . .
. . . . *L. striatum* / RIDGESTEM YELLOW FLAX

Linum medium (Planchon) Britton
Common yellow flax   (FACW)

Perennial herb; plants smooth. **Stems** 2–6 dm long,
unbranched below head. **Leaves** mostly alternate, narrowly lance-shaped, 1–2.5 cm long and 2–5 mm wide,
smaller upward; margins entire; petioles absent. **Flowers**
in a branched head, the branches stiffly ascending, the
flowers on stalks 2–3 mm long; outer sepals lance-shaped,
entire, 2–3 mm long, inner sepals shorter with gland-tipped
hairs or teeth on margins; petals yellow, 4–8 mm long. **Fruit** a
persistent, ± round capsule, 2 mm long, often purple-tinged
near top. June–Sept. Ours are var. *texanum*. ❧ Sandy, calcium-rich shores, moist places between dunes. ⊕ se Wisc, c and
s LP of Mich, ne Ill and nw Ind. Atlantic coast from Maine to
Fla, w to s Ont, Mich, Ill, Kans and e Tex.

capsule

Linum striatum Walter
Ridgestem yellow flax   FACW-

STATUS
Indiana - T

Perennial herb; plants smooth. **Stems** erect, 3–9 dm
long, 1 or several from base of plant, with 3
sharp, narrow wings extending downward from
base of each leaf. **Leaves** mostly opposite, oval to
obovate, the larger leaves 1–3 cm long and 4–9
mm wide. **Flowers** in an open panicle, the panicle
branches short and spreading; flower stalks
sharply angled, 1–3 mm long; sepal margins
mostly entire; petals yellow, 3–5 mm long. **Fruit** a
± round capsule, soon splitting into 10 segments.
June–July. ❧ Sandy shores and marshes (especially
near Lake Michigan); also in dry pine woods. ⊕ w LP
of Mich and nw Ind. Mass to Mich, s to n Fla, e Mo
and e Tex.

Lythraceae
Loosestrife Family

Annual or perennial herbs, sometimes woody at base (*Decodon*). **Leaves** simple, opposite, or both opposite and alternate, or whorled, margins entire, ± stalkless. **Flowers** 1 or several in leaf axils or in spikelike heads at ends of stems; perfect (with both male and female parts), regular or irregular; sepal lobes 4 or 6; petals 4 or 6, separate, pink or purple, deciduous; stamens usually 2x number of petals. **Fruit** a dry, many-seeded capsule.

▶**KEY TO LYTHRACEAE**

1 Plants arching, woody near base; leaves with petioles and mostly whorled . . . . *Decodon verticillatus* . . . . SWAMP OR WHORLED LOOSESTRIFE
1 Plants annual or perennial herbs; leaves opposite, or if whorled, leaves without petioles. **2**

2 Plants perennial; flowers in spikelike heads at ends of stems; petals and sepals 6 . . . . *Lythrum* / LOOSESTRIFE
2 Plants annual; flowers from leaf axils; petals and sepals 4 or 5 (when present). **3**

3 Flowers mostly 2–5 per leaf axil; flowers purple-tinged. . . . . *Ammannia robusta* / TOOTH-CUP; SCARLET LOOSESTRIFE
3 Flowers mostly 1 per axil, not purple. **4**

4 Submersed leaves lance-shaped, broadest at base, less than 3 mm wide . . . . *Didiplis diandra* / WATER-PURSLANE
4 Leaves oval, widest near middle, larger leaves 3 mm or more wide . . . . *Rotala ramosior* / TOOTH-CUP; WHEELWORT

▶**Ammannia** L. / Tooth-cup

Ammannia robusta Heer & Regel
Tooth-cup; Scarlet loosestrife   OBL
Annual herb; plants smooth. **Stems** erect, 2–8 dm long, often branched from base. **Leaves** opposite, linear, 2–8 cm long and 3–15 mm wide, heart-shaped and clasping at base; margins entire; petioles absent. **Flowers** stalkless, in clusters of 1–3 per leaf axil; petals 4 (rarely 5), 2–3 mm long, rose-purple, sometimes with a purple midvein at base; stamens 4 or 8. **Fruit** a round, 4-parted capsule, 3–5 mm wide, tipped by the persistent style. July–Oct. *A. coccinea.* ≋ Exposed mud flats and marshes, disturbed open wet areas; sometimes where calcium-rich. ⊕ Local in wc Minn and along Minn and Miss Rivers in s Minn; uncommon in far se LP of Mich and ne Ill. Ohio to SD, s to Ky and Tex; Calif, Mex, c Amer; n S Amer and islands of Caribbean.

▶**Decodon** J. F. Gmelin / Water-willow

Decodon verticillatus (L.) Elliott
Swamp or whorled loosestrife   OBL

Perennial herb, woody near base. **Stems** slender, angled, smooth or slightly hairy, 1–3 m long, arching downward and rooting at tip when in contact with water or mud. **Leaves** in whorls of 3–4 or opposite, lance-shaped, 5–15 cm long and 1–3 cm wide, smooth above, sparsely hairy below; margins entire; petioles short. **Flowers** in dense clusters in upper leaf axils; sepals 5–7, short, triangular; petals pink-purple, tapered to base, 10–15 mm long; stamens 10 (rarely 8), alternately longer and shorter than petals. **Fruit** a ± round capsule, 5 mm wide. July–Sept. Great Lakes plants are var. *laevigatus*. ❦ Shallow water and margins of lakes, ponds, bogs, swamps and marshes; soils mucky. ⊕ ec Minn, Wisc, Mich LP (and uncommon in UP), ne Ill and nw Ind. NS and Que to Minn, s to e Tenn.

▶**Didiplis** Raf. / Water-purslane

Didiplis diandra (Nutt.) A. Wood
Water-purslane   OBL

Annual herb; plants underwater or on exposed shores. **Stems** weak, branched, 1–4 dm long. **Leaves** numerous, opposite; underwater leaves linear, straight across base, 1–2.5 cm long; emersed leaves shorter and wider, tapered at base; petioles absent. **Flowers** few, inconspicuous, green. **Fruit** a small round capsule. July–Aug. *Peplis diandra*. ❦ Shallow water and muddy pond margins. ⊕ Uncommon in far se Minn; sw Wisc, ne Ill and nw Ind. Ohio, Wisc and Minn, s to Va, Fla, Kans and Tex. ☞ Plants somewhat resemble **water-starwort** (*Callitriche*), but in water-starwort the underwater leaves have a shallow notch at tip and the capsule is flattened.

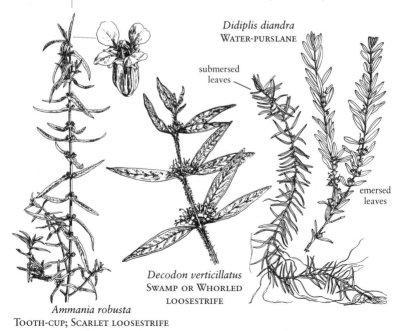

Didiplis diandra
WATER-PURSLANE

submersed leaves

emersed leaves

Decodon verticillatus
SWAMP OR WHORLED
LOOSESTRIFE

Ammania robusta
TOOTH-CUP; SCARLET LOOSESTRIFE

▶**Lythrum** L. / Loosestrife

Perennial herbs. **Stems** erect, sometimes rather woody at base, usually with ascending branches above, upper stems 4-angled. **Leaves** opposite, entire, alternate, or rarely whorled, lance-shaped, stalkless, reduced to bracts in the head. **Flowers** in showy, spikelike heads, 1 to several in axils of upper leaves, regular or somewhat irregular, the stamens and styles of 2 or 3 different lengths. Sepals joined into a tube, the calyx tube cylinder-shaped, green-striped with 8–12 nerves; petals 6, purple, not joined; stamens 6 or 12; ovary 2-chambered. **Fruit** an ovate capsule, enclosed by the calyx tube.

▶KEY TO LYTHRUM

1 Flowers single in upper leaf axils; stamens usually 6 . . . . . *L. alatum* . . . . WINGED LOOSESTRIFE
1 Flowers many in spikelike heads at ends of stems; stamens usually 12 (6 long and 6 short) . . . . *L. salicaria* / PURPLE LOOSESTRIFE

Lythrum alatum Pursh
Winged loosestrife OBL

Smooth perennial herb, spreading by rhizomes. **Stems** usually branched above, 2–8 dm long, somewhat woody at base. Lower **leaves** usually opposite, upper leaves alternate; lance-shaped, 1–4 cm long and 3–10 mm wide, rounded at base; margins entire; petioles absent. **Flowers** single in axils of upper, reduced leaves (bracts), short-stalked; calyx tube 4–6 mm long, smooth; petals 6, deep purple, 3–7 mm long; stamens usually 6. **Fruit** a capsule enclosed by the sepals. June–Aug. *L. dacotanum*. ⚘ Lakeshores, wet meadows, marshes, low prairie, calcareous fens, ditches; especially where sandy. ⊕ Common; wc and s Minn, Wisc, c and e UP, and LP (especially s) of Mich, ne Ill and nw Ind. Ont to ND and Wyo, s to Ga, Ala and Okla.

Lythrum salicaria L.
Purple loosestrife OBL

☞ To limit the spread of **purple loosestrife**, plants should be pulled (including roots), bagged, and removed from infested wetlands. Biological control by several insects also offers promise for long-term control.

Perennial herb, spreading and forming colonies by thick, fleshy roots which send up new shoots. **Stems** erect, 6–15 dm long, 4-angled, with many ascending branches. **Leaves** opposite or sometimes in whorls of 3, becoming alternate and reduced to bracts in the head; lance-shaped, 3–10 cm long and 0.5–2 cm wide, mostly heart-shaped and clasping at base; margins entire; petioles absent. **Flowers** large and showy, 2 or more in axils of reduced upper leaves (bracts), in spikes 1–4 dm long at ends of branches; sepals joined, the calyx tube 4–6 mm long, hairy; petals 6, purple-magenta, 7–10 mm long; stamens usually 12, the stamens and styles of 3 different lengths. **Fruit** a capsule enclosed by the sepals. June–Sept. ⚘ Introduced from Europe and sometimes planted as an ornamental, escaping to marshes, wet ditches, streambanks, cranberry bogs and shores, where a serious threat to our native flora and of little value to wildlife. In addition to spreading vegetatively, a single plant may produce several hundred thousand seeds each year. ⊕ Most common in c and s portions of our region. ec Minn near Miss River, local elsewhere; Wisc, Mich LP (especially s, local in UP), ne Ill and nw Ind. Naturalized over much of e and c USA, s Can; local in w USA.

▸**Rotala** L. / Tooth-cup

Rotala ramosior (L.) Koehne
Tooth-cup; Wheelwort   OBL

⚠
STATUS
Minnesota - T

Small, annual herb. **Stems** smooth, 4-angled, to 4 dm long, unbranched or branched from base, the branches spreading to upright. **Leaves** opposite, linear to oblong, 1–5 cm long and 2–12 mm wide; margins entire; stalkless or tapered to a short petiole. **Flowers** single and stalkless in leaf axils, calyx tube bell-shaped to cylindric, 2–5 mm long, not strongly nerved, the lobes alternating with appendages of same length; petals small, white to pink, 4, slightly longer than sepals; stamens 4. **Fruit** a round capsule enclosed by the sepals. July–Oct. ✤ Muddy or sandy shores, marshes (especially those that dry during growing season), low spots in fields, ditches and other seasonally flooded places. ⊕ ec Minn, Wisc, wc and s LP of Mich, ne Ill and nw Ind. Mass to Minn and SD, s to Fla and Tex; Pacific Coast and s into S Amer; Caribbean islands.

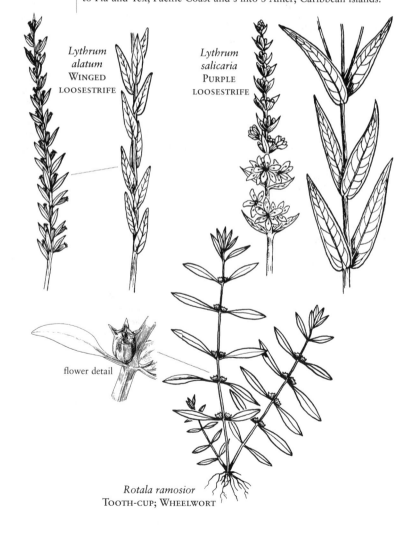

*Lythrum
alatum*
Winged
loosestrife

*Lythrum
salicaria*
Purple
loosestrife

flower detail

Rotala ramosior
Tooth-cup; Wheelwort

Malvaceae
Mallow Family

Annual or perennial herbs with upright stems. **Leaves** alternate, entire to lobed or dissected, often round or kidney-shaped, palmately veined. **Flowers** single or in small, narrow clusters from leaf axils, with 5 united sepals and 5 petals; stamens many and joined near base, forming a tube around the style. **Fruit** a capsule.

▶**KEY TO MALVACEAE**

1 Flowers perfect; pistil 5-parted, the fruit segments (carpels) united, not separating when mature . . . . *Hibiscus* / ROSE-MALLOW
1 Flowers either male or female and borne on separate plants; pistil 10-parted or more, the fruit segments separating when mature. . . . . . .
. . . . *Napaea dioica* / GLADE-MALLOW

▶**Hibiscus** L. / Rose-mallow

Large, upright perennial herbs. **Leaves** alternate, smooth or hairy, palmately divided. **Flowers** large and showy, pink to white; ovary divided into 5 segments (carpels). **Fruit** an ovate capsule.

▶**KEY TO HIBISCUS**

1 Leaves and stems without hairs . *H. laevis* / SMOOTH ROSE-MALLOW
1 Leaf undersides and upper stems with velvety hairs . *H. moscheutos*
. . . . SWAMP ROSE-MALLOW

Hibiscus laevis All.
Smooth rose-mallow   OBL

Perennial herb; stems and leaves smooth. **Stems** upright, 1–2 m long. **Leaves** triangular in outline, heart-shaped at base, sometimes with outward pointing basal lobes; margins with rounded teeth; petioles 3–15 cm long. **Flowers** large, from leaf axils or clustered at ends of stems or branches; petals pink with darker center, 5–8 cm long. **Fruit** an ovate capsule, enclosed by the calyx; seeds silky-hairy. Aug–Sept. *H. militaris.* ❦ Marshes, muddy shores and shallow water. ⊕ Uncommon in se Mich; ne Ill and nw Ind. Pa s to Fla and Tex, inland to Ohio, n Ind, n Ill and Minn.

Hibiscus moscheutos L.
Swamp rose-mallow   OBL

Large perennial herb. **Stems** upright, numerous from base of plant, 1–2 m long, upper stems gray-hairy. **Leaves** ovate, upper surface green and smooth, lower surface white velvety hairy; margins toothed; petioles 2–12 cm long. **Flowers** large and showy, 10–20 cm wide, pink or white, often red or purple in center, at ends of stalks near top of stems. **Fruit** a hairless, ovate capsule; seeds smooth. Aug–Sept. *H. palustris.* ❦ Marshes, streambanks and disturbed wet areas. ⊕ s Wisc, s Mich, ne Ill and nw Ind. Coastal marshes from Mass to Tex; occasional inland in NY, Ohio, Wisc and Mo; Calif.

▶**Napaea** L. / Glade-mallow

Napaea dioica L.

Glade-mallow   FACW-

⚠
STATUS
Minnesota - T

Large perennial herb. **Stems** erect, 1–2 m long. **Leaves** round in outline, 1–3 dm wide, deeply 5–9 lobed, the lobes coarsely toothed, on long petioles; upper leaves smaller, with short petioles. **Flowers** either male or female and on separate plants; many in large panicles at ends of stems; petals white, obovate, petals of male flowers 5–9 mm long, petals of female flowers smaller. **Fruit** a 10-parted capsule, the segments (carpels) 5 mm long, ribbed, and irregularly separating when mature. June–Aug. ❦ Moist floodplain forests, riverbanks. ⊕ Uncommon in se Minn; sw Wisc and n Ill. Va to Pa, w to Wisc, Ill and Iowa.

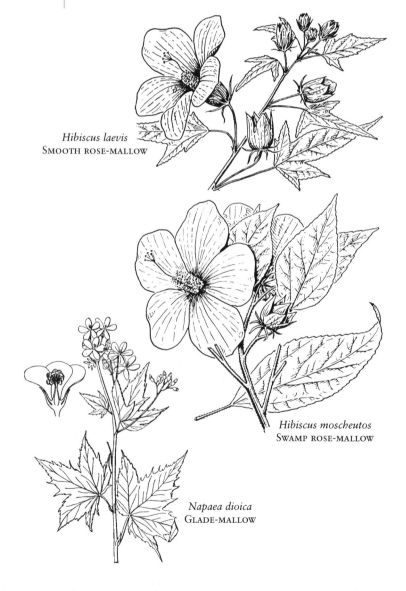

Hibiscus laevis
SMOOTH ROSE-MALLOW

Hibiscus moscheutos
SWAMP ROSE-MALLOW

Napaea dioica
GLADE-MALLOW

Melastomataceae
Melastome Family

▶**Rhexia** L. / Meadow-beauty; Meadow-pitchers

Perennial herbs; plants hairy. **Stems** round or square in cross-section. **Leaves** opposite, prominently 3–5-veined from base, margins with forward-pointing teeth and fringed with hairs; stalkless or short-petioled. **Flowers** large, pale to bright purple, rarely white, bell-shaped, in clusters of a few at ends of stems; sepals joined, 4-lobed; petals 4; stamens 8. **Fruit** a 4-chambered capsule.

▶**KEY TO RHEXIA**

1 Stems ± round in section. . . . . . *R. marina* / Dull meadow-beauty
1 Stems square or angled in section . . . . *R. virginica*
. . . . Virginia meadow-beauty; Deer-grass

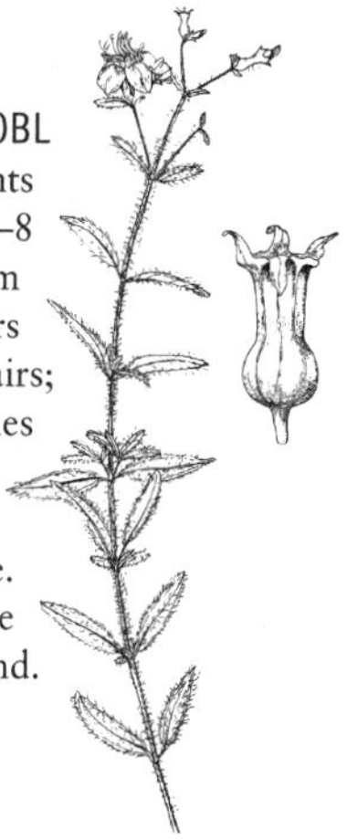

Rhexia marina L.
Dull meadow-beauty   OBL

⚠
STATUS
Indiana - E
Michigan - T

Weedy perennial herb, with shallow rhizomes; plants densely coarse-hairy. **Stems** ± round in section, 3–8 dm long, branched. **Leaves** lance-shaped, 2–6 cm long and 1–2 cm wide, spreading, with bristly hairs on both sides; margins toothed and fringed with hairs; petioles short. **Flowers** pale purple (sometimes white), stalked, in open clusters at ends of stems; petals 4, rounded at tip, 1–2 cm long. **Fruit** a capsule, enclosed by the glandular-hairy sepal tube. July–Sept. ≱ Moist openings and shores. ⊕ More common s and e of our range. Rare in s Mich and Ind. Mass to Fla, w to Mich, Ind, Mo and Tex.

Rhexia virginica L.
Virginia meadow-beauty; Deer-grass   OBL
Perennial herb, roots often with tubers. **Stems** simple, or branched above, 4-angled and winged, 2–6 dm long, usually with bristly hairs at nodes. **Leaves** opposite, ovate, 2–6 cm long and 1–3 cm wide, smooth or with short, stiff hairs on either side, tapered to a tip; margins finely toothed; stalkless. **Flowers** stalked, in clusters from ends of stems and upper leaf axils; sepals narrow, 2–4 mm long; petals purple, 10–20 mm long. **Fruit** a 4-chambered capsule. July–Sept. ≱ Open shores, thickets (often of *Aronia* and *Nyssa*); soils acidic, sandy or peaty. ⊕ wc and sw LP of Mich, ne Ill and nw Ind, NS to n Ill, s to Fla and Tex.

Menyanthaceae
Buckbean Family

▶**Menyanthes** L. / Buckbean

Menyanthes trifoliata L.
  Buckbean   OBL
Perennial herb, with thick rhizomes covered with old leaf bases; plants
smooth. **Leaves** alternate along rhizomes, palmately divided into 3
leaflets, the leaflets oval to ovate, 3–10 cm long and 1–5 cm wide, entire
or sometimes wavy-margined; petioles 5–30 cm long, the base of petiole
expanded and sheathing stem. **Flowers** in racemes on leafless stalks 2–4
dm long and longer than the leaves; bracts mostly 3–5 mm long; individual flowers on stalks 5–20 mm long; flowers perfect, regular, 5-part-
ed, often of 2 types, some with flowers with long stamens and a shorter
style, others with a long style and shorter stamens; sepal lobes 2–3 mm
long; corolla funnel-shaped, 8–12 mm long,
petals white, often purple-tinged, bearded
with white hairs on inner surface; stamens
5. **Fruit** a rounded capsule, 6–10 mm
wide; seeds shiny, yellow-brown.
May–July. ❦ Open bogs and fens
(especially in pools and outer moat),
cedar swamps, wet thickets. ⊕ Minn
(all but far sw and se), Wisc (all but
driftless area), Mich, ne Ill and nw
Ind. Circumboreal, s to Del, Va, Ohio,
Mo, SD, Colo and Calif.

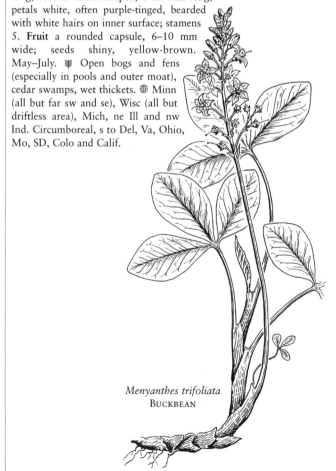

Menyanthes trifoliata
BUCKBEAN

Myricaceae
Bayberry Family

▶**Myrica** L. / Sweet gale; Bayberry

Myrica gale L.
Sweet gale   OBL

☞ Leaves of **sweet gale** emit a pleasant scent when rubbed.

Much-branched shrub, 6–15 dm tall; bark dark gray to red-brown with small pale lenticels; twigs hairy, dotted with glands. **Leaves** alternate, deciduous, wedge-shaped, tapered to base, broadest above middle, 3–6 cm long and 1–2 cm wide, tip rounded and toothed, dark green on upper surface, paler below, dotted with shiny yellow glands; petioles short, 1–3 mm long. Male and female **flowers** separate and on different plants, appearing before or with unfolding leaves; male flowers in catkins 10–20 mm long, with dark brown, shiny triangular scales; female flowers in conelike, brown clusters 10–12 mm long. **Fruit** a flattened, ovate achene, resin-dotted, 2–3 mm long. April–May.   *Gale   palustris.*   ≋ Lakeshores, marshes, swamps and bogs, often at water's edge or in shallow water. ⊕ ne and nc Minn, n Wisc, UP and n LP of Mich. Circumboreal, s to NJ, Pa, Minn and Ore.

female flower clusters

Myrica gale
SWEET GALE

Nelumbonaceae
Lotus-Lily Family

▶**Nelumbo** Adans. / Lotus-lily

Nelumbo lutea (Willd.) Pers.
   American lotus-lily   OBL

⚠
STATUS
Michigan - T

Perennial aquatic herb, from a large, horizontal rootstock. **Leaves** large and shield-shaped, 3–7 dm wide, ribbed, floating on water surface or held above water surface, smooth above, somewhat hairy below; petioles thick, attached at center of blade. **Flowers** pale yellow, single, 15–25 cm wide; petals obovate, blunt-tipped; receptacle flat-topped, to 1 dm wide. **Seeds** acornlike, 1 cm thick. July–Aug. ⚘ Lakes, ponds, backwater areas, marshes, where sometimes forming large colonies covering many acres. ⊕ se Minn and Wisc, mostly near Miss River; rare in s LP of Mich, ne Ill and nw Ind. s Ont and NY to s Minn, s to Fla and Tex.

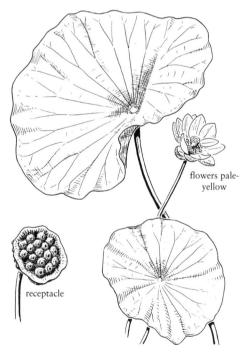

flowers pale-
yellow

receptacle

Nelumbo lutea
AMERICAN LOTUS-LILY

Nymphaeaceae
Water-Lily Family

Aquatic perennial herbs. **Stems** long and fleshy, from horizontal rhizomes rooted in bottom mud. **Leaves** large, leathery, mostly floating or emergent above water surface, heart-shaped to shield-shaped, notched at base, margins entire. **Flowers** showy, single on long stalks and borne at or above water surface, perfect (with both male and female parts), white or yellow, sepals 4–6, green or yellow; petals numerous, small (*Nuphar*) to large and showy (*Nymphaea*). **Fruit** a many-seeded, berrylike capsule, opening underwater when mature.

▸**KEY TO NYMPHACEAE**

1 Flowers yellow, often red-tinged, sepals petal-like, true petals small; leaf blades oblong to oval or heart-shaped . . . . *Nuphar*
. . . . YELLOW WATER-LILY; SPATTERDOCK
1 Flowers white (rarely pink), sepals green, true petals large and showy; leaf blades nearly round . . . . *Nymphaea* / WATER-LILY

▸**Nuphar** J.E. Smith / Yellow water-lily; Spatterdock

Aquatic herbs. **Leaves** large and floating or emergent. **Sepals** 5–6, yellow and petal-like, forming a saucer-shaped flower; **petals** small and numerous.

▸**KEY TO NUPHAR**

1 Leaves small, 5–10 cm wide; anther shorter than its stalk (filament); disk at base of stigma red; uncommon species of n Great Lakes region
. . . . *N. microphylla* / YELLOW WATER LILY
1 Leaves larger; anther longer than its stalk; disk at base of stigma green or yellow; widespread **2**

2 Leaf blades usually raised above water surface, basal lobes of blades close or touching; petioles round or oval in section . . . . *N. advena*
. . . . YELLOW WATER LILY
2 Leaf blades floating, basal lobes widely spreading; petioles flattened and narrowly winged . . . . *N. variegata* / BULLHEAD LILY

Nuphar advena (Aiton) Aiton f.
Yellow water lily   OBL
Aquatic perennial herb. **Leaves** mostly emergent and raised above water surface, 2–4 dm wide, with a broadly triangular notch at leaf base, petioles round or oval in section; underwater leaves absent. **Flowers** 3–6 cm wide; sepals 6, yellow, sometimes purple on inner surface; petals small, numerous; anthers 3–7 mm long and as long or longer than their stalks (filaments); disk at base of stigma green, 10–15 mm wide, with 14–18 rays. **Fruit** ovate, to 4 cm long. June–Sept. *N. fluviatilis*, *N. macrophylla*. ❦ Shallow to deep water of slow-moving streams, lakes and ponds. ⊕ n, c and se Wisc, s LP of Mich, ne Ill and nw Ind. Maine to Wisc, s to Fla, Cuba, Mo, Tex and n Mex.

Nuphar microphylla (Pers.) Fern.
Yellow water lily   OBL

Aquatic perennial herb. **Leaves** both underwater and floating; floating leaves 5–10 cm long and 3–8 cm wide, notch at base usually more than half as long as midvein; petioles flattened on upper side; underwater leaves membranous, somewhat larger. **Flowers** 1.5–2 cm wide, sepals 5, yellow on inner surface; petals small and many; anthers 1–3 mm long, shorter than the filaments; disk at base of stigma red, 3–6 mm wide, with 6–10 rays. **Fruit** ovate, 15 mm long. July–Aug. *N. luteum, N. pumila.* ❧ Lakes, ponds and slow-moving streams. ⊕ ne Minn, n Wisc, rare in Mich UP. Nfld to ne Minn, s to NJ and Pa.

Nuphar variegata Durand
Bullhead lily   OBL

Aquatic perennial herb. **Leaves** mostly floating, 10–25 cm wide, notch usually less than half as long as midvein, petioles flattened on upper side and narrowly winged; underwater leaves absent or few. **Flowers** 2.5–5 cm wide; sepals usually 6, yellow, red-tinged on inner surface; petals small and numerous; anthers 4–7 mm long, longer than filaments; disk at base of stigma green, 1 cm wide, with 10–15 rays. **Fruit** ovate, 2–4 cm long. June–Aug. *N. fraterna.* ❧ Ponds, lakes, quiet streams. ⊕ Minn, Wisc, Mich, ne Ill and nw Ind. Nfld to BC, s to Del, Ohio, Kans and Idaho.

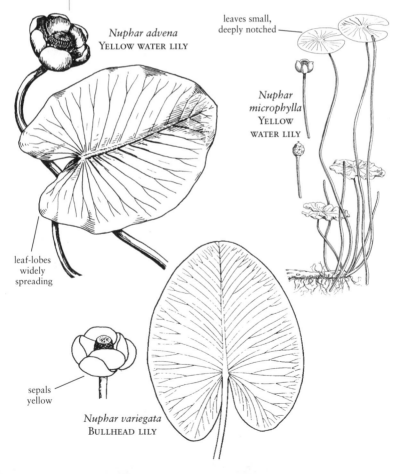

Nuphar advena
YELLOW WATER LILY

leaves small,
deeply notched

*Nuphar
microphylla*
YELLOW
WATER LILY

leaf-lobes
widely
spreading

sepals
yellow

Nuphar variegata
BULLHEAD LILY

▶**Nymphaea** L. / Water-lily

Large aquatic plants, from stout rhizomes, these sometimes with lateral tubers. **Leaves** floating, round, notched to the petiole, petioles not flattened or winged. **Flowers** white and showy; sepals 4, green; petals white or pink, showy, numerous and overlapping; stamens many, the outer stamens with broadened, petal-like filaments, anthers yellow, ovary depressed at tip with a rounded projection from center, stigmas 10–25. **Fruit** round, covered with persistent petal and stamen bases, maturing under water; seeds numerous, each enclosed within a sac (aril).

▶KEY TO NYMPHAEA

1 Leaves round in outline, narrowly notched; flowers large and showy, usually fragrant; common . . . . *N. odorata* / WHITE WATER-LILY
1 Leaves oval in outline, notch more widely spreading; flowers smaller and scarcely fragrant; rare in far n Minn and Isle Royale, Mich . . . . *N. tetragona* / PYGMY WATER-LILY

Nymphaea odorata Aiton
White water-lily   OBL

Aquatic perennial herb, rhizomes sometimes with knotty tubers. **Leaves** floating, round, 1–3 dm wide, with a narrow notch, green and shiny on upper surface, usually purple or red below. **Flowers** white (rarely pink), usually fragrant, 7–20 cm wide, often opening in morning and closing in late afternoon (or remaining open on cool, cloudy days); sepals 4, green, 3–10 cm long; petals 17–25, about as long as sepals, oval, tapered to a rounded tip; stamens 40–100. **Fruit** round, mostly covered by the sepals; seeds 2–4 mm long. June–Aug. *Castalia tuberosa, N. tuberosa.* ☙ Shallow water of ponds and lakes, quiet water of rivers. ⊕ e Minn (and uncommon in w), Wisc, Mich, ne Ill and nw Ind. Newf to Minn and Man, s to Fla and Tex.

Nymphaea tetragona Georgi
Pygmy water-lily   OBL

⚠
STATUS
Michigan - T
Minnesota - T

Aquatic perennial herb, rhizomes ascending. **Stems** arising from tip of rhizomes. **Leaves** 7–12 cm long and to 3/4 as wide, notch fairly wide, upper surface green, green or purple below. **Flowers** white, usually not fragrant, 4–8 cm wide, reported to open in afternoon; sepals 4, green, 2–3 cm long; petals 8–17, about as long as sepals; stamens 20–40. **Fruit** not covered by the erect sepals. Summer. *Castalia leibergii, Nymphaea leibergii.* ☙ Shallow water of ponds and lakes. ⊕ Far nc Minn and Isle Royale, Mich. Maine and Ont to n Minn and Wash; Eurasia.

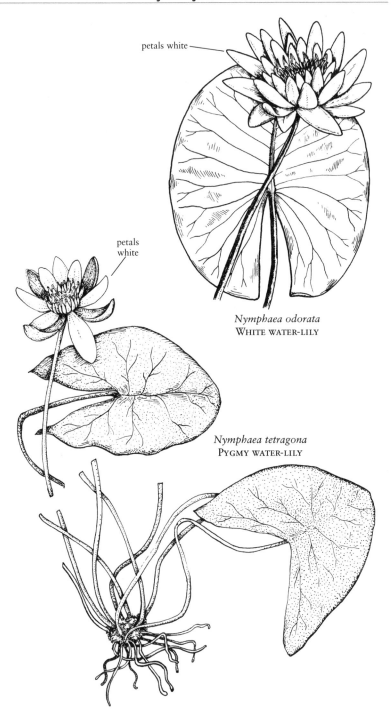

petals white

petals
white

Nymphaea odorata
WHITE WATER-LILY

Nymphaea tetragona
PYGMY WATER-LILY

Oleaceae
Olive Family

▶Fraxinus L. / Ash

Medium to large trees. **Leaves** deciduous, opposite, pinnately divided into leaflets. **Flowers** in clusters from axils of previous year's twigs, mostly single-sexed, male and female flowers on different trees, rarely perfect, petals absent. **Fruit** a 1-seeded, winged samara.

▶KEY TO FRAXINUS

1 Lateral leaflets ± stalkless . . . . *F. nigra* / BLACK ASH
1 Lateral leaflets short-stalked **2**

2 Twigs, petioles and leaf undersides hairy; widespread . . . .
. . . . *F. pennsylvanica* / GREEN ASH; RED ASH
2 Twigs, petioles and leaf undersides smooth; uncommon in s Mich and ne Ill (and possibly nw Ind) . . . . *F. profunda* / PUMPKIN ASH

Fraxinus nigra Marshall
　Black ash   FACW+

Tree to 15 m tall; trunk 30–60 cm wide, crown open and narrow; **bark** gray, thin, flaky; **twigs** smooth, round in section, dark green, becoming gray. **Leaves** opposite, pinnately divided into 7–11 stalkless (except for terminal) leaflets; **leaflets** lance-shaped to oblong, 7–13 cm long and 2.5–5 cm wide, long-tapered to a tip; margins with sharp, forward-pointing teeth. **Flowers** appear in spring before leaves, in open clusters on twigs of previous year; some perfect, some single-sexed, male and female flowers on different trees. **Fruit** a 1-seeded samara, 2.5–4 cm long and 6–10 mm wide, the wing broad and rounded at tip, deciduous or persisting until following spring. April–May. ⚘ Floodplain forests, cedar swamps, wet depressions in forests. ⊕ Minn (all but sw), Wisc, Mich, ne Ill and nw Ind. Nfld and Que to Man, s to Del, WVa, Ind and Iowa.

Fraxinus pennsylvanica Marshall
　Green ash; Red ash   FACW

Tree to 15 m tall; trunk 30–60 cm wide; **bark** dark gray or brown, thick, with shallow furrows and netlike ridges; **twigs** usually hairy for 1–3 years, becoming light gray or red-brown. **Leaves** opposite, pinnately divided into 7–9 leaflets; **leaflets** oblong lance-shaped to ovate, 7–13 cm long and 2.5–4 cm wide, upper surface smooth, underside smooth or hairy; margins entire or with few forward-pointing teeth; petioles short, smooth or hairy. **Flowers** appear in spring before or with leaves, in compact, hairy clusters on twigs of previous year; single-sexed, male and female flowers on different trees. **Fruit** a 1-seeded, slender samara, 2.5–5 cm long, in open clusters persisting until following spring. April–May. ⚘ Floodplain forests, swamps, shores, streambanks. ⊕ Minn, Wisc, Mich, ne Ill and nw Ind. NS and Que to Alberta, s to Fla and Tex. ☞ Both smooth and hairy forms *of F. pennsylvanica* occur, with trees becoming less hairy westward across our region. Trees with hairy twigs and leaves are called **red ash**. Hairless plants are called **green ash**.

Fraxinus profunda (Bush) Bush
Pumpkin ash   OBL

Tree to 30 m tall; trunk 30–60 cm wide; **bark** gray, scaly, with shallow furrows and netlike ridges; **twigs** gray or brown, velvety-hairy to smooth. **Leaves** opposite, pinnately divided into 7–9 leaflets; **leaflets** lance-shaped to oval, 15–20 cm long and 7–10 cm wide, long-tapered to a tip, upper surface smooth, underside velvety-hairy; margins entire or finely toothed; petioles 8–15 mm long. **Flowers** appear in spring before leaves, in elongated clusters on twigs of previous year; single-sexed, male and female flowers on different trees. **Fruit** a 1-seeded samara, linear or spatula-shaped, 4–7 cm long and 7–11 mm wide, the wing extending at least to middle of the round seed body. April–May. *F. tomentosa.* 🌱 Floodplain forests and swamps, especially where seasonally flooded. ⊕ Uncommon in extreme s Mich, ne Ill and nw Ind; more common s of our region. NJ to Fla, w to Ill, Mo and La.

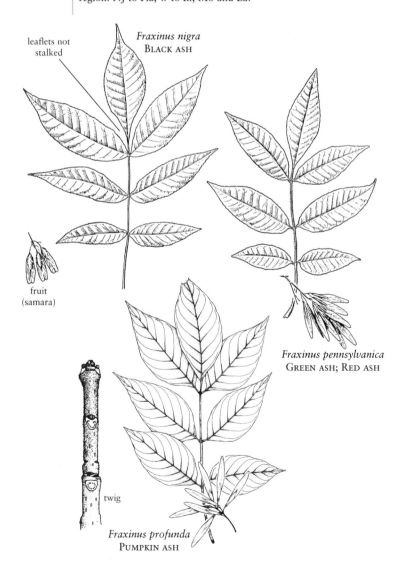

leaflets not
stalked

Fraxinus nigra
BLACK ASH

fruit
(samara)

Fraxinus pennsylvanica
GREEN ASH; RED ASH

twig

Fraxinus profunda
PUMPKIN ASH

Onagraceae
Evening-primrose Family

Annual or perennial herbs. **Leaves** opposite to alternate, simple to pinnately divided, stalkless or short-petioled. **Flowers** usually large and showy, perfect (with both male and female parts), regular, borne in leaf axils or in heads at ends of stems; sepals 8 or 4; petals 4, white, yellow or pink to rose-purple; ovary 4-chambered. **Fruit** a 4-chambered capsule; seeds many, with or without a tuft of hairs (coma).

▶**KEY TO ONAGRACEAE**

1 Petals 2, white; leaves opposite; fruit with bristly hairs . . . .
. . . . *Circaea alpina* / SMALL OR ALPINE ENCHANTER'S NIGHTSHADE
1 Petals 4 (rarely absent), white, pink, or yellow; leaves opposite or alternate; fruit without bristly hairs **2**

2 Petals yellow (or absent); seeds without a tuft of hairs (coma). . . . .
. . . . *Ludwigia* / WATER-PRIMROSE; PRIMROSE-WILLOW
2 Petals pink, white or rose-purple; seeds with a tuft of hairs. . . . . . .
. . . . *Epilobium* / WILLOW-HERB

▶**Circaea** L. / Enchanter's nightshade

Circaea alpina L.
Small or Alpine enchanter's nightshade   FACW

⚠
STATUS
Illinois - E

Perennial herb, spreading from rhizomes thickened and tuberlike at ends. **Stems** weak, 1–3 dm long, mostly smooth. **Leaves** opposite, ovate, 2–5 cm long and 1–3 cm wide; margins coarsely toothed; petioles flat on upper side, underside thin-winged along center. **Flowers** white, in short racemes of 10–15 flowers, becoming 1 dm long in fruit; sepals 1–2 mm long; petals to 2 mm long. **Fruit** a 1-seeded capsule, 2–3 mm long, covered with soft hooked bristles. June–Aug. ❧ Cedar swamps (where often on rotting logs), low spots in forests. ⊕ e and c Minn, Wisc, Mich, possibly in ne Ill and nw Ind. Circumboreal, s to NY, NC, Tenn, Ind, Iowa and SD; NM.

flower

Circaea alpina
SMALL OR ALPINE
ENCHANTER'S
NIGHTSHADE

▶**Epilobium** L. / Willow-herb

Perennial herbs, often producing leafy rosettes or bulblike offsets (turions) at base of stem late in growing season. **Leaves** simple, opposite, alternate, or opposite below and becoming alternate above; stalkless or short-petioled. **Flowers** white to pink, single in axils of upper reduced leaves, or in spike or racemes at ends of stems; sepals 4; petals 4; stamens 8, the inner 4 stamens shorter than outer 4; ovary 4-chambered, maturing into a linear, 4-parted capsule, splitting from tip to release numerous brown seeds which are tipped with a tuft of fine hairs (coma).

▶**KEY TO EPILOBIUM**

1 Stigma deeply 4-lobed **2**
1 Stigma entire or slightly notched, not deeply lobed **3**

2 Petals 10–15 mm long, shallowly notched at tip; leaves ± clasping stem . . . . *E. hirsutum* / Hairy willow-herb
2 Petals 4–9 mm long, deeply notched at tip; leaves not clasping stem . . . . *E. parviflorum* / Hairy willow-herb

3 Leaves more than 1 cm wide, margins toothed, not rolled under; stems usually with lines of hairs **4**
3 Leaves less than 1 cm wide, margins ± entire, rolled under; stem hairs not in lines **5**

4 Tuft of hairs attached to tip of seeds (coma) ± white, seeds with a broad, short beak; margins of stem leaves with mostly 10–30 teeth on a side . . . . *E. ciliatum* / American willow-herb
4 Coma brown, seeds beakless; leaf margins with more than 30 teeth on a side . . . . *E. coloratum* / Purple-leaf willow-herb

5 Hairs spreading . . . . *E. strictum* / Downy willow-herb
5 Hairs flattened against stems and leaves **6**

6 Upper surface of leaves finely hairy . . . . *E. leptophyllum* . . . . Linear-leaf willow-herb
6 Upper surface of leaves ± smooth *E. palustre* / Marsh willow-herb

Epilobium ciliatum Raf.
American willow-herb   FACU

⚠
STATUS
Indiana - E

Perennial herb, with over-wintering leafy rosettes. **Stems** often branched, 3–10 dm long, smooth below, short-hairy above, especially in the head (where often with gland-tipped hairs). **Leaves** opposite, usually alternate near top; lance-shaped to ovate, 3–10 cm long and 0.5–3 cm wide; margins with few, small, forward-pointing teeth; stalkless or with short, winged petioles to 6 mm long. **Flowers** usually nodding when young, on stalks 3–10 mm long, on branches from upper leaf axils; sepals ovate, 2–5 mm long; petals white (or pink), notched at tip, 2–8 mm long. **Fruit** a linear capsule, 4–8 cm long, with gland-tipped hairs; seeds 1 mm long, the coma white. July–Sept. *E. adenocaulon.* ≋ Shores, streambanks, marshes, wet meadows, seeps, ditches and other wet places. ⊕ Occasional in Minn, Wisc, Mich, ne Ill and nw Ind. Newf and Labr to Alaska, s to NC, Tenn, Ohio, Iowa, Tex and Ariz; Mex and c Amer.

Epilobium coloratum Biehler

Purple-leaf willow-herb   OBL

Perennial herb, producing basal, leafy rosettes in fall; similar to **American willow-herb** (*E. ciliatum*) but larger. **Stems** 5–10 dm long, much-branched in the head, smooth below, short-hairy above with hairs often in lines; stems and leaves often purple-tinged. **Leaves** mostly opposite, becoming alternate and smaller above, lance-shaped, 5–15 cm long and 0.5–3 cm wide, long-tapered to a pointed tip; margins finely toothed, with irregular sharp teeth; short-petioled to stalkless. **Flowers** many on branches from upper leaf axils; sepals lance-shaped, 2–3 mm long; petals pink or white, 3–5 mm long, notched at tip; individual flowers on stalks to 10 mm long. **Fruit** a linear capsule, 3–5 cm long; seeds 1.5 mm long, the coma brown when mature. July–Sept. ❧ Shores, seeps, swamps and wet woods, wet meadows, fens, ditches. ⊕ Minn, Wisc, Mich, ne Ill and nw Ind. Maine and Que to Minn and se ND, s to NC, Ala, Ark, Okla and n Tex.

Epilobium hirsutum L.

Hairy willow-herb   FACW+

Perennial herb, spreading by rhizomes. **Stems** much-branched, 5–15 dm long, upper stems with a dense covering of soft, straight hairs. **Leaves** opposite (but bracts alternate), lance-shaped or oblong, 5–10 cm long and 1–3 cm wide, hairy on both sides, somewhat clasping at base; margins with sharp, forward-pointing teeth; petioles absent. **Flowers** upright on stalks from upper leaf axils, petals red-purple, 10–15 mm long, shallowly notched; stigma 4-lobed. **Fruit** a hairy, linear capsule, 5–8 cm long; coma nearly white. June–Sept. ❧ Introduced from Eurasia, now established in swamps, thickets, marshes, shores, wet meadows and ditches. ⊕ se Wisc, LP of Mich, ne Ill and nw Ind; mostly near Great Lakes. s Que and Maine to s Ont, n Ohio, Mich and n Ill, s to Md.

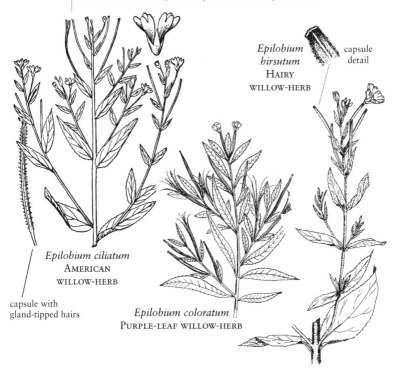

Epilobium hirsutum
HAIRY
WILLOW-HERB

capsule detail

Epilobium ciliatum
AMERICAN
WILLOW-HERB

capsule with gland-tipped hairs

Epilobium coloratum
PURPLE-LEAF WILLOW-HERB

Epilobium leptophyllum Raf.

Linear-leaf willow-herb   OBL

Perennial herb, similar to **marsh willow-herb** (*E. palustre*) but somewhat larger and more hairy. **Stems** simple or branched, 2–10 dm long, with short, incurved hairs. **Leaves** opposite or alternate, linear or linear lance-shaped, 2–7 cm long and 1–6 mm wide, upper surface hairy, underside hairy, at least on midvein, lateral veins indistinct; margins entire and rolled under; petioles short or ± absent. **Flowers** erect in upper leaf axils on short, slender stalks to 1 cm long; petals light pink, 3–5 mm long, entire or slightly notched at tip. **Fruit** a linear, finely hairy capsule, 4–5 cm long; the coma yellow-white. July–Sept. *E. lineare*. ❧ Swamps, marshes, open bogs, sedge meadows, shores, streambanks and springs. ⊕ Minn, Wisc, Mich, ne Ill and nw Ind. Maine and Que to Minn and ND, s to NC, Ala, Ark, Okla and n Tex.

Epilobium palustre L.

Marsh willow-herb   OBL

Perennial herb, from slender rhizomes or stolons. **Stems** simple or with a few branches above, 1–6 dm long, upper stem hairy with small incurved hairs. **Leaves** mostly opposite, lance-shaped, erect or ascending, 2–6 cm long and 3–15 mm wide, tapered to a rounded tip, upper surface smooth or with sparse hairs along midvein, underside smooth or finely hairy along midvein, lateral veins distinct; margins entire and often rolled under; stalkless. **Flowers** few in upper leaf axils, on short stalks; petals white to pink, 3–5 mm long, notched at tip. **Fruit** a linear, finely hairy capsule; coma pale. July–Aug. *E. oliganthum*. ❧ Open bogs and swamps. ⊕ Local in n and ec Minn, n Wisc, Mich UP and LP (especially nw). Circumboreal, s to Pa, Minn, Colo and Nev.

Epilobium parviflorum Schreber

Hairy willow-herb   (OBL)

Perennial herb, similar to *E. hirsutum* but plants smaller, and the petals only 4–7 mm long (vs. mostly 10–15 mm long in *E. hirsutum*). **Stems** 4–8 dm long. Lower **leaves** opposite, upper leaves often alternate; 2–8 cm long, not clasping at base; margins with sharp, forward-pointing teeth; ± stalkless. **Flowers** upright on stalks from upper leaf axils; petals red-purple, 4–7 mm long, deeply notched; stigma 4-lobed. **Fruit** a hairy, linear capsule; coma ± white. July–Sept. ❧ Swamps, shores and ditches. ⊕ n LP of Mich and s Ont.

Epilobium strictum Muhl.

Downy willow-herb   OBL

Perennial herb, spreading by slender rhizomes; plants densely soft white-hairy. **Stems** erect, simple or branched above, 3–6 dm long. Lower **leaves** opposite, upper leaves alternate; lance-shaped, ascending, 2–4 cm long and 3–8 mm wide, tapered to a rounded tip; margins mostly entire, rolled under; stalkless. **Flowers** on slender stalks from upper leaf axils; petals pink, 5–8 mm long, notched at tip. **Fruit** a linear, densely hairy capsule; coma pale brown. July–Aug. ❧ Conifer swamps, sedge meadows, calcareous fens, marshes. ⊕ Local in c Minn; Wisc, mostly s LP of Mich (and uncommon in UP), ne Ill and nw Ind. Que to Minn, s to Va, Ohio and n Ill.

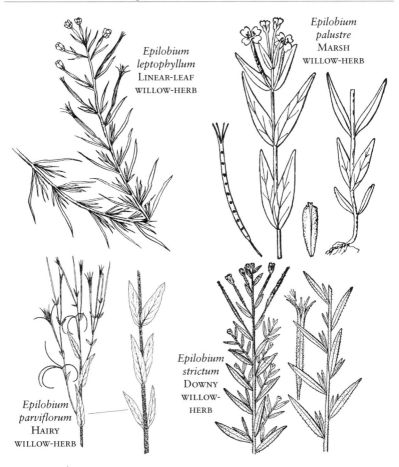

Epilobium leptophyllum LINEAR-LEAF WILLOW-HERB

Epilobium palustre MARSH WILLOW-HERB

Epilobium strictum DOWNY WILLOW-HERB

Epilobium parviflorum HAIRY WILLOW-HERB

▶**Ludwigia** L. / Water-primrose; Primrose-willow

Perennial herbs. **Stems** floating, creeping, or upright. **Leaves** simple, opposite or alternate, entire. **Flowers** single in leaf axils; sepals 4; petals 4 (or absent), yellow or green, large or very small; stamens 4; stigma unlobed. **Fruit** a 4-chambered, many-seeded capsule; seeds without a tuft of hairs at tip (coma).

▶KEY TO LUDWIGIA

1 Leaves opposite, stalked; stems floating or creeping and rooting at nodes. . *L. palustris* / COMMON WATER-PURSLANE; MARSH PURSLANE
1 Leaves alternate, ± stalkless; stems mostly erect **2**

2 Flower petals showy, yellow; flowers and fruit on stalks 3 mm or more long. . . . . *L. alternifolia*
. . . . SQUARE-POD WATER-PRIMROSE; SEED-BOX
2 Flower petals very small or absent; flowers and fruit stalkless **3**

3 Plants smooth (or leaves sometimes with hairs on margins). . . . . . .
. . . . *L. polycarpa* / TOP-POD WATER-PRIMROSE
3 Plants usually hairy. . . . . *L. sphaerocarpa*
. . . . ROUND-POD WATER-PRIMROSE

Ludwigia alternifolia L.
Square-pod water-primrose; Seed-box   OBL

Perennial herb, roots often with tubers; plants smooth or finely hairy. **Stems** erect, 4–10 dm long, branched. **Leaves** alternate, lance-shaped, 5–10 cm long, margins entire; stalkless or with short petioles. **Flowers** single from leaf axils, on stalks 3–5 mm long, with 2 lance-shaped bracts near the flower; petals 4, yellow, 3–4 mm long. **Fruit** a smooth capsule, 4–5 mm long and as wide, square above, sharp-angled and rounded below. July–Aug. ⚘ Swamps, thickets, marshes, shores, ditches; especially where sandy. ⊕ s Wisc, uncommon in s LP of Mich; ne Ill and nw Ind. Mass to s Ont, n Ind, Iowa and Neb, s to Fla and Tex.

Ludwigia palustris (L.) Elliott
Common water-purslane; Marsh purslane   OBL

Perennial herb. **Stems** weak, creeping and rooting at nodes or partly floating, simple to branched, 1–5 dm long, succulent, smooth or with sparse scattered hairs. **Leaves** opposite, lance-shaped to ovate, 0.5–3 cm long and 0.5–2 cm wide, shiny green or red, margins entire, tapered at base to a winged petiole to 2 cm long. **Flowers** single in leaf axils, stalkless; sepals broadly triangular, 1–2 mm long; petals usually absent, or small and red. **Fruit** a capsule, 2–5 mm long and 2–3 mm wide, somewhat 4-angled, with a green stripe on each angle. July–Sept. *Isnardia palustris.* ⚘ Shallow water or exposed mud of pond margins, lakeshores, streambanks, ditches, springs. ⊕ ec Minn, Wisc, Mich, ne Ill and nw Ind. NS to BC, s to Fla, Tex and Calif; Mex, S Amer, Eurasia and Africa.

Ludwigia polycarpa Short & Peter
Top-pod water-primrose   OBL

Perennial herb, producing leafy stolons from base in fall; plants smooth. **Stems** erect, 1–9 dm long, often branched, usually 4-angled. **Leaves** alternate, lance-shaped to oblong lance-shaped, 3–12 cm long and 5–15 mm wide; margins entire; ± stalkless. **Flowers** single in leaf axils, stalkless; sepals triangular, 2–4 mm long, usually persistent; petals green and very small or absent. **Fruit** a short-cylindric, rounded 4-angled capsule, 4–7 mm long and 3–5 mm wide. July–Sept. ⚘ Borders of swamps and marshes, muddy shores, wet depressions. ⊕ se Minn, Wisc, mostly ec and s LP of Mich, ne Ill and nw Ind. Maine and s Ont to Minn, s to Tenn, Mo and Kans; s Ala.

Ludwigia sphaerocarpa Elliott
Round-pod water-primrose   OBL

⚠
STATUS
Indiana - E
Michigan - T

Perennial herb, spreading by stolons; plants finely hairy or sometimes smooth. **Stems** to 1 m long, usually branched above. **Leaves** alternate, lance-shaped, 5–10 cm long and 1–2 cm wide, upper leaves much smaller; margins with low teeth; petioles absent. **Flowers** single and ± stalkless in leaf axils, greenish; sepal lobes ovate; petals absent. **Fruit** a ± round, finely hairy capsule, 3–4 mm long, not angled. July–Sept. ⚘ Swamp margins, lakeshores, often in shallow water. ⊕ Rare in sw LP of Mich and nw Ind. Mass to Fla and Tex; disjunct inland in Ind and sw Mich.

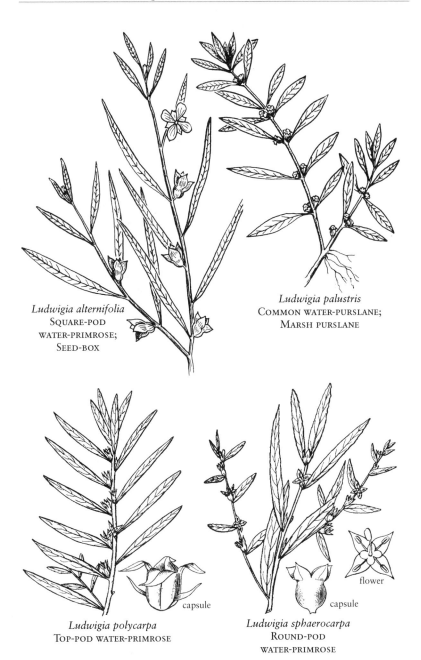

Ludwigia alternifolia
SQUARE-POD
WATER-PRIMROSE;
SEED-BOX

Ludwigia palustris
COMMON WATER-PURSLANE;
MARSH PURSLANE

Ludwigia polycarpa
TOP-POD WATER-PRIMROSE

capsule

Ludwigia sphaerocarpa
ROUND-POD
WATER-PRIMROSE

capsule

flower

Oxalidaceae
Wood Sorrel Family

▶**Oxalis** L. / Wood-sorrel

Oxalis acetosella L.
Northern wood-sorrel   (FACW)
Perennial herb, from slender, scaly rhizomes. **Leaves** single or 3–6 together, all from base of plant, on stalks 4–15 cm long, these joined at base; palmately divided into 3 leaflets, the leaflets notched at tips, sparsely hairy. **Flowers** perfect, broadly bell-shaped, single atop stalks 6–15 cm long (usually slightly taller than leaves), with a pair of small bracts above middle of stalk; sepals 5, much shorter than petals; petals 5, white or pink, with pink veins, 10–15 mm long. **Fruit** a smooth, nearly round capsule. May–July. *O. montana.* ❦ Hummocks in swamps, wet depressions in forests, moist wetland margins, usually where shaded. ⊕ Common in n portions of our region. ne Minn, n Wisc, UP and n LP of Mich. e Que to NY, Mich, n Minn and Sask, s to NC and Tenn.

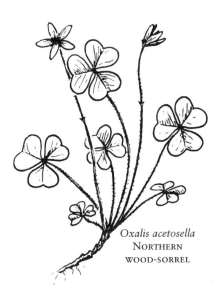

Oxalis acetosella
NORTHERN
WOOD-SORREL

Plantaginaceae
Plantain Family

Annual or perennial herbs. **Leaves** simple, entire, all from base of plant. **Flowers** perfect in a narrow spike (*Plantago*), each flower subtended by bracts, or single-sexed, the male and female flowers on same plant (*Littorella*); flower parts mostly in 4s. **Fruit** a capsule opening at tip.

▶**KEY TO PLANTAGINACEAE**

1 Flowers single at ends of stalks or stalkless, either male or female . . . . *Littorella uniflora* / SHOREWEED
1 Flowers many in spikes, perfect . . . . *Plantago* / PLANTAIN

▶**Littorella** P. Bergius / Shoreweed

Littorella uniflora (L.) Asch.
Shoreweed   OBL

Low perennial herb; plants clumped, often forming mats. **Leaves** bright green, linear, to 5 cm long and 2–3 mm wide, succulent; margins entire. **Flowers** only from emersed plants, single-sexed, male and female flowers on same plant; **male flowers** 1–2 on stalks to 4 cm long; **female flowers** stalkless among the leaves; sepals 4 (sometimes 3 in female flowers), lance-shaped, 2–4 mm long, with a dark green midrib and lighter margins; petals joined, 4-lobed; stamens 4, longer than the petals. **Fruit** a 1-seeded nutlet, 2 mm long and 1 mm wide. July–Aug. *L. americana.* ☙ Exposed lakeshores where sandy or mucky, or in water 1 m or more deep. ⊕ Along US-Canada border in ne Minn; n Wisc, UP of Mich. Nfld and Que to Ont and NY; n Great Lakes; Europe.

☞ Both native and introduced populations are reported for Littorella; native plants (var. *americana*) are somewhat smaller than the European variety.

flower detail

▶**Plantago** L. / Plantain

Perennial or annual herbs. **Leaves** all from base of plant, simple. **Flowers** small, perfect or single-sexed, green, ± stalkless in axils of small bracts, grouped into crowded spikes; sepals 4; petals 4. **Fruit** a capsule.

▶**KEY TO PLANTAGO**

1 Plants perennial; stamens 4; s portion of region, absent from Minn . . . . *P. cordata* / KING-ROOT; HEART-LEAF PLANTAIN
1 Plants annual; stamens 2; sw Minn only . . . . *P. elongata* . . . . SLENDER PLANTAIN

Plantago cordata Lam.
King-root; Heart-leaf plantain   OBL

⚠
STATUS
Illinois - E
Indiana - E
Michigan - E
Wisconsin - E

Smooth perennial herb, roots long and fleshy (to more than 1 cm wide). **Stems** stout, hollow, to 6 dm long, longer than leaves, often purple-tinged. **Leaves** large, broadly ovate, 10–25 cm long and 8–20 cm wide, pinnately veined, rounded or heart-shaped at base; margins entire or shallowly toothed; petioles winged near base of blade. **Flowers** green, in loose, interrupted spikes to 3 dm long; sepals ovate, about as long as bracts; petals joined, the 4 lobes spreading. **Fruit** a rounded capsule, 5–10 mm long, opening at or near the middle, usually with 2 seeds. April–June. ❦ Floodplain forests, wooded streambanks, sometimes in shallow water; usually where calcium-rich. ⊕ Uncommon in ec and se Wisc, s LP of Mich, ne Ill and nw Ind. Ohio and s Ont to s Wisc and Mo; occasional e and s to NY, Va, Ga and Ala.

Plantago elongata Pursh
Slender plantain   FACW

⚠
STATUS
Minnesota - T

Small annual herb with a slender taproot. **Stems** to 15 cm long, finely hairy. **Leaves** all from base of plant, narrow and linear, 3–8 cm long, tapered to a blunt tip; margins mostly entire; petioles absent. **Flowers** green, in slender spikes 3–8 cm long, with mix of male, female and some perfect flowers; sepals to 2 mm long and as long as bracts; petals joined, the lobes to 1 mm long, usually widely spreading. **Fruit** a capsule 2–3 mm long, opening at or near the middle; seeds 1–2 mm long. May–Aug. ❦ Moist, usually alkaline places. ⊕ Entering our range in far sw Minn. w Minn and Man to BC, s to Okla and Calif.

Plantago cordata
KING-ROOT;
HEART-LEAF
PLANTAIN

Plantago elongata
SLENDER PLANTAIN

flower

Platanaceae
Plane-Tree Family

▶**Platanus** L. / Sycamore

Platanus occidentalis L.
Sycamore   FACW
Large tree to 30 m tall or more; trunk to 2 m wide, crown broad and
spreading; **bark** red-brown when young, soon breaking into thin, flat
sections which fall away to expose white-green inner bark; **twigs** smooth,
light brown; **buds** light brown and pointed. **Leaves** alternate, to 20 cm
long and about as wide, divided into 3 or 5 shallow, sharp-pointed lobes,
bright green and smooth on upper surface, underside paler, smooth
except for sparse hairs on veins. Male and female **flowers** tiny, in dense
clusters, separate but on same tree. **Fruit** a round, light brown head, 2–3
cm wide, on a long, drooping stalk. May. ❦ Riverbanks, floodplain
forests and lakeshores. ⊕ Occasional in s Wisc and s Mich; ne Ill and nw
Ind. se Maine to s Wisc, n Ill and e Neb, s to Fla and e Tex.

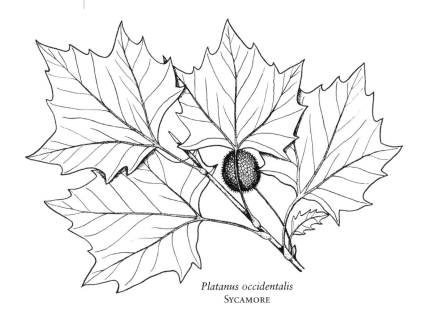

Platanus occidentalis
SYCAMORE

Polemoniaceae
Phlox Family

Annual or perennial herbs. **Leaves** opposite (*Phlox*) or pinnately divided (*Polemonium*). **Flowers** perfect (with both male and female parts), single or in clusters at ends of stems and from leaf axils; sepals and petals 5-parted and joined for part of length. **Fruit** a 3-chambered capsule, with usually 1 seed per chamber.

▸**KEY TO POLEMONIACEAE**

1 Leaves undivided. . . . . *Phlox* / PHLOX
1 Leaves pinnately divided into leaflets . . . . . *Polemonium occidentale*
. . . . WESTERN JACOB'S LADDER

▸**Phlox** L. / Phlox

Erect perennial herbs of southern portions of region. **Leaves** opposite, margins entire. **Flowers** pink, purple or rarely white, in stalked clusters at ends of stems and from upper leaf axils; sepals joined and tubelike; corolla 5-lobed, tubelike but flared outward at tip; stamens 5. **Fruit** a 3-chambered capsule.

▸**KEY TO PHLOX**

1 Flower head rounded, the individual flower clusters 1 to few, on stalks of unequal lengths . . . . *P. glaberrima* / SMOOTH PHLOX
1 Flower head ± cylinder-shaped, the clusters several or more, on stalks of about equal length . . . . *P. maculata*
. . . . SPOTTED PHLOX; WILD SWEET-WILLIAM

Phlox glaberrima L.
Smooth phlox   FACW

⚠
STATUS
Wisconsin - E

Perennial herb, plants usually smooth. **Stems** erect, unbranched, 5–10 dm long. **Leaves** opposite, firm, lance-shaped, long-tapered to a sharp tip, 5–12 cm long and 3–15 mm wide; margins entire; petioles absent (except on lowest leaves). **Flowers** 1.5–2 cm wide, in stalked clusters (cymes) at end of stems and from upper 1–4 pairs of leaf axils, the lower clusters long-stalked; sepals joined to form a sharp-tipped tube; petals pink, rounded at tip; style elongated. **Fruit** a 3-chambered capsule. June-Aug. ❦ Wet to moist, calcium-rich meadows and low prairies. ⊕ Uncommon in se Wisc; ne Ill and nw Ind. Md to n Ohio, n Ind and s Wisc, s to SC, Ala and Ark.

Phlox maculata L.
Spotted phlox; Wild Sweet-William   FACW+

⚠
STATUS
Michigan - T

Perennial herb. **Stems** erect, 3–8 dm long, simple or branched above, smooth or finely hairy, usually red-spotted. **Leaves** opposite, smooth, ± firm, lance-shaped, 5–12 cm long and 0.5–1.5 cm wide, long-tapered to a sharp tip; margins entire; petioles absent. **Flowers** 1–2 cm wide, in stalked clusters (cymes) at ends of stems and from several to many upper leaf axils, these short-stalked, forming a long, narrow head 10–20 cm long, the head finely hairy; sepals smooth, joined to form a sharp-tipped tube 6–8 mm long; petals pink or purple, rounded at tip; style elongated. **Fruit** a 3-chambered capsule. July-Sept. *P. pyramidalis*. ⚘ Fens, sedge meadows, springs. ⊕ se Minn, local in sw LP of Mich, ne Ill and nw Ind. s Que to Va and Ga, w to Minn, Iowa and Mo.

▶**Polemonium** L. / Jacob's ladder

Polemonium occidentale Green
Western Jacob's ladder OBL

⚠
STATUS
Minnesota - E

Perennial herb. **Stems** erect, to 10 dm long, single from upturned ends of short, unbranched rhizomes. **Leaves** alternate, pinnately divided with up to 27 leaflets, the **leaflets** 1–4 cm long, smaller upward; margins entire; petioles short or absent. **Flowers** blue, 10–15 mm wide, crowded in a long panicle composed of smaller clusters of flowers; sepals joined to form a tube; petal lobes longer than calyx tube; stamens shorter or equal to corolla; style longer than stamens. **Fruit** a 3-chambered capsule. July. ⚘ Cedar swamps and thickets. ⊕ Rare in ne Minn and n Wisc. Rocky Mts.

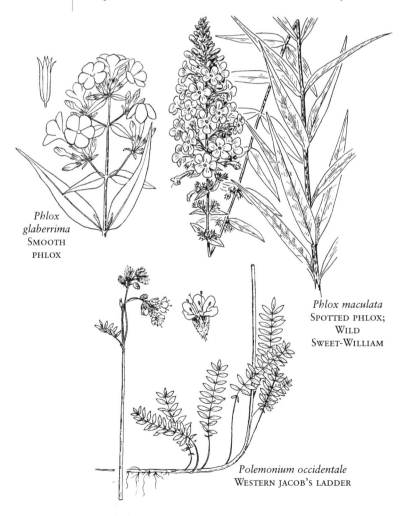

*Phlox
glaberrima*
Smooth
phlox

Phlox maculata
Spotted phlox;
Wild
Sweet-William

Polemonium occidentale
Western jacob's ladder

Polygalaceae
Milkwort Family

▶**Polygala** L. / Milkwort

Polygala cruciata L.
Drum-heads; Marsh milkwort   FACW+

⚠
STATUS
Minnesota - E

Annual herb. **Stems** erect, 4-angled, 1–4 dm long, usually branched above. **Leaves** mostly in whorls of 4, linear or oblong lance-shaped, 1–4 cm long and 1–5 mm wide, rounded and often with a short, sharp point at tip; margins entire; petioles short or absent. **Flowers** ± stalkless in cylindric racemes, 1–5 cm long and 1–1.5 cm wide; flowers pale purple or green purple; sepals 5, the 2 lateral sepals (wings) petal-like, 4–6 mm long and 3–4 mm wide at base; petals 3, joined into a tube; stamens 8 (sometimes 6). **Fruit** a 2-chambered capsule, with a single, ± hairy seed in each chamber. July–Sept. *P. ramosior*. ❦ Sandy or mucky lakeshores, wet areas between dunes. ⊕ Rare in ec Minn; s Wisc, s LP of Mich, ne Ill and nw Ind. Atlantic coastal plain from Maine to Tex; Ohio to Minn and s to Ky and Ill.

Polygala cruciata
DRUM-HEADS;
MARSH MILKWORT

Polygonaceae
Smartweed Family

Annual or perennial herbs, plants sometimes vining. **Leaves** alternate, simple, sometimes wavy-margined, otherwise entire. Stipules joined to form a membranous or papery sheath (ocrea) around stem at each node. **Flowers** in spikelike racemes or small clusters from leaf axils (*Polygonum*), or in crowded panicles at ends of stems (*Rumex*). **Flowers** small, perfect (with both male and female parts), regular, petals absent; in *Polygonum* the sepals petal-like, white to pink or yellow, mostly 5 (sometimes 4 or 6); in *Rumex* the sepals herbaceous, green to brown, in inner and outer groups, each group with 3 sepals, the 3 inner enlarging after flowering, becoming broadly winged, persisting to enclose the achene; stamens 4–8; ovary 1-chambered, styles 2–3. **Fruit** a 3-angled or lens-shaped achene.

▶**KEY TO POLYGONACEAE**

1 Flowers white to pink or green, in spikelike racemes or in groups of 1 to few in leaf axils, the sepals petal-like at least on margins . . . .
. . . . *Polygonum* / SMARTWEED; KNOTWEED; TEARTHUMB
1 Flowers green to brown, in panicles at ends of stems, the sepals not petal-like . . . . *Rumex* / DOCK

▶**Polygonum** L. / Smartweed; Knotweed: Tearthumb

Annual or perennial herbs. **Stems** erect to sprawling, often swollen at nodes. **Leaves** arrowhead-shaped to lance-shaped or oval; stipules joined to form a tubular sheath (ocrea) around the stem above each node; the ocreae (plural) membranous or papery, entire or with an irregular, jagged margin or fringed with bristles. **Flowers** small, green, white or pink, usually in slender racemes, the racemes at ends of stems or both terminal and from leaf axils, loosely to densely flowered; sepals usually 5, petal-like; green-white to pink; stamens 8 or less; styles 2–3. **Fruit** a brown to black achene, lens-shaped or 3-angled.

▶**KEY TO POLYGONUM**

1 Stems and leaf petioles with downward-curved prickles; leaves ± arrowhead-shaped **2**
1 Stems and petioles without prickles; leaves various, mostly lance-shaped or oval **3**

2 Basal lobes of leaves pointed downward; achenes 3-sided . . . .
. . . . *P. sagittatum* / ARROW-LEAVED TEARTHUMB
2 Basal lobes pointed outward; achenes 2-sided. . . . .
. . . . *P. arifolium* / HALBERD-LEAVED TEARTHUMB

3 Flowers rose-pink, in 1 (sometimes 2) terminal racemes at end of stem; plants perennial. . . . . *P. amphibium* / WATER SMARTWEED
3 Flowers white or pink, in numerous racemes from leaf axils and at

ends of stems; plants annual (except *P. hydropiperoides*)........ **4**

4 Ocreae (sheath around stem nodes) entire or with an irregular, jagged margin **5**
4 Ocreae fringed with bristles **6**

5 Outer sepals strongly 3-nerved, each nerve ending in an anchor shaped fork; racemes nodding to erect .... *P. lapathifolium* .... Dock-leaved smartweed
5 Outer sepals with faint, irregularly forked nerves; racemes erect ... . *P. pensylvanicum* / Pennsylvania smartweed

6 Flower stalks and ocreae with spreading hairs .... *P. careyi* .... Carey's hearts-ease
6 Flower stalks and ocreae with flattened hairs or hairs absent **7**

7 Sepals covered with shiny yellow glandular dots; plants peppery to taste **8**
7 Sepals without yellow glandular dots; plants not papery **9**

8 Ocreae swollen; sepals usually rose-colored at tips; achenes dull brown............. *P. hydropiper* / Water-pepper smartweed
8 Ocreae not swollen; sepals green or white-tipped; achenes smooth and shiny-black............... *P. punctatum* / Dotted smartweed

9 Plants perennial; racemes slender, over 3 cm long, loosely flowered and often interrupted; achenes 3-angled .... *P. hydropiperoides* .... False water-pepper
9 Plants annual; racemes 1–3 cm long, densely flowered and mostly continuous; achenes mostly lens-shaped (a few sometimes 3-angled) .... *P. persicaria* / Lady's thumb

Polygonum amphibium L.
Water smartweed   OBL
Perennial herb; plants either aquatic with floating leaves, or emergent and exposed, both types with spreading rhizomes. **Stems** to 1 m or more long, leaves and habit variable. **Submerged plants** smooth, usually branched, the branches floating, branch tips often upright and raised above water surface; **leaves** floating, leathery, oval, 4–20 cm long and 1–4 cm wide, rounded at tip; stipules (ocreae) membranous; petioles 1–8 cm long. **Exposed plants** hairy; leaves stalkless or with short petioles. **Flowers** pink to red, in 1–2 spikelike racemes from branch tips, the racemes 2–15 cm long and 1–2 cm wide; sepals 5-lobed to below middle, 4–5 mm long; stamens 5. **Fruit** a lens-shaped achene, 2–4 mm long, shiny dark brown. June–Sept. *P. coccineum, P. natans.* ≋ Ponds, lakes, marshes, bog pools, backwater areas, quiet streams. ⊕ Minn, Wisc, Mich, ne Ill and nw Ind. Widespread in N Hemisphere.

Polygonum arifolium L.
Halberd-leaved tearthumb   OBL

⚠
STATUS
Illinois - E

Annual herb, similar to **arrow-leaved tearthumb** (*P. sagittatum*). **Leaves** to 20 cm long and 15 cm wide, arrowhead-shaped at base but the triangular-shaped basal lobes pointing outward rather than downward as in *P. sagittatum*. **Flowers** in rounded heads at ends of stems or from leaf axils, flower stalks with glands; sepals pink, 2–3 mm long. **Fruit** a lens-shaped achene, 4–5 mm long. July–Sept. ≋ Swamps, wet woods, streambanks and shores. ⊕ Local in ec Minn, Wisc, s LP of Mich, ne Ill and nw Ind. NB to Minn, s to Ga and Mo.

Polygonum careyi Olney
Carey's hearts-ease FACW+

⚠
STATUS
Illinois - E
Indiana - T
Michigan - T

Annual herb. **Stems** upright, branched, to 1 m long, with gland-tipped hairs. **Leaves** lance-shaped; stipules (ocreae) fringed with bristles and covered with stiff, spreading hairs. **Flowers** in cylindric, drooping racemes 3–6 cm long; sepals pink or rose, 3 mm long; stamens 5 (sometimes to 8). **Fruit** a black, smooth, shiny achene, 2 mm wide. July–Aug. *Persicaria careyi*. ⚘ Sandy lakeshores and streambanks, marshes, recently burned wetlands. ⊕ Uncommon in ne Minn, Wisc, sw LP of Mich, ne Ill and nw Ind. Maine to ne Minn, s to Del and Ill.

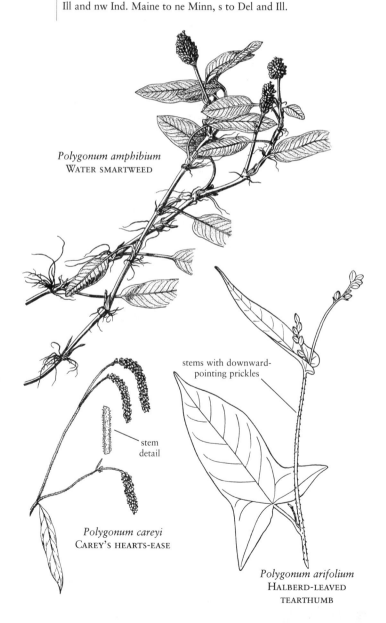

Polygonum amphibium
WATER SMARTWEED

stems with downward-
pointing prickles

stem
detail

Polygonum careyi
CAREY'S HEARTS-EASE

Polygonum arifolium
HALBERD-LEAVED
TEARTHUMB

Polygonum hydropiper L.
Water-pepper smartweed   OBL
Annual herb. **Stems** red, erect to sprawling, 2–6 dm long, sometimes rooting at lower nodes, branched or unbranched, peppery-tasting. **Leaves** lance-shaped, 3–8 cm long and to 2 cm wide, hairless except for short hairs on veins and margins, nearly stalkless or with a short petiole; stipules (ocreae) membranous, 5–15 mm long, swollen and fringed with bristles. **Flowers** green and usually white-margined, continuous in slender racemes, often nodding at tip; sepals 5, 3–4 mm long, with glandular dots; stamens 4 or 6. **Fruit** a dull, dark brown achene, 3-angled or lens-shaped, 2–3 mm long. July–Oct. *Persicaria hydropiper*. ⚘ Muddy shores, streambanks, floodplains, marshes, ditches and roadsides. Populations are apparently both native and introduced, the 2 races difficult to differentiate. ⊕ Minn, Wisc, Mich, ne Ill and nw Ind. Que to BC, s to Fla, Tex and Calif; Europe.

Polygonum hydropiperoides Michx.
False water-pepper   OBL

⚠
STATUS
Indiana - E

Perennial herb, spreading by rhizomes. **Stems** erect to sprawling with upright tips, to 1 m long, usually branched, nearly smooth or with short hairs. **Leaves** linear to lance-shaped, 4–12 cm long and to 2.5 cm wide, petioles short; stipules (ocreae) membranous, 5–15 mm long, with stiff hairs and fringed with bristles. **Flowers** green, white or pink, in 2 to several slender racemes, 1–6 cm long, often interrupted near base; sepals 2–3 mm long, 5-lobed to just below middle, without glandular dots or only the inner sepals slightly glandular; stamens 8. **Fruit** a black, shiny, 3-angled achene with concave sides, 2–3 mm long. July–Sept. ⚘ Shallow water or wet soil; ponds, marshes, swamps, bogs and fens, streambanks, lakeshores and ditches. ⊕ Local in extreme se Minn; Wisc, most of Mich (but uncommon in e UP), ne Ill and nw Ind. Que to BC, s through USA and into c and S Amer.

Polygonum lapathifolium L.
Dock-leaved smartweed   FACW+
Annual herb. **Stems** erect to sprawling, unbranched or few-branched, 2–15 dm long. **Leaves** lance-shaped, 4–20 cm long and 0.5–5 cm wide, smooth above, often densely short-hairy on leaf undersides; petioles to 2 cm long, smooth to glandular; stipules (ocreae) 5–20 mm long, entire or with irregular, jagged margins. **Flowers** deep pink, white or green, crowded in erect or nodding racemes 1–5 cm long; sepals 3–4 mm long, 4- or 5-lobed to below middle, the outer 2 sepals strongly 3-nerved; stamens usually 6. **Fruit** a brown, lens-shaped achene, 2–3 mm long. July–Sept. ⚘ Marshes, wet meadows, shores, streambanks, ditches and cultivated fields. ⊕ Common and weedy, in part introduced. Minn, Wisc, Mich, ne Ill and nw Ind. Circumboreal, s throughout most of USA; Europe.

Polygonum pensylvanicum L.
Pennsylvania smartweed   FACW+
Annual herb. **Stems** erect, 3–20 dm long, unbranched to widely branching. **Leaves** lance-shaped, 3–15 cm long and 1–4 cm wide, smooth except for short hairs on margins; petioles to 2.5 cm long; stipules (ocreae) 0.5–1.5 cm long, entire or with an irregular, jagged margin, hairless, not fringed with bristles. **Flowers** pink to white, in dense racemes 2–3 cm long, the flower stalks with gland-tipped hairs; sepals 3–5 mm long, 5-parted to below middle, the outer sepals faintly nerved; stamens 8 or less. **Fruit** a dark brown to black, shiny achene, lens-shaped, to 3 mm long.

June–Sept. ❦ Streambanks, exposed shores, marshes, fens, ditches and cultivated fields. ⊕ Mostly s Minn, Wisc, Mich, common in ne Ill and nw Ind. NS and Que to ND, s to Fla, Tex and Ariz.

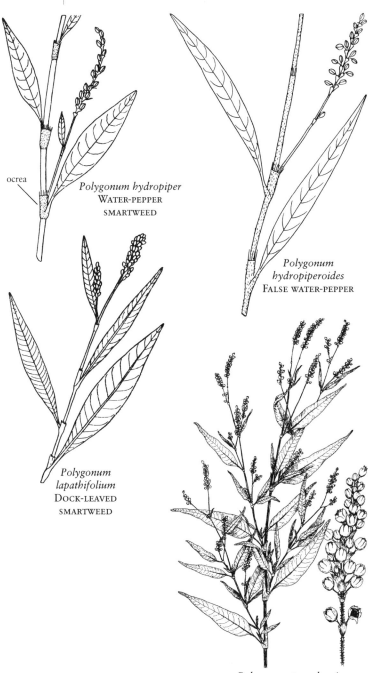

ocrea

Polygonum hydropiper
WATER-PEPPER
SMARTWEED

Polygonum hydropiperoides
FALSE WATER-PEPPER

Polygonum lapathifolium
DOCK-LEAVED
SMARTWEED

Polygonum pensylvanicum
PENNSYLVANIA SMARTWEED

Polygonum persicaria L.
Lady's thumb   FACW

Annual herb. **Stems** upright to spreading, 2–8 dm long, unbranched to branched, often red. **Leaves** lance-shaped, 3–15 cm long and 0.5–3 cm wide, smooth or with few hairs, underside usually dotted with small glands, leaves stalkless or on petioles to 1 cm long; ocreae 5–15 mm long, fringed with bristles, with short hairs. **Flowers** pink to rose, crowded in straight, cylindric racemes 1–4 cm long and 0.5–1 cm wide; sepals 2–4 mm long, 5-lobed to near middle; stamens 6. **Fruit** a black, shiny achene, lens-shaped or sometimes 3-angled, 2–3 mm long. July–Sept. ❧ Muddy shores, streambanks, ditches and cultivated fields, often weedy. ⊕ Minn, Wisc, Mich, ne Ill and nw Ind. Introduced from Europe and now throughout N Amer.

Polygonum punctatum Elliott
Dotted smartweed   OBL

Annual or perennial herb. **Stems** erect to spreading, 4–10 dm long, unbranched to branched. **Leaves** narrowly lance-shaped or oval, 4–15 cm long and 1–2 cm wide, smooth except for small short hairs on margins, underside usually dotted with small glands; petioles short; stipules (ocreae) 5–15 mm long, smooth or with stiff hairs and fringed with bristles. **Flowers** green-white; in numerous slender, loosely flowered racemes, interrupted in lower portion, to 10 cm long; sepals 3–4 mm long, with glandular dots, 5-parted to about middle; stamens 6–8. **Fruit** a dark, shiny achene, lens-shaped or 3-angled, 2–3 mm long. Aug–Sept. ❧ Floodplain forests, marshes, shores, streambanks and cultivated fields. ⊕ Minn, Wisc, most of Mich (but uncommon in ne LP), ne Ill and nw Ind. Throughout most of N Amer, s to S Amer.

Polygonum sagittatum L.
Arrow-leaved tearthumb   OBL

Slender annual herb. **Stems** 4-angled, weak, usually supported by other plants, 1–2 m long, with downward pointing prickles on stem angles, petioles, leaf midribs and flower stalks. **Leaves** lance-shaped to oval, arrowhead-shaped at base, 3–10 cm long and to 2.5 cm wide, the basal lobes pointing downward; petioles long on lower leaves, shorter above; stipules (ocreae) 5–10 mm long, with a few hairs on margins. **Flowers** white or pink; in round racemes to 1 cm long, on long slender stalks at ends of stems or from leaf axils; sepals 3 mm long, 5-parted to below middle. **Fruit** a brown to black, shiny achene, 3-angled, 2–3 mm long. July–Sept. ❧ Swamps, marshes, wet meadows and burned wetlands. ⊕ Minn (all but extreme w), Wisc, Mich, ne Ill and nw Ind. Newf and Que to Sask, s to Fla and Tex.

▶**Rumex** L. / Dock

Perennial, sometimes weedy, herbs (annual in *R. maritimus*). **Leaves** large and clustered at base of plants, or leafy-stemmed; mostly oblong to lance-shaped, flat to wavy-crisped along margins, usually with petioles. Membranous sheath around stem present at each node (ocrea). **Flowers** in crowded whorls in panicles at ends of stems; flowers small and numerous, green but turning brown; sepals in 2 series of 3, the inner 3 sepals (valves) enlarging, becoming winged and loosely enclosing the achene, giving the appearance of a 3-winged fruit, the midvein of the valve often swollen to produce a grainlike tubercle on the back; stamens 6; styles 3. **Fruit** a brown, 3-angled achene, tipped with a short slender beak.

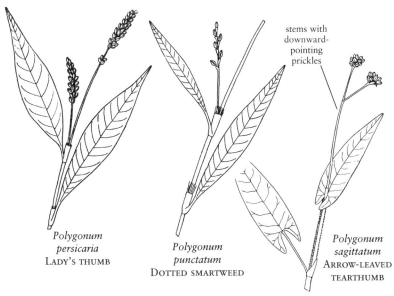

Polygonum persicaria
LADY'S THUMB

Polygonum punctatum
DOTTED SMARTWEED

stems with downward-pointing prickles

Polygonum sagittatum
ARROW-LEAVED TEARTHUMB

▶ **KEY TO RUMEX**

1 Margins of mature valves with coarse or spine-tipped teeth **2**
1 Margins of mature valves entire or shallowly lobed, not toothed . **4**

2 Plants annual, fibrous-rooted or with slender taproots; margins of valves dissected into spine-tipped teeth . . . . *R. maritimus* . . . . GOLDEN DOCK
2 Plants perennial from stout taproots; valve margins toothed or spine-tipped **3**

3 Grains 3, margins of valves coarsely toothed; w Minn . . . . *R. stenophyllus* / NARROW-LEAF DOCK
3 Grains 1; margins of valves with spine-tipped teeth; e Minn and eastward . . . . *R. obtusifolius* / BITTER DOCK
4 Flower stalks without a large swollen joint; grains 3, base of grain distinctly above base of valve . . . *R. orbiculatus* / GREAT WATER-DOCK
4 Flower stalks with a large swollen joint below the middle or near base; grains 1–3, base of grain even with base of valve **5**

5 Fruit with 3 grains, the grains projecting below the valves; flower stalks 2–5x longer than fruit . . . . *R. verticillatus* . . . . WATER-DOCK; SWAMP-DOCK
5 Fruit with 1–3 grains, the grains not projecting below the valves; flower stalks 1–2x longer than fruit **6**

6 Leaves crisp-margined (crinkled); grains 2/3 as wide as long . . . . *R. crispus* / CURLED DOCK
6 Leaf margins flat; grains narrower, up to half as wide as long **7**

7 Grains usually 1 (sometimes 2–3); leaves mostly less than 4x longer than wide . . . . *R. altissimus* / PALE DOCK
7 Grains usually 3; leaves mostly more than 4x longer than wide . . . . *R. salicifolius* / WILLOW DOCK

Rumex altissimus A. Wood
Pale dock   FACW-

Perennial herb, similar to **willow dock** (*R. salicifolius*). **Stems** 3–10 dm long, usually branched from base and with short branches above. **Leaves** all from stem, ovate to lance-shaped, 6–20 cm long and 2–6 cm wide, margins flat or slightly wavy. **Flowers** in panicles 1–3 dm long, the panicle branches short and ± upright; flower stalks short, 3–5 mm long, swollen and jointed near base; valves rounded, 4–6 mm long and as wide, flattened across base, margins smooth or irregularly toothed; grains usually well-developed on only 1 of the 3 valves, although sometimes present on 2–3 valves; the largest grain lance-shaped. **Fruit** a brown achene, 2–3 mm long. May–Aug. ❧ Marshes, shores, streambanks, ditches, disturbed areas. ⊕ sc and se Minn, c and s Wisc, mostly c and s LP of Mich, ne Ill and nw Ind. NH to Minn and Wyo, s to Ga, Tex and Ariz.

Rumex crispus L.
Curled dock   FAC+

Perennial herb, from a thick taproot. **Stems** stout, upright, usually single, 5–15 dm long. **Basal leaves** large, 10–30 cm long and 1–5 cm wide, on long petioles, often drying early in season; **stem leaves** smaller and with shorter petioles, oval to lance-shaped, margins strongly wavy-crisped (crinkled). **Flowers** in large branched panicles, the panicle branches ± upright; flower stalks drooping at tips, 5–10 mm long, swollen-jointed near base; valves heart-shaped to broadly ovate, 4–5 mm long and as wide, margins ± smooth; grains 3, swollen, often of unequal size, rounded at ends. **Fruit** a brown achene, 2–3 mm long. July–Sept. ❧ Wet meadows, shores, ditches, old fields, and other wet and disturbed areas; weedy. ⊕ Common; Minn, Wisc, Mich, ne Ill and nw Ind. Introduced from Eurasia, naturalized throughout USA, s Can and much of world.

Rumex maritimus L.
Golden dock   FACW+

Annual herb. **Stems** hollow, to 8 dm long, much-branched. **Leaves** mostly on stems, smaller upward, lance-shaped to linear, 5–20 cm long and 0.5–4 cm wide, wedge-shaped or heart-shaped at base, margins flat to wavy-crisped. **Flowers** in large open panicles, the panicle branches ± upright, leafy, the flower stalks jointed near base; valves triangular-ovate, 2–3 mm long, the margins lobed into 2–3 spine-tipped teeth on each side; grains 3. **Fruit** a light brown achene, 1–2 mm long. July–Aug. ❧ Marshes, shores, streambanks and ditches, sometimes where brackish. ⊕ Introduced. Minn (all but se), Wisc, local in w and c UP, e LP of Mich, ne Ill. Eurasia and most of N and S Amer.

Rumex obtusifolius L.
Bitter dock   FACW

Perennial herb. **Stems** stout, to 12 dm long, usually unbranched. **Lower leaves** oblong or ovate, to 30 cm long and 15 cm wide, heart-shaped or rounded at base; **upper leaves** smaller. **Flowers** in much-branched panicles, flower stalks longer than fruit, jointed near base; valves triangular-ovate, 4–5 mm long, with 2–4 spine-tipped teeth on each side; grains large and with tiny wrinkles. **Fruit** a shiny, red-brown achene. June–Aug. ❧ Floodplain forests and openings, cultivated fields and disturbed areas. ⊕ Extreme e Minn, Wisc, Mich, ne Ill and nw Ind. Introduced from Europe; naturalized from Que to BC, s to Fla and Ariz. FACW

Rumex orbiculatus A. Gray
Great water-dock   OBL

Perennial herb. **Stems** stout, unbranched, 2–2.5 m long. **Leaves** lance-shaped or oblong lance-shaped, lower leaves 30–60 cm long, upper leaves 5–15 cm long; margins flat. **Flowers** in panicles to 5 dm long; valves rounded, flat at base, 5–8 mm long and as wide, smooth or with small teeth; grains 3, narrowly lance-shaped, the base distinctly above base of valve. June–Aug. *R. britannica.* ⚘ Marshes, fens, streambanks and ditches, often in shallow water. ⊕ Minn, Wisc, Mich, ne Ill and nw Ind. Newf and Que to ND, s to NJ, Ohio, Ill, Iowa and Neb.

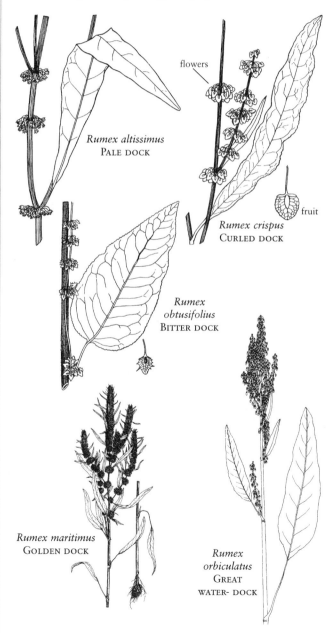

flowers

Rumex altissimus
PALE DOCK

Rumex crispus
CURLED DOCK

fruit

*Rumex
obtusifolius*
BITTER DOCK

Rumex maritimus
GOLDEN DOCK

*Rumex
orbiculatus*
GREAT
WATER- DOCK

Rumex salicifolius J. A. Weinm.
Willow dock   OBL

Perennial taprooted herb. **Stems** smooth, 3–10 dm long, usually branched from base and with short branches on stem. **Leaves** mostly on stems, not much smaller upward, narrowly lance-shaped, tapered at both ends, pale waxy green, 5–16 cm long and 1–3 cm wide, margins mostly flat. **Flowers** in panicles 1–3 dm long, panicle branches few and ± upright, with small linear leaves at base; flower stalks 2–4 mm long, swollen and jointed near base; valves thick, triangular, 3–6 mm long and wide, margins smooth or shallowly toothed; grains usually 3. **Fruit** a brown achene, 2 mm long. June–Aug. *R. mexicanus, R. triangulivalvis.* ⚘ Wet meadows, marshes, shores, streambanks, ditches and other low areas, sometimes where brackish. ⊕ UP, n and se LP of Mich, ne Ill and nw Ind. Que to Alaska, s to Pa, Ky, Tex, Calif and into Mex.

Rumex stenophyllus Ledeb.
Narrow-leaf dock   FACW

Perennial herb, similar to **curled dock** (*R. crispus*) but **leaves** less wavy-crisped and the valves with many small teeth on margins. Valves triangular to rounded, 4–6 mm long and as wide; grains 3. **Fruit** a brown achene, 2–3 mm long. July–Sept. ⚘ Wet meadows, shores, streambanks, ditches, and disturbed places, usually where brackish. ⊕ w Minn. Introduced from Europe, now from Minn to Man and Mont, s to Mo, Okla and n Tex.

Rumex verticillatus L.
Water-dock; Swamp-dock   OBL

Perennial taprooted herb. **Stems** stout, 1–1.5 m long, with many short branches from leaf axils. **Leaves** narrowly lance-shaped, tapered to base, margins flat. **Flowers** in leafless panicles 2–4 dm long, the panicle branches few and ± upright; flower stalks 10–15 mm long, jointed near base; valves triangular-ovate, 4–6 mm long and wide, thickened at center; grains 3, lance-shaped, the base blunt and projecting 0.5 mm below base of valve. June–Sept. *R. floridanus.* ⚘ Marshes, swamps, wet forests, backwater areas and muddy shores, often in shallow water. ⊕ se Minn, Wisc, c and s LP of Mich, ne Ill and nw Ind. Que and Ont to s Minn and Kans, s to Fla and Tex.

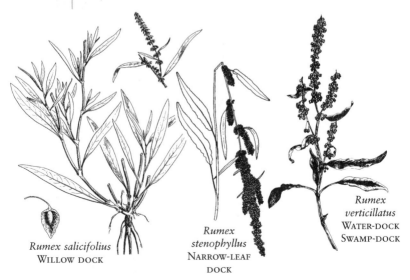

Rumex salicifolius
WILLOW DOCK

Rumex stenophyllus
NARROW-LEAF
DOCK

Rumex verticillatus
WATER-DOCK
SWAMP-DOCK

Portulacaceae
Purslane Family

▶**Montia** L. / Miner's-lettuce

Montia chamissoi (Ledeb.) Greene
Miner's-lettuce   OBL

⚠
STATUS
Minnesota - E

Smooth perennial herb, forming colonies from spreading rhizomes and stolons. **Stems** upright, 5–20 cm long. **Leaves** opposite, spatula-shaped to obovate, 2–5 cm long, margins entire. **Flowers** perfect, 3–10 in drooping racemes from ends of stems or upper leaf axils, flower stalks 1–3 cm long; petals 5, white to pink, 5–8 mm long, stamens 5. June–July. ⚘ Streambanks, springs and seeps. ⊕ Extreme se Minn and adjacent ne Iowa, where disjunct from Rocky Mts.

Montia chamissoi
MINER'S-LETTUCE

Primulaceae
Primrose Family

Perennial herbs (ours). **Leaves** simple, opposite (sometimes whorled in Lysimachia), or leaves all basal. **Flowers** perfect (with both male and female parts), regular, single from leaf axils, or in clusters at ends of stems; sepals 4–5, petals mostly 5 (varying from 4–9 or absent in *Glaux*), joined, tube-shaped below and flared above, deeply cleft to shallowly lobed at tip; ovary superior, style 1; stamens 5. **Fruit** a 5-chambered capsule.

▶**KEY TO PRIMULACEAE**

1 Leaves all from base of plant, leaf underside strongly whitened . . .
 . . . . *Primula mistassinica* / MISTASSINI PRIMROSE
1 Leaves from stem, green on both sides **2**

2 Flowers white to pink, single and stalkless in leaf axils; petals absent; sepals petal-like; nw Minn . . . . . . *Glaux maritima* / SEA-MILKWORT
2 Flowers yellow, single and stalked from leaf axils or in racemes from axils; sepals and petals present; widespread . . . . *Lysimachia*
 . . . . LOOSESTRIFE

▶Glaux L. / Sea-milkwort

Glaux maritima L.
Sea-milkwort   OBL

⚠
STATUS
Minnesota - E

Perennial herb, with shallow rhizomes; plants smooth, usually waxy blue-green, succulent. **Stems** leafy, 3–25 cm long, unbranched and erect to branched and spreading. **Leaves** fleshy, opposite, sometimes alternate above, oval to linear, 3–20 mm long and 1–5 mm wide, blunt-tipped; margins entire; petioles absent. **Flowers** small, white to pink, single and stalkless in leaf axils; sepals petal-like, bell-shaped, 3–4 mm long; petals absent; stamens equal or slightly longer than sepals. **Fruit** a rounded capsule, 2–3 mm long; seeds several, black, oval and flattened. June–Sept. ❧ Wet meadows, seeps, wet alkaline flats. ⊕ Rare in far nw Minn. Circumboreal, s to Va, Neb, NM and Ore.

▶Lysimachia L. / Loosestrife

Perennial herbs, spreading by rhizomes. **Stems** erect. **Leaves** opposite (sometimes appearing whorled), ovate or lance-shaped. **Flowers** 5-parted, yellow, single on stalks from leaf axils or in racemes or panicles; sepals green; petals bright to pale yellow. **Fruit** a capsule. ☞ **Garden looses-**

*Lysimachia
vulgaris*
GARDEN
LOOSESTRIFE

☞ **Purple
loosestrife**
(*Lythrum sali-
caria*), an
introduced
weed of
wetlands,
is a member
of the
Loosestrife
Family
(Lythraceae).

trife (*Lysimachia vulgaris* L.), with densely hairy stems and leaves and mostly whorled leaves, is occasional on mudflats along rivers and in wet meadows, mostly in s portion of our region. This introduced species sometimes escapes from cultivation in ne and c USA (FACW).

▶**KEY TO LYSIMACHIA**

1 Plants creeping; leaves round, on short, smooth petioles . . . .
. . . . *L. nummularia* / MONEYWORT; CREEPING JENNIE
1 Plants upright, leaves longer than wide; petioles hairy or absent . . **2**

2 Flowers in dense clusters at ends of stems or from leaf axils **3**
2 Flowers single from leaf axils **4**

3 Flowers in clusters at ends of stems . *L. terrestris* / SWAMP CANDLES
3 Flowers in clusters from leaf axils . . . . *L. thyrsiflora*
. . . . SWAMP LOOSESTRIFE

4 Leaves rounded or heart-shaped at base; petioles 1–3 cm long, fringed with hairs . . . . *L. ciliata* / FRINGED LOOSESTRIFE
4 Leaves tapered at both ends; petioles absent or short, smooth or fringed with hairs **5**

5 Leaves narrowly linear, to 5 mm wide; margins smooth and rolled under . . . . *L. quadriflora* / SMOOTH LOOSESTRIFE
5 Leaves lance-shaped to oval, usually greater than 9 mm wide; margins finely hairy or rough-to-touch **6**

6 Leaves and flowers with red or black dots or streaks; petals entire at tip . . . . *L. quadriflora* / SMOOTH LOOSESTRIFE
6 Leaves and flowers without red or black dots or streaks; petals ragged-fringed at tip . . . . *L. hybrida* / LOWLAND LOOSESTRIFE

Lysimachia ciliata L.
Fringed loosestrife   FACW
Perennial herb, spreading by rhizomes. **Stems** upright, 3–12 dm long, unbranched or with few branches above. **Leaves** ovate to lance-shaped, 4–15 cm long and 2–6 cm wide, rounded to heart-shaped at base, green above, slightly paler below; margins fringed with short hairs; petioles 0.5–5 cm long, fringed with hairs. **Flowers** yellow, single from upper leaf axils, on stalks 2–7 cm long; sepal lobes lance-shaped, 4–8 mm long, often with 3–5 parallel red-brown veins; petal lobes rounded and finely ragged at tip, 4–10 mm long and 3–9 mm wide, with a short slender tip. **Fruit** a capsule, 4–7 mm wide. June–Aug. *Steironema ciliata.* ⚘ Usually shaded wet areas, such as shores, streambanks, wet meadows, ditches, floodplains, wet woods and thickets. ⊕ Minn, Wisc, Mich, ne Ill and nw Ind. Que to Alaska, s to Fla, Tex, NM, Utah and Ore.

Lysimachia hybrida Michx.
Lowland loosestrife   OBL
Perennial herb, spreading by rhizomes. **Stems** usually erect, 2–8 dm long, unbranched or sometimes branched from base, usually branched above. **Leaves** narrowly lance-shaped to ovate, 3–10 cm long and 1–2 cm wide, tapered to base, upper surface green, underside green or slightly paler; lower leaves opposite, stalked, withering, petioles fringed with hairs at least near base; upper leaves ± whorled and stalkless, persistent. **Flowers** yellow, single from leaf axils but often appearing crowded, on stalks 1–4

cm long; sepal lobes lance-shaped, 3–6 mm long; petal lobes rounded and finely fringed at tip, 5–10 mm long and 4–10 mm wide, with a short slender tip. **Fruit** a capsule, 4–6 mm wide. July–Aug. *L. verticillata*. ❦ Wet meadows, marshes, streambanks, ditches and shores, sometimes in shallow water. ⊕ ne, c and se Minn, uncommon in s LP of Mich, ne Ill and nw Ind. Maine to s Sask, s to n Fla, Tenn, Ark and Kans; NM and Ariz.

Lysimachia nummularia L.
Moneywort; Creeping Jennie   FACW+

Perennial herb, often forming mats. **Stems** creeping, to 5–6 dm long. **Leaves** opposite, dotted with black glands, round or broadly oval, 1–2.5 cm long; petioles short. **Flowers** single in leaf axils, on stalks to 2.5 cm long; sepals leaflike, triangular, 6–8 mm long; petals yellow, dotted with dark red, 10–15 mm long. **Fruit** a capsule, shorter than sepals. June–Aug. ❦ Swamps, floodplain forests, streambanks, shores, meadows and ditches. ⊕ ec and se Minn, c and s Wisc, Mich (especially s), ne Ill and nw Ind. Native of Europe; occasional in Great Lakes area.

Lysimachia quadriflora Sims
Smooth loosestrife   OBL

Perennial herb, spreading by rhizomes which form clusters of basal rosettes. **Stems** upright, 3–10 dm long. **Leaves** opposite, sometimes appearing whorled; stem leaves stalkless, often ascending, linear, 3–8 cm long and 2–7 mm wide, margins smooth or rolled under, sometimes fringed with a few hairs near base. **Flowers** yellow, single in clusters at ends of stems and branches, on stalks 1–4 cm long; sepal lobes lance-shaped, 4–6 mm long; petal lobes oval, 7–12 mm long and 5–9 mm wide, entire or finely ragged at tip. **Fruit** a capsule, 3–5 mm wide. July–Aug. *L. longifolia*. ❦ Wet meadows, pond and marsh margins, low prairie, calcareous fens; often where sandy and calcium-rich. ⊕ wc and s Minn, Wisc, LP of Mich (plus uncommon in s UP), ne Ill and nw Ind. Mass to s Man, s to Ga, Ala and Neb.

Lysimachia terrestris (L.) BSP.
Swamp candles   OBL

Perennial herb, spreading by shallow rhizomes. **Stems** smooth, 4–8 dm long, usually branched. **Leaves** opposite, dotted with glands, narrowly lance-shaped, 5–10 cm long and 2–4 cm wide; small bulblike structures produced in leaf axils late in season; bracts awl-like, 3–8 mm long. **Flowers** yellow, in a single, crowded, upright raceme, 1–3 dm long; sepals lance-shaped; petal lobes oval, 5–7 mm long, with dark lines, on stalks 8–15 mm long. **Fruit** a capsule, 2–3 mm wide. June–Aug. ❦ Marshes, fens, thickets, muddy shores, and ditches. ⊕ e Minn, Wisc, Mich. Nfld to Sask, s to SC, Tenn and Iowa.

Lysimachia thyrsiflora L.
Swamp loosestrife   OBL

Perennial upright herb, spreading by rhizomes; plants conspicuously dotted with dark glands. **Stems** smooth or with patches of brown hairs, 3–7 dm long, unbranched or branched on lower stem. **Leaves** opposite, linear to lance-shaped, 4–12 cm long and 0.5–4 cm wide, smooth above, smooth or sparsely hairy below; petioles absent. **Flowers** yellow, crowded in dense racemes from leaf axils, on spreading stalks 2–5 cm long; mostly 6-parted; sepal lobes awl-shaped, 1–3 mm long; petal lobes linear, 3 mm long; stamens 2x longer than petals. **Fruit** a capsule, 2–4 mm wide. June–Aug. ❦ Many types of wetlands: thickets, shores, fens and bogs, marshes, low places in conifer and deciduous swamps, often in shallow water. ⊕ Minn, Wisc (occasional), Mich, ne Ill and nw Ind. Circumboreal, s to NJ, Ohio, Ill, Mo, Neb, Colo, Idaho and Calif.

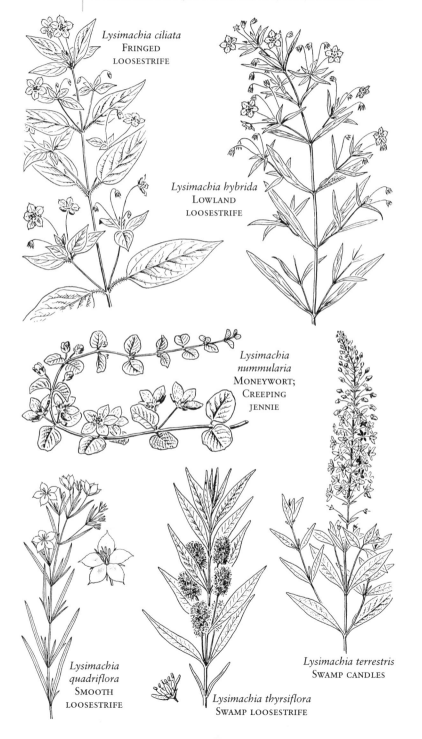

Lysimachia ciliata
Fringed
LOOSESTRIFE

Lysimachia hybrida
Lowland
LOOSESTRIFE

*Lysimachia
nummularia*
Moneywort;
Creeping
JENNIE

*Lysimachia
quadriflora*
Smooth
LOOSESTRIFE

Lysimachia thyrsiflora
Swamp LOOSESTRIFE

Lysimachia terrestris
Swamp candles

▶Primula L. / Primrose

Primula mistassinica Michx.

Mistassini primrose   FACW

Perennial herb. **Stems** to 25 cm long. **Leaves** all at base of plant, oblong lance-shaped, 2–7 cm long, long tapered to base, smooth on upper surface, smooth or often white-yellow powdery below; margins with outward pointing teeth; bracts below flowers awl-shaped, 3–6 mm long. **Flowers** 1–2 cm wide, 2–10 in a cluster atop a leafless stalk; sepals joined, shorter than petals; petals joined, tubelike and flared at ends, pink and sometimes with a yellow center. **Fruit** an oblong, upright capsule to 1 cm long. May–June. *P. intercedens*. ❦ Lake Superior shoreline in nw Minn, ne Wisc near Lake Michigan, w Wisc on moist ledges in St. Croix, Wisc and Kickapoo River valleys; UP and n LP of Mich near Great Lakes in moist, calcium-rich meadows and interdunal wetlands, also inland in calcareous fens and on sandstone cliffs; often with **violet butterwort** (*Pinguicula vulgaris*). Labr to Alaska, s to Maine, n NY, Mich, n Ill and Minn.

▶Samolus L. / Water pimpernel

Samolus floribundus HBK.

Water pimpernel   OBL

Perennial herb. **Stems** 1–3 dm long, branched above. **Leaves** in a basal cluster and alternate on stem, obovate, blunt or rounded at tip, 2–10 cm long; margins entire; lower leaves with petioles, upper leaves often stalkless. **Flowers** white, 2–3 mm wide, on slender spreading stalks 5–15 mm long, in loosely flowered racemes 3–15 cm long. **Fruit** a round capsule, 2–3 mm wide. June–Sept. *S. parviflorus*. ❦ Muddy and sandy streambanks, where often in shade; ditches and salt marshes. ⊕ c and s LP of Mich, uncommon in ne Ill and nw Ind. Atlantic coast, inland to Mich and n Ill; BC.

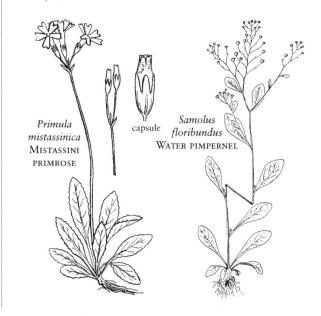

*Primula
mistassinica*
MISTASSINI
PRIMROSE

capsule

*Samolus
floribundus*
WATER PIMPERNEL

Pyrolaceae
Shinleaf Family

Perennial herbs or half-shrubs, most dependent on wood-rotting fungi (mycotrophic). **Leaves** alternate to sometimes opposite or nearly whorled, often shiny, evergreen in *Pyrola*, deciduous in *Moneses*. **Flowers** perfect (with both male and female parts), 5-parted, waxy and nodding. **Fruit** a capsule.

▶KEY TO PYROLACEAE

1 Flowers white, single and nodding at ends of stems . . . .
. . . . *Moneses uniflora* / ONE-FLOWERED SHINLEAF
1 Flowers pink, several in racemes . *Pyrola asarifolia* / PINK SHINLEAF

▶**Moneses** Salisb. / One-flowered shinleaf

Moneses uniflora (L.) A. Gray
  One-flowered shinleaf   FAC
Low perennial herb, roots creeping. **Stems** to 10 cm long. **Leaves** deciduous, mostly at base of plant, opposite or in whorls of 3, nearly round, margins entire or finely toothed. **Flowers** white, single at end of long stalk, nodding, 1–2 cm wide; petals 5. **Fruit** a round capsule, opening from top downward. July–Aug. *Pyrola uniflora*. ❦ Cedar swamps, wet conifer or mixed conifer and deciduous forests. ⊕ nc and ne Minn, n and ec Wisc, UP and n LP of Mich. Circumboreal, s to Conn, NY, Great Lakes and NM.

▶**Pyrola** L. / Shinleaf; Wintergreen

Pyrola asarifolia Michx.
  Pink shinleaf   FACW

STATUS
Indiana - E

Perennial herb, spreading by rhizomes. **Stems** to 3 dm long. **Leaves** persisting over winter, all near base of plant, kidney-shaped, 3–4 cm long and 3–5 cm wide, margins shallowly rounded-toothed; flower stalk with 1–3 small, scalelike leaves. **Flowers** nodding in a raceme; sepals triangular, 2–3 mm long; petals 5, 5–7 mm long, pink to pale purple. **Fruit** a capsule opening from base upward. June–Aug. *P. uliginosa*. ❦ Cedar swamps, peatlands, marly wetlands, and interdunal wetlands. ⊕ n and c Minn, n, c and se Wisc, Mich (especially n). n Ind. Nfld to Alaska, s to NY, n Ind, Minn and NM.

Ranunculaceae
Buttercup Family

Annual or perennial, aquatic or terrestrial herbs (or vines in *Clematis*). **Leaves** simple to compound, usually alternate, sometimes opposite or whorled, or all at base of plant. **Flowers** mostly white or yellow, usually with 5 (occasionally more) separate petals and sepals, or petals absent and then with petal-like sepals; sepals leafy and green or petal-like and colored; flowers perfect (with both male and female parts), stamens usually numerous; pistils several to many, ripening into beaked achenes or dry capsules (follicles).

▶**KEY TO RANUNCULACEAE**

1 Vines; leaves opposite; fruit with a long, feathery style. . . . *Clematis*
. . . . CLEMATIS
1 Herbs; leaves alternate or from base of plant; fruit not with a long, feathery style. **2**

2 Leaves linear, 1–2 mm wide, all from base of plant; sepals spurred at base; achenes in a spikelike cluster to 6 cm long. *Myosurus minimus*
. . . . MOUSE-TAIL
2 Leaves not linear; sepals not spurred; achenes in round to short-cylindric heads **3**

3 Flowers irregular, purple to blue; uncommon plant of driftless area of sw Wisc and ne Iowa . . . . *Aconitum noveboracense*
. . . . NEW YORK OR NORTHERN MONKSHOOD
3 Flowers regular, yellow to white. **4**

4 Leaves from base of plant except for 2–3 whorled, leafy bracts below flowers . . . . *Anemone canadensis* / CANADA ANEMONE
4 Stems leafy, the leaves alternate, *or* leaves all from base of plant . . **5**

5 Flowers yellow, *or* leaves simple and unlobed, *or* plants aquatic . . **6**
5 Flowers not yellow; leaves divided into leaflets; plants not aquatic **7**

6 Leaves all alike, unlobed; sepals yellow, large and petal-like; petals absent
. . . . *Caltha* / MARSH-MARIGOLD; COWSLIP
6 Leaves usually of 2 types (stem leaves different from basal leaves), *or* leaves deeply lobed or divided; sepals green; petals yellow or white.
. . . . *Ranunculus* / BUTTERCUP; CROWFOOT; SPEARWORT

7 Leaves all from base of plant, flowers single at ends of leafless stalks
. . . . *Coptis trifolia* / ALASKA GOLDTHREAD
7 Stems leafy; flowers many in panicles at ends of stems . . *Thalictrum*
. . . . MEADOW-RUE

▶**Aconitum** L. / Monkshood

Aconitum noveboracense A. Gray.
New York or Northern monkshood (FACW)

Perennial herb, from a thickened rootstock, ⚠poisonous. **Stems** upright, to 1.5 m long. **Leaves** divided into 5–7 coarsely toothed segments. **Flowers** few in a raceme, showy, irregular, purple to blue, the upper sepal rounded, domelike, covering the petals; stamens many, pistils 3–5. **Fruit** a follicle. July–Aug. *A. columbianum.* ⚘ Ledges and bases of shaded cliffs, streambanks. ⊕ Driftless area of sw Wisc and ne Iowa; c NY and ne Ohio.

▶**Anemone** L. / Anemone

Anemone canadensis L.
Canada anemone FACW

Perennial herb, from slender rhizomes, often forming large patches. **Stems** erect, 1–6 dm long, unbranched below the head. **Leaves** all from base of plant and with long petioles except for 2–3 stalkless leafy bracts below the head; 4–15 cm wide, deeply 3–5-lobed, round to kidney-shaped in outline, underside with long silky hairs, margins sharp-toothed. **Flowers** mostly single at ends of stalks, white and showy, 2–5 cm wide; sepals 5, petal-like, 1–2 cm long; petals absent; stamens and pistils many. **Achenes** clustered in a round, short-hairy head; achene body flat, 3–5 mm long and wide, beak 2–4 mm long. May–Aug. ⚘ Wet openings, streambanks, thickets, low prairie, ditches and roadsides. ⊕ Minn, Wisc, Mich, ne Ill and nw Ind. e Que to Alberta, s to Md, WVa, Mo, Kans and NM.

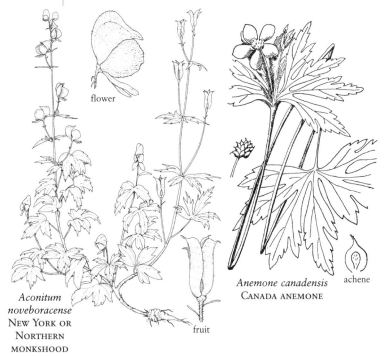

flower

Anemone canadensis
CANADA ANEMONE
achene

*Aconitum
noveboracense*
NEW YORK OR
NORTHERN
MONKSHOOD

fruit

▶Caltha L. / Marsh-marigold; Cowslip

Succulent perennial herbs. **Leaves** simple, mostly from base of plant, becoming smaller upward, heart-shaped; margins entire or rounded-toothed. **Flowers** mostly bright yellow (*C. palustris*), to pink or white (*C. natans*), single at ends of stalks; sepals large and petal-like; petals absent; stamens many. **Fruit** a follicle.

▶**KEY TO CALTHA**

1 Flowers bright yellow; common . . . . *C. palustris*
. . . . COMMON MARSH-MARIGOLD
1 Flowers pink or white; uncommon in ne Minn and nw Wisc. . . . . .
. . . . *C. natans* / FLOATING MARSH-MARIGOLD

Caltha natans Pallas
Floating marsh-marigold   OBL

⚠
STATUS
Minnesota - E
Wisconsin - E

Perennial herb. **Stems** floating or creeping, branched, rooting at nodes. **Leaves** heart- or kidney-shaped, 2–5 cm wide, notched at base, upper leaves smaller. **Flowers** pink or white, 1 cm wide; sepals oval; petals absent; stamens 12–25. **Fruit** a follicle, 4–5 mm long, in dense heads of 20–40. July–Aug. ☙ In shallow water and shores of ponds and slow-moving streams. ⊕ Rare in ne Minn, nw Wisc. Circumboreal, s to n Wisc and ne Minn.

Caltha palustris L.
Common marsh-marigold   OBL

☞ **Common marsh-marigold** may form large colonies; its flowers provide a brilliant display of color in spring.

Loosely clumped perennial herb. **Stems** smooth, 2–6 dm long, hollow. **Leaves** heart-shaped to kidney-shaped, 4–10 cm wide, usually with 2 lobes at base; margins smooth or shallowly toothed; lower leaves with long petioles, stem leaves with shorter petioles. **Flowers** bright yellow, showy at ends of stems or in leaf axils, 2–4 cm wide; sepals 4–9, petal-like, 12–20 mm long; petals absent; stamens many; pistils 4–15, with short styles. **Fruit** a follicle, 10–15 mm long. March–June. ☙ Shallow water, swamps, wet woods, thickets, streambanks, calcareous fens, marshes, springs. ⊕ Common; Minn, Wisc, Mich, ne Ill and nw Ind. Circumboreal; s to NC, WVa, Tenn, Ind, Ill, Iowa and Neb.

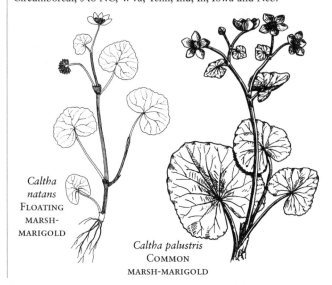

Caltha natans FLOATING MARSH-MARIGOLD

Caltha palustris COMMON MARSH-MARIGOLD

▶**Clematis** L. / Clematis

Clematis virginiana L.
Virgin's bower   FAC

☞ **Purple clematis** (*Clematis occidentalis*, illustrated below) is an uncommon vine of rocky streambanks in ne Minn, n Wisc and UP of Mich. It has 1–3 large, blue to purple flowers which open early in spring with the unfolding leaves.

Perennial, woody vine. **Stems** slender, to 5 m long or more, trailing on ground or over shrubs, smooth, brown to red-purple. **Leaves** opposite, divided into 3 leaflets, the **leaflets** ovate, 4–8 cm long and 2.5–5 cm wide; margins sharp-toothed or lobed; petioles 5–9 cm long. Male and female **flowers** separate and on separate plants, in many-flowered, open clusters from leaf axils, on stalks 1–8 cm long, usually shorter than leaf petioles; sepals 4, creamy-white, 6–10 mm long; petals absent. **Fruit** a rounded head of hairy brown achenes tipped with feathery, persistent styles 2.5–4 cm long. July–Sept. ❦ Thickets, streambanks, moist to wet woods, rocky slopes. ⊕ Minn, Wisc, Mich, ne Ill and nw Ind. NS to s Man, s to Ga and Kans.

▶**Coptis** Salisb. / Goldthread

Coptis trifolia (L.) Salisb.
Alaska goldthread   FACW

Perennial herb, with slender, bright yellow rhizomes. **Leaves** from base of plant on long petioles, evergreen, divided into 3-leaflets, the **leaflets** shallowly lobed, with rounded teeth tipped by an abrupt point. **Flowers** single, white, 10–15 mm wide, on a stalk 5–15 cm long from base of plant; sepals 4–7, petal-like; petals absent; pistils 3–7, narrowed to a short, slender style. **Fruit** a beaked follicle 8–13 mm long. May–June. C. *groenlandica*. ❦ Wet conifer woods and swamps, often on mossy hummocks. ⊕ n and c Minn (absent from far west), Wisc (especially n, confined to peatlands in s), Mich and nw Ind. Greenland to Alaska, s to NC, n Ind, Iowa and s BC; e Asia.

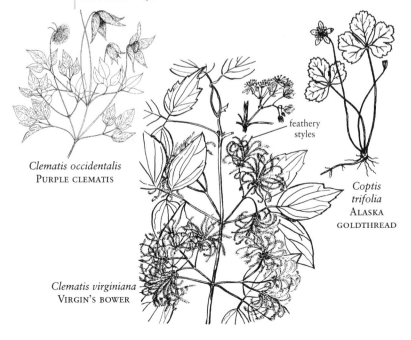

feathery styles

Clematis occidentalis
PURPLE CLEMATIS

Coptis trifolia
ALASKA GOLDTHREAD

Clematis virginiana
VIRGIN'S BOWER

▶**Myosurus** L. / Mouse-tail

Myosurus minimus L.
Mouse-tail   FACW

Small, inconspicuous, annual herb. **Stems** 4–15 cm long. **Leaves** in a basal tuft, hairless, linear, mostly less than 1 mm wide. **Flowers** small, few to many, in a spike above leaves on a slender stalk to 6 cm long when mature; sepals 5, green, upright, with a spur at base; petals 5 or sometimes absent, small, white or pink; stamens 5–10; pistils many, in an elongate receptacle. **Fruit** an achene, 2–3 mm long and 1 mm wide, with a small beak. April–June. ❦ Wet to moist places such as streambanks and floodplains, sometimes temporarily in shallow water; also in disturbed drier areas. ⊕ sw Minn (especially near Minn River), s Wisc, n Ill and n Ind. Ont to BC, s to Fla, Tex and Calif; also Europe, Asia and Australia.

▶**Ranunculus** L. / Buttercup; Crowfoot; Spearwort

Aquatic, semi-aquatic, or terrestrial annual and perennial herbs. **Stems** erect to sprawling, sometimes floating in water. **Leaves** simple, or compound and finely dissected, often variable on same plant; alternate on stem or all from base of plant; petioles short to long. **Flowers** borne above water surface in aquatic species; sepals usually 5, green; petals usually 5, yellow or white, often fading to white, usually with a small nectary pit covered by a scale near base of petal; stamens and pistils numerous. **Achenes** many in a round or cylindric head; achene body thick or flattened, tipped with a beak.

▶KEY TO RANUNCULUS

1 Flowers white; leaves divided into linear or threadlike segments; plants typically aquatic . . . . *R. aquatilis* / WHITE WATER-CROWFOOT

1 Flowers yellow; leaves simple to deeply lobed or divided into narrow segments; plants aquatic, emergent, or terrestrial **2**

2 Sepals 3 (rarely 4); uncommon in n portions of region . . . .
. . . . *R. lapponicus* / LAPPLAND BUTTERCUP
2 Sepals 5 (or rarely more) **3**

3 All leaves simple and entire, or shallowly lobed with rounded teeth . **4**
3 All, or at least stem leaves, deeply lobed, divided or compound. . . **5**

4 Leaves ovate to round or kidney-shaped, shallowly lobed with rounded teeth; achenes with longitudinal ribs . . . . *R. cymbalaria*
. . . . SEASIDE CROWFOOT
4 Leaves oval to lance-shaped or linear, entire to sharp-toothed; achenes not ribbed . . . . *R. flammula* / CREEPING SPEARWORT

5 Basal and stem leaves distinctly different in shape, the basal leaves mostly entire or with rounded teeth, the stem leaves deeply divided.
. . . . *R. abortivus* / SMALL-FLOWERED CROWFOOT

5 Basal and stem leaves similar, all deeply lobed, divided or compound **6**

6 Achenes swollen, without a sharp margin. **7**
6 Achenes flattened, with a sharp or winglike margin **9**

7 Petals 2–4 mm long; achenes to 1.2 mm long, nearly beakless; plants terrestrial or in water only part of season . . . . *R. sceleratus* . . . . Cursed crowfoot
7 Petals 4–14 mm long; achenes 1.2–2.5 mm long, beaked; plants underwater or exposed later in season **8**

8 Petals more than 7 mm long; achene body more than 1.6 mm long, achene margin thickened and white-corky below middle. . . . . *R. flabellaris* / Yellow water-crowfoot
8 Petals less than 7 mm long; achene body less than 1.6 mm long, achene margin rounded but not thickened. . . . . *R. gmelinii* . . . . Small yellow water-crowfoot

9 Petals 7–15 mm long; stems often recurved and rooting at nodes. **10**
9 Petals 2–5 mm long; stems not rooting at nodes **11**

10 Leaves deeply divided but outer segment not on a petiole; style short, curved; plants weedy . . . . . *R. acris* / Common or Tall buttercup
10 Leaves compound, the outermost lobe on a petiole; style long and straight; plants not weedy. . . . . *R. hispidus* . . . . Northern swamp buttercup

11 Beak of achene strongly hooked *R. recurvatus* / Hooked crowfoot
11 Beak of achene straight or only slightly curved **12**

12 Petals shorter than sepals; achenes in cylindric heads longer than wide; widespread. . . . . *R. pensylvanicus* / Bristly crowfoot
12 Petals equal or longer than sepals; heads ovate or round; uncommon in ne Minn and on Isle Royale . . . *R. macounii* / Marsh crowfoot

Ranunculus abortivus L.
Small-flowered crowfoot   FACW-
Biennial or perennial herb. **Stems** upright, 2–5 dm long, branched above, smooth or with fine hairs. **Leaves** at base of plant round to kidney-shaped, margins with rounded teeth, some leaves lobed; petioles long; stem leaves 3–5-divided into linear segments, margins entire or broadly toothed, petioles absent. **Flowers** yellow, petals 2–3 mm long, shorter than sepals. **Achenes** in a short, round head; achene body swollen, 1–2 mm long, with a very short, curved beak. April–June. ❧ Wet to moist woods, floodplains, wet meadows, thickets, ditches; especially where soils disturbed or compacted. ⊕ Common; Minn, Wisc, Mich. Labr to Alaska, s to Fla, Tex and Colo.

Ranunculus acris L.
Common or Tall buttercup   FACW-
Perennial herb, with fibrous roots. **Stems** hairy, to 1 m long, with few branches, most leaves on lower part of stem. **Leaves** kidney-shaped, deeply 3–7-divided, the segments again lobed or dissected; branch leaves much smaller, 3-parted. **Flowers** numerous; sepals 5, half length of petals; petals 5, bright yellow, 6–15 mm long, obovate, often with a

rounded notch at tip. **Achenes** in a round head; achene body flat, 2–3 mm long, beak 0.5 mm long. June–Aug. ≫ Common weed of fields, thickets, ditches and shores. ⊕ Minn (especially ne and ec), Wisc, Mich, ne Ill and nw Ind. Introduced from Europe; throughout e USA.

Ranunculus aquatilis L.
White water-crowfoot   OBL

☞ **White water-crowfoot** may form large patches, and is especially conspicuous in summer when flowering.

Perennial aquatic herb; plants mostly smooth. **Stems** underwater or floating (sometimes stranded on muddy shores in late summer), 2–8 dm long, unbranched or with a few branches, rooting from lower nodes. **Leaves** round to kidney-shaped in outline, 2–3x divided into narrow threadlike segments 1–2 cm long; stiff and not collapsing when removed from water; petioles absent or to 4 mm long. **Flowers** at or below water surface, single from upper leaf axils, 1–1.5 cm wide; sepals 5, purple-green, spreading, 2–4 mm long; petals 5, white, yellow at base, 4–9 mm long. **Achenes** many in a round head; achene body obovate, ridged, the beak thin and straight, 1–1.5 mm long. May–Aug. *R. trichophyllus.* ≫ Ponds, lakes, streams, rivers and ditches. ⊕ Minn, Wisc, Mich, ne Ill and nw Ind. Que to Sask, s to Del, Ala, Ark, Tex, NM, and Nev.

Ranunculus cymbalaria Pursh
Seaside crowfoot   OBL

⚠
STATUS
Illinois - E
Michigan - T

Perennial herb, spreading by stolons and forming dense mats. **Stems** 3–20 cm long, smooth. **Leaves** all from base of plant, ovate to kidney-shaped, 5–25 mm long and 4–30 mm wide, heart-shaped at base; margins with rounded teeth, often with 3 prominent lobes at tip; petioles sparsely hairy. **Flower** stalks longer than leaves, unbranched or with a few branches, with 1 to several flowers; sepals 5, green-yellow, 3–5 mm long, deciduous; petals usually 5, yellow, turning white with age, 3–5 mm long; stamens 10–30. **Achenes** numerous in a cylindric head to 10 mm long; achene body 1.5–2 mm long, longitudinally nerved, beak short and straight. June–Sept. ≫ Wet meadows, streambanks, shores, ditches and seeps, often in wet mud or sand; Lake Michigan shores; often where brackish. ⊕ Uncommon in w and sc Minn (plus uncommon in ne), far e and nw Wisc, w UP of Mich and ne Ill. Throughout much of N and S Amer; Eurasia.

Ranunculus flabellaris Raf.
Yellow water-crowfoot   OBL

Perennial herb; plants smooth or sometimes hairy when growing out-of-water. **Stems** floating, or upright from a sprawling base when exposed, branched, rooting at lower nodes, 3–7 dm long. **Underwater leaves** 3-parted into linear segments 1–2 mm wide, **exposed leaves** (when present) round to kidney-shaped in outline, 2–10 cm long and 2–12 cm wide, divided into 3 segments, the segments again 3-divided. **Flowers** 1 to several at ends of stems; sepals 5, green-yellow, 4–8 mm long; petals 5–8, bright yellow, 6–15 mm long. **Achenes** 50–75 in a round to ovate head; achene body obovate, to 2 mm long, the margin thickened and corky below middle, beak broad, flat, 1–1.5 mm long. May–July. ≫ Shallow water or muddy shores of ponds, quiet streams, swamps, woodland pools, marshes and ditches. ⊕ Minn, Wisc, s LP of Mich (local in e UP), ne Ill and nw Ind. Maine to BC, s to NJ, Va, Ohio, Ill, La, Utah, Nev and Calif.

Ranunculus flammula L.
Creeping spearwort   FACW

Perennial herb, spreading by stolons; plants often covered with appressed

☞ Sterile underwater plants of **creeping spearwort** may be recognized by the arching green stolons and threadlike, blunt-tipped leaves.

hairs. **Stems** sprawling, rooting at nodes, unbranched or few-branched, with upright shoots 4–15 cm long. **Leaves** in small clusters at nodes, simple, linear or threadlike, 1–5 cm long and 1.5 mm wide, margins ± entire; upper leaves smaller and with shorter petioles than lower. **Flowers** single at ends of stems; sepals 5, yellow-green, 2–4 mm long, with stiff hairs; petals 5, yellow, obovate, 3–5 mm long. **Achenes** 10–25 in a round head; achene body swollen, obovate, 1–1.5 mm long, smooth, the beak short, to 0.5 mm long. June–Aug. ≋ Sandy, gravelly, or muddy shores; shallow to deep water, water usually acid. ⊕ ne, nc and ec Minn, n Wisc, UP and n and w LP of Mich. Circumboreal, s to Mass, Pa, Minn, ND, NM, Ariz and Calif.

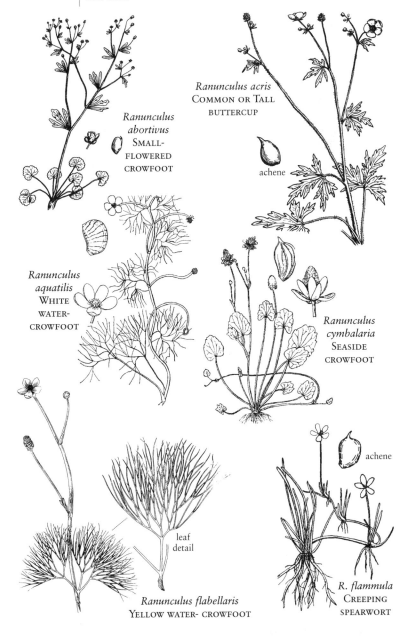

Ranunculus abortivus
SMALL-FLOWERED CROWFOOT

Ranunculus acris
COMMON OR TALL BUTTERCUP

achene

Ranunculus aquatilis
WHITE WATER-CROWFOOT

Ranunculus cymbalaria
SEASIDE CROWFOOT

leaf detail

achene

R. flammula
CREEPING SPEARWORT

Ranunculus flabellaris
YELLOW WATER- CROWFOOT

Ranunculus gmelinii DC.
Small yellow water-crowfoot   FACW+

Perennial herb, similar to **yellow water-crowfoot** (*R. flabellaris*) but plants aquatic or at least partly underwater; smooth or sometimes with coarse hairs. **Stems** usually sprawling and rooting at nodes, 1–5 dm long, sparsely branched. **Leaves** all on stem or with a few basal leaves on long petioles, deeply 3-lobed or dissected, the segments again forked 2–3 times; underwater leaf segments 2–4 mm wide; exposed leaves to 2 cm long and 1.5–2.5 cm wide. **Flowers** usually 1 to several at ends of stems; sepals 5, green-yellow, 3–6 mm long; petals 5–8, yellow, 4–8 mm long. **Achenes** 50–70 in a round to ovate head; achene body obovate, 1–1.5 mm long, the margin rounded, not corky-thickened, the beak broad and thin, 0.4–0.7 mm long, somewhat curved. May–Aug. ⚘ Streambanks and lakeshores, springs, pools in swamps and bogs. ⊕ n and ec Minn, uncommon in n Wisc; e and c UP, n and se LP of Mich. Circumboreal, s to Maine, Mich, Iowa, ND, Colo, Nev and Ore; Asia.

Ranunculus hispidus Michx.
Northern swamp buttercup   FACW+

Perennial herb; stems and leaves variable. **Stems** upright, 2–9 dm long, smooth or strongly coarse-hairy. **Leaves** from base of plant and on stems, the basal leaves larger and with longer petioles than stem leaves; 3-lobed, heart-shaped in outline, 3–14 cm long and 4–20 cm wide, with appressed hairs on veins, upper leaves usually strongly toothed. **Flowers** 1 to several; sepals 5, yellow-green, 5–11 mm long, hairy; petals 5–8, yellow, fading to white, 7–15 mm long and 3–10 mm wide. **Achenes** 15–30 or more in a round head; achene body obovate, 2–4 mm long, smooth, winged on margin, the beak straight, 2–3 mm long. May–July. *R. septentrionalis.* ⚘ Wet woods, floodplains and swamps, thickets, lakeshores, wet meadows and fens. ⊕ Minn, Wisc, Mich, ne Ill and nw Ind. Labr to s Man, s to Fla and Tex.

Ranunculus lapponicus L.
Lappland buttercup   OBL

Perennial herb, spreading by rhizomes. **Stems** prostrate, 1–2 dm long, sending up 1 shoot from each node, the shoots with 1–2 basal leaves, sometimes with a single smaller leaf above. **Leaves** kidney-shaped, deeply 3-cleft, margins with rounded teeth or shallowly lobed. **Flowers** single at ends of shoots; petals yellow with orange veins, 8–12 mm wide; sepals 3, curved downward. **Achenes** in a round head; achene body 2–3 mm long, swollen near base, flattened above, beak slender, sharply hooked. June–July. ⚘ Cedar swamps and bogs. ⊕ Uncommon in nc and ne Minn and e UP of Mich. Circumboreal, s to n Maine, n Mich and Minn; BC.

Ranunculus macounii Britton
Marsh crowfoot   OBL

Annual or short-lived perennial herb, similar to **bristly crowfoot** (*R. pensylvanicus*) but uncommon; plants smooth to densely hairy. **Stems** erect or reclining, hollow, 2–7 dm long, branched, the branches again branched. **Leaves** from base of plant and on stems, the basal leaves larger and with longer petioles than stem leaves; triangular in outline, 4–14 cm long and 6–16 cm wide, 3-lobed or divided into 3 segments, the segments themselves 3-lobed and coarsely toothed. **Flowers** several at ends of branches; sepals 5, yellow, 3-5 mm long; petals 5, yellow, 3–5 mm long, equal or longer than sepals; stamens 15–35. **Achenes** 30–50 in an ovate to round head; achene body flat, 3 mm long, smooth or shallowly pitted, with a stout, slightly curved or straight beak 1–2 mm long.

June–Aug. ❦ Wet meadows, marshes, shores, streambanks and ditches. ⊕ nw Minn (plus rare in ne), Isle Royale in Mich. Labr to Alaska, s to Que, Iowa, Neb, NM, Ariz and Calif; Asia.

Ranunculus pensylvanicus L. f.
Bristly crowfoot   OBL

Annual or short-lived perennial herb. **Stems** erect, hollow, 3–8 dm long, branched or unbranched. **Leaves** at base of plant withering early, larger and with longer petioles than the few stem leaves; 4–12 cm long and 4–15 cm wide, with appressed hairs, 3-lobed and coarsely toothed, the terminal leaflet stalked. **Flowers** few, on short stalks; sepals 5, yellow, 4–5 mm long; petals 5, pale yellow, fading to white, shorter than the sepals, 2–4 mm long; stamens 15–20. **Achenes** many, in a rounded cylindric head 10–15 mm long; achene body flattened, 2–3 mm long, smooth, the beak stout, 0.5–1.5 mm long. July–Aug. ❦ Marshes, wet meadows, ditches and streambanks, often in muck. ⊕ Minn, Wisc, Mich, ne Ill and nw Ind. Newf to Alaska, s to NJ, Pa, Ohio, n Ill, n Iowa, Neb, Colo, Ariz and Ore; e Asia.

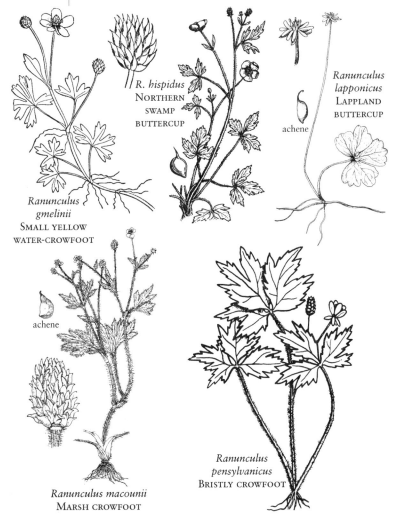

R. hispidus
NORTHERN
SWAMP
BUTTERCUP

Ranunculus lapponicus
LAPPLAND
BUTTERCUP

achene

Ranunculus gmelinii
SMALL YELLOW
WATER-CROWFOOT

achene

Ranunculus macounii
MARSH CROWFOOT

Ranunculus pensylvanicus
BRISTLY CROWFOOT

Ranunculus recurvatus Poiret
Hooked crowfoot   FACW

Perennial herb. **Stems** 2–7 dm long, usually hairy, branches few. **Leaves** broadly kidney-shaped or round in outline, 3-parted to below middle, covered with long, soft hairs; petioles present on all but uppermost leaves. **Flowers** on stalks at ends of stems; sepals curved downward, to 6 mm long; petals pale yellow, 4–6 mm long; styles strongly hooked. **Achenes** in a short-cylindric head; achene body flat, round, sharp-margined, to 2 mm long; beak 1 mm long, hooked or coiled. May–June. ⚘ Moist deciduous forests (especially in openings), swamps; also in drier woods; s in our region also in partial shade in calcareous fens. ⊕ ne, ec and se Minn, all but w Wisc, Mich, ne Ill and nw Ind. Que and Maine to Minn, s to Ga, Miss and Okla.

Ranunculus sceleratus L.
Cursed crowfoot   OBL

Weedy annual herb; plants smooth, sometimes partly submersed in shallow water. **Stems** upright, hollow, 1–6 dm long, branched above and with many flowers. **Leaves** from base of plant less deeply parted and with longer petioles than stem leaves; upper stem leaves small; leaves deeply 3-parted, the main lobes again lobed, heart-shaped at base, rounded at tip, 1–6 cm long and 3–8 cm wide. **Flowers** numerous at ends of stalks from upper leaf axils and branches; sepals 5, 2–3 mm long, yellow-green, tips curved downward; petals 5, light yellow, fading to white, 3–5 mm long. **Achenes** numerous in a short-cylindric head 4–11 mm long; achene body obovate, 1 mm long, slightly corky-thickened on margins; beak tiny, blunt. May–Sept. ⚘ Muddy shores, streambanks, wet meadows, ditches, marshes and other wet places. ⊕ Minn (all but ne), e Wisc (plus local in wc), Mich, ne Ill and nw Ind. Circumboreal, s to Fla, La, Ark, Tex, NM and Calif.

achene

*Ranunculus
recurvatus*
HOOKED
CROWFOOT

*Ranunculus
sceleratus*
CURSED
CROWFOOT

▶Thalictrum L. / Meadow-rue

Perennial herbs. **Leaves** alternate, compound. Male and female **flowers** separate, in panicles on separate plants; sepals 4–5, green or petal-like but soon deciduous; petals absent; stamens numerous, the stalks (filaments) long and slender; pistils several to many. **Fruit** a ribbed or nerved achene.

▶**KEY TO THALICTRUM**

1 Leaflets mostly with 4 or more teeth or lobes, often appearing 3-lobed, each lobe tipped with 1–3 teeth . . . . *T. venulosum*
. . . . NORTHERN MEADOW-RUE
1 Leaflets with 2 or 3 lobes, the lobes usually not toothed **2**

2 Underside of leaflets with very short hairs (rarely smooth); not glandular; leaves odorless; common . . . . *T. dasycarpum*
. . . . PURPLE MEADOW-RUE
2 Underside of leaflets with small beads and hairs tipped with gray or amber exudate; leaves with strong odor when crushed; uncommon (more frequent s of our region). *T. revolutum* / SKUNK MEADOW-RUE

Thalictrum dasycarpum Fischer & Ave-Lall.
Purple meadow-rue   FACW-
Perennial herb, from a short rootstock. **Stems** purple-tinged, 1–2 m long, branched above. **Leaves** divided into 3–4 groups of leaflets; **leaflets** 15 mm or more long, mostly tipped with 3 pointed lobes, dark green above, underside sparsely short-hairy, not waxy and without gland-tipped hairs; margins usually slightly turned under; stem leaves mostly without petioles. **Flowers** in panicles at ends of stems; male and female flowers separate and on different plants (sometimes with some perfect flowers); sepals 3–5 mm long, lance-shaped; anthers linear and sharp-tipped, 2–3 mm long, filaments white; stigmas straight, 2–4 mm long. **Achenes** 4–6 mm long, ribbed, in a round cluster. June–July. ☙ Wet to moist meadows, low prairie, swamps, thickets, streambanks. ⊕ Minn, Wisc, Mich, ne Ill and nw Ind. s Ont to Alberta and Wash, s to Ohio, Ill, Mo, Okla and Ariz.

Thalictrum revolutum DC.
Skunk meadow-rue   FAC
Perennial herb, from short rootstocks, with strong odor when crushed. **Stems** ± smooth, often purple-tinged, 0.5–1.5 m long. Lowest **leaves** on petioles, middle and upper leaves stalkless; leaves divided into 3–4 groups of leaflets; **leaflets** variable in shape and size, usually 3-lobed, some 1–2 lobed, upper surface smooth, underside leathery and conspicuously net-veined, finely hairy with gland-tipped hairs, margins turned under. **Flowers** in panicles at ends of stems; male and female flowers separate and on different plants (sometimes with some perfect flowers); anthers linear, 2–3 mm long, filaments threadlike, 2–5 mm long; pistils 6–12, stigmas 2–3 mm long. **Fruit** an oval or lance-shaped achene, 4–5 mm long, ridged, with tiny gland-tipped hairs. June–July. ☙ Streambanks, thickets, moist meadows and prairies. ⊕ Local in ne Minn, se Wisc, se LP and w UP of Mich, ne Ill and nw Ind. Mass to s Ont, Ohio, Ill and Mo, s to Fla, Ala and La.

Thalictrum venulosum Trelease
Northern meadow-rue   FACW
Perennial herb, spreading by rhizomes; plants pale green, waxy. **Stems** erect, 3–10 dm long. **Leaves** divided into 3–4 groups of leaflets; **leaflets** firm, nearly circular or obovate in outline, tipped by 3–5 lobes, underside veiny, appearing wrinkled, usually sparsely covered with gland-tipped hairs; lower leaves on petioles, upper leaves stalkless. **Flowers** in

narrow panicles at ends of stems, the panicle branches nearly erect; male and female flowers separate and on different plants; stamens 8–20, anthers linear and pointed at tip, filaments slender. **Fruit** an ovate achene, 4–6 mm long, tapered to a short-beak. June–July. Ours are var. *confine. T. confine.* 🌿 Streambanks, thickets and wet, calcium-rich shores of Lakes Huron and Mich. ⊕ n and c Minn, n Wisc, UP of Mich. Labr to BC, s to New Eng, NY, n Great Lakes, Wyo and Ore. ☞ Distinguished from **skunk meadow-rue** (*T. revolutum*) by its less glandular leaflets and its elongate horizontal rhizomes (*T. revolutum* has an erect rootstock). Hybrids with *T. dasycarpum* have been reported.

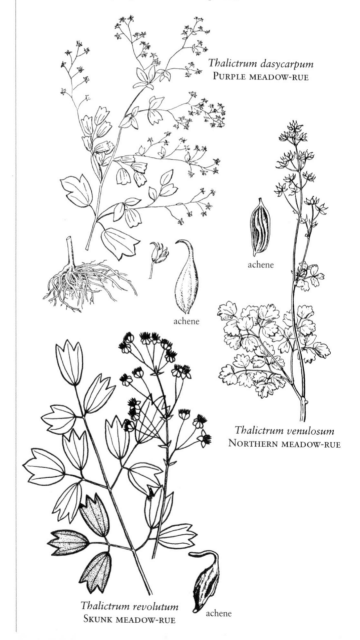

Thalictrum dasycarpum
PURPLE MEADOW-RUE

achene

achene

Thalictrum venulosum
NORTHERN MEADOW-RUE

Thalictrum revolutum
SKUNK MEADOW-RUE   achene

Rhamnaceae
Buckthorn Family

▶**Rhamnus** L. / Buckthorn

Shrubs or small trees. **Leaves** simple, alternate (opposite in *R. cathartica*), pinnately veined, usually with stipules. **Flowers** perfect, or male or female, regular, single or few from leaf axils; sepals joined, 4- or 5-parted; petals 4 or 5. **Fruit** a purple-black, berrylike drupe with 2–4, 1-seeded stones. ☞ **Common buckthorn** (*R. cathartica*, illustration on next page) is frequent in disturbed or heavily grazed, moist to dry woods in s portions of the region (especially in ne Ill). Its stems are often tipped with thorns and its leaves are mostly opposite.

▶**KEY TO RHAMNUS**

1 Leaf margins ± entire; flowers perfect . . . . *R. frangula*
. . . . GLOSSY BUCKTHORN
1 Leaf margins with small, forward-pointing teeth; flowers either male or female **2**

2 Flowers 5-parted; petals absent; widespread. . . . . *R. alnifolia*
. . . . ALDER-LEAF BUCKTHORN
2 Flowers 4-parted; petals present; ne Ill and s Wisc. . . . *R. lanceolata*
. . . . LANCE-LEAVED BUCKTHORN

Rhamnus alnifolia L'Her.
Alder-leaf buckthorn   OBL

⚠
STATUS
Illinois - E

Shrub to 1 m tall, forming low thickets. **Leaves** alternate, oval to ovate, 6–10 cm long and 3–5 cm wide, green above, paler green below; margins with low, rounded teeth; petioles grooved, 5–12 mm long; stipules linear, to 1 cm long, deciduous before fruits mature. **Flowers** appearing with leaves in spring, in clusters of 1–3 flowers from leaf axils; yellow-green, usually 5-parted, 3 mm wide, on short stalks, with both stamens and pistils but one or other is nonfunctional, sepals 1–2 mm long, petals absent. **Fruit** a purple-black, berrylike drupe, 6–8 mm wide, with 1–3 nutletlike stones. May–June. ≋ Conifer swamps, thickets, sedge meadows, wet depressions in deciduous forests; usually where calcium-rich. ⊕ n and e Minn, Wisc (all but wc), Mich, local in ne Ill and nw Ind. Nfld and Que to BC, s to NJ, Pa, Tenn, n Ill, Iowa; Mont; Calif.

Rhamnus frangula L.
Glossy buckthorn   FAC+

☞ **Glossy
buckthorn** is a
serious weed of
disturbed peat-
lands, especial-
ly in s portions
of the region.
It also occurs
in upland
woods.

Shrub or small tree to 5 m tall. **Stems** with pale lenticels. **Leaves** mostly alternate but some leaves often nearly opposite, oval or obovate, 5–8 cm long and 3–5 cm wide, tapered to a blunt or sharp tip; margins entire or slightly wavy; petioles stout, 1–2 cm long. **Flowers** appearing after leaves in spring, single or in clusters of 2–8 in leaf axils, perfect, green-yellow, 5-parted, to 5 mm wide; petals 1–2 mm long. **Fruit** a purple-black, berry-like drupe, 7 mm wide, with 2–3 nutlike stones. May–Aug. ≋ Conifer swamps, thickets, calcareous fens, lakeshores, especially where disturbed or cleared; also invading drier woods. ⊕ Occasional in w Minn, s Wisc,

LP and UP of Mich, ne Ill and nw Ind. ☞ Introduced from Eurasia; escaping from cultivation into disturbed wetlands in ne and c N Amer.

Rhamnus lanceolata Pursh
Lance-leaved buckthorn   (OBL)

Shrub to 1–2 m tall. **Leaves** alternate, lance-shaped to oval, 3–7 cm long and 1–3 cm wide, tapered to a short tip; margins with small, incurved, forward-pointing teeth; petioles to 1 cm long. **Flowers** appearing with leaves in spring, male and female flowers separate, male flowers usually 2–3 in leaf axils, female flowers usually single; sepals green-yellow, 4-lobed, petals to 1 mm long. **Fruit** a black, berrylike drupe, with 2 nutlike stones. ☙ Uncommon in calcareous fens. ⊕ Local in ne Ill and s Wisc. Ohio to SD, s to Ky, Ark and Kans.

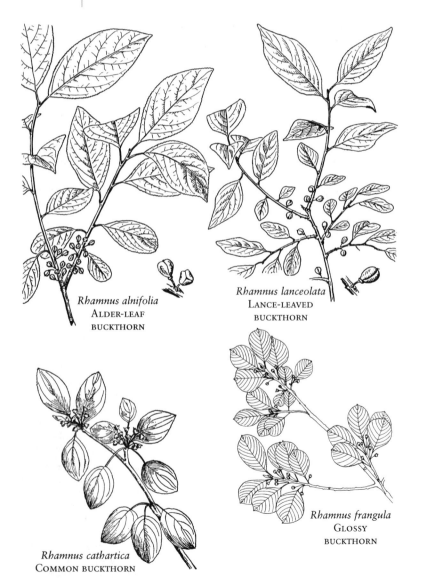

Rhamnus alnifolia
Alder-leaf
buckthorn

Rhamnus lanceolata
Lance-leaved
buckthorn

Rhamnus cathartica
Common buckthorn

Rhamnus frangula
Glossy
buckthorn

Rosaceae
Rose Family

Shrubs, or perennial, biennial, or annual herbs. **Leaves** evergreen or deciduous, mostly alternate and simple or compound. **Flowers** perfect (with both male and female parts), regular, with 5 sepals and petals; stamens numerous. **Fruit** an achene, capsule, or fleshy fruit with numerous embedded seeds (drupe, as in a strawberry), or a fleshy fruit with seeds within (pome, as in apples and pears).

▶**KEY TO ROSACEAE**

1 Leaves simple **2**
1 Leaves divided into leaflets **5**

2 Fruit dry; ovary superior **3**
2 Fruit fleshy; ovary inferior **4**

3 Leaves 3–5 lobed . . . . *Physocarpus opulifolius* / EASTERN NINEBARK
3 Leaves simple . . . . *Spiraea* / SPIRAEA

4 Leaf margins with gland-tipped teeth; flowers less than 1 cm wide .
. . . . *Aronia melanocarpa* / BLACK CHOKEBERRY
4 Leaves without gland-tipped teeth; flowers 1 cm or more wide . . . .
. . . . *Amelanchier bartramiana* / MOUNTAIN JUNEBERRY

5 Plants shrubs or brambles **6**
5 Plants herbs **8**

6 Plants without thorns or bristles; flowers yellow *Potentilla fruticosa*
. . . . SHRUBBY CINQUEFOIL
6 Plants with thorns or bristles; flowers white or pink **7**

7 Leaves pinnately divided into 7 leaflets; petals pink . . *Rosa palustris*
. . . . SWAMP ROSE
7 Leaves palmately divided into 3–5 leaflets; petals white . . . . . *Rubus*
. . . . RASPBERRY; DEWBERRY

8 Leaves divided into 3 equal leaflets . . . . *Rubus pubescens*
. . . . DWARF RASPBERRY
8 Leaves not divided into 3 equal leaflets **9**

9 Flowers white or pink, in large panicles . . . . *Filipendula rubra*
. . . . QUEEN OF THE PRAIRIE
9 Flowers yellow, white, or red-purple, single or in few-flowered clusters, or in narrow, spikelike racemes **10**

10 Flowers in long, narrow, spikelike racemes . . . *Agrimonia parviflora*
. . . . SWAMP AGRIMONY
10 Flowers not in long, narrow, spikelike racemes **11**

11 Flowers white, in many-flowered cylindric spikes; sepals 4, petals absent . . . . *Sanguisorba canadensis* / AMERICAN BURNET

11 Flowers yellow or red-purple, single or in few-flowered clusters; sepals
5, petals present. **12**

12 Leaves deeply parted or divided; styles long, jointed near middle. . .
. . . . *Geum* / AVENS
12 Leaves pinnately or palmately divided; styles short, not jointed . . . .
. . . . *Potentilla* / CINQUEFOIL

▶**Agrimonia** L. / Agrimony

Agrimonia parviflora Aiton
Swamp agrimony   FAC+

Perennial herb. **Stems** stout, 1–1.5 m long, densely covered with coarse, brown hairs; the stem in the inflorescence is also glandular. **Leaves** pinnately divided into mostly 11–23 leaflets, the **leaflets** lance-shaped, with much smaller leaflets intermixed with larger leaflets, smooth above, hairy and glandular below; margins with sharp, forward-pointing teeth; stipules present and deeply toothed. **Flowers** on short, erect stalks, in a long, narrow, spikelike raceme at end of stem; petals 5, small, yellow. **Fruit** a dry achene, at ends of spreading stalks. July–Aug. ❀ Streambanks, wet meadows, wet woods, ditches. ⊕ s Wisc, s LP of Mich, ne Ill and nw Ind. Conn to s Wisc, s to Fla and Mex.

☞ Agrimonia striata (similar to *A. parviflora*) sometimes occurs in cedar swamps, thickets and along shores. Its uppermost stem is not glandular.

▶**Amelanchier** Medikus / Serviceberry; Shadbush

Amelanchier bartramiana (Tausch) Roemer
Mountain juneberry   FAC

Shrub to 2 m tall, often forming clumps; **twigs** purplish, ± smooth. **Leaves** alternate, ovate to oval, 2–5 cm long and 1–2.5 cm wide, tapered to a blunt or sharp tip and often tipped with a small spine, green above, paler below, often purple-tinged when unfolding; margins with small, sharp, forward-pointing teeth; petioles to 1 cm long. **Flowers** 1 cm or more wide, single or in groups of 2–4 at ends of branches or on stalks 1–2 cm long from leaf axils; sepals lance-shaped; petals white, oval to oblong, 6–10 mm long. **Fruit** a dark purple, edible, berrylike pome, 1 cm long. May–Aug. ❀ Conifer swamps, open bogs, thickets. ⊕ n Minn, Mich UP (uncommon in LP). Labr to James Bay and Man, s to New Eng, Mich and Minn. ☞ Hybrids are frequent between various species of *Amelanchier*, making positive identification difficult. Most other species of serviceberry occur in drier habitats, especially where rocky or sandy.

▶**Aronia** L. / Chokeberry

Aronia melanocarpa (Michx.) Elliott
Black chokeberry   FACW-

Shrub, 1–2.5 m tall; **twigs** gray to purple, smooth or hairy. **Leaves** alternate, oval or obovate, 3–8 cm long and 1–4 cm wide, upper surface dark green and smooth (except for dark, hairlike glands along midveins), underside paler, smooth or hairy; margins with small, rounded, forward-pointing teeth, the teeth gland-tipped; petioles to 1 cm long. **Flowers** 5–10 mm wide, in clusters of 5–15 at ends of stems and short, leafy branches; sepals usually glandular; petals white, 4–6 mm long. **Fruit** a dark purple, berrylike pome, 5–10 mm wide. May–June. *A. arbutifolia, A. prunifolia.* ❦ Tamarack swamps, open bogs, thickets, marshes and shores. ⊕ nc, ne and ec Minn, Wisc, Mich, ne Ill and nw Ind. Nfld and Labr to Minn, Iowa and se Mo, s to n Ga and Ala.

▶**Filipendula** Miller / Queen of the prairie

Filipendula rubra (Hill) B. L. Robinson
Queen of the prairie   FACW+

STATUS
Illinois - E
Michigan - T

☞ **Queen of the prairie** is sometimes planted as an ornamental in gardens.

Large perennial herb. **Stems** smooth, 1–2 m long. **Leaves** large, lower leaves to 8 dm long and to 2 dm wide, pinnately parted or divided into 5–9 segments, the segments opposite, stalkless, with 3–5 deep or shallow lobes; margins sharply toothed. **Flowers** pink-purple, fragrant, 7–10 mm wide, in a panicle 1–2 dm wide at ends of stems; petals 5, 2–4 mm long; stamens many. **Fruit** an erect, smooth capsule, 6–8 mm long. June–July. ❦ Wet meadows and shores, calcareous fens; soils usually calcium-rich. ⊕ Uncommon in w LP of Mich, ne Ill and nw Ind. NY to n Ill, s to NC and Ky.

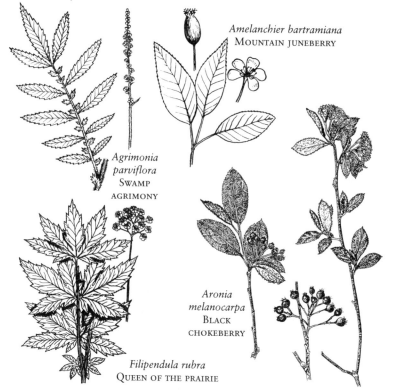

Amelanchier bartramiana
MOUNTAIN JUNEBERRY

Agrimonia parviflora
SWAMP
AGRIMONY

Aronia melanocarpa
BLACK
CHOKEBERRY

Filipendula rubra
QUEEN OF THE PRAIRIE

▶**Geum** L. / Avens

Perennial herbs. **Lower leaves** pinnately lobed or divided, **upper leaves** smaller, less divided or entire. **Flowers** yellow, white or purple; 1 to many in clusters at ends of stems; petals 5; stamens 10 to many. **Fruit** an achene.

▶KEY TO GEUM

1 Flowers nodding; sepals red-purple, upright or ascending at flowering time. . . . . *G. rivale* / PURPLE AVENS

1 Flowers erect; sepals green, curved downward at tip. **2**

2 Petals white . . . . *G. laciniatum* / ROUGH AVENS

2 Petals yellow. **3**

3 Terminal and lateral segment of basal leaves similar in size and shape . . . . *G. allepicum* / YELLOW AVENS

3 Terminal segment much larger than lateral segments. . . . . *G. macrophyllum* / LARGE-LEAF AVENS

Geum allepicum Jacq.
Yellow avens   FAC+

Perennial herb. **Stems** erect or ascending, to 1 m long, branched above, covered with coarse hairs. **Leaves** variable, **basal leaves** pinnately divided into 5–7 oblong leaflets, wedge-shaped at base, petioles long-hairy; **stem leaves** divided into 3–5 segments, stalkless or short-petioled; margins coarsely toothed. **Flowers** 1 to several, short-stalked, on branches at ends of stems; sepals lance-shaped; petals 5, yellow; style jointed. **Fruit** an achene, usually with long hairs. June–July. ❦ Swamps, wet forests, wet meadows, marshes, calcareous fens, ditches and roadsides. ⊕ Minn, Wisc, Mich, ne Ill and nw Ind. Nfld and Que to Yukon, s to NJ, Ill, Iowa and NM.

Geum laciniatum Murray
Rough avens   FACW

Perennial herb. **Stems** 4–10 dm long, covered with long, mostly downward-pointing hairs. **Lower leaves** pinnately divided, the segments pinnately lobed; **upper leaves** divided into 3 leaflets or lobes; margins coarsely toothed; petioles hairy. **Flowers** mostly single at ends of densely hairy stalks from ends of stems; sepals triangular, 4–10 mm long; petals 5, white, 3–5 mm long. **Fruit** an achene, 3–5 mm long (excluding style), grouped into round heads 1–2 cm long. May–June. ❦ Wet woods, floodplain forests, ditches. ⊕ Local in e and c Minn, Wisc, c and s LP of Mich, ne Ill and nw Ind. NS to s Ont and Minn, s to Va, Ky and Mo.

Geum macrophyllum Willd.
Large-leaf avens   FACW+

Perennial herb. **Stems** to 1 m long, unbranched, or branched above, bristly-hairy. **Leaves** pinnately divided, **basal leaves** stalked, the terminal segment large, 3–7-lobed, with much smaller segments intermixed; **stem leaves** smaller, deeply 3-lobed or divided into 3 leaflets, short-stalked or stalkless; margins sharply toothed. **Flowers** 1 to several on branches at ends of stems; sepals triangular, bent backward; petals yellow, obovate, 4–7 mm long; style jointed. **Fruit** a finely hairy achene. May–July. ❦ Moist to wet forest openings, streambanks, wet meadows, ditches. ⊕ n and c Minn, local in nw Wisc, occasional in Mich UP. Nfld and Labr to Alaska, s to New Eng, NY, Minn and Calif; e Asia.

Geum rivale L.
Purple avens   OBL

⚠
STATUS
Indiana - E

Perennial herb. **Stems** erect, 3–8 dm long, mostly unbranched, hairy. **Basal leaves** large, 1–4 dm long, pinnately divided, the terminal 1–3 leaflets much larger than other segments, stalked; **stem leaves** smaller,

2–5 on stem, pinnately divided or 3-lobed, short-stalked or stalkless; margins shallowly lobed and coarsely toothed. **Flowers** mostly nodding, few on branches at ends of stems, the branches with short, gland-tipped hairs and long, coarse hairs; sepals 5, purple, triangular, 6–10 mm long, ascending; petals 5, yellow to pink with purple veins, tapered to a claw-like base; stamens many; styles jointed above middle, the portion above joint deciduous, lower portion persistent and curved in fruit. **Fruit** a long-beaked, hairy achene, 3–4 mm long, grouped into round heads. May–July. ⚘ Conifer swamps, wet forests, bogs, fens, wet meadows; often where calcium-rich. ⊕ n and c Minn, n and c Wisc (especially e along Lake Michigan), Mich, local in ne Ill and nw Ind. Newf to BC, s to NJ, Ill, Mo, SD, NM and Wash.

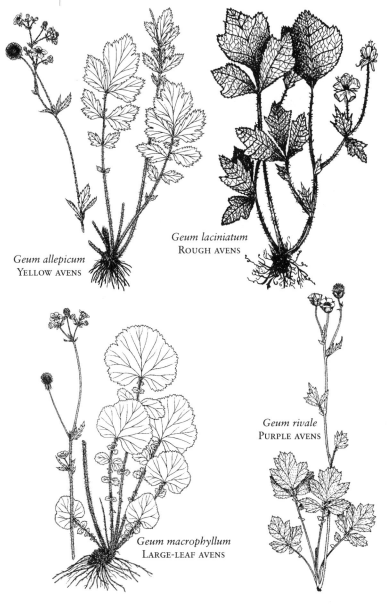

Geum allepicum
YELLOW AVENS

Geum laciniatum
ROUGH AVENS

Geum macrophyllum
LARGE-LEAF AVENS

Geum rivale
PURPLE AVENS

▶**Physocarpus** Maxim. / Ninebark

Physocarpus opulifolius (L.) Maxim.
   Eastern ninebark   FACW-
Much-branched shrub, 2–3 m long; **twigs** greenish, slightly angled or
ridged, smooth or finely hairy; **bark** of older stems shredding in long thin
strips. **Leaves** alternate, ovate in outline, mostly 3-lobed, dark green
above, paler and often sparsely hairy below; margins irregularly toothed;
petioles 1–2 cm long, with a pair of small, deciduous stipules at base.
Flowers 5-parted, white, 5–10 mm wide, many in stalked, rounded clusters at ends of branches. **Fruit** a red-brown pod, 5–10 mm long, in round
clusters; seeds 1–2 mm long, shiny, 3–4 in each pod. June–July. ⚘
Streambanks, lakeshores, swamps, rocky shores of w Lake Superior. ⊕
e Minn, especially near Lake Superior and Miss River; Wisc, Mich, ne Ill
and nw Ind. Que to ND and Colo, s to NC, Tenn and Ark.

fruit cluster

Physocarpus opulifolius
Eastern ninebark

▶**Potentilla** L. / Cinquefoil

Shrubs (*P. fruticosa*) and annual or perennial herbs. **Leaves** pinnately or
palmately divided, alternate or mostly from base of plant. **Flowers** perfect, regular; sepals 5, alternating with small bracts, the sepals and
bractlets joined at base to form a saucer-shaped hypanthium; petals 5,
yellow, or dark red in *P. palustris*; stamens many; pistils numerous. **Fruit**
a group of many small achenes, surrounded by the persistent hypanthium.

▶**KEY TO POTENTILLA**

1 Petals dark red-purple; plants often in shallow water, ± woody and
   creeping at base .... *P. palustris* / Marsh-cinquefoil
1 Petals yellow..2

2 Plants shrubs . . . . *P. fruticosa* / SHRUBBY CINQUEFOIL
2 Plants herbs **3**

3 Plants spreading by stolons; leaves densely white-hairy on underside
. . . . *P. anserina* / SILVER-WEED
3 Stolons absent; leaves green, smooth to hairy below **4**

4 Leaves pinnately divided, with 7–11 leaflets . . . . *P. paradoxa*
. . . . BUSHY CINQUEFOIL
4 Leaves palmately divided, with 3–7 leaflets . . . . *P. rivalis*
. . . . DIFFUSE CINQUEFOIL

Potentilla anserina L.
Silver-weed   FACW+

⚠
STATUS
Indiana - T

Perennial clumped herb, with a stout rootstock and spreading by stolons to 1 m long. **Leaves** all at base of plant except for a few clustered leaves on stolons, pinnately divided into 7–25 leaflets; **leaflets** oblong or obovate, 1.5–5 cm long and 0.5–2 cm wide, lower leaflets much smaller; upper surface green and smooth to gray-green and silky-hairy, underside densely white-hairy; margins with deep, sharp, forward-pointing teeth; stipules brown, membranous, at base of petiole. **Flowers** single from leafy axils of stolons, on stalks 5–15 cm long; sepals ovate, white silky-hairy; petals yellow, oval to obovate, 5–10 mm long; stamens 20–25. **Fruit** a light brown achene. May–Sept. ❦ Wet meadows, shallow marshes, sandy and gravelly shores and streambanks, ditches; soils often calcium-rich. ⊕ nc, c and w Minn, mostly near Great Lakes in Wisc, Mich, ne Ill and nw Ind. Circumboreal, s to NY, Ind, Iowa, Neb, NM and Calif.

Potentilla fruticosa L.
Shrubby cinquefoil   FACW

Much-branched shrub, 0.5–1 m tall; **twigs** brown to red, covered with long, silky- white hairs; **bark** of older branches shredding. **Leaves** alternate, pinnately divided; **leaflets** 3–7 (mostly 5), the terminal 3 leaflets often joined at base, oval to oblong, 1–2 cm long and 3–7 mm wide, tapered at each end, upper surface dark green, underside paler, with silky hairs on both sides or at least on underside; margins entire, often rolled under; short-stalked. **Flowers** 5-parted, bright yellow, 1–2.5 cm wide, 1 to few in clusters at ends of branches; bracts lance-shaped, much narrower than the ovate sepals; stamens 15–20. **Fruit** a small head of hairy achenes surrounded by the 10-parted calyx. June–Sept. *P. floribunda.* ❦ Calcareous fens, lakeshores, open bogs, conifer swamps, wet meadows. ⊕ n and c Minn (especially near Lake Superior), mostly e and s Wisc, Mich (but uncommon in w UP), ne Ill and nw Ind. Circumboreal, s to NJ, n Ind, n Ill, SD and Ariz.

Potentilla palustris (L.) Scop.
Marsh-cinquefoil   OBL

Perennial herb, from long, stout rhizomes. **Stems** 3–8 dm long, ascending to sprawling or floating in shallow water, often rooting at nodes, ± woody at base; lower stems smooth, upper stems sparsely hairy. **Leaves** all from stem, pinnately divided or nearly palmate, with 3–7 leaflets; **leaflets** oblong to oval, 3–10 cm long and 1–3 cm wide, mostly rounded at tip, underside waxy; margins with sharp, forward-pointing teeth; lower leaves long-petioled, upper leaves nearly stalkless; stipules forming wings around petioles of lower leaves, becoming shorter upward. **Flowers** single or paired from leaf axils, or in open clusters; sepals dark red or purple (at least on inner surface), ovate to lance-shaped, 6–20 mm long; petals 5 (sometimes 10), very dark red, 3–5 mm long, with a short slender tip; stamens about 25, dark red. **Achenes** red to brown, smooth, 1 mm long. June–Aug. *Comarum palustre.* ✹ Open bogs (especially in pools and wet margins), conifer swamps, shores. ⊕ Minn (all but extreme w and s), Wisc (all but sw), Mich, ne Ill and nw Ind. Greenland and Labr to Alaska, s to NJ, Ohio, Iowa, ND, Wyo and Calif.

Potentilla paradoxa Nutt.
Bushy cinquefoil   FACW+

⚠
STATUS
Michigan - T

Annual or short-lived perennial herb, taprooted. **Stems** erect to reclining on ground with tip upright, 1–6 dm long, unbranched or branched from base, smooth below to long-hairy above. **Leaves** mostly on stem, pinnately divided into 7–11 leaflets; **leaflets** oval to obovate, 1–4 cm long and 0.5–2 cm wide, finely hairy; margins with rounded teeth; stipules ovate, to 1.5 cm long; lower leaves long-petioled, upper leaves with short petioles. **Flowers** usually numerous in leafy-bracted clusters at ends of stems; sepals ovate, 2–4 mm long; petals yellow, obovate, 2–3 mm long, about as long as sepals; stamens 15–20. **Achenes** brown, 1 mm long. June–Sept. ✹ Shores, ditches, floodplains and flats, often where sandy or gravelly. ⊕ nc, c and s Minn, Mich. Ont to BC, s to Pa, Ill, Mo, La, Mex and Wash.

Potentilla rivalis Nutt.
Diffuse cinquefoil   FACW+

Annual or biennial herb, taprooted. **Stems** upright to spreading, 2–9 dm long, with soft, long hairs, unbranched or branched from base, upper stems branched. **Leaves** mostly on stems, palmately divided, with 3–7 leaflets, or lower leaves pinnately divided; **leaflets** obovate to oval, 1.5–5 cm long and 0.5–2.5 cm wide, sparsely hairy; margins with coarse, forward-pointing teeth; stipules ovate, to 1.5 cm long; petioles present, but uppermost leaves nearly stalkless. **Flowers** in leafy, branched clusters at ends of stems; sepals triangular, 3–6 mm long; petals yellow, obovate, 1–2 mm long, half as long as sepals (or shorter); stamens 10–15. **Achenes** yellow, less than 1 mm long, smooth. June–Aug. *P. millegrana, P. pentandra.* ✹ Wet meadows, streambanks, shores and ditches. ⊕ Local in n and c Minn. Minn to BC, s to Mo, Tex, Mex and Calif.

▶**Rosa** L. / Rose

Rosa palustris Marshall
Swamp rose   OBL

Much-branched, prickly shrub to 2 m tall; **twigs** red-brown, smooth, with a pair of broad-based, downward-curved prickles at nodes; bristles between nodes absent. **Leaves** alternate, pinnately divided into usually 7 leaflets; **leaflets** oval or obovate, 2–6 cm long and 1–2 cm wide; underside midrib often soft-hairy; margins finely toothed; stipules narrow; petioles present. **Flowers** single at ends of leafy branches, or in small clusters of 2–5; petals pink, 2–3 cm long; flower stalks, sepals and hypanthium with stalked glands. **Fruit** ± round, red-orange, 6–10 mm wide, with gland-tipped hairs. July–Aug. ✹ Open bogs, conifer swamps, thickets, shores and streambanks; increasing in disturbed wetlands. ⊕ c and e Wisc, Mich, ne Ill and nw Ind. NS to Wisc, s to Fla and Tex.

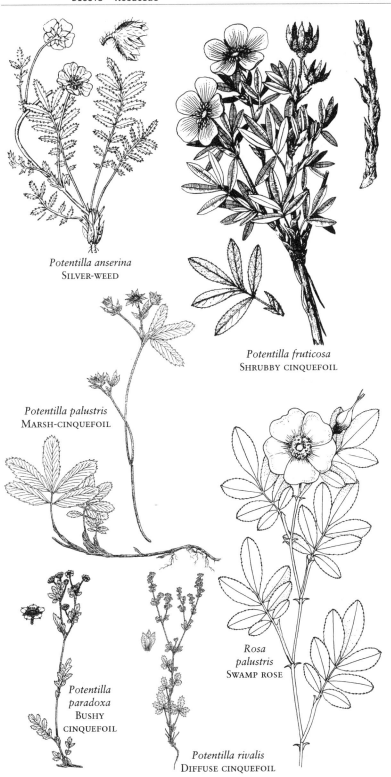

Potentilla anserina
SILVER-WEED

Potentilla fruticosa
SHRUBBY CINQUEFOIL

Potentilla palustris
MARSH-CINQUEFOIL

*Rosa
palustris*
SWAMP ROSE

*Potentilla
paradoxa*
BUSHY
CINQUEFOIL

Potentilla rivalis
DIFFUSE CINQUEFOIL

▶**Rubus** L. / Raspberry; Dewberry; Blackberry

Perennials, woody at least at base, usually with bristly stems. **Stems** biennial in some species, the first year's canes called *primocanes*, the second year's growth termed *floricanes*. **Leaves** alternate, palmately lobed or divided. **Flowers** 5-parted, usually perfect, white to pink or rose-purple; stamens many. **Fruit** a group of small, 1-seeded drupes forming a berry.

▶**KEY TO RUBUS**

1 Stems without bristles or prickles. **2**
1 Stems with bristles or prickles **3**

2 Flowering stems 1 or several from a short base; petals light to deep pink, 1–2 cm long; n portions of region. . . . . *R. acaulis*
. . . . NORTHERN DWARF RASPBERRY; ARCTIC RASPBERRY
2 Flowering stems single from a creeping stem; petals green-white, 0.5–1 cm long; widespread . . . . . *R. pubescens* / DWARF RASPBERRY

3 Leaves gray-hairy on underside; fruit separating from receptacle when ripe (raspberries) . . . . *R. idaeus* / WILD RED RASPBERRY
3 Leaves green on both sides, underside veins hairy; fruit detaching with receptacle when ripe **4**

4 Plants tall (to 1.5 m); stems erect or arching; flowers mostly more than 10 in a cluster; fruit black (blackberries) . . . . *R. setosus*
. . . . BRISTLY BLACKBERRY
4 Plants low and trailing (less than 0.5 m tall); flowers 1 to several in a cluster; fruit red to red-purple (dewberries). **5**

5 Stems with prickles, these hooked at tip and broad at base; leaves thin and deciduous; petals more than 1 cm long . . . . *R. flagellaris*
. . . . NORTHERN DEWBERRY
5 Stems with coarse hairs and slender bristles; leaves leathery and often evergreen; petals less than 1 cm long. . . . . *R. hispidus*
. . . . BRISTLY BLACKBERRY; SWAMP DEWBERRY

Rubus acaulis Michx.

Northern dwarf raspberry; Arctic raspberry   OBL

Perennial, woody at base. **Stems** herbaceous, 5–10 cm long, bristles or prickles absent. **Leaves** alternate, divided into 3 leaflets, 1–4 cm long and 0.5–3 cm wide, terminal leaflet stalked, lateral pair of leaflets nearly stalkless, lateral leaflets often with a shallow lobe, upper surface smooth, underside finely hairy; margins with blunt, forward-pointing teeth; petioles long, finely hairy; stipules small, ovate. **Flowers** single at ends of erect stems; sepals lance-shaped, to 1 cm long; petals 5, light to dark pink, 1–2 cm long. **Fruit** red, nearly round, 1 cm wide, edible. June–Aug. *R. arcticus* var. *grandiflorus*. ❧ Conifer swamps, open bogs. ⊕ nc and ne Minn, rare in c UP of Mich. Labr to Alaska, s to e Que, Minn and Colo.

Rubus flagellaris Willd.

Northern dewberry   FACW

Shrub. **Stems** long-trailing, 2–4 m long, often rooting at tip, brown to red-purple, with curved, broad-based prickles; bristles absent. **Leaves** alternate; primocane leaves divided into 3–5 leaflets, the terminal leaflet 2–6 cm long and 1–5 cm wide, often with small lobes above middle; floricane leaves smaller, usually divided into 3 leaflets; **leaflets** ovate to obovate, upper and lower surface ± smooth, or underside veins with appressed hairs; margins with forward-pointing teeth; petioles finely hairy, with scattered, hooked prickles. **Flowers** mostly 2–7 (sometimes 1), on upright, finely hairy stalks, the stalks with scattered prickles; sepals joined, the lobes narrowed to dark tips; petals 5, white, 10–15 mm long. **Fruit** red, ± round, composed of large, juicy drupelets, edible, not easily separating from receptacle. May–June. *R. baileyanus.* ❧ Swamps, wetland margins; also in drier sandy woods, prairies and openings. ⊕ ne, c and se Minn, local in c Wisc, Mich (but uncommon in UP), ne Ill and nw Ind. e Can (especially along shores of Lakes Huron, Erie and Ontario), to Mich and Minn, occasional s to Ga and Ark.

Rubus hispidus L.
Bristly blackberry; Swamp dewberry   FACW
Shrub. **Stems** trailing or low-arching, often rooting at tip, with slender bristles or spines 2–5 mm long, these sometimes gland-tipped, not much widened at base. **Leaves** alternate, divided into 3 leaflets (rarely 5);, the **leaflets** ovate to obovate, 2–5 cm long and 1–3 cm wide, upper surface dark green and slightly glossy, slightly paler and ± smooth below, some leaves persisting through winter; margins with rounded teeth; petioles finely hairy and bristly; stipules linear, persistent. **Flowers** single in upper leaf axils or in open clusters of 2–8 at ends of short branches; sepals joined, the lobes ovate, tipped with a small dark gland; petals 5, white, 5–10 mm long. **Fruit** red-purple, less than 1 cm wide, sour, not easily separated from receptacle. June–Aug. ❧ Conifer swamps, wet hardwood forests, thickets, wetland margins, sandy interdunal swales. ⊕ Wisc, Mich, ne Ill and nw Ind. Que and NS to Wisc, s to NC and Mo.

Rubus idaeus L.
Wild red raspberry   FACW-

☞ *Rubus ideaus is the familiar edible red raspberry.*

Shrub. **Stems** erect or spreading, to 1.5 m long, biennial; young stems bristly with slender, often gland-tipped hairs; older stems brown, smooth, **Leaves** alternate, pinnately divided; primocane leaves divided into 3 or 5 leaflets, floricane leaflets usually 3; **leaflets** ovate to lance-shaped, upper surface dark green and smooth or sparsely hairy, underside gray-hairy; margins with sharp, forward-pointing teeth; petioles with bristly hairs; stipules slender, soon deciduous. **Flowers** in clusters of 2–5 at ends of stems and 1–2 from upper leaf axils; sepals with gland-tipped hairs; petals 5, white, shorter than the sepals. **Fruit** red, about 1 cm wide, edible, separating from receptacle when ripe. May–Aug. *R. strigosus.* ❧ Thickets, moist to wet openings, streambanks; often where disturbed. ⊕ Minn, Wisc, Mich, ne Ill and nw Ind. Nfld to Alaska, s to Pa, Ind, Ill, Iowa and Ariz.

Rubus pubescens Raf.
Dwarf raspberry   FACW+

⚠
STATUS
Illinois - T

Low perennial. **Stems** long-creeping at or near soil surface, with upright, hairy branches 1–3 dm long; the branches herbaceous but woody at base, bristles absent; sterile branches arching to trailing, often rooting at nodes; flowering branches erect, with few leaves. **Leaves** alternate, divided into 3 leaflets; **leaflets** oval, 2–6 cm long and 1–4 cm wide, tapered to a sharp point; margins with coarse, forward-pointing teeth, often entire near base; petioles hairy; stipules ovate. **Flowers** on glandular-hairy stalks, 1–3 in loose clusters at ends of erect branches, sometimes with 1–2 flowers from leaf axils; petals 5, white or pale pink, to 1 cm long. **Fruit** bright red, round, 5–15 mm wide, the drupelets large, juicy, edible, not separating easily from receptacle. May–July. *R. triflorus.* ❧ Conifer swamps, wet deciduous woods, rocky shores. ⊕ Common in n portions of region. Minn (all but sw), Wisc, Mich, ne Ill and nw Ind. Labr to Yukon and BC, s to NH, WVa, Ind, Ill, Colo and Wash.

Rubus setosus Bigel.
   Bristly blackberry   FACW-

Shrub. **Stems** erect to spreading or arching, to 1.5 m long; **branches** covered with spreading bristles 1–4 mm long; older canes red-brown, ridged, not rooting at tip. **Leaves** alternate; primocane leaves divided into 3–5 leaflets; floricane leaves 3-divided; **leaflets** ovate to obovate, upper and lower surface ± smooth but often hairy on underside veins; margins with sharp, forward-pointing teeth; petioles bristly; stipules linear, 1–2 cm long. **Flowers** few to many in elongate clusters at ends of stems, with small, leafy bracts throughout the head; petals 5, white, to 1 cm long. **Fruit** red, ripening to black, round, to 1 cm wide, dry, poor eating quality. June–Aug. *R. wheeleri.* ⚘ Wetland margins, shores, occasional in open bogs; also in drier sandy prairie. ⊕ ec Minn, nw Wisc, Mich, ne Ill, Ind. Que to Minn, s to Va and Ill.

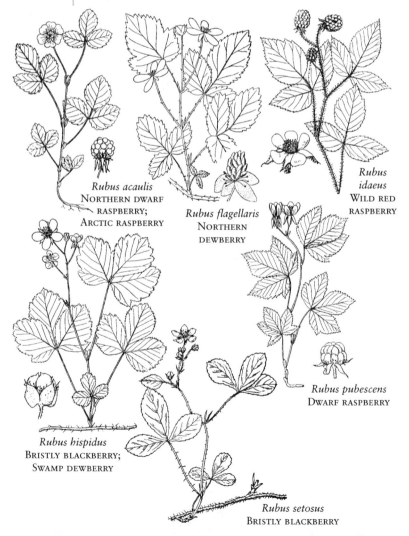

Rubus acaulis
NORTHERN DWARF
RASPBERRY;
ARCTIC RASPBERRY

Rubus flagellaris
NORTHERN
DEWBERRY

Rubus idaeus
WILD RED
RASPBERRY

Rubus pubescens
DWARF RASPBERRY

Rubus hispidus
BRISTLY BLACKBERRY;
SWAMP DEWBERRY

Rubus setosus
BRISTLY BLACKBERRY

▶**Sanguisorba** L. / Burnet

Sanguisorba canadensis L.
American burnet   FACW+

⚠
STATUS
Illinois - E
Indiana - E
Michigan - T

Perennial herb, from a thick rhizome. **Stems** erect, to 1.5 m long, usually simple below, branched above, ± smooth. **Leaves** alternate, to 3–4 dm long, pinnately divided into 7–15 leaflets; **leaflets** ovate to oval, 3–7 cm long; margins with sharp, forward-pointing teeth; petioles long on lower leaves, becoming shorter upward; stipules large. **Flowers** perfect, numerous, in 1 to several spikes 4–15 cm long, the spikes erect on long stalks; calyx 4-lobed, white, 2-3 mm long; petals absent; stamens 4, the filaments white, to 1 cm long. **Fruit** an achene, 2 mm long, enclosed by the persistent sepals. Aug–Sept. ❦ Wet meadows, low prairie; soils often calcium-rich. ⊕ Local in s LP of Mich, ne Ill, Ind. Nfld and Labr to Man, s to NJ, WVa, NC, Ky, Ohio and ne Ill.

▶**Spiraea** L. / Spiraea

Shrubs with alternate, undivided **leaves**. **Flowers** 5-parted, white to pink, perfect, numerous in clusters at ends of stems. **Fruit** a cluster of dry, 1-chambered follicles containing small seeds.

▶**KEY TO SPIRAEA**

1 Leaves smooth on both sides; flowers white . . . . *S. alba*
. . . . Meadowsweet
1 Leaf underside densely covered with light brown woolly hairs; flowers rose-pink . . . . *S. tomentosa* / Hardhack; Steeple-bush

---

Spiraea alba Duroi
Meadowsweet   FACW+

Much-branched shrub, often forming colonies. **Stems** somewhat angled or ridged, 0.5–1.5 m long, smooth or short-hairy when young, becoming red-brown and smooth. **Leaves** alternate, often crowded on stems, oval to oblong lance-shaped, 3–7 cm long and 1–2 cm wide, smooth on both sides; margins with sharp, forward-pointing teeth; petioles 2–8 mm long; stipules absent. **Flowers** small, 6–8 mm wide, many in a narrow, pyramid-shaped panicle 5–25 cm long at ends of branches; sepals 5, triangular; petals 5, white. **Fruit** a group of 5–8 small follicles, each with several seeds; the fruiting branches often persistent over winter. June–Aug. ❦ Wet meadows, streambanks, lakeshores, conifer swamps; soils often sandy. ⊕ Minn, Wisc, Mich, ne Ill and nw Ind. Newf and n Que to Alberta, s to Va, NC, Ind, n Mo and SD.

Spiraea tomentosa L.
Hardhack; Steeple-bush   FACW

Sparsely branched shrub to 1 m tall. Young **stems** covered with brown woolly hairs, becoming smooth and red-brown. **Leaves** alternate, lance-shaped to ovate, 2–5 cm long and 0.5–2 cm wide; ± smooth above, underside gray-green to tan, densely covered with feltlike hairs, the veins prominent; tapered to a pointed or blunt tip; margins with coarse, forward-pointing teeth; petioles 1–4 mm long or absent. **Flowers** small, 3–4 mm wide, in narrow panicles 5–15 cm long at ends of stems, the panicle branches covered with reddish woolly hairs; petals 5, pink or rose (rarely white). **Fruit** a cluster of small, hairy follicles, often persisting over winter. July–Sept. ❦ Open bogs, conifer swamps, thickets, lakeshores, wet meadows; soils usually sandy. ⊕ c Minn, Wisc, Mich, ne Ill and nw Ind. NS and NB to Que and Minn, s to NC, Tenn and Ark.

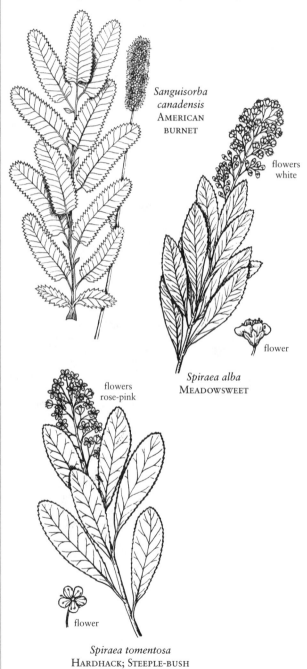

Sanguisorba canadensis AMERICAN BURNET

flowers white

flower

Spiraea alba MEADOWSWEET

flowers rose-pink

flower

Spiraea tomentosa HARDHACK; STEEPLE-BUSH

Rubiaceae
Madder Family

Shrubs (*Cephalanthus*), or herbs (*Galium*). **Leaves** simple, opposite or whorled. **Flowers** small, perfect (with both male and female parts), white to green, single or in loose or round clusters; petals joined, 3–4-lobed; stamens 3–4; ovary 2-chambered. **Fruit** a round head of cone-shaped nutlets (*Cephalanthus*), or a bristly to smooth capsule (*Galium*).

▶**KEY TO RUBIACEAE**

1 Shrub . . . . *Cephalanthus occidentalis* / BUTTONBUSH
1 Herbs . . . . *Galium* / BEDSTRAW

▶**Cephalanthus** L. / Buttonbush

Cephalanthus occidentalis L.
Buttonbush   OBL

Shrub or small tree, 1-4 m tall. Young **stems** green-brown, with lighter lenticels; older stems gray-brown. **Leaves** opposite or in whorls of 3, oval to ovate, 8–20 cm long and to 7 cm wide, upper surface bright green and shiny, paler or finely hairy below; margins entire or slightly wavy; petioles grooved, to 2 cm long. **Flowers** small, perfect, in round, many-flowered heads 2–4 cm wide, on long stalks at ends of stems or from upper leaf axils; petals 4, creamy white, 5–8 mm long; styles longer than petals and swollen at tip. **Fruit** a round head of brown, cone-shaped nutlets, tipped by 4 teeth of persistent sepals. June–Aug. ❧ Hardwood swamps, floodplain forests, thickets, streambanks, marshes, open bogs; often in standing water or muck. ⊕ se Minn, wc and s Wisc, LP of Mich, common in ne Ill and nw Ind. NS, NB and Que to s Minn, s to W Indies and Mex.

Cephalanthus occidentalis
BUTTONBUSH

▶Galium L. / Bedstraw

☞ **Boreal bedstraw** (*Galium kamtschaticum*; MI E) is found in moist, shaded swales in the e UP of Michigan. More common north of our region, it is distinguished from our other *Galiums* by its low, trailing habit, and plants with only 3-5 whorls of broadly ovate leaves.

Perennial herbs (our species), from slender rhizomes. **Stems** 4-angled, ascending to reclining, smooth or bristly. **Leaves** entire, in whorls of 4–6. **Flowers** small, perfect, regular, 1 to several from leaf axils or in clusters at ends of stems; sepals absent; petals joined, 3–4-lobed, white; stamens 3–4; styles 2, ovary 2-chambered and 2-lobed, maturing as 2 dry, round fruit segments which separate when mature.

▶**KEY TO GALIUM**

1 Fruit bristly. **2**
1 Fruit ± smooth **3**

2 Leaves in whorls of 4. . . . . *G. boreale* / NORTHERN BEDSTRAW
2 Leaves in whorls of 6. . . . *G. triflorum* / SWEET-SCENTED BEDSTRAW

3 Leaves sharp-tipped. . . . . *G. asprellum* / ROUGH BEDSTRAW
3 Leaves rounded or blunt at tip. **4**

4 Corolla lobes mostly 3, the lobes wider than long. **5**
4 Corolla lobes 4, the lobes longer than wide **6**

5 Leaves in whorls of 4–6; fruit on smooth, straight stalks. . . . .
. . . . *G. tinctorium* / SOUTHERN THREE-LOBED BEDSTRAW
5 Leaves in whorls of 4; fruit on rough, curved stalks. . . . *G. trifidum*
. . . . NORTHERN THREE-LOBED BEDSTRAW

6 Leaves bent strongly downward, less than 1.5 cm long and 1–2 mm wide; fruits 1–1.5 mm wide . . . . *G. labradoricum*
. . . . LABRADOR-BEDSTRAW
6 Leaves spreading, more than 2 cm long and usually more than 2 mm wide; fruits 2 mm or more wide. **7**

7 Larger leaves linear to lance-shaped, 3 cm or more long; flowers many in panicles at ends of stems . . . . *G. boreale* / NORTHERN BEDSTRAW
7 Leaves narrowly oval, up to 3 cm long; flowers 1–3 on stalks at ends of stems . . . . *G. obtusum* / BLUNTLEAF-BEDSTRAW

Galium kamtschaticum BOREAL BED-STRAW

Galium asprellum Michx.
Rough bedstraw   OBL
Perennial herb. **Stems** spreading or reclining on other plants, much-branched, to 2 m long, 4-angled, with rough, downward-pointing hairs on stem angles (which cling tightly to clothing). **Leaves** 6 in a whorl or 5-whorled on branches, narrowly oval, usually widest above middle, 1–2 cm long and 4–6 mm wide, tapered to a sharp tip; underside midvein and margins with rough hairs; petioles absent. **Flowers** in loose, few-flowered clusters at ends of stems and from upper leaf axils; corolla 4-lobed, white, 3 mm wide. **Fruit** smooth. July–Sept. ❀ Swamps, streambanks, thickets, marshes, wet meadows, calcareous fens. ⊕ n and c Minn, Wisc, Mich, ne Ill and nw Ind. Nfld to Minn, s to NC and Mo.

Galium boreale L.
Northern bedstraw   FAC
Perennial herb. **Stems** erect, 2–8 dm long, 4-angled, smooth or with short hairs at leaf nodes, sometimes slightly rough-to-touch. **Leaves** in whorls of 4, linear to lance-shaped, 1.5–4 cm long and 3–8 mm wide, 3-nerved,

tapered to a small rounded tip; margins sometimes fringed with hairs; petioles absent. **Flowers** many, 3–6 mm wide, in branched clusters at ends of stems; corolla lobes 4, white. **Fruit** with short, bristly hairs, or smooth when mature. June–Aug. ❧ Streambanks, shores, thickets, swamps, moist meadows; also in drier woods and fields. ⊕ Common; Minn, Wisc, Mich, ne Ill and nw Ind. Circumboreal, s to Del, Ky, Mo and Calif.

Galium labradoricum (Wieg.) Wieg.
Labrador-bedstraw   OBL

⚠
STATUS
Illinois - T

Perennial herb. **Stems** simple or branched, 1–3 dm long, 4-angled, hairy at leaf nodes, smooth on stem angles. **Leaves** in whorls of 4, soon curved downward, oblong lance-shaped, 1–1.5 cm long and 1–2 mm wide, blunt-tipped; underside midvein and margins with short, bristly hairs; petioles absent. **Flowers** single or in small groups on stalks from leaf axils; corolla lobes 4, white. **Fruit** smooth, dark. June–July. ❧ Conifer swamps, sphagnum bogs, fens, sedge meadows. ⊕ Minn (all but sw), Wisc (all, especially e), Mich, ne Ill and nw Ind. Newf and Labr to Alberta, s to Pa, Ohio, Ill, Minn and e SD.

Galium obtusum Bigel.
Bluntleaf-bedstraw   FACW+

Perennial herb. **Stems** branched, 2–6 dm long, 4-angled, hairy at leaf nodes, otherwise smooth. **Leaves** mostly in whorls of 4 (sometimes 5 or 6), ascending to spreading, linear to lance-shaped or oval, 1–3 cm long and 3–5 mm wide, blunt-tipped; margins with short, bristly hairs and often somewhat rolled under; petioles absent. **Flowers** in clusters at ends of stems; corolla lobes 4, white. **Fruit** smooth, dark, often with only 1 segment maturing. May–July. ❧ Wet deciduous forests, wet meadows, streambanks, thickets, floodplains, moist prairie. ⊕ Minn (mostly s), s Wisc (local in n), LP of Mich, ne Ill and nw Ind. NS and Que to Minn and SD, s to Fla and e Tex.

Galium tinctorium L.
Southern three-lobed bedstraw   OBL

☞ Plants are
similar to
Galium
trifidum and
sometimes
considered a
variety of
that species.

Perennial herb. **Stems** slender, weak, 4-angled, with rough hairs on angles. **Leaves** in whorls of 4 or sometimes 5–6, linear to oblong lance-shaped, 1–2.5 cm long, tapered to a narrow base, dark green and dull; underside midvein and margins with rough hairs; petioles absent. **Flowers** in clusters of 2–3, on slender, smooth, straight stalks at ends of stems; corolla lobes 3, white. **Fruit** smooth. July–Sept. *G. claytonii.* ❧ Conifer swamps, open bogs, fens, thickets, wet shores and marshes. ⊕ nw and e Minn, Wisc, Mich, ne Ill and nw Ind. Nfld to Minn, s to Fla, Mo, Tex and Mex.

Galium trifidum L.
Northern three-lobed bedstraw   FACW+

Perennial herb. **Stems** slender, weak, 2–6 dm long, much-branched, sharply 4-angled, with rough, downward-pointing hairs on stem angles. **Leaves** in whorls of 4, linear to oblong lance-shaped, 5–20 mm long and 1–3 mm wide, blunt-tipped, dark green and dull on both sides; underside midvein and margins often rough-hairy; petioles absent. **Flowers** small, on 2–3 slender stalks from leaf axils or at ends of stems, the stalks much longer than the leaves; corolla lobes 3, white. **Fruit** dark, smooth. June–Sept. Includes plants sometimes considered a separate species (*G. brevipes*). ❧ Lakeshores, streambanks, swamps, marshes, bogs, springs. ⊕ Minn (all but sw), Wisc, Mich, ne Ill and nw Ind. Circumpolar, s to Ga, Okla, Calif and Mex.

Galium triflorum Michx.

Sweet-scented bedstraw   FACU+

Perennial herb. **Stems** prostrate or scrambling, 2–8 dm long, 4-angled, smooth or with rough, downward-pointing hairs on stem angles. **Leaves** shiny, in whorls of 6 (or 4 on smaller branches), narrowly oval to oblong lance-shaped, 2–5 cm long and to 1 cm wide, l-nerved, tipped with a short, sharp point, slightly vanilla-scented, underside midvein with rough hairs, margins with rough, forward-pointing hairs; petioles absent. **Flowers** 2–3 mm wide, on slender stalks from leaf axils and at ends of stems, the stalks with 3 flowers or branched into 3 short stalks, each with 1–3 flowers; corolla lobes 4, green-white. **Fruit** 2-lobed, covered with hooked bristles. June–Aug. ❦ Moist to wet woods, hummocks in cedar swamps, wetland margins and shores, clearings. ⊕ Common; Minn, Wisc, Mich, ne Ill and nw Ind. Circumboreal, s in Amer to Fla and Mex.

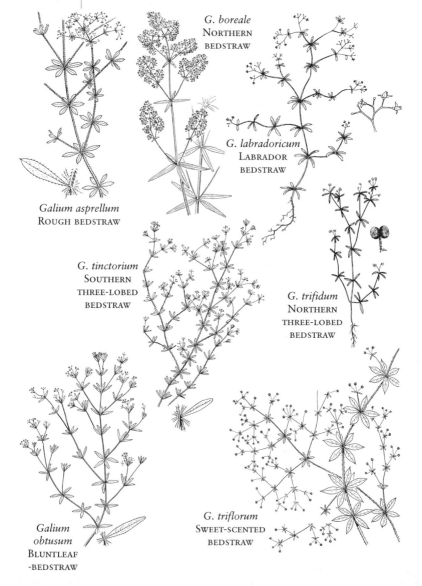

G. boreale
NORTHERN
BEDSTRAW

G. labradoricum
LABRADOR
BEDSTRAW

Galium asprellum
ROUGH BEDSTRAW

G. tinctorium
SOUTHERN
THREE-LOBED
BEDSTRAW

G. trifidum
NORTHERN
THREE-LOBED
BEDSTRAW

Galium obtusum
BLUNTLEAF
-BEDSTRAW

G. triflorum
SWEET-SCENTED
BEDSTRAW

Salicaceae
Willow Family

Deciduous trees or shrubs. **Leaves** alternate, margins entire or toothed; stipules often present at base of leaf petiole, these usually soon falling. **Flowers** borne in catkins near ends of branches, imperfect (the male and female flowers on separate plants), usually appearing before leaves open, or in a few species after leaves open; flowers without petals or sepals, each flower with either 1 or 2 enlarged basal glands (*Salix*) or a cup-shaped disk (*Populus*). **Fruit** a dry, many-seeded capsule; seeds small, covered with long, silky hairs.

▶**KEY TO SALICACEAE**

1 Large trees; leaves heart-shaped to ovate, mostly less than 2x as long as wide; buds often sticky and covered by 2 or more overlapping scales; catkins drooping, flowers subtended at base by a cup-shaped disk; stamens many, 12–80 . . . . . *Populus* / POPLAR; COTTONWOOD
1 Shrubs and trees; leaves ovate, lance-shaped or linear, 2x or more longer than wide; buds covered by 1 scale; catkins upright or drooping, flowers subtended by 1 or 2 enlarged glands; stamens 2–8 . . . . *Salix* / WILLOW

▶**Populus** L. / Poplar; Cottonwood

☞ **Quaking aspen** (*P. tremuloides*, illustrated) may occur as scattered trees in wetlands of the region. It is more common in uplands where it may form large groves.

Trees with deciduous, ovate to triangular **leaves**. **Flowers** in drooping catkins that develop and mature before and with leaves in spring; male and female flowers on separate trees; base of flower with a cup-shaped disk; stamens 10–80. **Fruit** a 2–4 chambered capsule with many small seeds, these covered with long, white hairs which aid in dispersal by the wind.

▶**KEY TO POPULUS**

1 Leaf petioles strongly flattened *P. deltoides* / EASTERN COTTONWOOD
1 Leaf petioles round in section **2**

2 Leaves rounded at tip, underside veins hairy, underside not brown-stained; s Mich only (more common s and e of our region) . . . . *P. heterophylla* / SWAMP-COTTONWOOD; DOWNY POPLAR
2 Leaves tapered to a sharp tip, smooth, underside often stained brown from resin; widespread . . . . *P. balsamifera* / BALSAM-POPLAR

Populus balsamifera L.
Balsam-poplar   FACW

⚠ STATUS Illinois - E

Medium to large tree to 20 m or more tall, trunk 30–60 cm wide, crown open, somewhat narrow; **bark** smooth when young, becoming dark gray and furrowed; **twigs** red-brown when young, becoming gray; **leaf buds** fragrant, very resinous and sticky. **Leaves** resinous, ovate to broadly lance-shaped, 8–13 cm long and 4–7 cm wide, tapered to a long tip, rounded or somewhat heart-shaped at base, dark green and somewhat

shiny above, white-green or silvery and often stained with rusty brown resin below; margins with small, rounded teeth; petioles round in section, 3–4 cm long. **Catkins** densely flowered, drooping, appearing before leaves; scales fringed with long hairs, early deciduous; female catkins 10–13 cm long; female flowers with 2 spreading stigmas; stamens 20–30. **Capsules** ovate, 6–8 mm long, crowded on short stalks. April–May. ❀ Swamps, floodplain forests, shores, streambanks, forest depressions, moist dunes. ⊕ Minn (all but sw), Wisc, UP and n LP of Mich (local in s LP) and ne Ill. Labr to Alaska, s to Conn, n Pa, n Ind, n Ill, n Iowa, Neb and Colo.

Populus deltoides Marsh.
Eastern cottonwood   FAC+

Large tree to 30 m or more tall, with a large trunk (often 1 m or more wide) and a broad, rounded crown; **bark** gray to nearly black, deeply furrowed; **twigs** olive-brown to yellow, turning gray with age; **leaf buds** very resinous and sticky, shiny, covered by several tan bud scales. **Leaves** smooth, broadly triangular, 8–14 cm long and 6–12 cm wide, short-tapered to tip, heart-shaped or squared-off at base; margins with forward-pointing, incurved teeth, 2–5 large glands usually present at base of blade near petiole; petioles strongly flattened, 3–10 cm long; stipules tiny, early deciduous. **Catkins** loosely flowered, drooping, appearing before leaves; scales fringed, soon falling; flowers subtended by a cup-shaped disk 2–4 mm wide; **female catkins** green, 7–12 cm long in flower, to 20 cm long in fruit; female flowers with 3–4 spreading stigmas; **male catkins** dark red, soon deciduous; stamens 30–80. **Capsules** ovate, 6–12 mm long, on stalks 3–10 mm long. April–May. ❀ Floodplains, streambanks and bars, shores, wet meadows, ditches. ⊕ Minn (all but ne), c and s Wisc, LP of Mich (especially s), common in ne Ill and nw Ind. Que to Sask, s to Fla, Tex and Ariz.

Populus heterophylla L.
Swamp-cottonwood; Downy poplar   OBL

⚠
STATUS
Michigan - E

Large tree to 20 m or more tall; **bark** dull brown and shaggy; **leaf buds** hairy, not resinous. **Leaves** broadly ovate, 12–20 cm long, blunt or rounded at tip, heart-shaped at base; upper surface densely hairy when young, becoming smooth except near base of blade, underside smooth except hairy on main veins; margins with incurved teeth; petioles round in section. **Catkins** loosely flowered, scales fringed with long hairs; female flowers with 2–3 spreading stigmas; stamens 12–20. **Capsules** ovate, 7–12 mm long, on stalks 10–15 mm long. May. ❀ Floodplain forests. ⊕ Rare in s Mich and ne Ill; nw Ind. Conn to s Mich and ne Ill, s mainly along Atlantic coast to Fla and La.

▶Salix L. / Willow

Shrubs and trees. **Leaves** variable in shape, petioles glandular in some species; stipules early deciduous or persistent, sometimes absent. **Catkins** stalkless or on leafy branchlets, usually shed early in season. Male and female flowers on separate plants; male flowers with mostly 2–3 stamens (to 8 in some species). **Fruit** a 2-chambered, stalked or stalkless capsule.

▶KEY TO SALIX

1 Leaves opposite; young branches often dark purple . . . . *S. purpurea*
. . . . Basket willow; Purple-osier
1 Leaves alternate; branches various colors 2

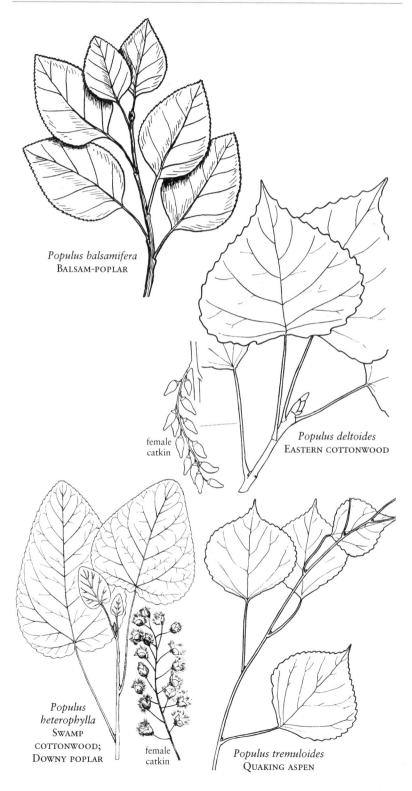

Populus balsamifera
BALSAM-POPLAR

Populus deltoides
EASTERN COTTONWOOD

female
catkin

*Populus
heterophylla*
SWAMP
COTTONWOOD;
DOWNY POPLAR

female
catkin

Populus tremuloides
QUAKING ASPEN

2 Leaf petioles with glands at or near base of leaf blade **3**
2 Petioles without glands **8**

3 Trees, usually with a single trunk; leaves narrow **4**
3 Small trees or shrubs, usually with several to many stems; leaves broader **5**

4 Leaves often curved sideways (scythe-shaped), tapered to a long, slender tip; stipules large on vigorous shoots . *S. nigra* / BLACK WILLOW
4 Leaves not curved sideways, tapered to a short tip; stipules small and early deciduous . . . . *S. alba* / WHITE WILLOW

5 Leaves not waxy on underside . . . . *S. lucida* / SHINING WILLOW
5 Leaves waxy-coated on underside **6**

6 Leaf tips rounded or with a short point; leaf base heart-shaped or rounded; young leaves thin and translucent; buds and leaves with a balsam-like scent. . . . . *S. pyrifolia* / BALSAM-WILLOW
6 Leaves tapered to tip; leaf base blunt or rounded; young leaves not translucent; buds and leaves not balsam-scented **7**

7 Young leaves sparsely hairy; margins with small forward-pointing teeth; flowering in early summer . . . . *S. amygdaloides* . . . . PEACH-LEAF WILLOW
7 Young leaves without hairs; margins with small, gland-tipped, forward-pointing teeth; flowering summer or fall . . . . *S. serissima* . . . . AUTUMN-WILLOW

8 Mature leaves hairy, at least on underside **9**
8 Mature leaves without hairs (sometimes hairy on petiole and midvein) **16**

9 Leaves linear or narrowly lance-shaped **10**
9 Leaves broadly lance-shaped, oblong or oval **13**

10 Underside of leaves with feltlike covering of white tangled hairs; young twigs white-hairy; plant of peatlands, often where calcium-rich . . . . *S. candida* / HOARY OR SAGE-LEAVED WILLOW
10 Leaves not with feltlike hairs; twigs smooth or sparsely hairy . . . **11**

11 Leaf margins smooth and turned under; leaf underside with shiny white hairs; uncommon in n portions of region . . . . *S. pellita* . . . . SATINY WILLOW
11 Leaf margins with gland-tipped teeth; leaf underside with few long hairs **12**

12 Leaf margins with widely spaced sharp teeth; petioles 1–5 mm long; colony-forming shrub of sandy banks *S. exigua* / SANDBAR-WILLOW
12 Leaf margins with small teeth at least above middle of blade; petioles 3–10 mm long; stems clustered but not forming large colonies . . . . *S. petiolaris* / MEADOW-WILLOW

13 Leaves rounded or heart-shaped at base; margins with gland-tipped, forward-pointing teeth; stipules present and persistent . . . . *S. eriocephala* / DIAMOND WILLOW
13 Leaves tapered to base; margins smooth or toothed; stipules usually deciduous early in season **14**

14 Leaves linear to lance-shaped, more than 5x longer than wide, underside velvety with shiny white hairs; uncommon in n portions of region . . . . *S. pellita* / SATINY WILLOW

14 Leaves oval or obovate, less than 5x longer than wide, underside hairs not shiny **15**

15 Small branches widely spreading; young leaves with white hairs; catkins appearing with leaves in spring; catkin bracts yellow or straw-colored . . . . *S. bebbiana* / BEBB'S OR BEAKED WILLOW

15 Small branches not widely spreading; young leaves with some red or copper-colored hairs; catkins appearing before leaves in spring; catkin bracts dark brown to black . . . . *S. discolor* / PUSSY-WILLOW

16 Leaves green on both sides or slightly paler on underside, not waxy or white below **17**

16 Leaves waxy or white-hairy on underside **18**

17 Many-stemmed shrub; stipules small or absent . . . . *S. exigua* . . . . SANDBAR-WILLOW

17 Single-stemmed tree; stipules large . . . . . . *S. nigra* / BLACK WILLOW

18 Leaf margins entire to shallowly lobed or with irregular teeth, sometimes rolled under **19**

18 Leaf margins distinctly and regularly toothed **23**

19 Leaf margins entire and somewhat rolled under **20**

19 Leaf margins irregularly toothed **21**

20 Stems to 1 m tall, or creeping and rooting in moss; upper surface of leaves with raised, netlike veins; catkins appearing with leaves; capsules not hairy . . . . *S. pedicellaris* / BOG-WILLOW

20 Stems 1–4 m tall; leaf veins not netlike; catkins appearing before leaves; capsules hairy; n portions of region . . . . *S. planifolia* . . . . TEA-LEAF WILLOW

21 Leaves dull green above, wrinkled below; catkins appearing with leaves; bracts of female catkins green-yellow to straw-colored. . . . . *S. bebbiana* / BEBB'S OR BEAKED WILLOW

21 Leaves dark green and shiny above; catkins appearing before leaves; bracts of female catkins dark brown to black **22**

22 Stipules large on vigorous shoots; capsules on distinct stalks 2 mm or more long . . . . *S. discolor* / PUSSY-WILLOW

22 Stipules lance-shaped and soon deciduous, or absent or very small; capsules stalkless or on short stalks less than 2 mm long; n portions of region . . . . *S. planifolia* / TEA-LEAF WILLOW

23 Leaves lance-shaped. **24**

23 Leaves broadly oval, ovate, or oblong lance-shaped **27**

24 Leaves ± equally tapered at tip and base **25**

24 Leaves unequally tapered, the tip tapered to a point, the base usually rounded or heart-shaped **26**

25 Young leaves with few to many coppery hairs mixed with white hairs; mature leaves smooth on both sides or hairy above; lateral veins not prominent; capsules lance-shaped . *S. petiolaris* / MEADOW-WILLOW

25 Young leaves densely silky hairy, without copper-colored hairs; underside of mature leaves silky-hairy with conspicuous, riblike, lateral veins; capsules ovate and rounded at tip; s portions of region . . . . *S. sericea* / SILKY WILLOW

26 Young twigs hairless; stipules small or absent; bracts of female catkins pale yellow and soon deciduous . . . . *S. amygdaloides* . . . . PEACH-LEAF WILLOW
26 Young twigs gray-hairy; stipules large; bracts of female catkins dark brown to black, persistent . . . . . *S. eriocephala* / DIAMOND WILLOW

27 Leaves balsam-scented (especially when dried), underside net-veined; stipules tiny or absent; catkins appearing with leaves, on leafy or leafless branches . . . . *S. pyrifolia* / BALSAM-WILLOW
27 Leaves not balsam-scented, not net-veined; stipules large on vigorous shoots; catkins appearing before or with leaves, stalkless or on short, leafy branches . . . . *S. myricoides* / BAYBERRY WILLOW

Salix alba L.

White willow   FACW

☞ Hybrids between Salix alba and two other introduced species— **weeping willow** (*S. babylonica*) and **crack-willow** (*S. fragilis*)— are common.

Tree to 20 m tall; **twigs** golden-yellow, often with long, silky hairs. **Leaves** lance-shaped, 4–10 cm long and 1–2.5 cm wide, dark green and shiny above, waxy white below, smooth to sparsely hairy on both sides, margins with small gland-tipped teeth; petioles 2–8 mm long, with silky hairs; stipules lance-shaped, 2–4 mm long, early deciduous. **Catkins** appearing with leaves in spring; **female catkins** 3–6 cm long, on leafy branches 1–4 cm long; **male catkins** 3–5 cm long, stamens 2; catkin bracts pale yellow, hairy near base, early deciduous. **Capsules** ovate, 3–5 mm long, without hairs, stalkless or on stalks to 1 mm long. May–June. ☙ Introduced from Europe and sometimes escaping to streambanks and other wet areas. ⊕ Mostly s Minn, se Wisc, mostly s LP of Mich, ne Ill and nw Ind. Widely established in temperate N Amer.

Salix amygdaloides Andersson

Peach-leaf willow   FACW

Shrub or tree to 15 m tall, often with several trunks; **twigs** gray-brown to light yellow, shiny and flexible. **Leaves** smooth, lance-shaped, long-tapered to tip, 5–12 cm long and 1–3 cm wide, yellow-green above, waxy-white below, margins finely toothed; petioles 5–20 mm long and often twisted; stipules small and early deciduous. **Catkins** appearing with leaves, linear and loosely flowered; female catkins 3–12 cm long, on leafy branches 1–4 cm long; catkin bracts deciduous, pale yellow, long hairy especially on inner surface; stamens 3–7 (usually 5). **Capsules** smooth, ovate, 3–7 mm long, on stalks 1–3 mm long. May–June. ☙ Floodplains, streambanks, lake and pond borders. ⊕ Minn (but not far ne), Wisc (but local in far n), Mich LP, ne Ill and nw Ind. Que and NY to se BC and Wash, s to Pa, Ky, Mo, n Tex, NM and Ariz.

Salix bebbiana Sarg.

Bebb's or Beaked willow   FACW+

Shrub or small tree to 8 m tall, stems 1 to several; **twigs** yellow-brown to dark brown, usually with short hairs. **Leaves** oval to ovate or obovate, tapered to tip, 4–8 cm long and 1–3 cm wide, dull gray-green, hairy or sometimes smooth on upper surface, waxy-gray, hairy and wrinkled below, the veins distinctly raised on lower surface; margins entire to shallowly toothed; petioles 5–15 mm long; stipules deciduous or persistent on vigorous shoots. **Catkins** appearing before leaves in spring; female catkins loose, 2–6 cm long, on short leafy branches to 2 cm long; catkin bracts persistent, red-tipped when young, turning brown, long hairy; stamens 2. **Capsules** ovate, 5–8 mm long, finely hairy, on stalks 2–6 mm long. May–June. ⚘ Swamps, thickets, wet meadows, streambanks, marsh borders. ⊕ Common; Minn, Wisc, Mich, ne Ill and nw Ind. Newf to Alaska, s to Md, Ohio, Ill, Iowa, Neb, Ariz, NM and Calif.

Salix candida Fluegge
Hoary or Sage-leaved willow   OBL
Low shrub to 1.5 m tall; **twigs** much-branched, covered with dense, matted white hairs. **Leaves** linear-oblong, tapered at tip, 4–10 cm long and 0.5–2 cm wide, dull, dark green and sparsely hairy above, veins sunken, densely white-hairy below; margins entire and rolled under; petioles 3–10 mm long; stipules persistent, 2–10 mm long, white-hairy. **Catkins** appearing with leaves in spring; female catkins 1–5 cm long, on leafy branches 0.5–2 cm long; catkin bracts persistent, brown, hairy; stamens 2. **Capsules** ovate, 4–8 mm long, white-hairy, on stalks to 1 mm long. May–June. ⚘ Fens, bogs, open swamps, streambanks, usually where calcium-rich. ⊕ Minn (all but far s), nw and e Wisc, c and e UP and LP of Mich, ne Ill and nw Ind. Labr to Alaska, s to NJ, Pa, Ohio, Ill, SD, Colo, Idaho and s BC.

Salix discolor Muhl.
Pussy-willow   FACW
Shrub or small tree to 5 m tall; **twigs** yellow-brown to red-brown, dull, smooth with age or with patches of fine hairs. **Leaves** oval and short-tapered to tip, 3–10 cm long and 1–4 cm wide, dark green and smooth above, underside red-hairy when young, becoming white-waxy, smooth and not wrinkled; margins entire or with few rounded teeth; petioles without glands; stipules deciduous, or often persistent on vigorous shoots. **Catkins** appearing and maturing before leaves in spring; female catkins 4–8 cm long, stalkless, sometimes with 2 or 3 small, brown, bractlike leaves at the base; stamens 2. **Capsules** ovate with a long neck, 6–10 mm long, densely gray-hairy, on stalks 2–3 mm long. April–May. ⚘ Swamps, fens, streambanks, floodplains, marsh borders. ⊕ Common; Minn (all but sw), Wisc, Mich, ne Ill and nw Ind. Newf to BC, s to Del, n Ga, Ky, Ill, n Mo, SD, Wyo and Idaho.

Salix eriocephala Michx.
Diamond willow   FACW
Shrub or small tree to 6 m tall; **twigs** red-brown to dark brown, hairy when young. **Leaves** lance-shaped or oblong lance-shaped, 5–12 cm long and 1–3 cm wide, red-purple and hairy when young, upper surface becoming smooth and dark green, underside becoming pale-waxy; margins finely toothed; petioles without glands, 3–15 mm long; stipules persistent (especially on vigorous shoots), ovate or kidney-shaped, to 12 mm long, hairless, toothed. **Catkins** appearing with or slightly before leaves in spring; female catkins 2–6 cm long, on short leafy branches to 1 cm long; catkin bracts persistent, brown to black, hairy; stamens 2. **Capsules** ovate with a long neck, 4–6 mm long, without hairs, on stalks 1–2 mm long. April–May. *S. lutea, S. rigida.* ⚘ Shores, streambanks, floodplains, ditches and wet meadows, especially along major rivers. ⊕ Minn (all but ne), Wisc, Mich (especially LP), ne Ill and nw Ind. NS and s Que to Sask and Mont, s to Va, Ga, Mo and Kans.

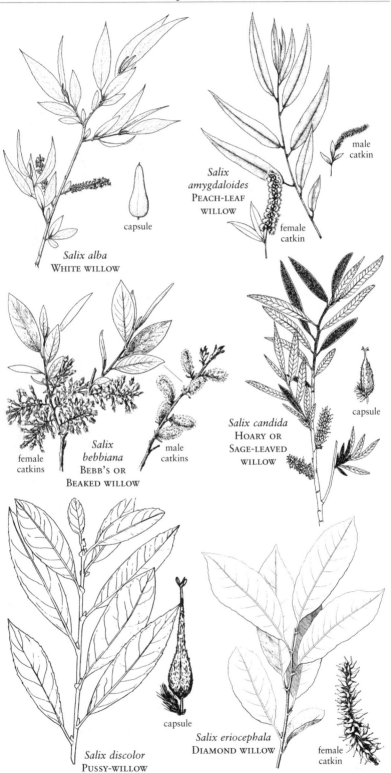

capsule

Salix alba
WHITE WILLOW

Salix amygdaloides
PEACH-LEAF
WILLOW

male
catkin

female
catkin

female
catkins

Salix bebbiana
BEBB'S OR
BEAKED WILLOW

male
catkins

Salix candida
HOARY OR
SAGE-LEAVED
WILLOW

capsule

capsule

Salix discolor
PUSSY-WILLOW

Salix eriocephala
DIAMOND WILLOW

female
catkin

Salix exigua Nutt.
Sandbar-willow OBL

Shrub to 4 m tall, spreading by rhizomes and often forming dense thickets; **twigs** yellow-orange to brown, smooth. **Leaves** linear to lance-shaped, tapered at tip and base, 5–14 cm long and 5–15 mm wide, green on both sides but paler below, at first hairy but soon usually smooth; margins with widely spaced, large teeth; petioles without glands, 1–5 mm long; stipules tiny or absent. **Catkins** appearing with leaves in spring on short leafy branches (and plants sometimes again flowering in summer); female catkins loosely flowered, 2–8 cm long; catkin bracts deciduous, yellow; stamens 2. **Capsules** narrowly ovate, 5–8 mm long, hairy when young, smooth when mature, on stalks to 2 mm long. May–June. *S. interior*. ⚘ Shores, streambanks, sand and mud bars, ditches and other wet places; often colonizing exposed banks. ⊕ Common; Minn, Wisc, Mich, ne Ill and nw Ind. NB and Que to Alaska and BC, s to Va, Tenn, La, Tex, Colo and Mont.

Salix lucida Muhl.
Shining willow FACW+

☞ On sunny days, the shiny leaves of Salix lucida are distinctive even from a distance.

Shrub or small tree to 5 m tall; **twigs** yellow-brown or dark brown, smooth and shiny. **Leaves** lance-shaped to ovate, long-tapered and asymmetric at tip, 4–12 cm long and 1–4 cm wide, shiny green above, pale below, red-hairy when young, but soon smooth; margins with small, gland-tipped teeth; petioles with glands near base of leaf; stipules often persistent, strongly glandular. **Catkins** appearing with leaves in spring; female catkins 2–5 cm long, on leafy branches 1–3 cm long; catkin bracts deciduous, yellow, sparsely hairy; stamens 3–6. **Capsules** ovate with a long neck, 4–7 mm long, not hairy, on short stalks to 1 mm long. May. ⚘ Swamps, shores, wet meadows, moist sandy areas. ⊕ n and e Minn; Wisc (but uncommon in sw), Mich, ne Ill and nw Ind. Labr and Newf to Sask, s to Del, Ohio, Iowa and SD.

Salix myricoides Muhl.
Bayberry willow FACW

Shrub to 4 m tall; **twigs** yellow to dark brown, hairy when young. **Leaves** thickened, lance-shaped to ovate or oval, 4–12 cm long and 1.5–5 cm wide, dark green above, strongly waxy-white below; margins with gland-tipped teeth; petioles 5–12 mm long; stipules 5–10 mm long. **Catkins** appearing shortly before or with leaves; female catkins 2–8 cm long, on leafy branches 5–15 mm long; catkin bracts deciduous, 1–2 mm long, brown-black and long hairy; stamens 2. **Capsules** lance-shaped, 5–8 mm long, not hairy, on stalks 1–3 mm long. May. *S. glaucophylloides*. ⚘ Dune hollows and sandy shorelines, fens, mostly near Great Lakes; inland on wet, calcium-rich sites. ⊕ e and c Wisc, e and c UP and LP of Mich, ne Ill and nw Ind. Nfld, Que and Maine, to Hudson Bay and Wisc, s to Ill.

Salix nigra Marshall
Black willow OBL

Medium tree to 15 m tall, trunks 1 or several, crown rounded and open; **bark** dark brown, furrowed, becoming shaggy; **twigs** bright red-brown, often hairy when young. **Leaves** commonly drooping, linear lance-shaped, 6–15 cm long and 0.5–2 cm wide, long tapered to an often curved tip, green on both sides but satiny above and paler below, lateral veins upturned at tip to form a ± continuous vein near leaf margin; margins finely toothed; petioles 3–8 mm long, hairy, usually glandular near base of blade; stipules to 12 mm long, heart-shaped, usually deciduous.

Catkins appearing with leaves in spring; female catkins 3–8 cm long, on leafy branches 1–3 cm long; stamens usually 6 (varying from 3–7); catkin bracts yellow, hairy, deciduous. **Capsules** ovate, 3–5 mm long, without hairs, on a short stalk to 2 mm long. May. ❦ Streambanks, lakeshores and wet depressions; not tolerant of shade. ⊕ ec and s Minn, all but far n Wisc, s LP of Mich (rare in n LP and UP), common in ne Ill and nw Ind. NB to Minn, s to Fla, Tex, Calif and into Mex.

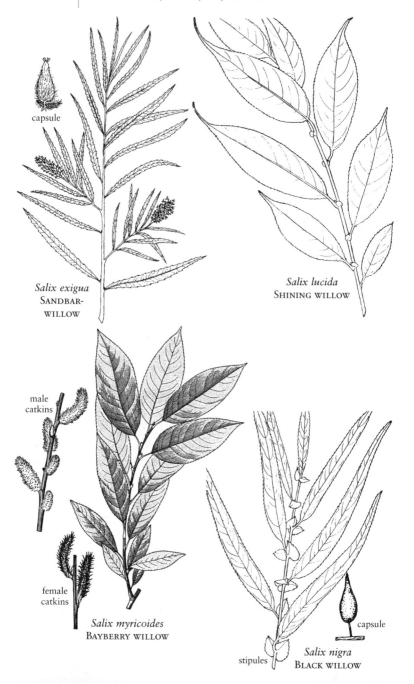

capsule

Salix exigua
SANDBAR-
WILLOW

Salix lucida
SHINING WILLOW

male
catkins

female
catkins

Salix myricoides
BAYBERRY WILLOW

capsule

stipules

Salix nigra
BLACK WILLOW

Salix pedicellaris Pursh
  Bog-willow   OBL
Short, sparsely branched shrub 4–15 dm tall; **twigs** dark brown and
smooth. **Leaves** oblong-lance-shaped to obovate, tapered to tip or blunt
and often with a short point, 3–6 cm long and 0.5–2 cm wide, silky hairy
when young, becoming hairless and thick and leathery with age, green on
upper surface, white-waxy below, veins pale-colored and slightly raised
on both sides; margins entire, often slightly rolled under; petioles without glands, 2–8 mm long; stipules absent. **Catkins** appearing with leaves
in spring; female catkins 2–4 cm long, on leafy branches 1–3 cm long;
catkin bracts persistent, yellow-brown, hairy on inner surface near tip;
stamens 2. **Capsules** lance-shaped, 4–7 mm long, without hairs, on stalks
2–3 mm long. May–June. ☙ Bogs, fens, sedge meadows, interdunal wetlands. ⊕ n and c Minn (but not far w), Wisc (but absent from driftless
area), Mich, ne Ill and nw Ind. Newf to NW Terr and BC, s to NY, n
Iowa, ND, n Idaho and Wash.

Salix pellita Andersson
  Satiny willow   FACW
Shrub, 3–5 m tall; **twigs** easily broken, yellow to olive-brown or red-
brown, smooth or sparsely hairy when young, becoming waxy. **Leaves**
lance-shaped, 4–12 cm long and 1–2 cm wide, short-tapered to a tip,
upper surface without hairs, veins sunken, underside waxy and satiny
hairy but becoming smooth with age, with numerous, parallel lateral
veins; margins rolled under, entire or with rounded teeth; petioles to 1 cm
long; stipules absent. **Catkins** appearing and maturing before leaves in
spring; female catkins 2–5 cm long, stalkless or on short branches to 1
cm long; catkin bracts black, long hairy; male catkins uncommon.
Capsules lance-shaped, 4–6 mm long, silky hairy, ± stalkless. May. ☙
Streambanks, sandy shores and rocky shorelines. ⊕ Uncommon in ne
Minn and n UP and ne LP of Mich. Nfld and Labr to s Sask, s to n
Maine, NH, Vt and Minn.

Salix petiolaris J. E. Smith
  Meadow-willow   FACW+
Shrub to 5 m tall; **twigs** red-brown to dark brown, sometimes with short,
matted hairs when young, smooth with age. **Leaves** narrowly lance-
shaped, 4–10 cm long and 1–2.5 cm wide, hairy when young, becoming
smooth, dark green above, white-waxy below,; margins entire or with
small, gland-tipped teeth; petioles without glands, 3–10 mm long; stipules absent. **Catkins** appearing with leaves in spring; female catkins 1–4
cm long, stalkless or on short branches to 2 cm long; catkin bracts persistent, brown, with a few long, soft hairs; stamens 2. **Capsules** narrowly lance-shaped, 4–8 mm long, finely hairy, on stalks 2–4 mm long. May.
S. gracilis. ☙ Wet meadows, fens, streambanks, shores, open bogs, floating sedge mats, ditches. ⊕ Common; Minn, Wisc, Mich, ne Ill and nw
Ind. NB to Alberta, s to NJ, Ohio, Ill, Iowa, and n Mont, with outliers
in SD, n Neb and Colo.

Salix planifolia Pursh
  Tea-leaf willow   OBL
⚠
STATUS
Michigan - T
Shrub to 3 m tall; **twigs** dark red-brown, short hairy when young, soon
smooth and shiny. **Leaves** oval to oblong-lance-shaped, 3–6 cm long and
1–3 cm wide, short-hairy when young, becoming smooth, green above,
paler or waxy below; margins entire or with a few small, rounded teeth;
petioles 3–6 mm long, without glands; stipules small and deciduous.
Catkins appearing before leaves in spring; female catkins 2–5 cm long,

stalkless; catkin bracts 2–3 mm long, persistent, black, with long, soft hairs; stamens 2. **Capsules** lance-shaped, 4–8 mm long, finely hairy, stalkless or on short stalks to 0.5 mm long. May. *S. phylicifolia* subsp. *planifolia*. ☙ Rocky lakeshores, cedar swamps, black spruce bogs, streambanks, and margins of sedge meadows. ⊕ ne and nc Minn, n Wisc, rocky shores of Isle Royale in Mich. Newf and Labr to Alaska, s to Maine, NH, Vt, Minn, SD, NM and n Calif.

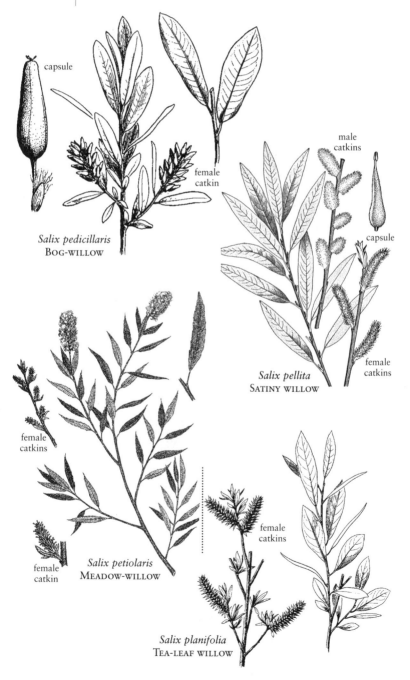

capsule

female
catkin

Salix pedicillaris
BOG-WILLOW

male
catkins

capsule

female
catkins

Salix pellita
SATINY WILLOW

female
catkins

female
catkin

Salix petiolaris
MEADOW-WILLOW

female
catkins

Salix planifolia
TEA-LEAF WILLOW

Salix purpurea L.
Basket willow; Purple-osier   FACW

Shrub to 2.5 m tall; **twigs** smooth, green-yellow to purple. **Leaves** ± opposite (unique among our willows), smooth, linear to oblong lance-shaped, 4–9 cm long and 7–16 mm wide, purple-tinged, somewhat waxy below, veins raised and netlike on both sides; margins entire near base, irregularly toothed near tip; petioles short; stipules absent. **Catkins** appearing with and maturing before leaves in spring; female catkins 2–3.5 cm long, stalkless; catkin bracts black; stamens 2 but often joined. **Capsules** ovate, 3–4 mm long, short-hairy, stalkless. May–June. ❦ Introduced from Europe, occasionally escaping to lakeshores and streambanks. ⊕ Mostly near Great Lakes in Wisc, Mich LP and ne Ill.

Salix pyrifolia Andersson
Balsam-willow   FACW+

Shrub or small tree to 5 m tall; **twigs** smooth, yellow when young, becoming shiny red. **Leaves** smooth, ovate to lance-shaped, often rounded at tip, rounded to heart-shaped at base, 4–12 cm long and 2–4 cm wide, red-tinged and translucent when unfolding; green on upper surface, waxy and finely net-veined below; with balsam fragrance (especially when dried); margins with small gland-tipped teeth; petioles 1–2 cm long; stipules absent or small and 1–2 mm long. **Catkins** appearing with or after leaves in spring; female catkins loosely flowered, 2–6 cm long, on leafy branches 1–3 cm long; catkin bracts red-brown, white-hairy, 2 mm long; stamens 2. **Capsules** lance-shaped, beaked at tip, 6–8 mm long, smooth, on stalks 2–4 mm long. May–June. *S. balsamifera.* ❦ Conifer swamps, bogs, rocky shores, wet depressions in boreal forests. ⊕ nc, ne and ec Minn, n and c Wisc, Mich UP and occasional in LP. Labr and Que to BC, s to n New Eng, n NY and n Minn.

Salix sericea Marshall
Silky willow   OBL

Shrub to 4 m tall; **twigs** brown, brittle, densely gray or brown hairy when young, becoming smooth except at leaf nodes. **Leaves** lance-shaped, short tapered to tip, 6–12 cm long and 1–2.5 cm wide, upper surface dark green and smooth or finely hairy, waxy and with short silky hairs below; margins with small, gland-tipped teeth; petioles finely hairy, 5–10 mm long; stipules broadly lance-shaped, to 1 cm long, mostly deciduous. **Catkins** appearing before leaves in spring; female catkins 1–4 cm long, stalkless or on leafy branches to 1 cm long; catkin bracts black, long-hairy, 1 mm long; stamens 2. **Capsules** obovate, blunt-tipped, 3–5 mm long, short-hairy, on stalks to 1 mm long. May. ❦ Streambanks, lakeshores, bogs, ditches; often in water. ⊕ s Wisc, s LP of Mich, ne Ill and nw Ind. NS and NB to n Ill and e Iowa, s to SC, n Ga and Ark.

Salix serissima (L. H. Bailey) Fernald
Autumn-willow   OBL

Shrub to 4 m tall; **twigs** gray, yellow or dark brown, shiny and smooth. **Leaves** smooth, oval to lance-shaped, 4–10 cm long and 1–3 cm wide, red and hairless when young; green and shiny above, usually white-waxy below; margins with small gland-tipped teeth; petioles with glands near base of leaf; stipules usually absent. **Catkins** appearing with or after leaves in spring; female catkins 2–4 cm long, on leafy branches 1–4 cm long; catkin bracts deciduous, light yellow, long hairy; stamens 3–7. **Capsules** narrowly cone-shaped, 7–10 mm long, smooth, on stalks to 2 mm long. Late May–July; our latest blooming willow. ❦ Fens, cedar and tamarack swamps, marshes, floating sedge mats, streambanks and shores, often where calcium-rich. ⊕ n and ec Minn, nw and e Wisc, Mich (all but far w UP), ne Ill and Ind. Newf to Alberta, s to Pa, n Ohio, n Ill, Minn, ND, Mont and Colo.

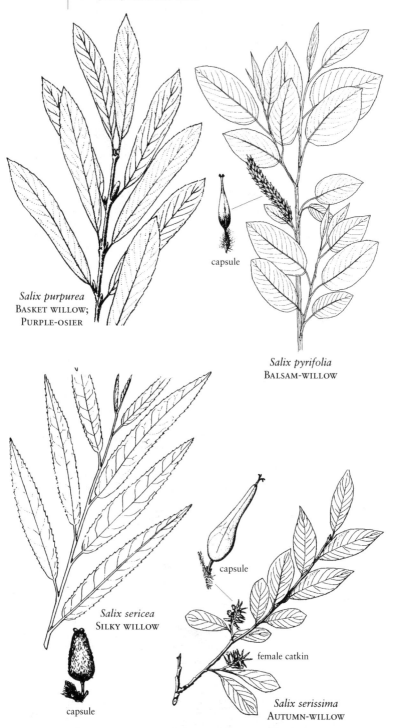

Salix purpurea
BASKET WILLOW;
PURPLE-OSIER

capsule

Salix pyrifolia
BALSAM-WILLOW

Salix sericea
SILKY WILLOW

capsule

capsule

female catkin

Salix serissima
AUTUMN-WILLOW

Santalaceae
Sandalwood Family

▶**Geocaulon** Fern. / Toadflax

Geocaulon lividum (Richardson) Fern.
Northern red-fruit toadflax   FACW-

⚠
STATUS
Wisconsin - E

Perennial herb, from a slender rhizome; at least partially parasitic on other plants. **Stems** smooth, 1–3 dm long. **Leaves** alternate, oval or ovate, 1–3 cm long and 1–1.5 cm wide, rounded at tip; margins entire; petioles short. **Flowers** usually 3 on slender stalks from leaf axils, the lateral 2 flowers typically male, the middle flower perfect; sepals 4–5, triangular, 1–2 mm long; petals absent; style very short. **Fruit** a round, orange or red drupe, about 6 mm wide. June–Aug. *Comandra livida*. ⚘ Cedar swamps, open bogs; more commonly in sandy conifer woods and forested dune edges. ⊕ Local in ne and far n Minn, uncommon in e Wisc (Door Peninsula), occasional in Mich UP and n LP (mostly near Great Lakes). Labr and Nfld to BC and Alaska, s to New Eng, n Great Lakes and Mont.

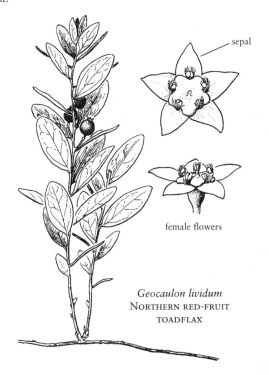

sepal

female flowers

Geocaulon lividum
Northern red-fruit
toadflax

Sarraceniaceae
Pitcher-Plant Family

▶Sarracenia L. / Pitcher-plant

Sarracenia purpurea L.
Pitcher-plant   OBL

⚠
STATUS
Illinois - E

☞ Insects are attracted by the reddish color and scent of pitcher-plant leaves; they are then trapped by the downward-pointing hairs which prevent their escape. Enzymes then digest the insect which becomes a source of nitrogen and other nutrients for the plant.

Perennial insectivorous herb. **Flower stalks** leafless, 3–6 dm long. **Leaves** clumped, hollow and vaselike, curved and upright from base of plant, 1–2 dm long and 1–5 cm wide, green or veined with red-purple, winged, smooth on outside, upper portion of inside with downward-pointing hairs, tapered to a short petiole at base. **Flowers** large and nodding, 5–6 cm wide, single at ends of stalks, perfect; sepals 5; petals 5, obovate, dark red-purple, curved inward over yellow style; ovary large and round. **Fruit** a 5-chambered capsule; seeds small and numerous. May–July. ⚘ Sphagnum bogs, floating bog mats, occasional in calcium-rich wetlands. ⊕ n and c Minn (absent from far w), Wisc (all but sw), Mich, ne Ill (state endangered) and nw Ind. Labr and Nfld to Man and Sask, s to Md, Ohio, Ind, n Ill and Minn; also n Fla to La, n to Va and Tenn. ☞ Plants lacking the maroon pigment and with yellow flowers have been reported from n LP of Mich. These plants have been called *S. purpurea* form *heterophylla*, and are listed as state threatened.

Sarracenia purpurea
PITCHER-PLANT

Saururaceae
Lizard's-Tail Family

▶**Saururus** L. / Lizard's tail

Saururus cernuus L.
Lizard's tail   OBL
Perennial, succulent herb. **Stems** branched, jointed, 5–12 dm tall. **Leaves** alternate, heart-shaped to ovate, 6–15 cm long, base of main veins loosely hairy with jointed hairs; margins entire; base of petiole surrounds stem. **Flowers** in 1–2 fuzzy spikes at ends of stems, 6–15 cm long, often nodding at tip when young; petals and sepals absent; stalks of stamens (filaments) white, much longer than pistils. **Fruit** a rough nutlet, 2–3 mm wide. June–Aug. ⚘ Wet or swampy deciduous woods, cedar swamps, shallow pools, mudflats, ditches, marshes. ⊕ c and s Mich, ne Ill and nw Ind. New Eng and s Que to n Ind and n Ill, s to Fla and Tex.

Saururus cernuus
Lizard's tail

Saxifragaceae
Saxifrage Family

Perennial herbs with alternate, opposite or basal leaves. **Flowers** perfect (with both male and female parts), regular, single on stalks or in narrow heads; sepals 5; petals 5 or absent (*Penthorum*); stamens 5 or 10, stigmas 2 or 4. **Fruit** mostly a 2-parted capsule.

▶KEY TO SAXIFRAGACEAE

1 Leaves all on stem **2**
1 Leaves all (or nearly all) from base of plant **3**

2 Leaves mostly opposite; plants low and trailing . . . .
   . . . . *Chrysosplenium americanum* / AMERICAN GOLDEN-SAXIFRAGE
2 Leaves alternate; plants upright . . . . *Penthorum sedoides*
   . . . . DITCH-STONECROP

3 Leaves with rounded teeth . . . . *Mitella nuda* / SMALL BISHOP'S-CAP
3 Leaves entire **4**

4 Flowers single atop a smooth stalk; leaves more than 2x longer than
   wide . . . . *Parnassia* / GRASS-OF-PARNASSUS
4 Flowers numerous in a panicle, the stalk hairy; leaves less than 2x
   longer than wide . . . . . . *Saxifraga pensylvanica* / SWAMP-SAXIFRAGE

▶Chrysosplenium L. / Golden-saxifrage

Chrysosplenium americanum Schwein.
American golden-saxifrage   OBL

STATUS
Indiana - T

Small, perennial herb, often forming large mats. **Stems** creeping, branched, 5–20 cm long. Lower **leaves** opposite, the upper often alternate, broadly ovate, 5–15 mm long and as wide, margins entire or with rounded teeth or lobes; petioles short. **Flowers** single and stalkless from leaf axils, 4–5 mm wide; sepals 4, green-yellow or purple-tinged; petals absent; stamens usually 8 from a red or green disk, anthers red. **Fruit** a 2-lobed capsule. April–June. ❦ Springs, shallow streams, shady wet depressions; soils mucky. ⊕ ne and ec Minn, n and c Wisc, Mich, nw Ind. Que and Ont to Sask, s to Va, Ky, Ind and Minn. ☞ Chrysosplenium iowense Rydb., more common in arctic regions, occurs on wet, mossy, rocky slopes in the driftless area of ne Iowa and se Minn (⚠ state E). It differs from *C. americanum* by having leaf margins with 5–7 large rounded teeth.

▶Mitella L. / Mitrewort; Bishop's-cap

Mitella nuda L.
Small Bishop's-cap   FACW
Small perennial herb, spreading by rhizomes or stolons. **Leaves** all from

base of plant, or with 1 small leaf on flower stalk, rounded heart-shaped, 1–3.5 cm wide, both sides with sparse coarse hairs; margins with rounded teeth; petioles 2–8 cm long. **Flowers** small, green, on short stalks, in racemes of 3–12 flowers, on a glandular-hairy stalk 10–25 cm tall; calyx lobes 5, 1–2 mm long; petals green, pinnately divided into usually 4 pairs of threadlike segments, the segments 2–4 mm long; stamens 10. **Fruit** a capsule, splitting open to reveal the black, shiny, 1 mm long seeds. June–July. ❦ Hummocks in swamps and alder thickets, ravines, seeps, moist mixed conifer and deciduous forests. ⊕ n and c Minn (local in se), mostly n Wisc (occasional in c and se Wisc in tamarack swamps), Mich. Labr to Alaska, s to Pa, Mich, Minn, ND, Mont and Wash; e Asia.

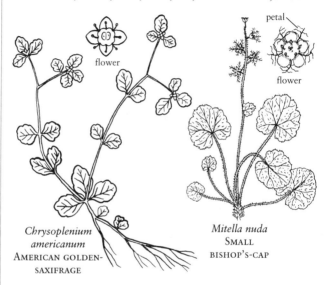

*Chrysoplenium
americanum*
AMERICAN GOLDEN-
SAXIFRAGE

flower

petal

flower

Mitella nuda
SMALL
BISHOP'S-CAP

▶**Parnassia** L. / Grass-of-parnassus

Smooth perennial herbs. **Leaves** all from base of plant but often with 1 stalkless leaf near middle of stalk, margins entire; petioles present. **Flowers** large, white, single at ends of stalks; calyx 5-lobed; petals white, veined, spreading; fertile stamens 5, alternating with petals; staminodes (infertile stamens) attached to base of petals and divided into threadlike segments tipped with glandular knobs; stigmas 4. **Fruit** a 4-chambered capsule with numerous seeds.

▶KEY TO PARNASSIA

1 Sepals with narrow translucent margins; staminodes (sterile stamens) 3-parted, not widened at base. . . . . *P. glauca*
. . . . AMERICAN GRASS-OF-PARNASSUS
1 Sepal margins green; staminodes 5 to many-parted **2**

2 Leaves broadly rounded or heart-shaped at base . . . . . . *P. palustris*
. . . . NORTHERN GRASS-OF-PARNASSUS
2 Leaves narrowed to base . . . . *P. parviflora*
. . . . SMALL-FLOWERED GRASS-OF-PARNASSUS

Parnassia glauca Raf.
American grass-of-parnassus   OBL

Smooth perennial herb. **Leaves** from base of plant and usually with 1 ± stalkless stem leaf; broadly ovate to nearly round, 2–7 cm long and 1–5 cm wide, rounded to a blunt or somewhat pointed tip; margins entire; petioles long. **Flowers** single atop a stalk 1–4 dm long; sepals ovate, 2–5 mm long, with a narrow, translucent margin; petals white with green veins, 1–2 cm long; staminodes 3-parted from near base, shorter than to equal to stamens. **Fruit** a capsule about 1 cm long. Aug–Sept. ❦ Calcareous fens and wet meadows. ⊕ Minn (but not ne or ec), Wisc, Mich, ne Ill and nw Ind. Que and NB to Sask, s to Va, Ind, Iowa and SD.

Parnassia palustris L.
Northern grass-of-parnassus   OBL

⚠
STATUS
Michigan - T
Wisconsin - T

Smooth perennial herb. **Leaves** from base of plant and usually with 1clasping, heart-shaped leaf below middle of stalk; ovate to nearly round, 1–3 cm long, rounded or blunt at tip; margins entire; petioles long and slender. **Flowers** single atop a stalk 1.5–4 dm long; sepals lance-shaped, to 1 cm long, green throughout; petals white with green veins, ovate, 1–1.5 cm long, longer than sepals; staminodes many-parted from the widened tip, 5–9 mm long. **Fruit** a capsule. July–Sept. ❦ Calcareous fens, shores, streambanks and wet meadows. ⊕ n and c Minn, nw Wisc, Mich. Circumboreal, s to NY, Minn, n SD, Colo, Nev and Calif.

Parnassia parviflora DC.
Small-flowered grass-of-parnassus   OBL

⚠
STATUS
Wisconsin - E

Smooth perennial herb. **Leaves** from base of plant, with a stalkless non-clasping leaf near middle of stalk; oval to ovate, 1–3 cm long, blunt to rounded at tip, narrowed to base; margins entire; petioles present. **Flowers** single atop slender stalks 0.5–3 dm long; sepals ovate, 3–7 mm long, nearly as long as petals, green throughout; petals white with green veins, oval, 5–10 mm long; staminodes 5–7-parted near the slightly widened tip, shorter than the stamens. **Fruit** a capsule. July–Sept. ❦ Calcareous fens, moist, sandy lakeshores, limestone shores, streambanks. ⊕ e Wisc (Door Peninsula), Mich. Labr to BC, s to Que, Ont, Mich, Mont and n Idaho.

▶Penthorum L. / Ditch-stonecrop

Penthorum sedoides L.
Ditch-stonecrop   OBL

Perennial herb, spreading by rhizomes; plants often red-tinged. **Stems** 1–6 dm long, smooth and round in section below, upper stem often angled and with gland-tipped hairs. **Leaves** alternate, lance-shaped to narrowly oval, 2–10 cm long and 0.5–3 cm wide, tapered to tip and base; margins with small, forward-pointing teeth; stalkless or on petioles to 1 cm long. **Flowers** star-shaped, perfect, 3–6 mm wide, on short stalks, in branched racemes at ends of stems; sepals 5, green, triangular, 1–2 mm long; petals usually absent; stamens 10; pistils 5, joined at base and sides to form a ring. **Fruit** a many-seeded capsule, the seeds about 0.5 mm long. July–Sept. ❦ Streambanks, muddy shores and ditches. ⊕ Minn (all but far ne), Wisc, Mich, common in ne Ill and nw Ind. Maine to Man, s to Fla and Tex.

▶**Saxifraga** L. / Saxifrage

Saxifraga pensylvanica L.
Swamp-saxifrage   OBL

Perennial herb. **Stems** stout, erect, 3–10 dm long, with sticky hairs.
Leaves all from base of plant, ovate to oblong ovate, 1–2 dm long and
4–8 cm wide, smooth or hairy; margins entire to slightly wavy or with
irregular rounded teeth; petioles wide. **Flowers** small, in clusters atop
stem, the head elongating with age; sepals bent backward, 1–2 mm long;
petals green-white or purple-tinged, lance-shaped, 2–3 mm long; stamens
10, the filaments threadlike. **Fruit** a follicle. May–June. ❦ Swamps, wet
deciduous forests, marshes, moist meadows and low prairie; often where
calcium-rich. ⊕ nc, c and se Minn; c and s Wisc (and near Lake Superior
in nw), Mich, ne Ill and nw Ind. Maine to Minn, s to Va and Mo.

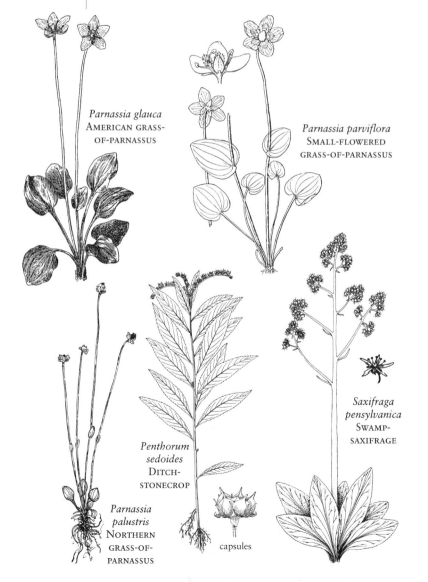

Parnassia glauca
AMERICAN GRASS-
OF-PARNASSUS

Parnassia parviflora
SMALL-FLOWERED
GRASS-OF-PARNASSUS

*Penthorum
sedoides*
DITCH-
STONECROP

*Saxifraga
pensylvanica*
SWAMP-
SAXIFRAGE

*Parnassia
palustris*
NORTHERN
GRASS-OF-
PARNASSUS

capsules

Scrophulariaceae
Figwort Family

Annual, biennial or perennial herbs. **Leaves** opposite, alternate, or (rarely) all from base of plant (*Limosella*). **Flowers** single or few from leaf axils, or numerous in clusters at ends of stems or leaf axils, perfect, usually with a distinct upper and lower lip; sepals and petals 4–5 (petals sometimes absent); stamens usually 4; pistil 2-chambered. **Fruit** a several- to many-seeded capsule.

▶**KEY TO SCROPHULARIACEAE**

1 Leaves all clustered at base of plant; w Minn only . . . .
. . . . *Limosella aquatica* / NORTHERN MUDWORT
1 Leaves all or mostly from stem **2**

2 Sepals (or calyx lobes) 4 or less **3**
2 Sepals (or calyx lobes) 5 . . . . **6**

3 Most leaves pinnately lobed *Pedicularis lanceolata* / SWAMP-LOUSEWORT
3 Leaves entire or toothed, not lobed **4**

4 Leaves whorled . . . . . . *Veronicastrum virginicum* / CULVER'S ROOT
4 Leaves opposite. **5**

5 Stamens 2, flowers blue (occasionally white) . *Veronica* / SPEEDWELL
5 Stamens 4, flowers white or pale yellow . . . . . *Melampyrum lineare*
. . . . AMERICAN COW-WHEAT

6 Flowers in spikes at ends of stems **7**
6 Flowers single from leaf axils. **8**

7 Leaves whorled . . . . . . *Veronicastrum virginicum* / CULVER'S ROOT
7 Leaves opposite . . . . *Chelone* / TURTLEHEAD
. . . .
8 Leaves pinnately lobed . *Leucospora multifida* / OBE-WAN-CONOBEA
8 Leaves not lobed **9**

9 Sepals joined to form a tube. **10**
9 Sepals not joined, free to their base **11**

10 Leaves linear, usually rough-to-touch; corolla ± regular. . . . *Agalinis*
. . . . AGALINIS
10 Leaves broader, smooth; corolla 2-lipped *Mimulus* / MONKEY-FLOWER

11 Leaves about as long as wide; corolla regular; upper sepal much wider than other 4 sepals . . . . *Bacopa rotundifolia* / WATER-HYSSOP
11 Leaves longer than wide; corolla 2-lipped; sepals all about same width
. . . . **12**

12 Petals white to yellow; stamens 2; plants with gland-tipped hairs (at least in upper portion) . . . . *Gratiola* / HEDGE HYSSOP
12 Petals blue-violet; stamens 4; plants smooth throughout . . . .
. . . . *Lindernia dubia* / FALSE PIMPERNEL

▶**Agalinis** Raf. / Agalinis

Annual herbs. **Stems** slender, erect, branched, 4-angled. **Leaves** opposite, linear, stalkless, smooth, or rough-to-touch on upper surface. **Flowers** showy, in clusters at ends of branches; sepals joined, the calyx 5-lobed, bell-shaped; petals united, corolla 5-lobed, bell-shaped, and slightly 2-lipped, pink to purple; stamens 4, of 2 different lengths. **Fruit** a ± round, many-seeded capsule.

▶**KEY TO AGALINIS**

1 Plants yellow-green; petals pink; uncommon in s portion of our region
. . . . *A. skinneriana* / PALE FALSE FOXGLOVE
1 Plants deep green, often tinged with purple; petals purple; widespread
. . . . **2**

2 Flowers on short stalks 2–5 mm long. . . . . *A. purpurea*
. . . . SMOOTH AGALINIS
2 Flower stalks 1 cm or more long . *A. tenuifolia* / COMMON AGALINIS

Agalinis purpurea (L.) Pennell
Smooth agalinis   FACW
Annual herb. **Stems** slender, 2–8 dm long, 4-angled, smooth to slightly rough, branched and spreading above. **Leaves** opposite, spreading, linear, 1–5 cm long and 1–3 mm wide; margins entire; petioles absent. **Flowers** on spreading stalks 2–5 mm long, in racemes on the branches; calyx 4–6 mm long; corolla purple, 2–3 cm long, the lobes spreading, 5–10 mm long. **Fruit** a round capsule, 4–6 mm wide. Aug–Sept. *Gerardia purpurea*. ❀ Wet meadows, fens, shores of Great Lakes and along inland lakes and ponds, moist areas between dunes, ditches; usually where sandy, sometimes where calcium-rich. ⊕ nw, c and se Minn, Wisc, Mich, ne Ill and nw Ind. Maine to Minn and Neb, s to Fla and Tex. ☞ Our most common agalinis.

Agalinis skinneriana (A. Wood) Britton
Pale false foxglove   (FACW)

⚠
STATUS
Illinois - T
Indiana - E
Michigan - E
Wisconsin - E

Annual herb; plants rough-to-touch. **Stems** slender, 1.5–4 dm long, ridged or narrowly 4-winged, usually with a few upright branches. **Leaves** opposite, upright, narrow and bristlelike, 1–2.5 cm long and 1–2 mm wide, smaller above; margins entire; petioles absent. **Flowers** on stalks from leaf axils, the stalks longer than the calyx, calyx teeth very small; corolla pink to light purple, to 2 cm long, the lobes to 2 cm wide. **Fruit** an oblong capsule, longer than the calyx. Aug–Sept. ❀ Sandy, calcium-rich, moist prairie; also in drier prairie and pine barrens. ⊕ Uncommon in sc and se Wisc, ec LP of Mich, ne Ill and nw Ind. sw Ont to Ohio and s Wisc, s to Mo and Kans.

Agalinis tenuifolia (M. Vahl) Raf.
Common agalinis   FACW
Annual herb. **Stems** slender, erect, 2–6 dm tall, smooth, usually with many branches. **Leaves** opposite, spreading, linear, 1–5 cm long and 1–3 mm wide, upper surface slightly rough; margins entire; petioles absent. **Flowers** on slender, ascending stalks, 1–2 cm long; calyx 3–5 mm long, with short teeth; corolla purple (rarely white), often spotted, 10–15 mm long, the lobes 3–5 mm long. **Fruit** a round capsule, 4–6 mm wide. Aug–Sept. *A. besseyana*, *Gerardia tenuifolia*. ❀ Wet meadows, low prairie, fens, shores, streambanks and ditches, usually where sandy. ⊕

Minn (all but far ne), Wisc, Mich (all but w UP), ne Ill and nw Ind.
Maine to Man, s to Fla, Tex and e Colo.

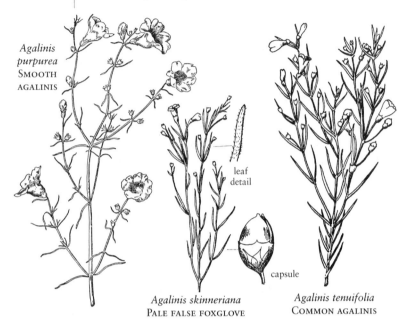

*Agalinis
purpurea*
Smooth
agalinis

leaf
detail

capsule

Agalinis skinneriana
Pale false foxglove

Agalinis tenuifolia
Common agalinis

▶Bacopa Aublet / Water-hyssop

Bacopa rotundifolia (Michx.) Wettst.
Water-hyssop   OBL

⚠
STATUS
Indiana - E

Perennial succulent herb, spreading by stolons. **Stems** creeping, 0.5–4 dm
long, rooting at leaf nodes, smooth when underwater, usually hairy when
emersed. **Leaves** opposite, obovate to nearly round, 1–3.5 cm long and
1–2.5 cm wide, smooth, palmately veined, rounded at tip, clasping at
base; margins entire or slightly wavy; petioles absent. **Flowers** 1–2 from
leaf axils, on hairy stalks to 1.5 cm long and shorter than the leaves;
sepals 5, unequal, 4–5 mm long; corolla white with a yellow throat, 2-
lipped, bell-shaped, 5–10 mm long, the 5 lobes shorter than the tube; stamens 4. **Fruit** a round capsule, about as long as sepals. Aug–Sept. *B. sim-
ulans, Hydranthelium roundifolium.* ⚘ Mud flats and shallow water of
ponds and marshes. ⊕ wc and sw
Minn, uncommon in ne Ill (where
probably introduced from further
s). Ind to Mont, s to Miss, Tex and
Ariz.

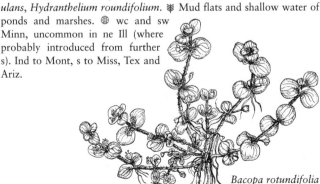

Bacopa rotundifolia
Water-hyssop

▶**Chelone** L. / Turtlehead

Perennial herbs. **Leaves** opposite, with toothed margins. **Flowers** large, 5-parted, perfect, white or rose-purple, 2-lipped, the lower lip 3-lobed and woolly on inner surface; stamens 5 (4 fertile and 1 sterile and smaller), anthers woolly; style threadlike. **Fruit** a many-seeded capsule.

▶**KEY TO CHELONE**

1 Petals creamy white; leaves nearly stalkless; widespread . . *C. glabra*
. . . . WHITE TURTLEHEAD
1 Petals rose-purple; leaves stalked; uncommon in s portions of region
. . . . *C. obliqua* / PURPLE TURTLEHEAD

Chelone glabra L.

White turtlehead   OBL

Perennial herb. **Stems** erect, 5–10 dm long, rounded 4-angled, unbranched or sometimes branched above. **Leaves** opposite, lance-shaped, to 15 cm long and 1–3 cm wide, tapered to a sharp tip; margins with sharp, forward-pointing teeth; petioles very short or absent. **Flowers** in dense spikes at ends of stems, 3–8 cm long; sepals 5; corolla white or light pink, 2.5–3.5 cm long. **Fruit** an ovate capsule. Aug–Sept. ❦ Swamp openings, thickets, streambanks, shores, wet meadows, marshes, calcareous fens. ⊕ nc and e Minn, Wisc, Mich, ne Ill and nw Ind. Nfld to Minn, s to Ga and Ala.

Chelone obliqua L.

Purple turtlehead   OBL

⚠
STATUS
Michigan - E

Perennial herb. **Stems** 3–6 dm long. **Leaves** opposite, lance-shaped, 5–15 cm long and 2–5 cm wide; margins with sharp, somewhat spreading teeth; petioles 5–15 mm long. **Flowers** in dense spikes at ends of stems, 2–6 cm long; sepals 5, fringed with hairs; corolla 2.5–3.5 cm long, rose-purple. **Fruit** an ovate capsule. Aug–Oct. ❦ Thickets and riverbanks. ⊕ Reported from s Minn; rare in se LP of Mich near Ann Arbor, and in ne Ill (where may be an escape from cultivation). Atlantic coast from Md to Ala; inland in s Mich and ne Ill, s to Ark.

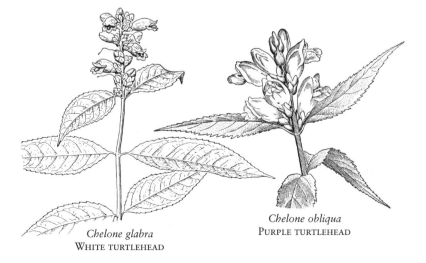

Chelone obliqua
PURPLE TURTLEHEAD

Chelone glabra
WHITE TURTLEHEAD

▶Gratiola L. / Hedge hyssop

Low annual or perennial herbs of shallow water and shores. **Leaves** opposite. **Flowers** on stalks from leaf axils; sepals 5; corolla white or yellow, 2-lipped, the upper lip entire or 2-lobed, the lower lip 3-lobed; fertile stamens 2. **Fruit** a 4-chambered capsule.

▶KEY TO GRATIOLA

1 Plants perennial, spreading by rhizomes; flowers bright yellow; leaves entire, widest at base; uncommon in Mich UP . . . . *G. aurea*
. . . . GOLDEN HEDGE HYSSOP
1 Plants annual, rhizomes absent; flowers white; leaves toothed, widest near middle of blade **2**

2 Flowers on slender, spreading stalks 1–2 cm long; upper stems with fine, gland-tipped hairs; widespread . . . . *G. neglecta*
. . . . CLAMMY HEDGE HYSSOP
2 . Flowers on stout, erect stalks to 5 mm long; stems smooth; uncommon in s portion of region . . . . *G. virginiana*
. . . . ROUND-FRUIT HEDGE HYSSOP

Gratiola aurea Pursh
Golden hedge hyssop OBL

Perennial herb. **Stems** ascending or creeping, 1–3 dm long, somewhat 4-angled, smooth or glandular hairy. **Leaves** opposite, lance-shaped to ovate, 1–2.5 cm long, with dark, glandular dots; margins entire or with a few small teeth; petioles absent. **Flowers** on slender stalks 5–15 mm long from leaf axils; sepals lance-shaped, 4–5 mm long; corolla bright yellow, 10–15 mm long. **Fruit** a round capsule, 2–3 mm long, about as long as sepals. July–Sept. *G. lutea.* ⚘ Shallow water of lakes, wet sandy or gravelly shores. ⊕ e and w UP of Mich (Gogebic County and Drummond Island). Atlantic coast from Nfld and Que to Fla; locally inland to n Mich and ND.

⚠ STATUS Michigan - T

☞ *G. aurea* sometimes forms colonies of small sterile plants in water to 1 m or more deep.

Gratiola neglecta Torr.
Clammy hedge hyssop OBL

Annual herb. **Stems** erect to horizontal, 5–25 cm long, usually branched, glandular-hairy above. **Leaves** opposite, linear to lance-shaped, 5–25 mm long and 1–10 mm wide, clasping at base; margins entire to wavy-toothed; petioles absent. **Flowers** single in the leaf axils, on slender stalks 1–2 cm long, subtended by a pair of small narrow bracts; sepals 5, unequal, 3–6 mm long, enlarging after flowering; corolla white, tube-shaped, slightly 2-lipped, 6–10 mm long; stamens 2. **Fruit** an ovate capsule, 3–5 mm long. June–Sept. ⚘ Mud flats, shores of ponds and marshes. ⊕ Minn (all but nw), Wisc, Mich, ne Ill and nw Ind. Maine and Que to BC, s to Ga, Tex and Ariz.

Gratiola virginiana L.
Round-fruit hedge hyssop OBL

Annual-biennial herb. **Stems** upright, 1–4 dm long, ± smooth, simple or branched. **Leaves** opposite, oval or obovate, 2–4 cm long and 1–2 cm wide, 3–5-veined; margins coarsely toothed; petioles absent. **Flowers** single on stalks from leaf axils, the stalks erect, 1–5 mm long, subtended by a pair of bracts about as long as sepals; sepals narrowly lance-shaped, 5 mm long; corolla white, 8–12 mm long, inner surface with purple lines. **Fruit** a round capsule, 5–9 mm long. June–Aug. *G. sphaerocarpa.* ⚘

⚠ STATUS Michigan - T

Marshes, shores, wet sand flats; sometimes in shallow water. ⊕ Uncommon in extreme sw LP of Mich, ne Ill and nw Ind. NJ to Ohio, Ill and Iowa, s to Fla and Tex.

▶**Leucospora** Nutt. / Obe-wan-conobea

Leucospora multifida (Michx.) Nutt.

Obe-wan-conobea   FACW+

Annual herb; plants with fine, sticky hairs. **Stems** leafy, 1–2 dm long, branched. **Leaves** opposite, 1–3 cm long, pinnately divided into 3–7 segments; margins entire or deeply lobed; petioles present. **Flowers** mostly single on slender stalks 5–10 mm long from leaf axils; sepals awl-shaped; corolla pale lavender, tube-shaped, 2-lipped, the upper lip 2-lobed, the lower 3-lobed; stamens 4 of 2 different lengths. **Fruit** a smooth, narrow, many-seeded capsule, about same length as sepals. July–Sept. *Conobea multifida*. ❀ Low prairie, sandy ditches, calcium-rich wetlands. ⊕ se LP of Mich, ne Ill and nw Ind. s Ont and Ohio to Neb, s to Ga, Ala and Tex.

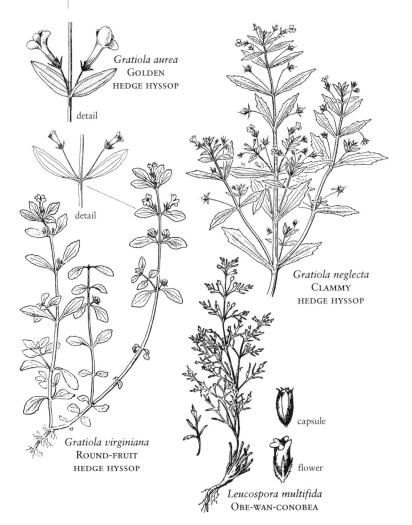

Gratiola aurea
GOLDEN
HEDGE HYSSOP

detail

detail

Gratiola neglecta
CLAMMY
HEDGE HYSSOP

Gratiola virginiana
ROUND-FRUIT
HEDGE HYSSOP

capsule

flower

Leucospora multifida
OBE-WAN-CONOBEA

▶**Limosella** L. / Mudwort

Limosella aquatica L.
Northern mudwort   OBL

Small annual herb (sometimes perennial by stolons); plants smooth, succulent. **Stems** 3–10 cm long. **Leaves** from base of plant, linear but wider at tip, the tip emersed or floating, 1–2.5 cm long and 2–8 mm wide, tapered to a long petiole; margins entire. **Flowers** small, single on stalks from base of plant, the stalks shorter than the leaves; calyx lobes triangular, corolla white or pink, 1–3 mm wide, slightly longer than sepals; stamens 4. **Fruit** an ovate capsule, 2–3 mm long. June–Sept. ❀ Streambanks, shores and mud flats of temporary ponds and marshes. ⊕ Extreme w Minn. ± circumboreal, s in c and w USA to Tex, Calif and Mex.

▶**Lindernia** All. / False pimpernel

Lindernia dubia (L.) Pennell
False pimpernel   OBL

Annual herb. **Stems** smooth, 1–2 dm long, widely branched. **Leaves** opposite, ovate to obovate, 5–30 mm long and 3–10 mm wide, the upper leaves smaller; margins entire or with small, widely spaced teeth; petioles absent. **Flowers** single, on slender stalks 0.5–2.5 cm long from leaf axils; sepals 5, linear; corolla light blue-purple, 5–10 mm long, 2-lipped, the upper lip 2-lobed, the lower lip 3-lobed and wider than upper lip; fertile stamens 2, staminodes (sterile stamens) 2. **Fruit** an ovate capsule, 4–6 mm long. June–Sept. *L. anagallidea.* ❀ Mud flats, sandbars, shores of temporary ponds and marshes, streambanks. ⊕ c and s Minn, Mich, ne Ill and nw Ind. NH and Que to ND, s to Fla and Tex; also Pacific Coast, s to S Amer.

▶**Melampyrum** L. / Cow-wheat

Melampyrum lineare Desr.
American cow-wheat   FAC-

Annual herb, partially parasitic on other plants, often red-tinged when in open habitats. **Stems** usually branched, 1–4 dm long. **Leaves** opposite, lower leaves oblong lance-shaped, upper leaves linear or lance-shaped, often tootherd near base; petioles short or absent. **Flowers** from upper leaf axils; sepals joined, calyx lobes 5 and awl-shaped; corolla about 1 cm long, 2-lipped, the upper lip white, the lower pale yellow. **Fruit** a capsule to 1 cm long. Summer. ❀ Common in a wide variety of habitats, ranging from wet to dry forests and openings; in wetlands occasional in swamps and on hummocks in open fens. ⊕ n and c Minn; n, c and se Wisc; Mich; ne Ill and nw Ind. Nfld to BC, s to Ga, Ill, Mont, and Wash.

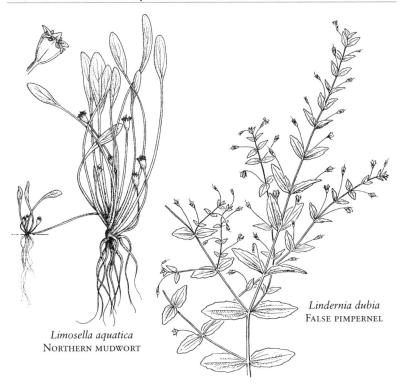

Lindernia dubia
FALSE PIMPERNEL

Limosella aquatica
NORTHERN MUDWORT

▶**Mimulus** L. / Monkey-flower

Perennial herbs (or sometimes annual in *M. guttatus*). **Leaves** opposite, margins shallowly toothed. **Flowers** often large and showy, single on stalks from leaf axils or in leafy racemes at ends of stems; sepals joined, the calyx tube-shaped; corolla 2-lipped, the upper lip 2-lobed, the lower lip 3-lobed, yellow or blue-violet; stamens 4, of 2 different lengths; stigmas 2. **Fruit** a cylindric capsule.

▶KEY TO MIMULUS

1 Flowers blue to violet 2
1 Flowers yellow 3

2 Leaves with petioles; flowers on stalks to 1 cm long . . . . . *M. alatus*
. . . . SHARPWING MONKEY-FLOWER
2 Leaves stalkless and clasping stem; flowers on stalks 2–4 cm long . .
. . *M. ringens* / ALLEGHENY OR SQUARE-STEMMED MONKEY-FLOWER

3 Calyx lobes lance-shaped and all ± same length . . . . . *M. moschatus*
. . . . MUSKY MONKEY-FLOWER
3 Calyx lobes broadly triangular, upper lobe longer than other lobes **4**

4 Stems weak, plants spreading or creeping; corolla to 2.5 cm long . .
. . . . *M. glabratus* / ROUND-LEAF MONKEY-FLOWER
4 Stems stout, erect; corolla more than 2.5 cm long . . . . . *M. guttatus*
. . . . COMMON YELLOW MONKEY-FLOWER

Mimulus alatus Aiton
Sharpwing monkey-flower   OBL

Smooth perennial herb. **Stems** erect, 3–7 dm long, 4-angled and winged, unbranched or branched above. **Leaves** opposite, smaller upward, ovate, 5–12 cm long and 2.5–4 cm wide; margins coarsely toothed; petioles 1–2 cm long, narrowly winged. **Flowers** blue-violet, single on stalks from leaf axils, the stalks shorter than the sepals; calyx 1–2 cm long, the lobes sharp-pointed; corolla 2-lipped, 2–3 cm long, nearly closed at throat, upper lip upright to bent backward, lower lip longer and spreading. **Fruit** an oblong capsule, about 1 cm long. Aug–Sept. ✿ Streambanks, floodplains, muddy shores, ditches, often in shade. ⊕ se Mich (once known from near Detroit), uncommon in ne Ill and nw Ind. Conn, NY, s Ont and Neb, s to n Fla and Tex.

Mimulus glabratus HBK.
Round-leaf monkey-flower   OBL

Perennial herb, spreading by stolons and often forming large mats. **Stems** succulent, smooth, 0.5–5 dm long, creeping and rooting at nodes, the stem ends angled upward. **Leaves** opposite, nearly round to broadly ovate, 1–2.5 cm wide, palmately veined, rounded at tip, hairy when young, becoming smooth; margins shallowly toothed or entire; petioles short and winged, or the upper leaves stalkless. **Flowers** yellow, on stalks from leaf axils and at ends of stems; calyx 5–9 mm long, barely toothed, irregular, the upper lobe large, the other lobes smaller; corolla 2-lipped, 9–15 mm long, the throat open and bearded on inner surface. **Fruit** an ovate capsule, 5–6 mm long. June–Aug. ✿ Cold springs, seeps, and banks of spring-fed streams; usually where calcium-rich. ⊕ c and s Minn, s Wisc, UP and n and w LP of Mich ne Ill. Mich to Man and Mont, s to Tex, Ariz, Nev and into Mex and S Amer. ☞ Most plants of our region are var. *jamesii* (synonym var. *fremontii*). Var. *michiganensis* is extremely rare in e UP (Mackinac County) and n LP of Mich (which is the total range of this variety; ⚠ federally and state endangered). It is distinguished from var. *jamesii* by its longer styles and corollas [see *Michigan Flora*, Vol. 3, by E.G. Voss (1996) for a complete discussion].

Mimulus guttatus DC.
Common yellow monkey-flower   OBL

Annual or perennial herb, spreading by stolons or rhizomes; plants smooth or short-hairy. **Stems** 0.5–6 dm long, unbranched or branched. **Leaves** opposite, ovate to obovate, 2–8 cm long and 1–4 cm wide, reduced to bracts in the head; margins with irregular, coarse teeth; petioles short on lower leaves, upper leaves stalkless or clasping. **Flowers** yellow, showy, in loose racemes at ends of stems; flowers on stalks 1–2.5 cm long; calyx irregular, 10–15 mm long, the upper lobe largest; corolla yellow, often spotted with red or purple, 2-lipped, 2.5–5 cm long, lower lip bearded at base. **Fruit** an ovate capsule, about as long as calyx tube. July–Sept. ✿ Springs and spring-fed streams; wet, seepy woods. ⊕ Rare in w UP of Mich (where may be an introduction). Rocky Mts from Alaska to Mex, occasional as an escape from cultivation in e USA.

Mimulus moschatus Douglas
Musky monkey-flower   OBL

Perennial herb; plants long-hairy, sticky, with a musky odor. **Stems** 2–4 dm long, lower stems creeping, the tips ascending. **Leaves** opposite, ovate, 3–6 cm long and 1–2 cm wide, pinnately veined; margins entire or with spaced, coarse teeth; petioles short. **Flowers** single from upper leaf axils, on slender stalks 1–2 cm long; calyx about 1 cm long, the lobes about equal; corolla yellow, open in the throat, 1.5–2.5 cm long and 2–3x longer than sepals. **Fruit** a capsule. July–Aug. ❧ Shores, swamp margins, wet streambanks, springs, ditches, wet forest trails. ⊕ w and c UP and n LP of Mich. Nfld and Que to n Mich, s to WVa; Rocky Mts.

Mimulus ringens L.

Allegheny or Square-stemmed monkey-flower   OBL

Smooth perennial herb, from stout rhizomes. **Stems** usually erect, 3–8 dm long, 4-angled and sometimes winged. **Leaves** opposite, oblong to lance-shaped, 4–12 cm long and 1–3.5 cm wide, upper leaves smaller; margins with forward-pointing teeth; petioles absent, the base of leaf clasping stem. **Flowers** single from upper leaf axils, on slender stalks 1–5 cm long and longer than the sepals; calyx regular, angled, 1–2 cm long, the lobes awl-shaped, 3–5 mm long; corolla blue-violet, 2-lipped, 2–3 cm long, the throat nearly closed, the upper lip erect and bent upward, lower lip longer and bent backward. **Fruit** a capsule, about as long as calyx tube. July–Aug. ❧ Streambanks, oxbow marshes, swamp openings, floodplain forests, muddy shores, ditches; sometimes where disturbed. ⊕ Common; Minn, Wisc, Mich, ne Ill and nw Ind. NS and Que to Sask, s to Fla, La and Okla.

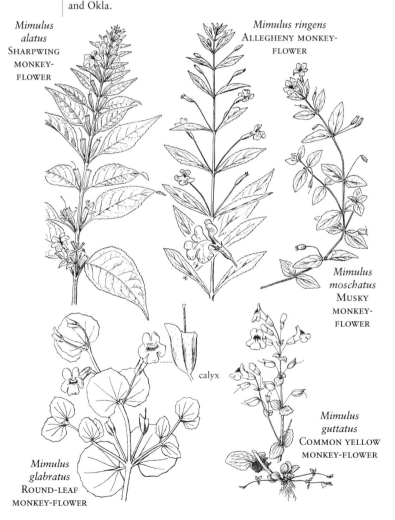

Mimulus alatus
SHARPWING MONKEY-FLOWER

Mimulus ringens
ALLEGHENY MONKEY-FLOWER

Mimulus moschatus
MUSKY MONKEY-FLOWER

calyx

Mimulus guttatus
COMMON YELLOW MONKEY-FLOWER

Mimulus glabratus
ROUND-LEAF MONKEY-FLOWER

▶**Pedicularis** L. / Lousewort

Pedicularis lanceolata Michx.

Swamp-lousewort   FACW+

Perennial herb; plants at least partially parasitic on other plants. **Stems** 3–8 dm long, ± smooth, unbranched or few-branched. **Leaves** opposite, or in part alternate, mostly lance-shaped, 4–9 cm long and 1–2 cm wide, pinnately lobed; margins with small rounded teeth; lower leaves short-petioled, upper leaves stalkless. **Flowers** ± stalkless, in spikes at ends of stems and from upper leaf axils; the spikes 2–10 cm long; calyx 2-lobed; corolla yellow, about 2 cm long, the upper lip entire and arched, lower lip upright. **Fruit** an unequally ovate capsule, mostly shorter than the sepals. July–Sept. ≱ Wet meadows, calcareous fens, wetland margins, springs, streambanks. ⊕ Minn (all but ne), Wisc, LP and s UP of Mich, ne Ill and nw Ind. Mass to ND, s to NC, Mo and Neb.

▶**Veronica** L. / Speedwell

Annual or perennial herbs. **Leaves** opposite, or becoming alternate in the head. **Flowers** single or in racemes from leaf axils or at ends of stems; sepals deeply 4-parted, enlarging after flowering; corolla blue or white, 4-lobed, somewhat 2-lipped, the tube shorter than the lobes; stamens 2. **Fruit** a flattened capsule, lobed at tip; styles usually persistent on fruit.

▶**KEY TO VERONICA**

1 Flowers in racemes at ends of stems; flower stalks 1–2 mm long ..
. . . . *V. peregrina* / PURSLANE-SPEEDWELL
1 Flowers in racemes from leaf axils; flower stalks longer than 2 mm
. . . . **2**

2 Leaves with short petioles . . . *V. americana* / AMERICAN SPEEDWELL
2 Petioles absent **3**

3 Leaves with sharp forward-pointing teeth, or entire; upper leaves clasping stem; capsules swollen. . . . . *V. anagallis–aquatica*
. . . . WATER SPEEDWELL
3 Leaves with small, gland-tipped, outward-pointing teeth; leaves narrowed to base, not clasping stem; capsules strongly flattened . . . . .
. . . . *V. scutellata* / NARROW-LEAVED SPEEDWELL

Veronica americana L.

American speedwell   OBL

Perennial herb, spreading by rhizomes; plants smooth and succulent. **Stems** erect to creeping, 1–6 dm long. **Leaves** opposite, ovate to lance-shaped (or lower leaves oval), 2–8 cm long and 0.5–3 cm wide, upper leaves tapered to a tip, lower leaves often rounded; margins with forward-pointing teeth; petioles short. **Flowers** in stalked racemes from leaf axils; the racemes with 10–25 flowers and to 15 cm long; corolla 4-lobed, blue (sometimes white), often with purple stripes. **Fruit** a ± round, compressed capsule, 3–4 mm long, slightly notched at tip, the styles persistent, 2–4 mm long. July–Sept. *V. beccabunga*. ≱ Streambanks and wet shores, hummocks in swamps, springs. ⊕ c and e Minn, Wisc (all but se), Mich, uncommon in ne Ill. Newf to Alaska, s to NC, Tex, Calif and into Mex; ne Asia.

Veronica anagallis-aquatica L.
Water speedwell OBL

Biennial or short-lived perennial herb, spreading by stolons or leafy shoots produced in fall; plants ± smooth. **Stems** erect to spreading, 1–6 dm long, often rooting at lower nodes. **Leaves** opposite, lance-shaped to ovate, 2–10 cm long and 0.5–5 cm wide, tapered to a blunt or rounded tip; margins entire or with fine, forward-pointing teeth; petioles absent, the leaves often clasping. **Flowers** in many-flowered racemes from leaf axils, the racemes 5–12 cm long; corolla 4-lobed, blue or striped with purple, about 5 mm wide. **Fruit** a round, compressed capsule, 2–4 mm long, notched at tip, the styles persistent, 1–2 mm long. June–Sept. *V. catenata, V. comosa.* ⚘ Wet, sandy or muddy streambanks and ditches; often in shallow water. ⊕ Minn, Wisc, Mich, ne Ill and nw Ind. Evidently introduced from Eurasia and naturalized throughout most of N Amer.

Veronica peregrina L.
Purslane-speedwell FACW+

Small annual herb. **Stems** upright, 0.5–3 dm long, unbranched or with spreading branches, usually glandular-hairy. **Lower leaves** opposite, becoming alternate and smaller in the head, oval to linear, 5–25 mm long and 1–5 mm wide, rounded at tip; margins of lower leaves sparsely toothed, **upper leaves** entire; petioles short or absent. **Flowers** small, on short stalks from upper leaf axils; corolla 4-lobed, ± white, about 2 mm wide. **Fruit** an oblong heart-shaped capsule, 2–4 mm long, notched at tip, the styles not persistent. May–July. ⚘ Mud flats, shores, ditches, temporary ponds, swales; also weedy in cultivated fields, lawns and moist disturbed areas. ⊕ Minn, c and s Wisc, Mich, ne Ill and nw Ind. Temperate N and S Amer; Europe.

Veronica scutellata L.
Narrow-leaved speedwell OBL

Perennial herb, spreading by rhizomes or leafy shoots produced in fall; plants smooth (or sometimes with sparse hairs). **Stems** slender, erect to reclining, 1–4 dm long, often rooting at lower nodes. **Leaves** opposite, linear to narrowly lance-shaped, 3–8 cm long and 2–10 mm wide, tapered to a sharp tip; margins entire or with small, irregularly spaced teeth; petioles absent. **Flowers** in racemes from leaf axils, the racemes with 5–20 flowers, as long or longer than the leaves; corolla 4-lobed, blue, 6–10 mm wide. **Fruit** a strongly flattened capsule, 3–4 mm long, notched at tip, the styles persistent, 3–5 mm long. June–Sept. ⚘ Marshes, pond margins, hardwood swamps, thickets, springs, streambanks, wet swales and depressions. ⊕ n and e Minn, Wisc, Mich, ne Ill and nw Ind. Newf and Labr to Yukon, s to Va, Iowa, ND, Colo and Calif; Eurasia.

▶**Veronicastrum** Fabr. / Culver's root

Veronicastrum virginicum (L.) Farw.
Culver's root FAC

Erect perennial herb, 1–2 m tall, usually with several upright branches. **Leaves** in whorls of 3–6, lance-shaped; margins with fine, forward-pointing teeth; petioles to 1 cm long. **Flowers** in erect, spikelike racemes to 15 cm long, the flowers crowded and spreading; corolla white, nearly regular, 4–5-parted, the lobes shorter than the tube; stamens 2, long-exserted from the corolla mouth. **Fruit** a   capsule, 4–5 mm long. June–Aug.

Veronica virginicum, Leptandra virginicum. ❦ Moist to wet prairie, fens and streambanks; also in drier deciduous woods and sandy grasslands. ⊕ Minn, Wisc, Mich (especially LP), ne Ill and nw Ind. New Eng to Ont and Man, s to Ga and La.

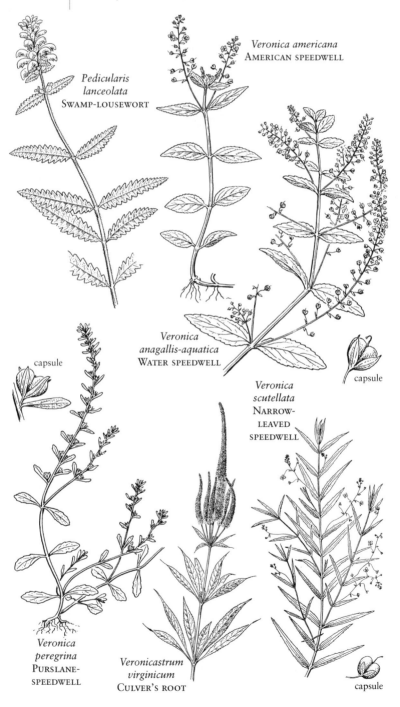

*Pedicularis
lanceolata*
SWAMP-LOUSEWORT

Veronica americana
AMERICAN SPEEDWELL

*Veronica
anagallis-aquatica*
WATER SPEEDWELL

capsule

*Veronica
scutellata*
NARROW-
LEAVED
SPEEDWELL

capsule

capsule

*Veronica
peregrina*
PURSLANE-
SPEEDWELL

*Veronicastrum
virginicum*
CULVER'S ROOT

capsule

Styraceae
Storax Family

▶**Styrax** L. / Storax

Styrax americanus Lam.
American snowbell OBL

⚠ STATUS
Illinois - T

Shrub, 1–3 m tall. **Leaves** alternate, smooth, oval, 3–10 cm long and 1–3 cm wide; margins entire or with small sharp teeth; petioles to 1 cm long. **Flowers** single or paired in leaf axils, or in few-flowered racemes on somewhat drooping lateral branches, the flower stalks and sepals with glandular dots; calyx 3–4 mm long, persistent in fruit; corolla white, 5-parted, the lobes 10–12 mm long and longer than the tube. **Fruit** a dry, ± round capsule, 6–8 mm wide. June. ❀ Floodplain forests. ⊕ Local in ne Ill and nw Ind. Atlantic coast from Va to Fla and La, and n to to s Ind; occasional northward and elsewhere in e USA.

capsule

Styrax americanus
AMERICAN SNOWBELL

Ulmaceae
Elm Family

▶**Ulmus** L. / Elm

Ulmus americana L.
American elm   FACW-
Tree to 25 m tall, trunk to 1 m wide, crown broadly rounded or flat-topped, smaller **branches** usually drooping; **bark** gray, furrowed, breaking into thin plates with age; **twigs** brown, smooth or with sparse hairs, often zigzagged; **buds** red-brown. **Leaves** alternate, simple, to 15 cm long and 7–8 cm wide, oval, pointed at tip, base strongly asymmetrical, upper surface dark green and smooth, lower surface pale and smooth or soft-hairy; margins coarsely double-toothed; petioles short, usually yellow. **Flowers** small, green-red, hairy, in drooping clusters of 3–4; appearing before leaves unfold in spring. **Fruit** 1-seeded, oval, 1 cm wide, with a winged, hairy margin, notched at tip. ≋ Floodplain forests, streambanks and moist, rich woods; less common now than formerly due to losses from Dutch elm disease. ⊕ Minn, Wisc, Mich, ne Ill and nw Ind. NS and Que to Sask, s to Fla and Tex.

fruit

Ulmus americana
AMERICAN ELM

Urticaceae
Nettle Family

Annual or perennial herbs with watery juice, sometimes with stinging hairs. **Leaves** alternate or opposite, simple, with petioles. **Flowers** small, green, in simple or branched clusters from leaf axils, male and female flowers usually separate, on same or separate plants; sepals joined, 3–5-lobed; petals absent; ovary superior, 1-chambered. **Fruit** an achene, often enclosed by the sepals which enlarge after flowering.

▶**KEY TO URTICACEAE**

1 Plants with stiff stinging hairs **2**
1 Plants without stinging hairs; smooth or with sparse small hairs . **3**

2 Leaves alternate . . . . *Laportea canadensis* / WOOD-NETTLE
2 Leaves opposite . . . . *Urtica dioica* / STINGING NETTLE

3 Flowers in cylindric spikes from leaf axils; achene shorter than and hidden by sepals . . . . *Boehmeria cylindrica* / FALSE NETTLE
3 Flowers in dense short clusters from leaf axils; achene equal or longer than sepals . . . . *Pilea* / CLEARWEED

▶**Boehmeria** Jacq. / False nettle

Boehmeria cylindrica (L.) Swartz
False nettle   OBL
Perennial, nettle-like herb, stinging hairs absent. **Stems** upright, 4–10 dm long, usually unbranched. **Leaves** opposite, rough-textured, ovate to broadly lance-shaped, narrowed to a pointed tip, with 3 main veins; margins coarsely toothed; petioles shorter than blades. **Flowers** tiny, green, male and female flowers usually on separate plants, in small clusters along unbranched stalks from upper leaf axils, forming cylindric, interrupted spikes of male flowers or continuous spikes of female flowers. **Fruit** an achene, enclosed by the enlarged bristly sepals and petals, ovate and narrowly winged. July–Aug. ❦ Floodplain forests, swamps, marshes and bogs. ⊕ ec and se Minn, c and s Wisc, LP and sc UP of Mich, ne Ill and nw Ind. Que and Ont to e Minn, s to Fla and NM.

Laportea Gaudich / Wood-nettle

Laportea canadensis (L.) Wedd.
Wood-nettle   FACW
Perennial herb, spreading by rhizomes. **Stems** somewhat zigzagged, 5–10 dm long. **Leaves** alternate, 8–15 cm long, ovate and narrowed to a tip, with small stinging hairs, margins coarsely toothed. **Flowers** small, green, male and female flowers separate but borne on same plant; **male flowers** in branched clusters from lower leaf axils, shorter than leaf petioles; **female flowers** in open, spreading clusters from upper axils, usually

much longer than petioles. **Fruit** a flattened achene, longer than the 2 persistent sepals. July–Sept. ❧ Floodplain forests, rich moist woods, low places in hardwood forests, streambanks. ⊕ Common; Minn, Wisc, Mich, ne Ill and nw Ind. NS to Man, s to Ga, Ala and Okla.

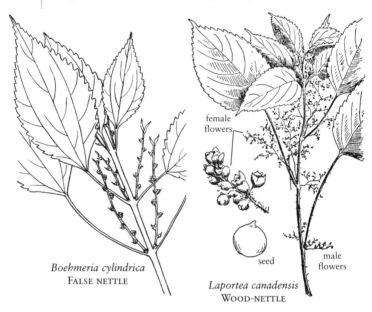

Boehmeria cylindrica
FALSE NETTLE

female flowers

seed

male flowers

Laportea canadensis
WOOD-NETTLE

▶**Pilea** Lindl. / Clearweed

Annual herb, sometimes forming colonies from seeds of previous year. **Stems** erect to sprawling, smooth, translucent and watery. **Leaves** opposite, stinging hairs absent, thin and translucent, ovate, with 3 major veins from base of leaf, margins toothed. **Flowers** green, male and female flowers separate, borne on same or different plants, in clusters from leaf axils; male flowers with 4 sepals and 4 stamens; female flowers with 3 sepals, ovary superior. **Fruit** a flattened, ovate achene.

▶KEY TO PILEA

1 Achenes olive-green to dark purple with a narrow pale margin, about as long as wide, covered with low bumps; leaf petioles 1/5–1/2 length of blade . . . . *P. fontana* / BOG CLEARWEED
1 Achenes to 1 mm wide, green to yellow, longer than wide, often marked with purple spots, smooth; petioles 1/3 to as long as blade
. . . . *P. pumila* / CLEARWEED

Pilea fontana (Lunell) Rydb.
Bog clearweed   FACW
Annual herb. **Stems** 1–4 dm long, often sprawling. **Leaves** opposite, 2–6 cm long and 1–4 cm wide; petioles 0.5–5 cm long. **Flowers** in clusters, male flowers usually innermost when mixed with female flowers. **Fruit** a dark olive-green to purple achene, 1–1.5 mm wide, with a narrow pale margin; sepals persistent, shorter to slightly longer than achene. Aug–Sept. ❧ Lakeshores, riverbanks, swamps, marshes and springs. ⊕ c and se Minn, Wisc, mostly c and s LP of Mich, ne Ill and nw Ind. PEI to Ind, ND and Neb, s to Va and Fla.

Pilea pumila (L.) A. Gray
Clearweed   FACW
Annual herb; plants similar to *P. fontana,* but sometimes taller (to 5 dm).
Leaves opposite, usually larger (to 12 cm long and 8 cm wide), thinner
and more translucent than in *P. fontana;* petioles to 8 cm long. The green
achenes, often marked with purple and to 1 mm wide, are best way to
identify this species. July–Sept. ≱ Swampy woods (often on logs), wooded streambanks, floodplain forests, wet depressions, rocky hollows; usually in partial shade. ⊕ c and s Minn, Wisc, mostly c and s LP of Mich,
common in ne Ill and nw Ind. Que to e ND, s to Fla, La and Okla.

Urtica L. / Nettle

Urtica dioica L.
Stinging nettle   FAC+
Stout perennial herb, often forming dense patches from spreading rhizomes. **Stems** 8–20 dm tall, usually unbranched, with stinging hairs on
stems and leaves, the hairs irritating to skin. **Leaves** opposite, ovate to
lance-shaped, 5–15 cm long and 2–8 cm wide; margins coarsely toothed;
petioles 1–6 cm long; stipules lance-shaped, 5–15 mm long. **Flowers**
small, green, male and female flowers separate but mostly on same
plants; flower clusters branched and spreading from leaf axils, the clusters usually longer than petioles, all of one sex or a mix of male and
female flowers, the female clusters usually above the male clusters when
both are present. **Fruit** an ovate achene, 1–2 mm long, enclosed by the
inner pair of sepals. July–Sept. *U. procera.* ≱ Moist woods, thickets,
ditches, streambanks and disturbed areas. ⊕ Common; Minn, Wisc,
Mich, ne Ill and nw Ind. Labr to Alaska, s through most of USA and
Mex; also S Amer and Eurasia.

CAUTION!
Stinging
hairs

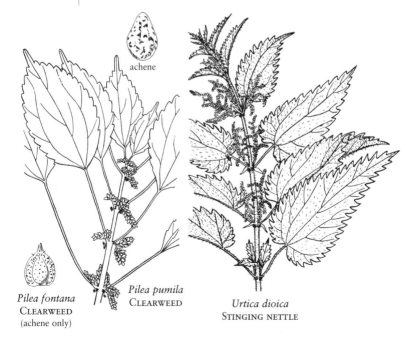

achene

Pilea pumila
CLEARWEED

Pilea fontana
CLEARWEED
(achene only)

Urtica dioica
STINGING NETTLE

Valerianaceae
Valerian Family

▶**Valeriana** L. / Valerian

Perennial, strongly scented herbs. **Leaves** from base of plant and oppo-site along stem, simple to pinnately divided. **Flowers** somewhat irregular, in branched heads at ends of stems; calyx inrolled when young, later expanding and spreading; petals joined into a tube-shaped, 5-lobed corolla; stamens 3. **Fruit** a 1-chambered achene.

▶**KEY TO VALERIANA**

1 Leaves thick, parallel-veined; plants from a stout, carrotlike taproot
. . . . *V. edulis* / COMMON VALERIAN; TOBACCO-ROOT
1 Leaves thin, net-veined; plants from a creeping or ascending rhizome
. . . . *V. uliginosa* / BOG VALERIAN

Valeriana edulis Nutt.
Common valerian; Tobacco-root   FACW+

⚠
STATUS
Indiana - E
Michigan - T
Minnesota - T

Perennial herb, from a stout taproot. **Stems** smooth, 3–12 dm long. **Leaves** thick, ± parallel-veined, often hairy when young, becoming smooth or with the margins fringed with hairs when mature; **basal leaves** oblong lance-shaped, 1–3 dm long and 1–2 cm wide, margins entire or with several lobes, tapered to a winged petiole; **stem leaves** stalkless, pin-nately divided into lance-shaped segments. **Flowers** both perfect and sin-gle-sexed, the different types often on different plants; perfect and male flowers 2–4 mm wide, female flowers to 1 mm wide, in widely branched panicles at ends of stems; corolla 5-lobed, yellow-white. **Fruit** an ovate achene, 3–4 mm long. May–June. *V. ciliata.* ☙ Wet meadows, calcareous fens, low prairie. ⊕ se Minn, ec and se Wisc, s LP of Mich, ne Ill and nw Ind. s Ont to Minn, s to Ohio, Ill and Iowa; Rocky Mts from s BC to Mex.

Valeriana uliginosa (T. & G.) Rydb.
Bog valerian   (OBL)

⚠
STATUS
Illinois - E
Indiana - E
Wisconsin - T

Perennial herb, from a stout rhizome or crown. **Stems** 3–8 dm long, ± smooth. **Leaves** thin, net-veined; **basal leaves** obovate, 6–14 cm long and 1–3 cm wide, tapered to a long petiole; margins entire or with several lobes; **stem leaves** 2–6 pairs, pinnately divided into 3–15 ovate segments, margins often fringed with fine hairs; petioles present. **Flowers** all per-fect, in clusters grouped into panicles at ends of stems; corolla 5-lobed, pale pink, 5–7 mm long. **Fruit** a smooth, ovate achene, 3–4 mm long. May–July. *V. septentrionalis* var. *uliginosa.* ☙ Conifer swamps (especial-ly of cedar and tamarack), marshes, calcareous fens, wet meadows; soils often alkaline. ⊕ Wisc, e UP and LP of Mich, uncommon in ne Ill and nw Ind. Maine and s Que to NY, n Ohio, Mich and ne Ill.

Valeriana edulis
COMMON VALERIAN;
TOBACCO-ROOT

achene

flower

Valeriana uliginosa
BOG VALERIAN

Verbenaceae
Vervain Family

Perennial herbs with 4-angled, erect or prostrate stems. **Leaves** oppo-site, toothed. **Flowers** small, numerous, perfect (with both male and female parts), in branched or unbranched spikes or heads at ends of stems or from upper leaf axils, the spikes elongating as flowers open upward from the base. Calyx 5-toothed (*Verbena*) or 2-parted (*Phyla*); corolla 5-lobed (*Verbena*) or 4-lobed (*Phyla*), somewhat 2-lipped; sta-mens 4, of 2 lengths. **Fruit** dry, enclosed by the sepals, splitting length-wise into 2 or 4 nutlets when mature.

▶KEY TO VERBENACEAE

1 Flowers in round heads or short-cylindric spikes on leafless stalks
   from leaf axils . . . . *Phyla lanceolata* / FOGFRUIT
1 Flowers in long spikes at ends of stems and from upper leaf axils . .
   . . . . *Verbena hastata* / COMMON VERVAIN; WILD HYSSOP

▶**Phyla** Lour. / Fogfruit

Phyla lanceolata (Michx.) Greene
Fogfruit   OBL
Perennial herb, sometimes forming mats; plants smooth or with sparse, short, forked hairs. **Stems** slender, weak, 4-angled, creeping to ascending, often rooting at nodes, the stem tips and lateral branches upright. **Leaves** opposite, ovate to oblong lance-shaped, 2–7 cm long and 0.5–3 cm wide, bright green, tapered to a sharp tip; margins with coarse, forward-point-ing teeth to below middle of blade; tapered to a short petiole. **Flowers** small, crowded in spikes from leaf axils, the spikes single, at first round, becoming short-cylindric, 0.5–2 cm long and 5–7 mm wide, on slender stalks 2–9 cm long; calyx 2-parted and flattened, about as long as corol-la tube; corolla pale blue or white, 3–4 mm long, 4-lobed and 2-lipped, the lower lip larger than upper lip; withering but persistent in fruit. **Fruit** round, enclosed by the sepals, separating into 2 nutlets. June–Sept. *Lippia lanceolata.* ❧ Margins of lakes, ponds, streams, ditches, mud flats; often where seasonally flooded. ⊕ s Minn, Wisc, s LP of Mich, ne Ill and nw Ind. Ont to Minn and SD, s to Fla, Tex, NM, Calif and n Mex.

▶**Verbena** L. / Vervain

Verbena hastata L.
Common vervain; Wild hyssop   FACW+
Perennial herb; plants with short, rough hairs. **Stems** stout, erect, 4–12 dm tall, 4-angled, sometimes branched above. **Leaves** opposite, lance-shaped to oblong lance-shaped, 4–12 cm long and 1–5 cm wide; margins with coarse, forward-pointing teeth and sometimes lobed near base; peti-oles short. **Flowers** small, numerous, slightly irregular, in long, narrow spikes 5–15 cm long at ends of stems, the spikes elongating as flowers

open upward from base; calyx unequally 5-toothed, 1–3 mm long; corolla dark blue to purple, 5-lobed, trumpet-shaped, slightly 2-lipped, 2–4 mm wide. **Fruit** 4-angled, splitting into 4 nutlets. July–Sept. ❦ Marshes, wet meadows, shores, streambanks, openings in swamps, ditches. ⊕ Common; Minn, Wisc, Mich, ne Ill and nw Ind. NS to BC, s to Fla and Ariz.

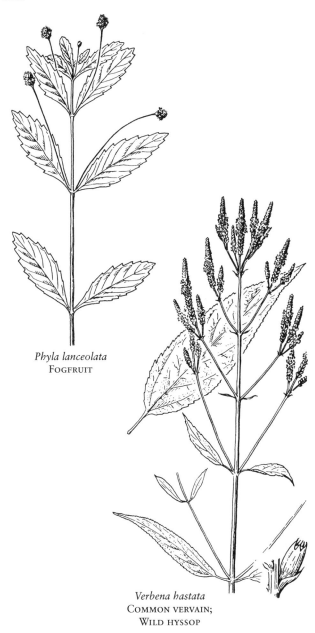

Phyla lanceolata
Fogfruit

Verbena hastata
Common vervain;
Wild hyssop

Violaceae
Violet Family

▶**Viola** L. / Violet

Perennial herbs, with or without leafy stems. **Leaves** all at base of plant or alternate on stems; petioles with membranous stipules. **Flowers** perfect, nodding and single at ends of stems, with 5 unequal sepals, 2 upper petals, 2 lateral, bearded petals, and 1 lower petal prolonged into a nectar-holding spur at the petal base. **Fruit** an ovate capsule which splits to eject the seeds.

▶**KEY TO VIOLA**

1 Plants with stems; leaves and flowers borne on the upright stems . **2**
1 Plants without stems; leaves and flowers directly from rootstock. . **3**

2 Flowers light blue or lavender . . *V. labradorica* / LABRADOR VIOLET
2 Flowers creamy-white . . . . *V. striata* / CREAMY VIOLET

3 Flowers white **4**
3 Flowers purple **8**

4 Leaves more than 1.5x longer than wide **5**
4 Leaves often wider than long, less than 1.5x longer than wide . . . **6**

5 Leaves lance-shaped, tapered to a narrow base . . . . . . *V. lanceolata*
. . . . LANCE-LEAVED VIOLET
5 Leaves broader, ovate, narrowly heart-shaped at base *V. primulifolia*
. . . . PRIMROSE-LEAVED VIOLET

6 Leaves dull, not shiny, upper and lower surface without hairs, lower surface not paler than upper; margins ± entire or with rounded teeth; petioles often with long soft hairs . . . . *V. macloskeyi*
. . . . WILD WHITE VIOLET
6 Leaves shiny and smooth on upper surface, *or* dull and hairy on either upper or lower surface; underside paler than upper surface; margins with sharp, forward-pointing teeth **7**

7 Plants with stolons and horizontal rhizomes; upper and lower surface of leaves sparsely to densely hairy with short hairs less than 1 mm long . . . . *V. blanda* / SWEET WHITE VIOLET
7 Plants without stolons, rhizomes upright; leaves often shiny and smooth on upper surface, *or* densely hairy on upperside with hairs about 1–2 mm long and smooth below . . . . *V. renifolia*
. . . . KIDNEY-LEAVED VIOLET

8 Leaves longer than wide **9**
8 Leaves as wide or wider than long **10**

9 Lateral petals with long, threadlike hairs on inner surface; spurred petal densely hairy within; s Mich only . . . . *V. affinis*
. . . . LeCONTE'S VIOLET

9 Lateral petals with short, knob-tipped hairs on inner surface; spurred petal without hairs; widespread. . *V. cucullata* / BLUE MARSH VIOLET

10 Sepals long-tapered to a sharp tip; lateral petals with short, knob-tipped hairs on inner surface; spurred petal without hairs . . . . *V. cucullata* / BLUE MARSH VIOLET
10 Sepals oblong to broadly lance-shaped, rounded at tip; lateral petals with long, threadlike hairs on inner surface **11**

11 Flowers held above leaves; leaves and stems without hairs, leaves rounded at tip, margins with rounded teeth; spurred petal densely hairy within; plant of open wetlands and peatlands. *V. nephrophylla* . . . . NORTHERN BOG VIOLET
11 Flowers overtopped by leaves; leaves and stems usually hairy, leaves tapered to a pointed tip, margins with sharp, forward-pointing teeth; spurred petal smooth to slightly hairy within; plant of moist forests . . . . *V. sororia* / COMMON BLUE VIOLET

Viola affinis Leconte
LeConte's violet   FACW
Perennial herb, spreading by rhizomes. **Leaves** all from base of plant, hairless, narrowly heart-shaped; margins with rounded teeth. **Flowers** violet, bearded within with long, threadlike hairs, atop stalks slightly longer than leaves. **Fruit** a purple-flecked capsule on horizontal or arching stalks, seeds dark. April–May. ⚜ Swamps, floodplain forests, streambanks and lakeshores, low prairie. ⊕ Minn, Wisc, occasional in Mich (especially s), ne Ill and nw Ind. Que to Ont, s to Mass, Fla and Tex.

Viola blanda Willd.
Sweet white violet   FACW-

STATUS
Illinois - E

Perennial herb, spreading by short rhizomes (and stolons later in season). **Stems** smooth. **Leaves** all from base of plant, heart-shaped, dark green and satiny, 2–5 cm wide, upper surface near base of blade usually with short, stiff white hairs; petioles usually red. **Flowers** white, fragrant, on stalks shorter than longer than leaves; lower 3 petals with purple veins near base, all ± beardless; upper 2 petals narrow, twisted backward, 2 side petals forward-pointing. **Fruit** a purple capsule 4–6 mm long, seeds dark brown. April–May. *V. incognita*. ⚜ Hummocks in swamps and bogs, low wet areas in deciduous and conifer forests. ⊕ Minn (all but nw and sw), Wisc (all but far s), Mich, ne Ill and nw Ind. NS to Ont and ND, s to Maine NC, e Tenn, n Ind and e Iowa.

Viola cucullata Aiton
Blue marsh violet   OBL
Perennial herb, spreading by short, branched rhizomes; plants smooth. **Leaves** all from base of plant, ovate to kidney-shaped, to 10 cm wide, heart-shaped at base; margins coarsely toothed; blade angled from the upright petioles. **Flowers** light purple or white, dark at center, on slender stalks longer than leaves; the 2 side petals densely bearded with short hairs, the hairs mostly knobbed or club-tipped. **Fruit** a cylinder-shaped capsule, seeds dark. April–June. *V. obliqua*. ⚜ Swamps, sedge meadows, shady seeps; occasionally in bogs and low areas in forests. ⊕ ne and ec Minn, Wisc, Mich, ne Ill and nw Ind. NS and Maine to Ont and Minn, s to Ga and Tenn.

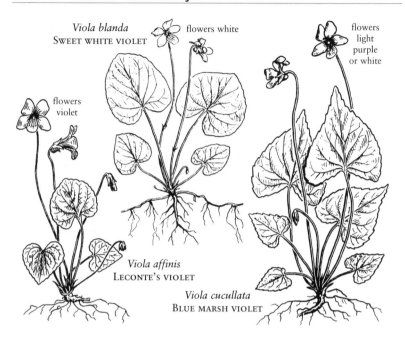

Viola blanda
SWEET WHITE VIOLET

flowers white

flowers
light
purple
or white

flowers
violet

Viola affinis
LECONTE'S VIOLET

Viola cucullata
BLUE MARSH VIOLET

Viola labradorica Schrank

Labrador Violet   FAC

⚠
STATUS
Illinois - T

Perennial herb; plants smooth. **Leaves** in clumps from rhizomes, at first
all from base of plants, later with leafy, horizontal stems to 15 cm long;
light green, ovate to kidney-shaped, 1–2.5 cm wide; margins with rounded teeth; petioles 2–6 cm long. **Flowers** pale blue, side petals bearded on
inner surface. **Fruit** 4–5 mm long, seeds dark brown. April–June. *V.
adunca* var. *minor, V. consperma.* ✻ Swamps, streambanks, moist hardwood forests. ⊕ n and c Minn, Wisc, Mich, ne Ill and nw Ind. NS and
Maine to Man, s to NJ, w SC, Ala, n Ill and se ND.

Viola lanceolata L.

Lance-leaved violet   OBL

⚠
STATUS
Minnesota - T

☞ The lance-
shaped leaves
are distinctive.

Perennial herb, spreading by rhizomes and stolons. **Leaves** from base of
plant, narrowly lance-shaped, more than 2x longer than wide, tapered to
base; margins toothed. **Flowers** white, all beardless; lower 3 petals purple-veined near base. **Fruit** a green capsule 5–8 mm long, seeds brown.
April–June. ✻ Open bogs, sedge meadows; soils sandy or mucky. ⊕
Uncommon in e Minn, n and sw Wisc, Mich (especially n and w LP), ne
Ill and nw Ind. NS and Maine to Ont and Minn, s to SC, Ala and Tex.

Viola macloskeyi F. Lloyd

Wild white violet   OBL

☞ Similar to
**sweet white
violet** (*V.
blanda*) but
differs by
having
hairless
leaves and
green rather
than purple
capsules.

Small perennial herb (our smallest violet), spreading by rhizomes and
stolons. **Leaves** all from base of plant, heart-shaped to kidney-shaped,
1–3 cm wide at flowering, later to 8 cm wide, underside orange-tinged;
margins with rounded teeth. **Flowers** white, on upright stalks equal or
longer than leaves, 3 lower petals purple-veined near base, 2 side petals
beardless or with sparse hairs. **Fruit** a green capsule 4–6 mm long, seeds
olive-black. April–July. *V. pallens.* ✻ Marshes, sedge meadows, open
bogs and swamps, alder thickets; sometimes in shallow water. ⊕ n and

ec Minn, Wisc, Mich, ne Ill and nw Ind. NS and Maine to Minn and Man, s to Ohio, n Ind, n Ala; disjunct in se Iowa and e Mo.

Viola nephrophylla Greene
Northern bog violet · · · · · · · · · · · · · · · FACW+

Low perennial herb, spreading by short rhizomes. **Leaves** all from base of plant, smooth, heart-shaped to kidney-shaped, 1–4 cm long and 2–6 cm wide, rounded at tip; margins with rounded teeth; petioles slender, 2–16 cm long. **Flowers** single, nodding on slender stalks, the stalks longer than leaves. **Flowers** violet, bearded near base on inside, or upper pair of petals not bearded. **Fruit** a capsule 5–10 mm long. May, sometimes again flowering in Aug or Sept. ❧ Wet meadows, fens, calcium-rich wetlands, low areas between dunes, streambanks, rocky shores. ⊕ Minn, mostly se Wisc (local in n), Mich, ne Ill and nw Ind. e Que to BC, s to Conn, NY, Wisc, ne Tex, NM and Wash.

Viola primulifolia L.
Primrose-leaved violet · · · · · · · · · · · · · · FACW+

⚠
STATUS
Illinois - E

Perennial herb, spreading by rhizomes and stolons. **Leaves** all from base of plant, oblong to ovate, rounded at tip, longer than wide; margins with small rounded teeth. **Flowers** white, on stalks shorter or equal to leaves, 3 lower petals purple-veined at base, 2 side petals beardless or with few hairs. **Fruit** a capsule 7–10 mm long; seeds red-brown to black. May. *V. lanceolata* x *pallens*, *V.* x *primulifolia*. ❧ Wet meadows and bogs, often in sphagnum moss; sandy streambanks. ⊕ Minn, Wisc, uncommon in UP and w LP of Mich, rare in ne Ill and nw Ind. NS and Maine to Ont, s to Fla, Ill, Minn and Tex.

Viola renifolia A. Gray
Kidney-leaved violet · · · · · · · · · · · · · · · FACW

Perennial herb, spreading by long rhizomes. **Leaves** all from base of plant, mostly kidney-shaped, rounded at tip, varying from smooth and shiny above to hairy on lower surface only; margins with few rounded teeth. **Flowers** white, all bearded or beardless, 3 lower petals purple-veined at base. **Fruit** a capsule 4–5 mm long, seeds brown and dark-flecked. May–July. ❧ Cedar swamps, sphagnum hummocks in peatlands. ⊕ ne, nc and ec Minn, n Wisc, UP and n and c LP of Mich. NS and Maine to Yukon and Alaska, s to Mass, Mich and Minn.

Viola sororia Willd.
Common blue violet · · · · · · · · · · · · · · · FACW

☞ Includes
plants
sometimes
separated as
V. novae-
angliae, which
has leaf blades
distinctly
longer than
wide (see
illustration).

Perennial herb, spreading by short rhizomes. **Leaves** all from base of plant, ovate to heart-shaped, sometimes expanding to 10 cm wide in summer, with long hairs; margins with rounded teeth; blades angled from the upright petioles. **Flowers** blue-violet, on stalks about as high as leaves, the 2 side petals densely bearded with hairs 1 mm long and not club-tipped. **Fruit** a purple-flecked capsule, seeds dark brown. April–June. ❧ Moist hardwood forests; occasionally in swamps, flood-plain forests and along rocky streambanks. ⊕ Common; Minn, Wisc, Mich, ne Ill and nw Ind. NS to BC, s to Fla and Tex.

Viola striata Aiton
Creamy violet · · · · · · · · · · · · · · · · FACW

Perennial herb, spreading by rhizomes. **Leaves** from base of plant and on leafy stems, smooth, leaves at base of plant and on lower stems rounded at tip, upper leaves heart-shaped and tapered to tip; margins with small teeth. **Flowers** many, creamy white with purple veins at center, on stalks raised well above leaves; side petals bearded, style tip bent. **Fruit** a rounded capsule 4–5 mm long, seeds light brown. April–June. *V. consperma* var. *masonii*. ❦ Floodplain forests, moist deciduous woods, streambanks, thickets; sometimes weedy. ⊕ Local in s Wisc, c and s LP of Mich, ne Ill and nw Ind. Mass to s Ont and s Wisc, s to SC and Ark.

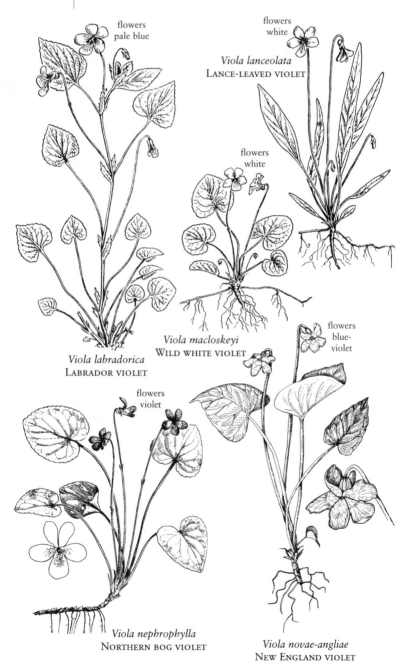

flowers
pale blue

flowers
white

Viola lanceolata
LANCE-LEAVED VIOLET

flowers
white

Viola macloskeyi
WILD WHITE VIOLET

Viola labradorica
LABRADOR VIOLET

flowers
blue-
violet

flowers
violet

Viola nephrophylla
NORTHERN BOG VIOLET

Viola novae-angliae
NEW ENGLAND VIOLET

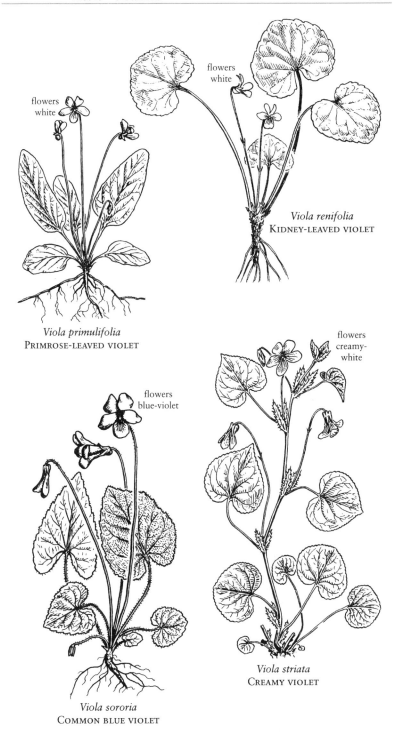

flowers
white

flowers
white

Viola renifolia
KIDNEY-LEAVED VIOLET

Viola primulifolia
PRIMROSE-LEAVED VIOLET

flowers
creamy-
white

flowers
blue-violet

Viola striata
CREAMY VIOLET

Viola sororia
COMMON BLUE VIOLET

Vitaceae
Grape Family

▶Vitis L. / Grape

Vitis riparia Michx.
  Riverbank grape   FACW-
Perennial, woody, climbing vine to 5 m or more long; young **branches** green or red, hairy, becoming smooth. **Leaves** alternate, heart-shaped in outline, 1–2 dm long and as wide, with a triangular tip and 2 smaller lateral lobes, leaf base with a U-shaped indentation, upper surface smooth, bright green, underside paler and sparsely hairy along veins; margins with coarse, forward-pointing teeth; petioles shorter than blades. **Flowers** small, sweet-scented, green-white to creamy, in stalked clusters 5–10 cm long. **Fruit** a dark blue to black berry, 6–12 mm wide, with a waxy bloom, sour when young, becoming sweeter when ripe in fall. May–July. Includes *V. vulpina*. ≋ Floodplain forests, moist sandy woods, streambanks, thickets; also on sand dunes. ⊕ Minn (all but far ne), Wisc, mostly LP of Mich, common in ne Ill and nw Ind. NB and Que to Minn and Mont, s to Va, Tenn, Ark and Tex.

Vitis riparia
RIVERBANK GRAPE

Angiosperms - Monocots

THE MONOCOTYLEDONEAE (or Liliopsida, the Monocots) include families with showy flowers such as members of the Liliaceae and Orchidaceae as well as families lacking petals and sepals such as the Cyperaceae (Sedge Family), Poaceae (Grass Family), and Juncaceae (Rush Family; see examples below). Identification of species within these three families is often dependent on characters of small floral parts, and a hand lens or dissecting microscope are often useful.

Arethusa bulbosa (Swamp-pink, Dragon's mouth), Orchidaceae

Calamagrostis canadensis (Bluejoint), Poaceae

Eriophorum viridicarinatum (Dark-scale cotton-grass), Cyperaceae

Juncus effusus (Soft rush), Juncaceae

Acoraceae
Sweet Flag Family

▶**Acorus** L. / Sweet flag

Acorus calamus L.
  Sweet flag   OBL
Perennial herb, from stout, aromatic rhizomes. **Leaves** linear, long and swordlike, leathery, 2-ranked, 5–15 dm long and 1–2 cm wide, sweet-scented when crushed; margins entire, sharp-edged, translucent near base. **Flowers** small, in a cylindric, yellow-green spadix, appearing lateral from a leaflike, tapered stalk; the spadix upright, 5–10 cm long and 1–2 cm wide; flowers perfect, yellow or brown, composed of 6 papery tepals and 6 stamens. **Fruit** a 1–3-seeded berry, dry outside and jellylike on inside. June–July. *A. americanus*. ✹ Marshes (often with **cat-tails**), bogs, streambanks. ⊕ Minn, Wisc, Mich, ne Ill and nw Ind. Native and in part introduced from Europe; widely established in N Amer from NS and Que to Alberta, s to Fla, Tex, Colo, n Idaho and Wash; Asia.

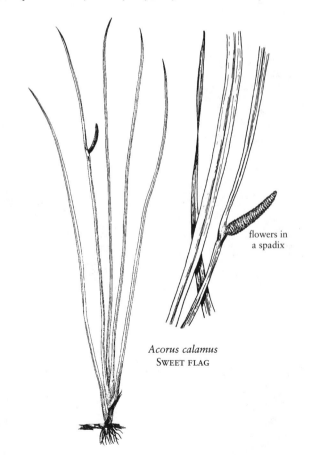

flowers in
a spadix

Acorus calamus
Sweet flag

Alismataceae
Water-Plantain Family

Perennial, aquatic or emergent herbs; plants swollen and tuberlike at base. **Leaves** all from base of plant and clasping an erect stem; underwater leaves often ribbonlike; emergent leaves broader. **Flowers** perfect (with both male and female parts) or imperfect, in racemes or panicles at ends of stems, with 3 sepals and 3 petals; stamens 6 or more. **Fruit** a compressed achene, usually tipped by the persistent style.

▶KEY TO ALISMATACEAE

1 Leaves never arrowhead-shaped; flowers perfect, in a panicle-like head; pistils or achenes in a single whorl on a small, flat receptacle. . . . . *Alisma* / WATER-PLANTAIN
1 Leaves often arrowhead-shaped; flowers mostly imperfect, whorled on stem; male flowers above female in the head; pistils or achenes in several series around a large, round receptacle, and forming a dense, round head. . . . . *Sagittaria* / ARROWHEAD

▶**Alisma** L. / Water-plantain

Perennial herbs, from cormlike rootstocks. **Leaves** emersed or floating, ovate to lance-shaped, never arrowhead-shaped; underwater leaves sometimes ribbonlike (in *A. gramineum*). **Flowers** perfect, in whorled panicles, sepals 3, green; petals 3, white or light pink; stamens 6. **Fruit** a flattened achene in a single whorl on a flat receptacle, style beak small or absent.

KEY TO ALISMA

1 Leaves lance-shaped to oval, or if underwater, leaves long and ribbonlike; flower stalks rarely longer than leaves; petals usually pink; local in w and c Minn . . . . *A. gramineum*
. . . . NARROW-LEAVED WATER-PLANTAIN
1 Leaves ovate; flower stalks much longer than leaves; petals white; widespread species. . . . . . . *A. plantago-aquatica* / WATER-PLANTAIN

Alisma gramineum Lej.
Narrow-leaved water-plantain OBL
Perennial herb. **Stems** upright to spreading, 0.5–3 dm tall. Emersed **leaves** lance-shaped to oval, 2–10 cm long and 1–3 cm wide, petioles mostly longer than blades; underwater leaves reduced to linear, ribbonlike petioles, to 6 dm long and 1 cm wide. **Flowers** many on spreading stalks, the stalks shorter to somewhat longer than the leaves; sepals 3; petals pink, 1–3 mm long. **Fruit** an achene, 2–3 mm long, with a central ridge and 2 lateral ridges. July–Sept. *A. geyeri*. ❧ Shallow, often brackish water, muddy shores, streambanks. ⊕ Local in w and c Minn. Circumboreal, in N Amer from Que to sw BC, s to NY, Minn, Neb, Colo, Idaho and n Ga.

Alisma plantago-aquatica L.
Water-plantain   OBL
Perennial herb. **Leaves** ovate to oval, 3–15 cm long and 2–12 cm wide,
rounded to nearly heart-shaped at base; petioles long. **Flowers** clustered
on slender stalks 1–10 dm long, in whorls of 3–10; sepals 3; petals white,
3–5 mm long. **Fruit** an achene, 2–3 mm long, with a central groove.
July–Sept. *A. brevipes, A. subcordatum, A. triviale.* ❦ Shallow water
marshes, shores, ditches. ⊕ Minn, Wisc, Mich, ne Ill and nw Ind. NS to
s BC, s to Pa, Mo and Calif.

Alisma gramineum
NARROW-LEAVED

*Alisma
plantago-aquatica*
WATER-PLANTAIN

▶**Sagittaria** L. / Arrowhead

Perennial or annual herbs, with fleshy rootstocks. **Leaves** sheathing, all
from base of plant, variable in shape and size. Emersed and floating
leaves usually arrowhead-shaped with large lobes at base, or sometimes
ovate to oval and without lobes; underwater leaves often linear in a basal
rosette, normally absent by flowering time. **Flowers** in a raceme of mostly 3-flowered whorls; upper flowers usually male, lower flowers usually
female or sometimes perfect; sepals 3, green, persistent; petals 3, white,
deciduous; stamens 7 to many; pistils crowded on a rounded receptacle.
Fruit a crowded cluster of achenes in ± round heads, the achenes flattened and winged, beaked with a persistent style.

▶KEY TO SAGITTARIA

1 Emersed leaves not arrowhead-shaped, basal lobes absent **2**
1 Emersed leaves all or mostly arrowhead-shaped, with large basal
    lobes. **3**

2 Female flowers and fruiting heads ± stalkless . . . . *S. rigida*
    . . . . SESSILE-FRUITED ARROWHEAD
2 Female flowers and fruiting heads obviously stalked . . . *S. graminea*
    . . . . GRASS-LEAVED ARROWHEAD

3 Plants annual, rhizomes absent; sepals appressed to fruiting heads; stalks of fruiting heads stout; uncommon in se Mich. . . . . *S. calycina*
 . . . . MISSISSIPPI ARROWHEAD; LONG-LOBED ARROWHEAD
3 Plants perennial, with rhizomes; sepals reflexed on fruiting heads; stalks of fruiting heads slender; widespread **4**

4 Bracts below flowers mostly less than 1 cm long; achene beak projecting horizontally from tip of achene . . . . *S. latifolia*
 . . . . COMMON ARROWHEAD; WAPATO
4 Bracts below flowers usually more than 1 cm long; achene beak erect or ascending **5**

5 Achene beak short, erect, to 0.4 mm long; basal lobes of leaves mostly shorter than terminal lobe . . . . *S. cuneata*
 . . . . NORTHERN ARROWHEAD; WAPATO
5 Achene beak larger, curved and ascending, 0.5 mm long or more; basal lobes of leaves usually equal or longer than terminal lobe . . .
 . . . . *S. brevirostra* / MIDWESTERN ARROWHEAD

Sagittaria brevirostra Mackenzie & Bush
Midwestern arrowhead OBL
Perennial herb. **Leaves** arrowhead-shaped, mostly 10–30 cm long and to 20 cm wide; basal lobes lance-shaped and usually equal or longer than terminal lobe; petioles long. **Flowers** in heads 1–2 cm wide, on a mostly unbranched stalk usually longer than leaves, the male flowers above the female flowers; bracts below flowers 1–5 cm long; female flowers on ascending stalks 0.5–2 cm long; sepals bent backward in fruit; petals white, 1–2 cm long. **Fruit** a winged achene, 2–3 mm long, separated from style beak by a saddlelike depression, the beak usually curved-ascending. July–Sept. *S. engelmanniana* var. *brevirostra*. ⚘ Shallow water and muddy shores, marshes. ⊕ Uncommon in wc and se Minn; s Wisc, ne and ec LP of Mich, ne Ill and nw Ind. Ohio and Mich to SD, s to Tex and NM.

Sagittaria calycina Engelm.
Mississippi or Long-lobed arrowhead OBL

STATUS
Michigan - T

Annual herb, rhizomes and tubers absent. **Leaves** erect to spreading; emersed blades arrowhead-shaped (the lobes sometimes outward spreading) or oval to ovate, 3–40 cm long and 2–25 cm wide, the basal lobes usually longer than terminal lobe; petioles and flower stalks spongy, round in cross-section. **Lower flowers** usually perfect; **upper flowers** usually male, in heads 1–2 cm wide Flowers from a stalk 1–10 dm tall, heads leaning when fruiting; bracts membranous, short and rounded at lower nodes, upper bracts longer (to 1 cm long) and tapered to a tip; sepals blunt-tipped, bent backward in flower but appressed to the head in fruit; petals white with a yellow base. **Fruit** an achene, 2–3 mm long, beak ± horizontal from top of achene. July–Sept. *Lophotocarpus calycina, S. montevidensis* subsp. *calycinus*. ⚘ Muddy shores. ⊕ Local in extreme se Mich. Ohio and Mich to SD, s to Va, Tenn, La, Tex, NM, Calif and into Mex.

Sagittaria cuneata Sheldon
Northern arrowhead; Wapato OBL
Perennial herb, with rhizomes and large, edible tubers. **Submerged leaves** (if present) often awl-shaped or reduced to bladeless, expanded petioles (phyllodes); **emersed leaves** long-stalked, usually arrowhead-shaped,

5–20 cm long and 2–15 cm wide, the basal lobes much shorter than terminal lobe; floating leaves often heart-shaped (unlike our other species of *Sagittaria*). **Flowers** imperfect, the male flowers above the female, in ± round heads 5–12 mm wide, with 2–10 whorls of heads on a stalk 1–6 dm tall, the stalks often branched at lowest node; bracts tapered to tip, 1–4 cm long; sepals ovate, bent backward in flower and fruit; petals white, 7–15 mm long. **Fruit** an achene, 2–3 mm long; beak erect, small, 0.1–0.4 mm long. June–Sept. ❦ Shallow water, lakeshores and streambanks. ⊕ Minn, Wisc, Mich (but uncommon in w UP), ne Ill and nw Ind. NS to BC, s to NY, Ind, Ill, n Tex, NM, Utah and Calif.

Sagittaria graminea Michx.
  Grass-leaved arrowhead   OBL

Perennial herb, with rhizomes. Underwater plants sometimes only a rosette of bladeless, ribbonlike petioles (phyllodes) to 1 cm wide; **emergent leaves** lance-shaped to oval, never arrowhead-shaped, 3–20 cm long and 0.5–3 cm wide, tapered to a blunt tip. **Flowers** imperfect, the male flowers usually above the female, clustered in ± round heads, 5–12 mm wide, the heads on spreading stalks 1–4 cm long; with 2–10 whorls of flowers along an unbranched stalk mostly shorter than leaves; bracts broadly ovate, joined in their lower portion, 2–8 mm long; sepals ovate, bent backward in fruit; petals white, equal or longer than sepals. **Fruit** a winged achene, 1–2 mm long, beak small or absent. June–Sept. *S. cristata*. ❦ Shallow water and shores. ⊕ n and c Minn, Wisc, Mich, ne Ill and nw Ind. Labr and Newf to SD, s to Fla and Tex; Cuba.

Sagittaria latifolia Willd.
  Common arrowhead; Wapato   OBL

Perennial herb, with rhizomes and edible tubers in fall. **Leaves** variable; emersed leaves arrowhead-shaped, mostly 8–40 cm long and 1–15 cm wide, lobes typically narrow on plants in deep water to broad on emersed plants; plants sometimes with bladeless, expanded petioles (phyllodes). **Flowers** male above and female below, clustered in ± round heads 1–2.5 cm wide, at ends of slender, spreading stalks 0.5–3 cm long, in whorls of 2–15 along a stalk 2–10 dm tall; bracts tapered to a tip or blunt, 0.5–1 cm long; sepals ovate, bent backward by fruiting time; petals white, 7–20 mm long. **Fruit** a winged achene, 2–4 mm long, the beak projecting horizontally, 1–2 mm long. July–Sept. ❦ Shallow water, shores, marshes, and pools in bogs. ⊕ Common; Minn, Wisc, Mich, ne Ill and nw Ind. NS and Que to BC, s to S Amer.

Sagittaria rigida Pursh
  Sessile-fruited arrowhead   OBL

Perennial herb, rhizomes present. **Stems** erect or lax. **Emersed leaves** lance-shaped to ovate, rarely with short, narrow basal lobes, (but not arrowhead-shaped), 4–15 cm long and to 7 cm wide; petioles sometimes bent near junction with blades; deep water plants often with only linear, bladeless, expanded petioles (phyllodes). **Flowers** in ± round heads to 1.5 cm wide, the heads stalkless and bristly when mature due to achene beaks; in 2–8 whorls on a stalk 1–8 dm tall, the stalk often bent near lowest node; flowers imperfect, male flowers above the female, male flowers on threadlike stalks 1–3 cm long, female flowers ± stalkless; bracts ovate, 5 mm long, joined at base; sepals ovate, 4–7 mm long, bent backward when in fruit; petals white, 1–3 cm long. **Fruit** a narrowly winged achene, 2–4 mm long; beak ascending, 1–1.5 mm long. June–Sept. ❦ Shallow water, shores and streambanks. ⊕ Minn (all but sw), Wisc, local in Mich (mostly c and s LP), ne Ill and nw Ind. Que to Minn, s to Va, Ky, Tenn, Mo and Neb.

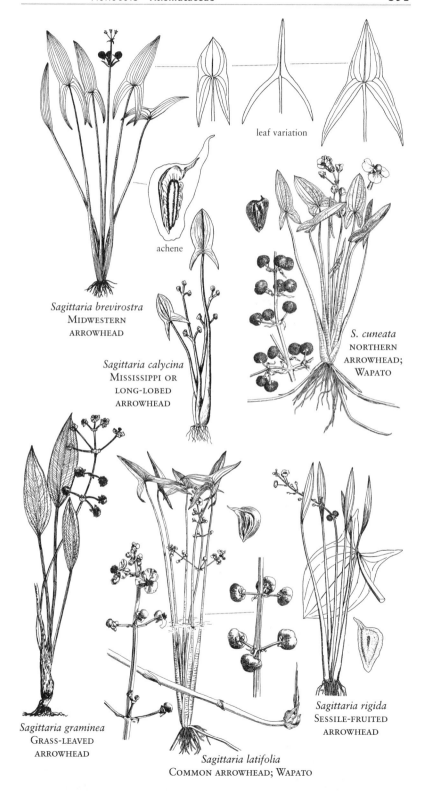

leaf variation

achene

Sagittaria brevirostra
MIDWESTERN
ARROWHEAD

Sagittaria calycina
MISSISSIPPI OR
LONG-LOBED
ARROWHEAD

S. cuneata
NORTHERN
ARROWHEAD;
WAPATO

Sagittaria graminea
GRASS-LEAVED
ARROWHEAD

Sagittaria latifolia
COMMON ARROWHEAD; WAPATO

Sagittaria rigida
SESSILE-FRUITED
ARROWHEAD

Araceae
Arum Family

Perennial herbs; **leaves** alternate, simple or compound, often fleshy. **Flowers** small and numerous, mostly single-sexed, male flowers usually above female, crowded in a cylindric or rounded spadix subtended by a leaflike spathe; sepals 4–6 or absent; petals absent; stamens mostly 2–6; pistils 1–3-chambered. **Fruit** a usually fleshy berry, containing 1 to few seeds, or the entire spadix ripening as a fruit.

▶**KEY TO ARACEAE**

1 Leaves compound . . . . *Arisaema* / Jack-in-the-pulpit
1 Leaves simple, not divided **2**

2 Leaves arrowhead-shaped, lobes 1/3 or more length of blade . . . . .
. . . . *Peltandra virginica* / Tuckahoe; Arrow-arum
2 Leaves heart-shaped or rounded at base **3**

3 Leaves broadly heart-shaped, abruptly tapered to a tip; spathe white, long-stalked; flowering late spring . . . *Calla palustris* / Water-arum
3 Leaves large, ovate, tapered to a rounded tip; spathe green-yellow to purple-brown, short-stalked or stalkless; flowering late winter to early spring . . . . *Symplocarpus foetidus* / Skunk-cabbage

▶**Arisaema** Martius / Jack-in-the-pulpit

Perennial herbs. **Leaves** compound. **Flowers** either male or female, on same or different plants; male flowers with 2–5, ± stalkless stamens, above the female flowers on a fleshy spadix, the spadix subtended by a green or purple-brown spathe; sepals and petals absent. **Fruit** a cluster of round, red berries, each berry with 1–3 seeds.

▶**KEY TO ARISAEMA**

1 Leaflets 7–13; spadix longer than spathe . . . . *A. dracontium*
. . . . Green dragon
1 Leaflets usually 3; spathe arching over spadix . . . . . . *A. triphyllum*
. . . . Jack-in-the-pulpit

Arisaema dracontium (L.) Schott
　Green dragon   FACW
Perennial herb, from corms. **Leaf** usually single, palmately branched into 7–15 leaflets, the **leaflets** oval to oblong lance-shaped, tapered to a point and narrowed at base, the central leaflets 1–2 dm long and to 8 cm wide, the outer leaflets progressively smaller; petioles 2–10 dm long. **Flowers** male or female and on different plants, or plants with both male and female flowers, the male above female, on a long, slender spadix exserted 5–10 cm beyond spathe; the spathe green, slender, rolled inward, 3–6 cm long; the flower stalk shorter than the leaf petiole. **Fruit** a cluster of red-orange berries. May–July. 🌿 Wet woods and floodplain forests. ⊕ se

Minn (mostly along Miss River), occasional in mostly c and s Wisc, c and s LP of Mich, ne Ill and nw Ind. Que to s Minn, s to Fla and Tex.

Arisaema triphyllum (L.) Schott

Jack-in-the-pulpit   FACW-

Perennial herb, from bitter-tasting corms. **Stems** 3–12 dm long. **Leaves** usually longer than the flower stalk, mostly 2, divided into 3 leaflets, the terminal leaflet oval to ovate, the lateral leaflets often asymmetrical at base. **Flowers** male or female and usually on separate plants, borne near base of a cylindric, blunt-tipped spadix, subtended by a green, purple-striped spathe, rolled inward below, expanded and arched over the spadix above, abruptly tapered to a tip. **Fruit** a cluster of shiny red berries. April–July. *A. atrorubens.* ❦ Moist forests, cedar swamps. ⊕ Minn, Wisc, Mich, ne Ill and nw Ind. NS to Ont, s to Fla, La, and Kans.

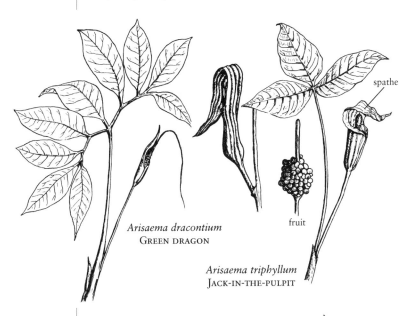

Arisaema dracontium
GREEN DRAGON

spathe

fruit

Arisaema triphyllum
JACK-IN-THE-PULPIT

▶Calla L. / Water-arum

Calla palustris L.

Water-arum   OBL

⚠
STATUS
Illinois - E
Indiana - E

Perennial herb, from rhizomes, the rhizomes creeping in mud or floating. **Leaves** broadly heart-shaped, abruptly tapered to a tip, 5–15 cm long and about as wide; petioles stout, 1–2 dm long (or longer when underwater). **Flowers** perfect or the uppermost male, on a short-cylindric spadix, 1.5–3 cm long, shorter than the spathe; the spathe white, ovate, tipped with a short, sharp point to 1 cm long; sepals and petals absent; stamens 6. **Fruit** a fleshy, few-seeded berry, turning red when ripe. May–July. ❦ Bog pools, swamps, shores and wet ditches. ⊕ n and c Minn, n and c Wisc (local in s), Mich, uncommon in ne Ill and nw Ind. Circumboreal, s to Md, Ind, Iowa, n ND, nw to Alaska.

▶**Peltandra** Raf. / Arrow-arum

Peltandra virginica (L.) Schott & Endl.
Arrow-arum; Tuckahoe   OBL

Perennial herb, with thick fibrous roots. **Leaves** all from base of plant on long petioles, bright green, oblong to triangular in outline, 1–3 dm long and 8–15 cm wide at flowering, to 8 dm long later; leaf base with pair of lobes. **Flowers** in white to orange spadix about as long as the spathe, atop a curved stalk 2–4 dm long; flowers either male or female, the male flowers covering upper 3/4 of the spadix, the female flowers on lower portion; spathe green with a pale margin, 1–2 dm long, the lower portion covering the fruit. **Fruit** a head of green-brown berries, the berries with 1–3 seeds surrounded by a jellylike material. June–July. *P. luteospadix.* ❦ Shallow water, shores, bog pools; often where shaded. ⊕ Wisc, mostly c and s LP of Mich, ne Ill and nw Ind. Maine to Mich, s to Fla and Tex.

Symplocarpus Salisb. / Skunk-cabbage

Symplocarpus foetidus (L.) Nutt.
Skunk-cabbage   OBL

☞ **Skunk-cabbage** is our earliest flowering plant, the flowers often appearing while still partially covered by snow.

Perennial foul-smelling herb, from thick rootstocks. **Leaves** all from base of plant, ovate to heart-shaped, 3–8 dm long and to 3 dm wide, strongly nerved; petioles short, channeled. **Flowers** appearing before leaves in late winter or early spring, perfect; the spathe ovate, curved over spadix, 8–15 cm long, green-purple and often mottled; sepals 4. **Fruit** round, 8–12 cm wide; seeds 1 cm thick. Feb–May. ❦ Floodplain forests, swamps, streambanks, calcareous fens, moist wooded slopes. ⊕ e Minn (especially ec and se), Wisc, common in Mich LP and Isle Royale (local in rest of UP), ne Ill and nw Ind. NS to Minn, s to NC and Iowa.

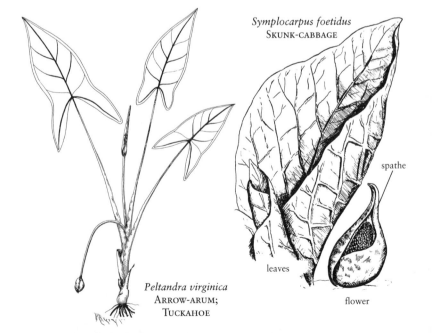

Symplocarpus foetidus
SKUNK-CABBAGE

spathe

leaves

flower

Peltandra virginica
ARROW-ARUM;
TUCKAHOE

Butomaceae
Flowering Rush Family

▶**Butomus** L. / Flowering rush

Butomus umbellatus L.
Flowering rush   OBL

☞ **Flowering rush** was introduced to N Amer from Eurasia, and is now established across much of n USA and s Canada.

Perennial herb, from creeping rhizomes. **Leaves** all from base of plant, erect when emersed, or floating when in deep water, linear, to 1 m long and 5–10 mm wide, parallel-veined; petioles absent. **Flowers** pink, perfect, 2–3 cm wide, stalked, in a many-flowered umbel, borne on a round stalk 1–1.2 m tall; with 4 lance-shaped bracts subtending the umbel; sepals 3, petal-like; petals 3; stamens 9; pistils 6. **Fruit** a dry, many-seeded capsule, splitting open on inner side. June–Aug. ✤ Marshes and lakeshores. ⊕ Local in wc and se Minn, e Wisc and se and n LP of Mich.

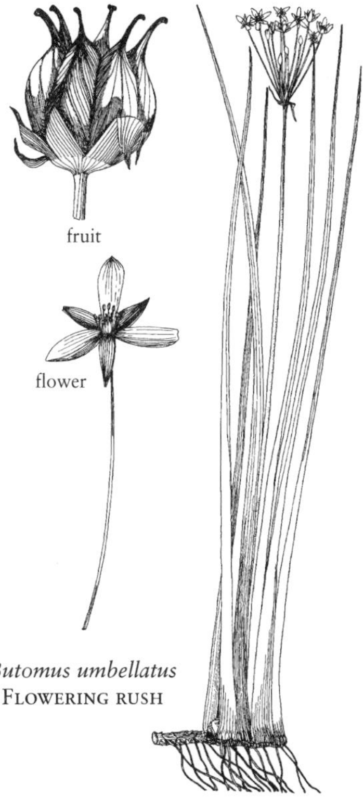

fruit

flower

Butomus umbellatus
FLOWERING RUSH

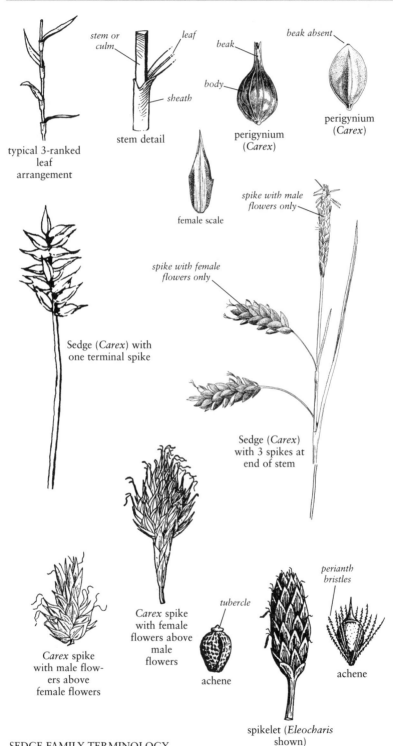

typical 3-ranked leaf arrangement

stem or culm

leaf

sheath

stem detail

beak

body

perigynium (*Carex*)

beak absent

perigynium (*Carex*)

female scale

spike with male flowers only

spike with female flowers only

Sedge (*Carex*) with one terminal spike

Sedge (*Carex*) with 3 spikes at end of stem

Carex spike with male flowers above female flowers

Carex spike with female flowers above male flowers

tubercle

achene

perianth bristles

achene

spikelet (*Eleocharis* shown)

SEDGE FAMILY TERMINOLOGY

Cyperaceae
Sedge Family

Mostly perennial, grasslike, rushlike or reedlike plants. **Stems** 3-angled or ± round in section, solid or pithy. **Leaves** 3-ranked or reduced to sheaths at base of stem; leaf blades, when present, grasslike, parallel-veined, often keeled; sheaths mostly closed around the stem. **Flowers** small, perfect (with both male and female parts), or single-sexed, each flower subtended by a bract (scale); perianth of 1 to many (often 6) small bristles, or a single perianth scale, or absent; stamens usually 3; ovary 2–3-chambered, contained in a saclike covering (perigynium) in *Carex*, maturing into an achene, stigmas 3 or 2. Flowers arranged in spikelets (termed spikes in *Carex*), the spikelets single as a terminal or lateral spike, or several to many in various types of heads, the head often subtended by 1 to several bracts.

▶**KEY TO CYPERACEAE**

1 Flowers either male or female; achene enclosed in a saclike perigynium . . . . *Carex* / SEDGE p. 398
1 Flowers perfect (except in *Scleria*); achene not in a sac **2**

2 Scales in 2 rows in the spikelets **3**
2 Scales overlapping in a spiral in the spikelets, or (rarely) spikelets not in spikes or heads **4**

3 Heads terminal at ends of stems; achene not subtended by bristles . . . . *Cyperus* / FLATSEDGE p. 456
3 Heads from leaf axils; achene subtended by bristles . . . . *Dulichium arundinaceum* / THREE-WAY SEDGE; DULICHIUM p. 461

4 Spikelets of 2 kinds on each plant; achenes exposed, ± round, white to gray . . . . *Scleria* / NUT-RUSH; STONE-RUSH p. 485
4 Spikelets ± all alike; achenes rarely white **5**

5 Base of style persistent as a swelling (tubercle) atop the achene, different in color and texture from achene body, or if style base not different from achene body, then the spikelets single at end of leafless stems **6**
5 Base of style persistent as a small beak atop achene, not different from achene body, or the style base not persistent; spikelets usually few to many, or if single, then on leafy stems **7**

6 Spikelets single at ends of leafless stems; leaves reduced to sheaths at base of plant . . . . *Eleocharis* / SPIKE-RUSH p. 461
6 Spikelets 1 to several, stems leafy at base of plant, leaves with narrow blades . . . . *Rhynchospora* / BEAK-RUSH p. 473

7 Sepals and petals of many long, white or coppery bristles, longer than the scales; spikelets with a cottony look . . . . *Eriophorum* . . . . COTTON-GRASS p. 469

7 Sepals and petals of 1–6 small bristles or scales, or the sepals and petals absent; spikelets not long-cottony **8**

8 Sepals and petals of 1–6 small bristles or absent; plants mostly perennial. **9**
8 Sepals and petals of 1 or 3 scales, sometimes absent; plants annual **11**

9 Sepals and petals absent; base of style deciduous and swollen above the attachment to achene . . . . *Fimbristylis* / FIMBRY p. 471
9 Sepals and petals of 1–6 bristles (or rarely absent); base of style not swollen, often persistent as a beak on achene **10**

10 Bracts 2 or more, leaflike *Cladium mariscoides* / TWIG-RUSH p. 456
10 Bracts 1, erect, appearing to be a continuation of stem. . . . . *Scirpus* . . . . BULRUSH p. 476

11 Sepals and petals reduced to 1 tiny scale or sometimes absent; spikelets to 5 mm long . . . . *Hemicarpha micrantha* . . . . DWARF-BULRUSH p. 473
11 Sepals and petals reduced to 3 stalked scales; spikelets mostly more than 5 mm long . . . . *Fuirena* / UMBRELLA-SEDGE p. 473

▶Carex L. / Sedge

Perennial grasslike plants. **Stems** mostly 3-angled. **Leaves** 3-ranked, margins often finely toothed. **Flowers** either male or female, with both sexes in same spike, or in separate spikes on same plant, or the male and female flowers on different plants. Male flowers with 3 or rarely 2 stamens; female flowers with style divided into 2 or 3 stigmas. **Achenes** lens-shaped or flat on 1 side and convex on other (in species with 2 stigmas), or achenes 3-angled or nearly round (in species with 3 stigmas), enclosed in a sac called the perigynium (singular) or perigynia (plural). ▶Sedges are the largest genus of wetland plants in the Great Lakes region. For unknown specimens, start with the Group Key below, followed by keys to 35 Sections of closely related *Carex* species. The Section Keys and species descriptions are arranged alphabetically after the Group Keys. ▶As evident in the following keys, identification of *Carex* species is often based on characteristics of the perigynium—the sac around the achene; these are illustrated in the sidebar next to each species' description. For small plants, a hand lens or dissecting scope may be needed to see diagnostic features of the perigynium.

▶KEY TO CAREX GROUPS

1 One terminal spike on each stem . . . . **GROUP 1**
1 Two or more spikes on each stem **2**

2 Achenes lens-shaped, or flat on 1 side and convex on other; stigmas 2 . . . . **GROUP 2**
2 Achenes 3-angled or nearly round; stigmas 3 . . . . **3**

3 Style persistent on achene and becoming firm . . . . **GROUP 3**
3 Style withering and usually deciduous as the achene matures **4**

4 Perigynia beaked, the beak prolonged into well-developed, usually stiff, sharp teeth . . . . **GROUP 4**
4 Perigynia beaked or beakless, the teeth small or soft and blunt . . . **5**

5 Terminal spike with some female flowers or perigynia . . . **GROUP 5**
5 Terminal spike entirely of male flowers **6**

6 Perigynia covered with hairs, at least around base of beak . . . .
. . . . **GROUP 6**
6 Perigynia without hairs **7**

7 Leafy bract of lowest female spike with a well-developed sheath enclosing the stem . . . . **GROUP 7**
7 Bract of lowest female spike without a well-developed sheath . . . .
. . . . **GROUP 8**

CAREX GROUP KEYS

▶**KEY TO CAREX GROUP 1**
1 Achenes lens-shaped or flat on 1 side and convex on other; stigmas 2
. . . . **2**
1 Achenes 3-angled or round in cross-section; stigmas 3 . . . . **3**

2 Plants spreading by long rhizomes . . . . **Dioiceae**
. . . . (*C. dioica* / NORTHERN BOG SEDGE)
2 Plants forming clumps, long rhizomes absent . . . . **Stellulatae**

3 Spikes with both male and female flowers, male *below* female . . . .
. . . . **Squarrosae**
3 Spikes with both male and female flowers, male *above* female . . . **4**

4 Perigynia long and narrow or awl-shaped, spreading or angled downward . . . **Orthocerates** (*C. pauciflora* / FEW-FLOWERED BOG SEDGE)
4 Perigynia wider and upright in spike . . . . **Polytrichoidae**
. . . . (*C. leptalea* / SLENDER SEDGE)

▶**KEY TO CAREX GROUP 2**
1 Spikes all similar, usually less than 1.5 cm long, and not on stalks. **2**
1 Spikes not alike, the top and bottom spikes distinctly different; side spikes with or without stalks; if without stalks, then the spikes usually long and slender **14**

2 Stems single or few together from rhizomes, stolons, or stems lying along ground **3**
2 Stems in clumps, rhizomes absent or very short **6**

3 Stems becoming horizontal, new stems upright from old leaf axils; plants in shallow water and wet peatlands . . . . **Chordorrhizae**
. . . . (*C. chordorrhiza* / CORDROOT SEDGE)
3 Stems from long rhizomes, not reclining; plants mostly not of peatlands **4**

4 Spikes separated from one another . . . . **Bracteosae**

4 Spikes crowded into dense heads **5**

5 Leaves well-developed and mostly clustered near base of plant; peri gynia usually without nerves, often sharp-edged but not thin-margined . . . . **Divisae** (*C. praegracilis* / EXPRESSWAY SEDGE)
5 Lowest leaves scalelike, leaves with blades located above base of plant; perigynia with nerves and usually thin-margined . . . .
. . . . **Intermediae** (*C. sartwellii* / RUNNING MARSH SEDGE)

6 Male flowers at top of some or all spikes **7**
6 Male flowers at base of some or all spikes **11**

7 Spikes single at each node; heads usually with less than 10 spikes **8**
7 Spikes two or more (at least at lowermost node) **9**

8 Side spikes with a few male flowers at tip; perigynia usually green even when mature . . . . **Bracteosae**
8 Side spikes either all male or all female; perigynia usually brown when mature . . . . **Stellulatae**

9 Perigynia firm, not spongy, the tip abruptly narrowed to a beak, olive-green to dark brown or nearly black . . . . **Paniculatae**
9 Perigynia often spongy and thickened at base, usually gradually tapered to a beak, pale green to light golden-brown **10**

10 Female scales awn-tipped, the awn 1–5 mm long; perigynia base slightly or not at all spongy-thickened . . . . **Multiflorae**
. . . . (*C. vulpinoidea* / BROWN FOX SEDGE)
10 Female scales unawned, or if awned, then perigynia base broad and spongy-thickened . . . . **Vulpinae**
. . . .

11 Perigynia margins thin-winged at least along upper part of body and lower beak . . . . **Ovales**
11 Perigynia mostly filled by achene, sometimes sharp edged but never thin-winged **12**

12 Perigynia nearly filled by the achene . . . . **Heleonastes**
12 Perigynia spongy at base; achene filling only upper half of perigynia
. . . . **13**

13 Perigynia (especially the lowest in spike) spreading or curved downward; perigynia often smaller or broader or shorter-beaked than in Deweyanae . . . . **Stellulatae**
13 Perigynia upright, 4–6 mm long and 3–5x as long as wide . . . .
. . . . **Deweyanae**

14 Lower female spikes spreading or drooping on slender stalks . . . . .
. . . . **Cryptocarpae**
14 Lower female spikes erect, stalkless or on short stalks **15**

15 Perigynia round and swollen, orange when mature (white-tinged when dried) . . . . **Bicolores** (*C. aurea* / GOLDEN SEDGE)
15 Perigynia flattened or lens-shaped, green or brown **16**

16 Perigynia dull; achene jointed with the style . . . . **Acutae**
16 Perigynia shiny; achene continuous with the persistent style . . . . . .
. . . . **Vesicariae**

▶KEY TO CAREX GROUP 3

1 Perigynia lance-shaped, 8–15 mm long and 1.5–3 mm wide, gradually tapered to a beak . . . . **Folliculatae**
1 Perigynia wider, ovate or oval 2

2 Lowest female spikes drooping on long stalks . . . . **Pseudocypereae**
2 Female spikes upright, stalked or stalkless 3

3 Perigynia thick-walled, usually not inflated . . . . **Paludosae**
3 Perigynia thin-walled, usually inflated 4

4 Perigynia broadest above middle, rounded or blunt at tip and abruptly narrowed to a beak . . . . **Squarrosae**
4 Perigynia broadest below middle, ovate or oval, tapered or rounded to a beak 5

5 Bract of lowest female spike with an obvious sheath around stem; perigynia large, 10–20 mm long . . . . **Lupulinae**
5 Bract of lowest female spike without an obvious sheath, or if sheath present, perigynia less than 10 mm long . . . . **Vesicariae**

▶KEY TO CAREX GROUP 4

1 Perigynia 10–20 mm long . . . . **Lupulinae**
1 Perigynia less than 8 mm long 2

2 Female scales awn-tipped; top third of terminal spike female, lower two-thirds male . . . . **Gracillimae**
2 Female scales unawned or with only a small point; terminal spike all male or sometimes with a few perigynia at top or bottom . . . .
. . . . **Sylvaticae**

▶KEY TO CAREX GROUP 5

1 Perigynia at bottom of terminal spike . . . . **Sylvaticae**
1 Perigynia at top or middle of terminal spike 2

2 Perigynia with an obvious beak 3
2 Perigynia beakless, or with a short beak not much different than body 4

3 Side spikes short-cylindric, upright, mostly without stalks; plants mostly of calcium-rich wetlands . . . . **Extensae**
3 Side spikes long-cylindric, spreading or drooping on slender stalks; habitats various . . . . **Sylvaticae**

4 Female spikes slender, spreading or drooping, 2–6 cm long; perigynia in several open rows; perigynia usually more than 4 mm long. . . . .
. . . . **Gracillimae**
4 Female spikes short-cylindric, mostly 1–2 cm long; perigynia in dense clusters; perigynia less than 4 mm long 5

5 Female scales longer than perigynia; spikes spreading or drooping on slender stalks . . . . **Limosae**
5 Female scales shorter than perigynia, or if longer, then the spikes stalkless 6

6 Terminal spike about half female, half male . . . . **Atratae**
6 Terminal spike with only one or several perigynia; plants mostly of calcium-rich wetlands . . . . **Paniceae**

▶**KEY TO CAREX GROUP 6**

1 Perigynia with 2 prominent ribs but without nerves . . . . . **Montanae**
. . . . (*C. deflexa* / NORTHERN SEDGE)
1 Perigynia with 2 prominent ribs and with several distinct nerves . **2**

2 Female spikes short-cylindric, upright and ± stalkless. . . . . . . **Hirtae**
2 Female spikes slender, spreading or drooping on stalks **3**

3 Plants clumped; perigynia lance-shaped, 5–8 mm long . . **Sylvaticae**
3 Plants spreading by rhizomes; perigynia obovate, 3–5 mm long . . .
. . . . **Anomalae** (*C. scabrata* / ROUGH SEDGE)

▶**KEY TO CAREX GROUP 7**

1 Perigynia with 2 prominent ribs, otherwise ± without nerves **2**
1 Perigynia with 2 ribs and usually many conspicuous nerves **5**

2 Perigynia beakless . . . . **Paniceae**
2 Perigynia beaked **3**

3 Female spikes ± upright, perigynia abruptly narrowed to a beak . .
Paniceae
3 Female spikes spreading or drooping, mostly on slender stalks, perigynia various **4**

4 Female spikes 1–6 cm long, if only 1 cm long, then the perigynia 3–6 mm long . . . . **Sylvaticae**
4 Female spikes 5–15 cm long, perigynia 2–3 mm long . . . . **Capillares**
. . . . (*C. capillaris* / HAIRLIKE SEDGE)

5 Female spikes ± stalkless, in dense short-cylindric to round heads; perigynia spreading (at least at their tips) and with conspicuous beaks
. . . . **Extensae**
5 Lower female spikes on short stalks, short to long cylindric; spikes densely or loosely clustered, the perigynia mostly upright, not curved downward **6**

6 Perigynia ovate or lance-shaped, distinctly narrowed to their base **7**
6 Perigynia ovate or oval, rounded at base **8**

7 Female spikes short, cylinder-shaped, upright . . . . **Oligocarpae**
. . . . (*C. conoidea* / PRAIRIE GRAY SEDGE)
7 Female spikes elongated, at least the lower spikes spreading or drooping . . . . **Sylvaticae**

8 Perigynia beakless **9**
8 Perigynia with a short but distinct beak **10**

9 Female spikes short, cylinder-shaped, 1–3 cm long, ± erect on short stalks . . . . **Oligocarpae** (*C. conoidea* / PRAIRIE GRAY SEDGE)
9 Female spikes very slender, 3–6 cm long, spreading or drooping on slender stalks . . . . **Gracillimae**

10 Leaf blades flat; plants of freshwater habitats . . . . **Granulares**
10 Leaf blades rolled inward; plants of brackish or calcium-rich habitats
. . . . **Extensae**

▶ **KEY TO CAREX GROUP 8**

1 Perigynia beakless or with only a short, soft tip **2**
1 Perigynia with a distinct, short or long beak. **4**

2 Female spikes short-cylindric on short stalks or stalkless, ± upright.
. . . . **Paniceae**
2 Female spikes short-cylindric on slender stalks, at least the lower
spikes spreading or drooping **3**

3 Female spikes usually less than 2x as long as wide; perigynia flattened
. . . . **Limosae**
3 Female spikes at least 3x as long as thick; perigynia 3-angled in section . . . . **Gracillimae**

4 Female spikes upright, stalkless or on short stalks . . . . **Extensae**
4 Female spikes spreading or drooping on slender stalks **5**

5 Female spikes 1–2 cm long and 6–8 mm wide . . . . **Sylvaticae**
5 Female spikes slender, 2–5 cm long and about 5 mm wide . . . .
. . . . **Gracillimae**

Carex Section ACUTAE

▶ **KEY TO ACUTAE**

1 Longest bract much longer than spikes **2**
1 Longest bract shorter or equal to spikes **3**

2 Plants forming large clumps or patches; leaves 3–8 mm wide; female
spikes 3–6 cm long; perigynia without nerves . . . . *C. aquatilis*
. . . . WATER SEDGE
2 Plants densely clumped, long rhizomes absent; leaves 2–3 mm wide;
female spikes 1.5–3 cm long; perigynia with a few prominent raised
nerves . . . . *C. lenticularis* / SHORE SEDGE

3 Lower sheaths rough-to-touch, red-brown, splitting into fibers . . . .
. . . . *C. stricta* / COMMON TUSSOCK SEDGE
3 Lower sheaths smooth, not splitting into fibers **4**

4 Perigynia olive-green with red dots, without nerves, or with 1–3 faint
nerves . . . . *C. haydenii* / LONG-SCALED TUSSOCK SEDGE
4 Perigynia green, becoming straw-colored, without red dots, usually
with several nerves . . . . *C. emoryi* / RIVERBANK SEDGE

Carex aquatilis Wahlenb.   Acutae
Water sedge   OBL
Large perennial, forming clumps or turfs; spreading by many slender rhizomes. **Stems** 3–l2 dm long and longer than the leaves, 3-angled, usually
rough-to-touch below the spikes. **Leaves** waxy blue-green, 2–7 mm wide;

perigynium

sheaths white or purple-dotted. **Spikes** 3–5, the upper spikes male, the middle and lower spikes female or often with male flowers borne above female, 2–5 cm long; **female scales** tapered to tip. **Perigynia** pale green to yellow-brown or red-brown, obovate, broadest near tip, not inflated, 2–3 mm long; beak tiny. **Achenes** lens-shaped, 1–2 mm long; stigmas 2. May–Aug. ⚘ Wet meadows, marshes, shores, streambanks, kettle lakes, ditches and fens. ⊕ n and c Minn (infrequent in s), e and n Wisc, Mich (but local in w UP), ne Ill and nw Ind. Circumboreal, s to NJ, Ind, Iowa, Kans, NM and Calif.

Carex emoryi Dewey
Acutae
Riverbank sedge
OBL

perigynium

Loosely clumped perennial from scaly rhizomes. **Stems** 3-angled, 4–12 dm long. **Leaves** 3–7 mm wide, lowest leaves reduced to red-brown sheaths; upper sheaths white or yellow-tinged and translucent, lower sheaths red-brown. **Spikes** 3-7, the terminal 1 or 2 all male, 2–4.5 cm long, the lateral spikes all female or with male flowers above the female, 2–10 cm long; lowest bract leaflike; **female scales** blunt or tapered to tip, narrower than the perigynia. **Perigynia** light green, becoming straw-colored at maturity, convex on both sides, oval or ovate, 1.5–3 mm long, stigmas 2. May–July. ⚘ Shores, streambanks, wet meadows and floodplain forests, sometimes forming pure stands. ⊕ Minn, especially along rivers (common in all but far ne), c and s Wisc, s LP of Mich, ne Ill and nw Ind. NY and NJ to Man, s to Fla, Tex and NM.

Carex haydenii Dewey
Acutae
Long-scaled tussock sedge
OBL

perigynium

Loosely clumped perennial, from short rhizomes. **Stems** arising from previous year's clumps of leaves (which are persistent at the base of the new leaves), 3-angled, 3–10 dm long, usually longer than the leaves, rough-to-touch above. **Leaves** green, 2–5 mm wide, the lower leaves bladeless and sheathlike; sheaths white to yellow on front, green on back, translucent. **Spikes** 3–6, the upper 1–3 male, the terminal one largest, 2–5 cm long, the others smaller; the lower 2–3 female or with male flowers above female, 1–3 cm long; lowest bract leaflike, usually shorter than the head; **female scales** tapered to tip, longer than the perigynia. **Perigynia** pale brown when mature, often with dark brown spots, convex on both sides, obovate, inflated at tip, 2–3 mm long; beak tiny. **Achenes** lens-shaped, 1 mm long; stigmas 2. May–July. ⚘ Wet to moist meadows and swales, marshes and streambanks; often with **dark-scaled sedge** (*C. buxbaumii*). ⊕ Occasional in e Minn (plus uncommon in w), Wisc, s LP of Mich (now extirpated), ne Ill and nw Ind. NB to ND, s to Pa, Ind, Mo and Neb.

Carex lenticularis Michx.
Acutae
Shore sedge
OBL

perigynium

Densely clumped perennial. **Stems** 1–6 dm long, upright, slender, usually shorter than leaves, brown at base. **Leaves** clustered on lower one-third of stem, upright, long-tapered to tip, 1–2 mm wide; sheaths dotted with yellow-brown on front. **Male spike** single, sometimes with a few female flowers, stalked, linear, 8–30 mm long and 2–3 mm wide; **female spikes** 3–5, upright, the upper stalkless, the lower stalked, the upper grouped, the lower separate, linear, 1–5 cm long and 3–4 mm wide; lowest bract leaflike, erect, much longer than the head, the upper bracts shorter; **female scales** ovate, red or red-brown, with a 3-veined, green center, the margins translucent near tip, narrower and usually shorter than the perigynia. **Perigynia** upright, soon deciduous, obovate, flattened, convex on both sides and sharply two-edged, 2–3 mm long and 1–1.5 mm wide, waxy blue-green, with a few yellow glandular dots or bumps, tapered or rounded at the abruptly pointed tip; the beak small, to 0.2 mm long. **Achenes** lens-shaped, 2 mm long, brown; stigmas 2. June–Sept. ✤ Rocky and sandy lakeshores, rock pools along Lake Superior, shallow ponds, sedge mats. ⊕ ne Minn, n and ec Wisc, UP and c LP of Mich. Labr to Alaska, s to Mass, NY, Minn Calif; e Asia.

Carex stricta Lam.   Acutae
  Common tussock sedge   OBL

perigynium

Densely clumped perennial from long scaly rhizomes, forming large, raised hummocks to 1 m tall. **Stems** 3-angled, 3–10 dm long, rough-to-touch, longer than leaves. **Leaves** 2–6 mm wide, the lower leaves reduced to sheaths around the base of stem; sheaths white to red-brown on front, green on back, the lower sheaths breaking into ladderlike thin strands. **Spikes** mostly all male or female (sometimes mixed), the upper 1–3 spikes male, the terminal spike 1.5–5 cm long, the lower 2–5 spikes female or some with male flowers borne above female, 2–8 cm long; lowest bract leaflike; **female scales** rounded or tapered to tip, equal or longer than the perigynia but narrower. **Perigynia** green at tip and margins, golden to yellow-brown in middle, with white or brown bumps, convex on both sides to nearly flat, ovate to oval, 2–3 mm long and 0.5–2 mm wide, 2-ribbed with a few faint nerves on both sides; beak short and tubelike, to only 0.3 mm long. **Achenes** lens-shaped, 1.5 mm long; stigmas 2. May–July. ✤ Sedge meadows, marshes, fens, shores, streambanks, ditches. ⊕ Common, and a dominant component of sedge meadow communities; Minn, Wisc, Mich, ne Ill and nw Ind. NJ to Man, s to Fla, Tex and Colo.

Carex Section ANOMALAE

Carex scabrata Schwein.   Anomalae
  Rough sedge   OBL

⚠
STATUS
Indiana - E

perigynium

Colony-forming perennial; plants rough-to-touch. **Stems** loosely clustered, 4–9 dm long. **Leaves** 4–14 mm wide, lowest leaves not reduced to scales. **Spikes** either male or female; male spike single, 2–4 cm long, short-stalked; female spikes 3–6, cylindric, 2–4 cm long, upright, the lower on long stalks, the upper stalkless or short-stalked; bracts leaflike; **female scales** lance-shaped, about as long as the perigynia, tapered to a tip. **Perigynia** obovate, 3-angled, 2-ribbed, 3–5 mm long, finely coarse-hairy, few-nerved, abruptly tapered to a slightly curved, notched beak. **Achenes** 3-angled; stigmas 3. May–Aug. ✤ Low shaded areas in forests, streambanks, seeps. ⊕ Wisc (mostly n), Mich, local in nw Ind. NS and Que to Wisc, s to NJ, n Ga, Ohi

Carex Section ATRATAE

▸**KEY TO ATRATAE**

1 Lowest leaves reduced to scales; stems not surrounded by dried sheaths of previous years; perigynia light gray-green, covered with many small bumps; female spikes 1–3 cm long; female scales brown to nearly black with a lighter midrib . . . . *C. buxbaumii*
. . . . Dark-scaled sedge

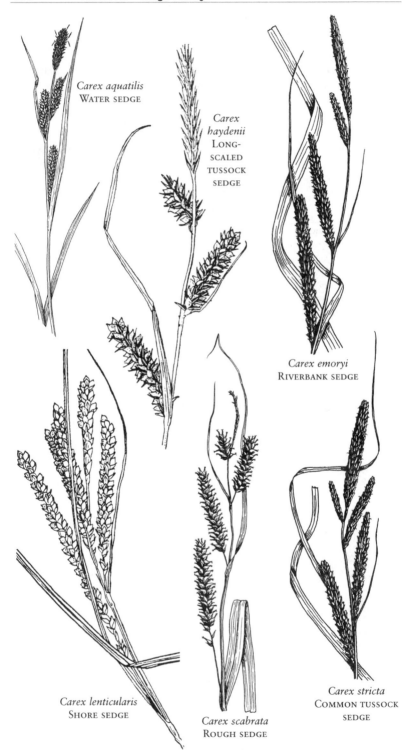

Carex aquatilis
WATER SEDGE

Carex haydenii
LONG-SCALED TUSSOCK SEDGE

Carex emoryi
RIVERBANK SEDGE

Carex lenticularis
SHORE SEDGE

Carex scabrata
ROUGH SEDGE

Carex stricta
COMMON TUSSOCK SEDGE

1 Lowest leaves well-developed or slightly scalelike; stems surrounded by dried sheaths of previous years; perigynia usually straw-colored but sometimes green or purple, without small bumps; side spikes usually less than 1 cm long; female scales black with white translucent margins **2**

2 Spikes short, the terminal spike 6–14 mm long, female scales dark purple; ne Minn, sw Wisc, Keweenaw Peninsula and Isle Royale of Mich UP . . . . *C. norvegica* / SCANDINAVIAN SEDGE
2 Spikes longer, the terminal spike 15–30 mm long, female scales straw-colored to brown; nw Minn . . . . *C. parryana* / PARRY'S SEDGE

Carex buxbaumii Wahlenb.   Atratae
  Dark-scaled sedge   OBL
Loosely clumped perennial, from long rhizomes. **Stems** single or few together, 3-angled, 3–10 dm long, rough-to-touch above, red-tinged near base. **Leaves** 1–3 mm wide, the lowest leaves without blades; lower sheaths shredding into thin strands, the upper sheaths membranous and purple-dotted. **Spikes** 2–5, 1–3 cm long, terminal spike with female flowers above male and larger than the lateral spikes, lateral spikes female, short-cylindric, stalkless or nearly so; bracts leaflike, the lowest shorter than the head; **female scales** dark brown, tapered to an awn at tip. **Perigynia** light green, golden brown near base, oval, 2.5–3.5 mm long, 2-ribbed, with 6–8 faint nerves on each side; beak tiny, notched. **Achenes**

perigynia

3-angled, 1–2 mm long; stigmas 3. May–Aug. ❦ Wet meadows and fens, shallow marshes, low prairie, hollows in patterned peatlands. ⊕ Minn (but not sw), Wisc, Mich, ne Ill and nw Ind. Circumboreal, s to NC, Ky, Ark, Kans, Colo, Utah and Calif.

Carex norvegica Retz.   Atratae
  Scandinavian sedge   FACW

⚠
STATUS
Michigan - T
Wisconsin - E

Loosely clumped perennial, from short rhizomes. **Stems** slender, not stiff, 2–8 dm long, smooth or slightly rough-to-touch above, sharply triangular above, much longer than the leaves, red-tinged at base. **Leaves** 7–15 and mostly near base of stem, pale-green, flat or margins slightly rolled under, 2–3 mm wide, rough-to-touch on margins, the dried leaves of previous year conspicuous; sheaths translucent. **Spikes** usually 3, densely flowered, the terminal with both male and female flowers, the male below the female, clustered, upright, oblong to nearly round in outline per spike, 4–8 mm long and 3–5 mm wide, stalkless; the lateral spikes female, on short stalks; lowest bract usually shorter than the head; **female scales** ovate, 2–3 mm long, purple-black, acute to rounded, margins white-translucent, nearly as wide as perigynia but much shorter.

perigynia

Perigynia obovate, 2–4 mm long and 1.5 mm wide, rounded 3-angled, slightly inflated, yellow-green to brown, two-ribbed, otherwise without nerves, tip rounded and abruptly beaked, the beak short (0.5 mm long), red-tinged, with a small notch. **Achenes** obovate, 1–2 mm long, 3-angled, yellow-brown; stigmas 3. July–Aug. *C. media.* ❦ Rocky streambanks, rocky Lake Superior shores, talus slopes. ⊕ Extreme ne Minn, sw Wisc, Keweenaw Peninsula and Isle Royale in UP of Mich. Circumboreal, s to Que, Wisc, Minn and Utah.

Carex parryana Dewey   Atratae
  Parry's sedge   (FACW)

Loosely clumped perennial, from short scaly rhizomes. **Stems** 2–6 dm long. **Leaves** clustered near base of plant, 2–4 mm wide, mostly less than 20 cm long. **Spikes** 1–5, upright, all female or the terminal spike male (or

perigynium

with both male and female flowers, the male usually below the female), 1–3 cm long; bract usually shorter than the head; **female scales** brown with translucent margins, shorter or longer than the perigynia. **Perigynia** obovate, 2–3 mm long, tapered to a short beak up to 0.5 mm long, often short-hairy near tip, 2-ribbed. **Achenes** 3-angled; stigmas 3. June–Aug. *C. hallii.* ☙ Prairie swales and wet meadows. ⊕ Extreme nw Minn. Interior w USA and s Can, e to nw Minn.

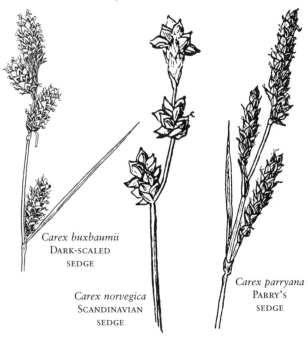

Carex buxbaumii
DARK-SCALED
SEDGE

Carex norvegica
SCANDINAVIAN
SEDGE

Carex parryana
PARRY'S
SEDGE

Carex Section BICOLORES

One wetland species in Great Lakes region . . . .*C. aurea*
. . . . GOLDEN SEDGE

Carex aurea Nutt.   Bicolores
Golden sedge   FACW+

perigynium

Small, loosely clumped perennial. **Stems** upright, 3-angled, 5–30 cm long. **Leaves** 1–4 mm wide. **Spikes** 2–5 per stem, the lower spikes stalked; spikes at ends of stems male, 3–18 mm long; lateral spikes female, 8–20 mm long; bract of lowest spike longer than the head; **female scales** white-tinged to yellow-brown, with a green midvein, tipped with a short, sharp point, shorter than the perigynia. **Perigynia** with short white hairs when young, becoming a distinctive gold-orange when mature (drying paler), round to obovate, beakless or with a very short beak, several-ribbed, 2–3 mm long. **Achenes** dark brown to black, lens-shaped, 1–1.5 mm long; stigmas 2. May–July. *C. garberi, C. hassei.* ☙ Moist to wet meadows, low prairie, swales, wet woods and along sandy or gravelly shores; often where calcium-rich. ⊕ Minn, Wisc, Mich, ne Ill and nw Ind. Newf to Alaska, s to Conn, Pa, Ind, Minn, Neb, NM and Calif.

Carex Section BRACTEOSAE

▶KEY TO BRACTEOSAE

1 Female scales brown or red-purple; perigynia 3 mm or more long; spikes many and crowded into a head; leaves 3–6 mm wide . . . . *C. alopecoidea* / BROWN-HEADED FOX SEDGE

1 Female scales green or green-white with translucent margin (or drying to pale brown); perigynia less than 3 mm long; spikes 2–5 and widely separated; leaves narrow, 1–2 mm wide . . . . . . *C. disperma* . . . . TWO-SEEDED SEDGE

Carex alopecoidea Tuckerman   Bracteosae
Brown-headed Fox sedge   FACW+

⚠
STATUS
Indiana - E

Clumped perennial. **Stems** soft, 4–10 dm long, 3-angled and sharply winged. **Leaves** 3–8 mm wide; sheaths purple-dotted, not cross-wrinkled. **Spikes** with both male and female flowers, male flowers above female, in heads 1.5–5 cm long; **female scales** tapered to tip or with a short sharp tip. **Perigynia** yellow-brown when mature, ovate, flat on 1 side and convex on other, 3–5 mm long, spongy-thickened at base, narrowed to a beak half to as long as the body. **Achenes** lens-shaped, 1–2 mm long; stigmas 2. May–July. 🌱 Swamps and floodplain forests, streambanks, swales and moist fields. ⊕ Minn (all but far ne), s Wisc, sw Mich, ne Ill and nw Ind. Que and Maine to Man, s to NJ, Ind and Iowa.

perigynium

Carex disperma Dewey   Bracteosae
Two-seeded sedge   OBL

⚠
STATUS
Illinois - E
Indiana - E

Small, loosely clumped perennial, from slender rhizomes. **Stems** slender, weak, 3-angled, 1–4 dm long, shorter to longer than leaves. **Leaves** soft and spreading, 1–2 mm wide; sheaths tight, translucent. **Spikes** 2–5, with both male and female flowers, male flowers borne above female, few flowered and small, with 1–6 perigynia and 1–2 male flowers, to 5 mm long, stalkless, separate or upper spikes grouped in interrupted heads 1.5–2.5 cm long; bracts sheathlike and resembling the female scales, or threadlike and to 2 cm long; **female scales** white, translucent except for the darker midrib, tapered to tip or short-awned, 1–2 mm long. **Perigynia** convex on both sides to nearly round in section, oval, 2–3 mm long, strongly nerved and rounded on the margins, beak tiny. **Achenes** lens-shaped, oval, 1–2 mm long; stigmas 2. May–July. 🌱 Hummocks in conifer swamps and alder thickets, usually where shaded, wetland margins. ⊕ n and c Minn, Wisc, Mich, local in ne Ill and nw Ind. Circumboreal, s to NJ, Ind, SD, NM, Utah and Ore.

spike with
several
perigynia

Carex Section CAPILLARES

One wetland species in Great Lakes region . . . .*C. capillaris* . . . . HAIRLIKE SEDGE

Carex capillaris L.   Capillares
Hairlike sedge   FACW

Small, densely clumped perennial. **Stems** slender, 3-angled, 1.5–4 dm long. **Leaves** mostly at base of plant and much shorter than stems, 1–3 mm wide; sheaths tight. **Spikes** either male or female; terminal spike male, 4–8 mm long; lateral spikes 1–4, separated on stem, loosely flowered, short-cylindric, 5–15 mm long, on threadlike, spreading to drooping stalks 5–15 mm long; **female scales** white, translucent on outer edges,

perigynium

perigynium

green or light brown in middle, blunt or acute at tip, shorter but usually wider than perigynia, deciduous. **Perigynia** shiny brown to olive-green, ovate, round in section, 2–4 mm long, 2-ribbed, otherwise without nerves, tapered to a translucent-tipped beak 0.5 mm or more long. **Achenes** 3-angled with concave sides, 1–1.5 mm long; stigmas 3. June–July. ⚘ Alder thickets, wetland margins, usually in shade. Occasional in n Minn, n Wisc, Mich (UP and n LP). ⊕ Circumboreal, s to NY, Mich, Minn, SD, NM, Utah, Nev and Ore.

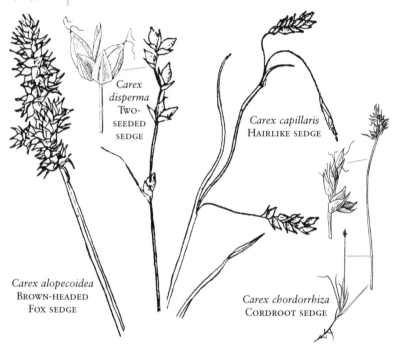

Carex disperma
Two-
SEEDED
SEDGE

Carex capillaris
HAIRLIKE SEDGE

Carex alopecoidea
BROWN-HEADED
FOX SEDGE

Carex chordorrhiza
CORDROOT SEDGE

Carex Section CHORDORRHIZAE

One wetland species in Great Lakes region . . . .*C. chordorrhiza*
. . . . CORDROOT SEDGE

Carex chordorrhiza L. f.   Chordorrhizae
Cordroot sedge   OBL

⚠
STATUS
Illinois - E
Indiana - E

perigynium

Perennial from long, creeping stems. **Flowering stems** upright, rounded 3-angled in section, 1–3 dm tall, single or several together, arising from axils of dried leaves on older, reclining sterile stems. **Leaves** several on stem, the lower ones often bladeless, 1–2 mm wide; sheaths translucent. **Spikes** 3–8, with both male and female flowers, male flowers borne above female, crowded in an ovate head 5–15 mm long; bracts absent; **female scales** dark brown, ovate, about equaling the perigynia. **Perigynia** brown, compressed, ovate, 2–3.5 mm long, leathery, with many nerves on both sides; beak short. **Achenes** lens-shaped; stigmas 2. May–Aug. ⚘ Open floating mats around lakes and ponds, fens, conifer swamps, interdunal hollows. ⊕ n and ec Minn, Wisc, Mich, uncommon in ne Ill and nw Ind. Circumboreal, s to Vt, NY, Ind, n Iowa, n ND, Sask and BC. ☞ The creeping stems which root at each flowering stem are distinctive.

Carex Section CRYPTOCARPAE

▶KEY TO CRYPTOCARPAE

1 Stem sheath smooth; perigynia inflated, obovate, rounded at tip but
abruptly tapered to a beak . . . . *C. crinita* / FRINGED SEDGE
1 Stem sheath rough-to-touch; perigynia flattened, oval, tapered from
near middle to a small beak . . . . . . *C. gynandra* / FRINGED SEDGE

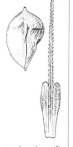

perigynium (l)
and female
scale (r)

Carex crinita Lam.   Cryptocarpae
Fringed sedge   FACW+

Large, densely clumped perennial. **Stems** 5–15 dm long and longer than
leaves. **Leaves** 7–13 mm wide, lowest stem leaves reduced to scales;
sheaths smooth. **Spikes** male or female, drooping on slender stalks; male
spikes 1–3, above female spikes, 4–10 cm long; female spikes 2–5, narrow cylindric, 4–12 cm long; bract leaflike, without a sheath; **female
scales** rounded and notched at tip with pale midvein prolonged into a
toothed awn to 10 mm long, scale edges copper-brown. **Perigynia** green,
2-ribbed, nerves faint or absent, round in cross-section, abruptly tapered
to a tiny beak. **Achenes** lens-shaped; stigmas 2. May–July. ≋ Swamps
and alder thickets, wet openings, ditches and potholes. ⊕ ne and ec
Minn, n and c Wisc, Mich, ne Ill and nw Ind. Nfld and Que to Minn, s
to Ga and Tex. ☞ Similar to *C. gynandra* but with smooth sheaths,
lower female scales rounded at tip, and perigynia inflated.

Carex gynandra Schwein.   Cryptocarpae
Fringed sedge   FACW+

Large, clumped perennial. **Stems** 5–15 dm long, longer than leaves.
Leaves 7–14 mm wide, lowest leaves reduced to scales; sheaths finely
hairy; bracts leaflike, lowest bract 1–3.5 dm long. **Spikes** either male or
female, spreading or drooping and often curved, stalked; male spikes
1–3, above female, 5–9 cm long; female spikes 2–5, long-cylindric, 5–12
cm long; lower **female scales** 5–6 mm long, with a pale midrib, tapered
to an awned tip about 5 mm long. **Perigynia** green, ovate to oval, not
inflated, 3–4 mm long. **Achenes** lens-shaped, stigmas 2. June–July. *C.
crinita* var. *gynandra*. ≋ Wet openings and swamps. ⊕ ne Minn, mostly
near Lake Superior; Wisc, UP and n and e LP of Mich. Nfld to ne Minn,
s to Va, n Ga, and Wisc. ☞ Similar to *C. crinita*, but with finely hairy
sheaths, lower female scales tapered to an awned tip, and perigynia
somewhat flattened and not inflated.

perigynium (l)
and female
scale (r)

Carex Section DEWEYANAE

▶KEY TO DEWEYANAE

1 Perigynia to 1.2 mm wide and 4–5x as long as wide, usually strongly
nerved on both sides . . . . *C. bromoides* / BROME HUMMOCK SEDGE
1 Perigynia 1.3–1.6 mm wide and 3–4x as long as wide, nerves faint or
absent . . . . *C. deweyana* / DEWEY'S HUMMOCK SEDGE

Carex bromoides Willd.   Deweyanae
Brome hummock sedge   FACW+

Densely clumped perennial. **Stems** very slender, 3–8 dm long. **Leaves** 1–2
mm wide. **Spikes** 3–7, narrowly oblong, 1–2 cm long, terminal spike
with both male and female flowers, the male below female; lateral spikes
all female or with a few male flowers at base, the spikes clustered or

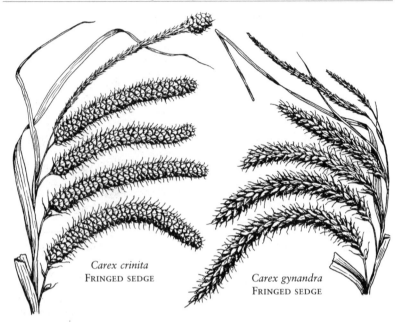

Carex crinita
FRINGED SEDGE

Carex gynandra
FRINGED SEDGE

perigynia

overlapping; **female scales** obovate, about as long as perigynia body, pale brown or orange-tinged with translucent margins, tapered to tip or short-awned. **Perigynia** lance-shaped, flat on 1 side and convex on other, light green, 4–6 mm long and 1–1.5 mm wide, nerved on both sides, gradually tapered to a finely sharp-toothed beak, the beak 1/2–2/3 as long as body. **Achenes** lens-shaped, to 2 mm long, in upper part of perigynium body; stigmas 2. April–July. ❦ Floodplain forests, old river channels, swamps. ⊕ Locally common in ec Minn; Wisc, Mich (w UP, s LP), ne Ill and nw Ind. NS, Que to Ont and Minn, s to Fla and Mex.

Carex deweyana Schwein.   Deweyanae
  Dewey's hummock sedge   FACU

Large, loosely clumped perennial from short rhizomes. **Stems** weak and spreading, 2–12 dm long, rough-to-touch below the head. **Leaves** shorter than stems, yellow-green to waxy blue-green, soft, flat, 2–5 mm wide; sheath tight. **Spikes** 2–6, the lower separate, the upper grouped, forming a head 2–6 cm long and often drooping near tip; terminal spike with male flowers at base, lateral spikes usually female, the perigynia upright; **female scales** ovate, blunt to short-awned at tip, thin and translucent with green center, slightly shorter than perigynia. **Perigynia** flat on 1 side and convex on other, 4–6 mm long and 1–2 mm wide, oblong lance-shaped, pale-green, very spongy at base, the beak 2–3 mm long, finely toothed and weakly notched. **Achenes** lens-shaped, nearly round, yellow-brown, 2 mm long; stigmas 2. May–Aug. ❦ Thickets, swamps and moist to dry woods. ⊕ In Minn, most common in n, occasional in sc and se, especially in tamarack swamps; Wisc and Mich. Labr, Nfld to NW Terr and BC, s to Pa, Mich, Iowa, Calif and Mex.

perigynia

Carex Section DIOICAE

Carex dioica L.   Dioicae
Northern bog sedge   OBL

perigynium

Small perennial, from long, slender rhizomes. **Stems** single or few together, 0.3–3 dm long, smooth, usually longer than the leaves, brown at base. **Leaves** clustered near base of plant, blades inrolled and threadlike, to 1 mm wide. **Spikes** only 1 per stem, all male or all female, or with both male and female flowers and with the male flowers borne above the female, 0.5–2 cm long; the male spike or portion of spike narrowly cylindric, the female spike or portion short-cylindric; bract absent; **female scales** brown or red-brown, obovate, tapered to tip, shorter but wider than perigynia. **Perigynia** 4–10, widely spreading, yellow to dark brown, shiny, plump, obovate, 2–4 mm long and 1–2 mm wide, spongy at base, abruptly contracted to the beak; beak nearly entire to unequally notched, 0.5 mm long. **Achenes** lens-shaped, 1–2 mm long; stigmas 2. June–July. *C. gynocrates*. ⚘ Conifer swamps and open peatlands, usually in sphagnum and wet, peaty soils. ⊕ Occasional in n and c Minn; ne Wisc, Mich (UP, n LP). Greenland to Yukon, s to Newf, Pa, Mich, Minn, ND, Colo, Utah and Ore; Siberia.

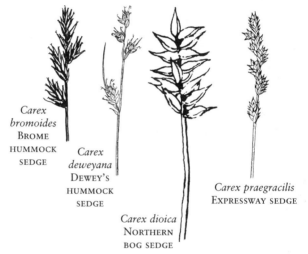

Carex bromoides BROME HUMMOCK SEDGE

Carex deweyana DEWEY'S HUMMOCK SEDGE

Carex dioica NORTHERN BOG SEDGE

Carex praegracilis EXPRESSWAY SEDGE

Carex Section DIVISAE

One wetland species in Great Lakes region . . . .*C. praegracilis*
. . . . EXPRESSWAY SEDGE

Carex praegracilis W. Boott   Divisae
Expressway sedge   FACW

perigynium

Colony-forming perennial, from long black rhizomes. **Stems** single or few together, 3-angled, 1–7 dm long, longer than the leaves. **Leaves** on lower part of stems, 2–3 mm wide; sheaths white-translucent. **Spikes** with both male and female flowers, male flowers above female, or spikes nearly all male or female, 4–8 mm long, upper spikes crowded, lower spikes separated, in narrowly ovate heads 1–4 cm long; bracts absent; **female scales** brown, shiny, shorter or equal to perigynia. **Perigynia** green-brown, turning dark brown, flat on 1 side and convex on other, ovate to lance-shaped, 3–4 mm long and 1 mm wide, sharp-edged, spongy at base, tapered to a finely toothed beak 2 mm long, unequally

notched. **Achenes** lens-shaped, 1–2 mm long; stigmas 2. May–June. ❧
Wet to moist meadows, shores, streambanks and ditches. ⊕ In s part of
region, most common along salted highways. Minn (especially w), s LP
of Mich (local in UP), ne Ill and nw Ind. Mich to Yukon, s to Ind, Ill, Mo,
Okla, n Mex and Calif.

Carex Section EXTENSAE

▶**KEY TO EXTENSAE**

1 Perigynia 2–3.3 mm long, achene filling most of perigynium . . . . .
. . . . *C. viridula* / GREEN YELLOW SEDGE

1 Perigynia 3.5–6 mm long, achene filling only lower half of perigynium **2**

2 Female scales conspicuous copper-brown, beak of perigynia rough-
margined . . . . *C. flava* / LARGE YELLOW SEDGE

2 Female scales inconspicuous, about same color as perigynia; beak
smooth . . . . *C. cryptolepis* / SMALL YELLOW SEDGE

Carex cryptolepis Mackenzie   Extensae
  Small yellow sedge   OBL

⚠
STATUS
Illinois - E

Clumped perennial. **Stems** 2–6 dm long and longer than leaves. **Leaves**
2–4 mm wide. **Spikes** male or female; male spikes short-stalked or stalkless, the stalk shorter than the female spikes; female spikes 3–4, the upper
2 spikes grouped, the third separate, the fourth spike lower on stem,
short-cylindric, 1–2 cm long, stalkless; bracts leaflike and spreading;
female scales narrowly ovate, same color as perigynia and as long as
perigynia body. **Perigynia** yellow-brown when mature, lower ones curved
outward and downward, body obovate, 3–5 mm long, 2-ribbed and several nerved, contracted into a smooth beak 1–1.5 mm long. **Achenes** 3-
angled; stigmas 3. June–Aug. ❧ Wet meadows and marshy areas, peatlands, swamp margins; often where calcium-rich. ⊕ Occasional in ne and
c Minn, Wisc, Mich, ne Ill and nw Ind. Nfld to Minn, s to NJ, Ohio and
Ill.

perigynium

Carex flava L.   Extensae
  Large yellow sedge   OBL

⚠
STATUS
Indiana - T

perigynium

Densely clumped perennial from short rootstocks. **Stems** stiff, 1–7 dm
high, usually longer than the leaves. **Leaves** 4–8 to a stem, mostly near
base, 3–5 mm wide. Terminal **spike** male (or rarely partly female), stalkless or short-stalked, linear, 0.5–2 cm long and 2–3 mm wide; female
spikes 2–5, sometimes with male flowers at tip, the uppermost spikes
nearly stalkless, the lower stalked, short-oblong to nearly round, 6–18
mm long and 7–12 mm wide, perigynia 15–35, crowded in several to
many rows, their beaks turned downward; bracts conspicuous, leaflike,
spreading outward, much longer than the head; **female scales** ovate, narrower and much shorter than the perigynia, red-tinged except for the
pale, three–nerved middle and the narrow translucent margins. **Perigynia**
4–6 mm long and 1–2 mm wide, obovate, yellow-green becoming yellow
with age, conspicuously ribbed, tapered to a slender, finely toothed beak
about as long as the body, the tip notched. **Achenes** 1.5 mm long, obovate, 3-angled, yellow-brown; stigmas 3. May–Aug. *C. laxior.* ❧ Wet,
peaty meadows, often where calcium-rich. ⊕ Uncommon in ne Minn, n
and c Wisc, Mich and nw Ind. Circumboreal, s to NJ, Ind, Idaho and BC.

Carex viridula Michx.   Extensae
Green yellow sedge   OBL

STATUS
Illinois - T

perigynium

Clumped perennial. **Stems** stiff, slightly 3-angled, 0.5–4 dm long, longer than leaves. **Leaves** 1–3 mm wide; sheaths white-translucent. **Spikes** either male or female (or sometimes mixed), the terminal spike male or with a few female flowers at tip or middle, 3–15 mm long, short-stalked or stalkless, longer than the female spikes or clustered with them; lateral spikes female, 2–6, ovate to short-cylindric, 5–10 mm long, clustered and stalkless above, the lower spikes often separate and on short stalks; bracts leaflike, usually upright, much longer than the heads; **female scales** brown on sides, rounded or with a short, sharp point, about equal to perigynia. **Perigynia** yellow-green to brown, rounded 3-angled, obovate, 2–4 mm long, 2-ribbed, tapered to a slightly notched beak 0.5–1 mm long. **Achenes** 3-angled, to 1.5 mm long; stigmas 3. May–Aug. ☙ Wet meadows, sandy lake margins, fens and seeps; often where calcium-rich. ⊕ Mostly n and c Minn (locally common with *C. lasiocarpa* in nw Minn, uncommon in s), Wisc, Mich, ne Ill and nw Ind. Newf to Alaska s to Conn, Ill, Minn, SD and NM.

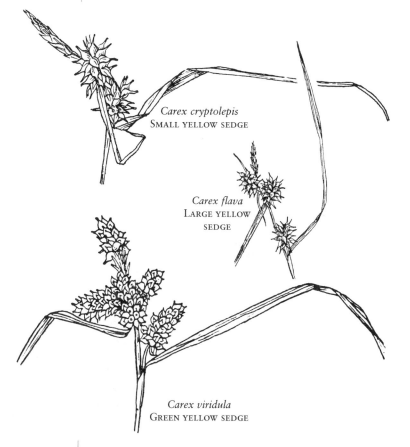

Carex cryptolepis
SMALL YELLOW SEDGE

Carex flava
LARGE YELLOW
SEDGE

Carex viridula
GREEN YELLOW SEDGE

Carex Section FOLLICULATAE

▶**KEY TO FOLLICULATAE**

1 Leaves 4–16 mm wide . . . . *C. folliculata* / FOLLICLE SEDGE
1 Leaves 1–4 mm wide . . . . *C. michauxiana* / MICHAUX'S SEDGE

Carex folliculata L. ... Folliculatae
Follicle sedge ... OBL

Large, clumped perennial. **Stems** to 1 m long. **Leaves** 5–15 mm wide. **Male spike** single, 10–25 mm long, long-stalked; **female spikes** 2–5, widely separated, upright, 15–30 mm long and as wide, stalked; **bracts** leaflike, longer than stems; **female scales** ovate, translucent or brown-tinged, green in center, much shorter than perigynia. **Perigynia** lance-shaped, many-nerved, 10–15 mm long, tapered to a long, finely toothed beak, the teeth upright. **Achenes** 3-angled; stigmas 3. June–Aug. ❦ Wet woods and cedar swamps. ⊕ Wisc, Mich (where local in w and c LP and UP) and local in nw Ind. Nfld, Que, to Wisc, s to Fla and La.

Carex michauxiana Boeckeler ... Folliculatae
Michaux's sedge ... OBL

perigynium

Clumped perennial. **Stems** 2–6 dm long. **Leaves** 2–4 mm wide. **Spikes** either male or female; terminal spike male, 0.5–1.5 cm long, stalkless or short stalked; female spikes 2–4, broadly ovate, 1.5–2.5 cm long, upright, the lower spikes stalked, the upper on shorter stalks; **bracts** leaflike, 1–3 mm wide, longer than the stems; **female scales** ovate, shorter than the perigynia, margins translucent or brown, with a green midrib, tapered to a tip. **Perigynia** narrowly lance-shaped, 8–13 long and to 2 mm wide, round in section, long-tapered to a beak with upright teeth 1 mm long. **Achenes** rounded 3-angled; stigmas 3. June–Aug. ❦ Wet meadows, sphagnum peatlands, ditches and swales. ⊕ Uncommon in ne Minn, nw Wisc, UP of Mich. Nfld, Ont, NY, ne Minn, Sask; e Asia.

perigynium

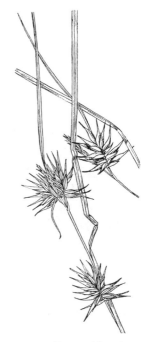

Carex folliculata
FOLLICLE SEDGE

Carex michauxiana
MICHAUX'S SEDGE

Carex Section GRACILLIMAE

▶**KEY TO GRACILLIMAE**

1 Perigynia sharply angled; plants brown or green at base . *C. prasina*
. . . . Drooping sedge
1 Perigynia somewhat 3-angled; plants purple at base . . . . . *C. davisii*
. . . . Awned graceful sedge

Carex davisii Schwein. & Torr.   Gracillimae
  Awned graceful sedge   FAC+

STATUS
Minnesota - T

Clumped perennial. **Stems** 3–10 dm long, purple at base. **Leaves** 4–8 mm wide, hairy on underside; sheaths hairy. Terminal **spike** male with female flowers near tip; female spikes 2–3, the upper 2 overlapping, cylindric, 2–4 cm long and 5–6 mm wide, upright to nodding on short stalks; **female scales** obovate, white or translucent with green center, tipped with a long awn, shorter or longer than perigynia. **Perigynia** ovate, dull orange when mature, 4–6 mm long and 2–3 mm wide, somewhat 3-angled, tapered to a notched beak to 1 mm long. **Achenes** 3-angled; stigmas 3. May–June. ❦ Floodplain forest and moist woods. ⊕ se Minn, Wisc, sw Mich, ne Ill and nw Ind. Mass, Vt, s Ont to Minn, s to MD, Neb and Tex.

perigynium

Carex prasina Wahlenb.   Gracillimae
  Drooping sedge   OBL

STATUS
Illinois - T
Wisconsin - T

Clumped perennial. **Stems** 3–8 dm long, brown or green at base. **Leaves** 3–5 mm wide. Terminal **spike** male or with a few female flowers at tip; female spikes 2–4, widely separated, cylindric, 2–5 cm long and 5 mm wide, curved or nodding, lower spikes on long stalks, the upper stalks much shorter; upper bract ± sheathless; **female scales** ovate to obovate, shorter than the perigynia, tipped with a short point. **Perigynia** 3–4 mm long, ovate, 3-angled, tapered to beak. **Achenes** 3-angled; stigmas 3. May–June. ❦ Low areas in deciduous woods, streambanks. ⊕ Uncommon in sc and nw Wisc, Mich LP, local in Ill and nw Ind. Que and Maine to Wisc, s to SC, Ga and Ala.

perigynium

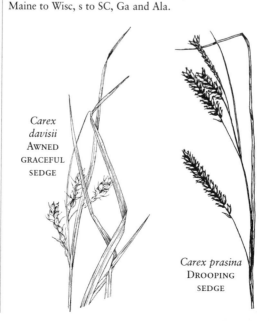

Carex davisii AWNED GRACEFUL SEDGE

Carex prasina DROOPING SEDGE

Carex Section GRANULARES

▶KEY TO GRANULARES

1 Male spike stalkless, or on a stalk shorter than uppermost female
spike . . . . *C. granularis* / PALE SEDGE
1 Stalk of male spike longer than uppermost female spike . *C. crawei*
. . . . EARLY FEN SEDGE

Carex crawei Dewey   Granulares
  Early fen sedge   FACW

STATUS
Illinois - T
Indiana - T

Perennial, from long-creeping rhizomes. **Stems** single or several together,
faintly 3-angled, 0.5–4 dm long. **Leaves** 1–4 mm wide; sheaths tight,
translucent. **Spikes** either male or female, cylindric, densely flowered,
1–3 cm long, terminal spike male; lateral spikes female, 2–5, separate,
the lowest spike near base of plant; bract leaflike with well-developed
sheath, its blade shorter than terminal spike; **female scales** red-brown
with a pale or green midrib, shorter and narrower than the perigynia.
Perigynia green to brown, ovate, 2–3.5 mm long, many-nerved; beak
absent or very short, entire to notched. **Achenes** 3-angled, 1–2 mm long;
stigmas 3. May–July. ❧ Wet to moist meadows and prairies, marly
lakeshores, ditches, especially where calcium-rich. ⊕ Mostly nw Minn,
local elsewhere in state; sc and se Wisc, Mich, ne Ill and nw Ind. Que to
s BC, s to NJ, Ala, Mo, Okla, Wyo and Utah.

perigynium

Carex granularis Muhl.   Granulares
  Pale sedge   FACW+

Clumped perennial, from short rhizomes. **Stems** rounded 3-angled, 1–5
dm long. **Leaves** often longer than stems, 3–13 mm wide; sheaths membranous on front, divided-with small swollen joints on back. **Spikes**
either all male or female, the terminal spike male, stalkless; the lateral
spikes female, clustered around the male spike; bracts longer than the
head; **female scales** brown, tapered to tip or with a short, sharp point,
half as long as perigynia. **Perigynia** crowded in several rows, green or
olive to brown, oval to obovate, 2–3 mm long and 1–2 mm wide, 2-
ribbed, strongly nerved; beak tiny or absent, entire to slightly notched.
Achenes 3-angled, 1–2 mm long; stigmas 3. May–July. ❧ Wet to moist
meadows and swales, streambanks and pond margins, especially where
calcium-rich. ⊕ Minn (all but ne), s and e Wisc, Mich, common in ne Ill
and nw Ind. Que and Maine to Sask, s to Fla, La and Tex.

perigynium

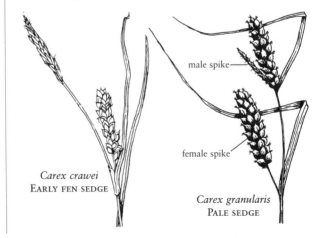

male spike

female spike

Carex crawei
EARLY FEN SEDGE

Carex granularis
PALE SEDGE

Carex Section HELEONASTES

Carex brunnescens (Pers.) Poiret   Heleonastes
Green bog sedge   FACW

⚠
STATUS
Illinois - E
Indiana - E

Densely clumped perennial from a short, fibrous rootstock. **Stems** slender,
sharply 3-angled, 0.5–5 dm long, smooth or slightly rough-to-touch below
the head, mostly longer than the leaves. **Leaves** 1–3 mm wide; sheaths
tight, thin and translucent. **Spikes** 5–10 in a head 2–5 cm long, all with
female flowers borne above male, 4–8 mm long, each spike with 5–15
perigynia, lower spikes separated; lowermost bract bristlelike, shorter or
longer than lowermost spike; **female scales** ovate, rounded or acute at tip,
shorter than the perigynia. **Perigynia** 3-angled, not winged or sharp-edged,
2–3 mm long, faintly nerved on both sides, not spongy-thickened at base,
tapered at tip to a short, minutely notched beak, the beak and upper body
finely toothed and white-dotted. **Achenes** lens-shaped, 1–1.5 mm long;
stigmas 2. June–Aug. ❦ Wet forests and swamps, peatland margins. ⊕ ne
and nc Minn, Wisc, Mich, local in ne Ill and nw Ind. Circumboreal, s to
NJ, Ga, Tenn, Ohio, n Ind, Minn, ND, Colo, Utah and Ore.

perigynium

Carex canescens L.   Heleonastes
Gray bog sedge   OBL

⚠
STATUS
Illinois - E

Clumped perennial. **Stems** 2–6 dm long. **Leaves** waxy blue- or gray-
green, 2–4 mm wide, mostly near base of plant and shorter than stems.
Spikes 4–8, silvery green or grayish, with both male and female flowers,
the male below the female, ovate to cylindric, 5–10 mm long, the lower
spikes ± separate, each spike with 10–30 perigynia. **Perigynia** flat on one
side and convex on other, 2–3 mm long and 1–2 mm wide, with a beak
to 0.5 mm long, not noticeably finely toothed on the margins; **female
scales** shorter than perigynia. **Achenes** lens-shaped; stigmas 2. May–July.
❦ Peatlands (including hummocks in patterned fens), tamarack swamps,
floating mats, alder thickets, wet forest depressions. ⊕ ne, nc, and c
Minn; Wisc, Mich, far ne Ill and nw Ind. Circumboreal, s to Va, Ohio,
Ind, Minn, SD, Ariz and Calif. ☞ Similar to **green bog sedge** (*C. brun-*

perigynium

nescens) but leaves waxy blue-green rather than green and spikes somewhat larger and silver-green vs. brown.

Carex heleonastes L. f.   Heleonastes
  Hudson Bay sedge   (OBL)

⚠
STATUS
Michigan -E

Perennial, in small clumps from long rhizomes. **Stems** slender and stiff, 2–5 dm long, sharply 3-angled, rough on upper stem angles, longer than leaves. **Leaves** 4–8 on lower stem, 5–12 cm long and 1–2 mm wide. **Spikes** 2–4, with both male and female flowers, the male below the female, grouped into a head 1–2 cm long and to 1 cm wide; **female scales** brown with pale margins, about as long as perigynia. **Perigynia** 5–10 per spike, oval, flat on one side and convex on other, 2–3 mm long, with sharp margins, tapered to a short beak to 0.5 mm long. **Achenes** lens-shaped, filling the perigynium; stigmas 2. June–Aug. ⚜ Open calcareous fens. ⊕ Rare in n Mich. Nearly circumboreal, s to n shore of Lake Superior and n Mich.

perigynium

Carex tenuiflora Wahlenb.   Heleonastes
  Small-headed bog sedge   OBL

Loosely clumped, delicate perennial, spreading from long, slender rhizomes. **Stems** very slender, 2–6 dm long. **Leaves** 1–2 mm wide. **Spikes** 2–4, with both male and female flowers, the male below the female, stalkless, clustered into a head 8–15 mm long; **female scales** white-translucent with green center, covering most of the perigynium. **Perigynia** 3–15, oval, flat on 1 side and convex on other, 3–4 mm long, dotted with small white depressions, sharp-edged, beakless. **Achenes** lens-shaped, nearly filling the perigynia; stigmas 2. June–Aug. ⚜ Hummocks in peatlands, floating mats, conifer swamps; mostly confined to tamarack swamps in s part of our region. ⊕ Occasional; ne, nc and sc Minn, Wisc, Mich, ne Ill and nw Ind. Circumboreal, s to Maine, NY, Minn, Sask and BC. ☞ Easily overlooked as plants are similar to **two-seeded bog sedge** (*C. disperma*) and **three-seeded bog sedge** (*C. trisperma*) and often growing with these species.

perigynium

Carex trisperma Dewey   Heleonastes
  Three-seeded bog sedge   OBL

⚠
STATUS
Illinois - E

Loosely clumped perennial, with short, slender rhizomes. **Stems** very slender and weak, 2–7 dm long. **Leaves** 1–2 mm wide. **Spikes** 1–3 (usually 2), stalkless, 1–4 cm apart in a slender, often zigzagged head, each spike with 2–5 perigynia and a few male flowers at the base; lowest spike subtended by a bristlelike bract 2–6 cm long; **female scales** ovate, translucent with a green center, shorter or equal to the perigynia. **Perigynia** flat on 1 side and convex on other, oval, 3–4 mm long, finely many-nerved, tapered near tip to a short, smooth beak 0.5 mm long. **Achenes** oval-oblong, filling the perigynia; stigmas 2. May–Aug. ⚜ Forested wetlands and conifer swamps, alder thickets, true bogs; a dominant species of forested peatlands in Red Lake peatland of Minn. ⊕ Common in n portions of region; n and ec Minn, Wisc, Mich, local in extreme ne Ill; nw Ind. Nfld to BC, s to Va, Ill and Minn.

perigynia

Carex Section HIRTAE

▸**KEY TO HIRTAE**

1 Leaves ± flat, mostly 2–5 mm wide . *C. lanuginosa* / WOOLLY SEDGE
1 Leaves folded along midrib and inrolled, only 1–2 mm wide . . . . .
  . . . . *C. lasiocarpa* / SLENDER SEDGE

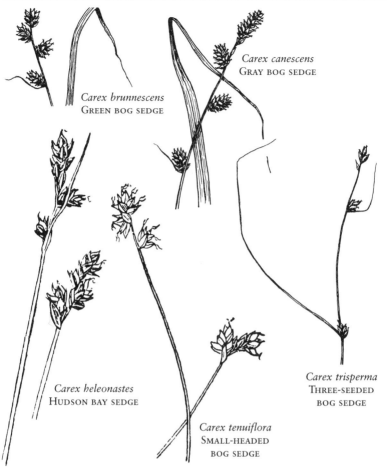

Carex canescens
GRAY BOG SEDGE

Carex brunnescens
GREEN BOG SEDGE

Carex heleonastes
HUDSON BAY SEDGE

Carex trisperma
THREE-SEEDED
BOG SEDGE

Carex tenuiflora
SMALL-HEADED
BOG SEDGE

perigynium

Carex lanuginosa Michx.   Hirtae
   Woolly sedge   OBL
Colony-forming perennial, from scaly rhizomes. **Stems** 3-angled, 2–10
dm long. **Leaves** 2–5 mm wide; sheaths thin and translucent, lower
sheaths often purple-tinged on back, shredding into a loose network of
fibers. **Spikes** either all male or female, the upper 1–3 male, 2–6 cm long;
the lower 1–3 spikes female, separate, stalkless or nearly so, cylindric,
1–4 cm long; bracts leaflike, the lowest usually longer than the head;
female scales brown to purple-brown, tapered to a tip to awned, shorter
or longer than the perigynia. **Perigynia** brown to yellow-green to gray-
brown, nearly round in section, obovate, 2.5–5 mm long, densely hairy,
many-nerved, contracted to a finely toothed beak 1–2 mm long, the beak
teeth spreading. **Achenes** 3-angled with concave sides, 1.5–2 mm long;
stigmas 3. June–Aug. *C. lasiocarpa* var. *latifolia, C. pellita*. ≋ Wet to
moist meadows and swales, marshes, shores, streambanks and other wet
places. ⊕ Common; Minn, Wisc, Mich, ne Ill and nw Ind. NB and Que
to BC, s to Va, Tenn, Ark, Tex and Calif.

Carex lasiocarpa Ehrh.   Hirtae
   Slender sedge   OBL
Colony-forming perennial, from long, scaly rhizomes. **Stems** loosely
clumped, 3-angled, 3–10 dm long. **Leaves** elongate and inrolled, 1–2 mm

perigynium

☞ Slender sedge is similar to **woolly sedge** (*C. lanuginosa*) but distinguished from it by the long, inrolled leaves to only 2 mm wide.

wide; sheaths tinged with yellow-brown. **Spikes** either all male or female, usually the upper 2 male; the male spikes slender, on a long stalk; the lower 1–3 spikes female, widely separate, ± stalkless, cylindric, 1–4 cm long; bracts leaflike, the lowest usually longer than the stem; **female scales** purple-brown with a green center, narrowly ovate, narrower and shorter or longer than the perigynia. **Perigynia** dull brown green, obovate, nearly round in section, 3–5 mm long, densely soft hairy, contracted to a beak about 1 mm long, the beak teeth erect. **Achenes** yellow-brown, 3-angled with concave sides, to 2 mm long; stigmas 3. June–Aug. North American plants are var. *americana* Fern. ≱ Peatlands and wet peaty soils, open bogs, pond margins (where a pioneer mat-former), hollows in Red Lake peatlands of Minn. ⊕ Common; Minn, Wisc, Mich, ne Ill and nw Ind. Circumboreal, Newf to Alaska s to NJ, Ohio, Iowa, ND, Mont, Idaho and Wash.

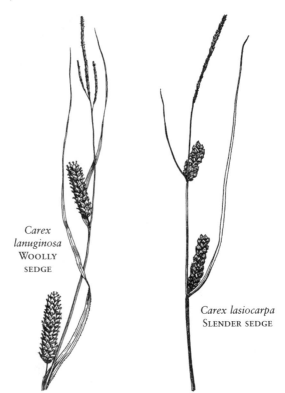

Carex lanuginosa WOOLLY SEDGE

Carex lasiocarpa SLENDER SEDGE

Carex Section INTERMEDIAE

One wetland species in Great Lakes region . . . .*C. sartwellii*
. . . . RUNNING MARSH SEDGE

Carex sartwellii Dewey   Intermediae
  Running marsh sedge   FACW+
Colony-forming perennial, from long black rhizomes. **Stems** single or few together, stiff, sharply 3-angled, 3–8 dm long, longer than the leaves. **Leaves** 2–4 mm wide, few per stem, the lowest leaves small and without

blades; sheaths with green lines on front, and a translucent ligule around stem. **Spikes** with both male and female flowers, male flowers above female, or upper spikes male; clustered or lower spikes separate, 5–10 mm long, in cone-shaped heads, 3–6 cm long; bracts small, the lower bracts sometimes bristlelike and longer than the spike; **female scales** brown with a prominent green midvein, acute or with a short sharp point, about equal to perigynia. **Perigynia** tan to brown, flat on 1 side and convex on other, ovate, 2.5–3.5 mm long and 1–2 mm wide, finely nerved on both sides, sharp-edged, tapered to a short, finely toothed beak. **Achenes** lens-shaped, 1–1.5 mm long; stigmas 2. May–July. ❀ Wet to moist meadows, marshes, fens and shores, often where calcium-rich. ⊕ Minn (all but ne), se Wisc, s LP Mich, ne Ill and nw Ind. NY and Ont to BC, s to Ind, Mo, Neb and Colo.

perigynia

Carex Section LIMOSAE

▶KEY TO LIMOSAE

1 Female scales oval, about as wide and long as the perigynia . . . . . .
. . . . *C. limosa* / MUD SEDGE
1 Female scales lance-shaped, narrower and longer than perigynia . .
. . . . *C. paupercula* / POOR SEDGE

Carex limosa L.   Limosae
  Mud sedge   OBL

⚠
STATUS
Indiana - E

perigynium
(l), scale (r)

Loosely clumped perennial, from long scaly rhizomes. **Stems** sharply 3-angled, 3–5 dm long, longer than leaves, usually rough-to-touch above. **Leaves** 1–3 mm wide; sheaths translucent, shredding into threadlike fibers near base. **Spikes** either all male or female, the terminal spike male, 1–3 cm long; the lower 1–3 spikes female, drooping on lax, threadlike stalks 1–3 cm long, ovate to short-cylindric, 1–2 cm long; **female scales** brown, rounded or with a short, sharp point, about same size as perigynia. **Perigynia** waxy blue-green, ovate, flattened except where filled by achene, 2.5–4 mm long and 1–2 mm wide, strongly 2-ribbed with a few faint nerves on each side; beak tiny. **Achenes** 3-angled, 2 mm long; stigmas 3. May–July. ❀ Open bogs and floating mats. ⊕ Common northward, less common in s where mostly confined to calcareous fens and tamarack swamps. n and c Minn, Wisc and Mich, ne Ill and nw Ind. Circumboreal, s to NJ, Ohio, Iowa, Neb, Mont, Idaho and Calif. ☞ **Poor sedge** (*C. paupercula*) is similar but has scales much narrower than the perigynia.

Carex paupercula Michx.   Limosae
  Poor sedge   OBL

Loosely clumped perennial, from slender branching rhizomes. **Stems** slender, 1–8 dm high, longer than the leaves, red-brown at base. **Leaves** 3–12 on lower half of stem, flat but with slightly rolled under margins, 2–4 mm wide, the dried leaves of previous year conspicuous; sheaths red-dotted. Terminal **spike** male (or sometimes with a few female flowers at tip), on a long stalk, linear, 4–12 mm long and 2–4 mm wide, usually upright; female spikes 1–4 (rarely with several male flowers at base), clustered, usually drooping on slender stalks, 4–20 mm long and 4–8 mm wide, nearly round to oblong; lowest bract leaflike, equal or longer than

perigynium
(l), scale (r)

the head. **Female scales** lance-shaped to ovate, tapered to a tip, narrower but usually longer than the perigynia, brown or green in center, margins brown. **Perigynia** broadly ovate or oval, 2–3 mm long and 1.5–2.5 mm wide, flattened and 2-ribbed, with several evident nerves, pale or somewhat waxy blue-green, covered with many small bumps, the tip rounded and barely beaked. **Achenes** 3-angled, obovate, 2 mm long; stigmas 3. July–Aug. ❦ Open bogs, partly shaded peatlands, floating mats, swamps and thickets, usually in sphagnum moss. ⊕ Occasional to common; n, c and se Minn, n Wisc (uncommon in s), Mich UP and LP (but not sw LP). Circumboreal, s to NJ, Pa, Minn, Colo, Utah and BC.

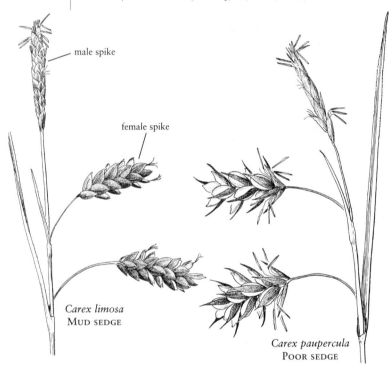

male spike

female spike

Carex limosa
MUD SEDGE

Carex paupercula
POOR SEDGE

Carex Section LUPULINAE

▶KEY TO LUPULINAE

1 Plants clumped; sheath of uppermost stem leaf (not bract) absent or less than 15 cm long; perigynium beak 1–4 mm long **2**
1 Plants usually with long rhizomes; sheath of uppermost leaf usually longer than 15 cm; perigynium beak 4–10 mm long **3**

2 Perigynia dull, tapered to the base; spikes with mostly 8–35 perigynia, these radiating in all directions . . . . *C. grayi* / COMMON BUR SEDGE
2 Perigynia shiny, convexly rounded to the base; spikes with 1–12 perigynia, these ascending or spreading . . . . *C. intumescens*
. . . . SHINING BUR SEDGE

3 Achene sides flat to slightly concave; achene angles smoothly curved; widespread species . . . . *C. lupulina* / COMMON HOP SEDGE
3 Achene sides strongly concave, achene angles pointed; plant of s LP of Mich. . . . . *C. lupuliformis* / KNOBBED HOP SEDGE

perigynium

Carex grayi Carey   Lupulinae
Common bur sedge   FACW+

Perennial, rhizomes absent. **Stems** single or forming small clumps, 3–9 dm long, rough on upper stem angles, sheaths at base of stem persistent, red-purple. **Leaves** 5–12 mm wide. **Spikes** either male or female; terminal spike male, 1–6 cm long, stalked; female spikes 1–2, rounded, stalked; bracts leaflike; female scales ovate, body shorter than perigynia but sometimes tipped with an awn to 7 mm long. **Perigynia** 10–30 per spike, spreading in all directions, not shiny, 10–20 mm long, strongly nerved, tapered from widest point to a notched beak 2–3 mm long. **Achenes** 3–5 mm long, with a persistent, withered style; stigmas 3. June–Sept. ❦ Floodplain forests and backwater areas (as along Miss River). ⊕ Uncommon in extreme ec and se Minn; local in Wisc; Mich (s and c LP, local in w UP), ne Ill and nw Ind. s Que and s Ont to Minn, s to Mass, Ga and Mo.

STATUS
Illinois - T

perigynium

Carex intumescens Rudge   Lupulinae
Shining bur sedge   FACW+

Perennial, rhizomes absent. **Stems** single or in small clumps, 3–9 dm long, rough on upper stem angles; sheaths at base of stem persistent, red-purple. **Leaves** 4–12 mm wide, bracts leaflike. **Spikes** either male or female, or sometimes male spikes with a few female flowers; terminal spike male, 1–6 cm long, stalked; female spikes 1–4, grouped, 1–3 cm long and wide, rounded, on stalks to 1.5 cm long; **female scales** narrowly ovate, shorter and narrower than perigynia. **Perigynia** 1–12 per spike, spreading in all directions, satiny (not dull), 10–17 mm long, tapered to a beak 2–4 mm long. **Achenes** 3–6 mm long, flattened; stigmas 3. May–Aug. ❦ Mixed and deciduous moist forests, kettle wetlands in woods, swamps and alder thickets. ⊕ Common in n portions of region; Minn (all but sw), Wisc, Mich, ne Ill and nw Ind. Nfld to se Man, s to Fla and Tex.

STATUS
Michigan - T
Wisconsin - E

perigynium

Carex lupuliformis Sartwell   Lupulinae
Knobbed hop sedge   FACW+

Loosely clumped perennial, from rhizomes. **Stems** stout, 3-angled, 4–10 dm long. **Leaves** longer than head, 5–15 mm wide. **Spikes** either all male or female, or female spikes sometimes with few male flowers at tip; the uppermost spike male, 3–8 cm long, stalked or stalkless; female spikes 3–6, clustered or overlapping, 3–6 cm long and 2–3 cm wide; bracts leaflike and much longer than head; **female scales** lance-shaped, shorter than the perigynia, tipped with a short awn. **Perigynia** ascending to spreading, yellow-brown when mature, lance-shaped, inflated, 10–20 mm long and 4–8 mm wide, tapered to a beak 5–10 mm long. **Achenes** 3–5 mm long, 3-angled with concave sides, each angle with a hard knob near the middle; stigmas 3. ❦ Low areas in forests (floodplains and seasonally wet depressions); swamps and marshes, often in shallow water. ⊕ Local in s Wisc, s LP of Mich, ne Ill and nw Ind. Vt and s Que to Ill, s to Va, Ky and Tex. ☞ Similar to **common hop sedge** (*C. lupulina*) but less common.

Carex lupulina Muhl.   Lupulinae
Common hop sedge   OBL

Loosely clumped perennial, from rhizomes. **Stems** stout, 3-angled, 3–12 dm long. **Leaves** much longer than head, 4–15 mm wide; upper sheaths white and translucent, the lower sheaths brown. **Spikes** either all male or female, the upper spike male, short-stalked, 2–5 cm long; female spikes 2–6, clustered or overlapping, the lowermost sometimes separate, 2.5–6

perigynium

cm long and 1.5–3 cm wide; bracts leaflike and spreading, much longer than head; **female scales** narrowly ovate, tapered to tip or with a short awn, much shorter than the perigynia. **Perigynia** many, upright, dull green-brown, lance-shaped, inflated, 10–20 mm long and 4–7 mm wide, many-nerved, tapered to a finely toothed beak 5–10 mm long, the beak teeth 1–2 mm long. **Achenes** 3-angled, 3–4 mm long; stigmas 3. June–Aug. ❧ Wet woods, swamps, wet meadows and marshes, ditches and shores. ⊕ nc, c and se Minn (most common in floodplain forests of Miss and St. Croix Rivers); Wisc, Mich, ne Ill and nw Ind. NS to Minn and Neb, s to Fla and Tex. ☞ **Shining bur sedge** (*C. intumescens*) is similar but differs from common hop sedge by having fewer, uncrowded perigynia which are olive-green and glossy.

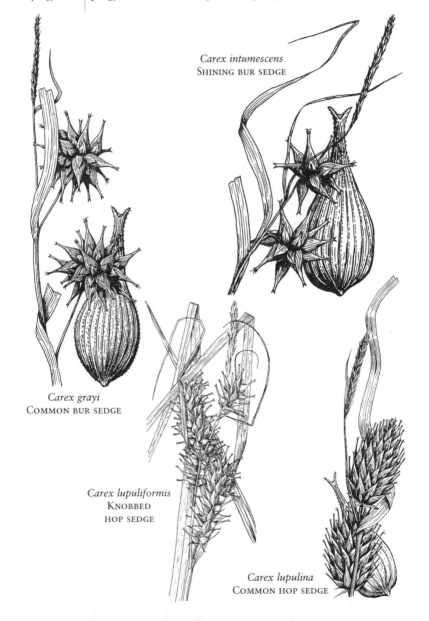

Carex intumescens
SHINING BUR SEDGE

Carex grayi
COMMON BUR SEDGE

Carex lupuliformis
KNOBBED
HOP SEDGE

Carex lupulina
COMMON HOP SEDGE

Carex Section MONTANAE

One wetland species in Great Lakes region . . . .*C. deflexa*
. . . . NORTHERN SEDGE

Carex deflexa Hornem.   Montanae
  Northern sedge   (NI)
Small, loosely clumped perennial. **Stems** 1–2 dm long, purple-tinged at
base, shorter than the leaves. **Leaves** soft, 1–3 mm wide. **Spikes** either
male or female; male spike short, to 5 mm long; female spikes on long,
slender stalks near base of plant and also 2–4 spikes on stem near male
spike; bract leaflike, to 2 cm long; **female scales** ovate, shorter than perigynia. **Perigynia** green, oblong-ovate, 2–3 mm long, covered with short
hairs, abruptly tapered to a small beak about 0.5 mm long. **Achenes** 3-
angled; stigmas 3. June–Aug. ❦ Moist woods and swamps, wetland margins. ⊕ Occasional in ne Minn and in w and e UP and n LP of Mich.

perigynium

Greenland to Alaska, s to Mass, NY, Minn, Man, BC.

Carex Section MULTIFLORAE

One wetland species in Great Lakes region . . . .*C. vulpinoidea*
. . . . BROWN FOX SEDGE

Carex vulpinoidea Michx.   Multiflorae
  Brown Fox sedge   OBL
Densely clumped perennial, from short rootstocks. **Stems** stiff, sharply 3-
angled, 3–9 dm long, shorter to longer than the leaves. **Leaves** 2–4 mm
wide; sheaths tight, cross-wrinkled and translucent on front, mottled
green and white on back. **Spikes** with both male and female flowers,
male flowers borne above female; heads oblong to cylindric, 3–9 cm
long, with several spikes per branch at lower nodes; bracts small and
bristlelike, longer than the spikes; **female scales** awn-tipped, the awns
equal or longer than the perigynia. **Perigynia** yellow-green, becoming
straw-colored or brown when mature, flat on 1 side and convex on other,
ovate to nearly round, 2–3 mm long and 1–2 mm wide, abruptly con-

perigynium

tracted to a notched, finely toothed beak 1 mm long. **Achenes** lens-
shaped, 1–2 mm long; stigmas 2. May–Aug. *C. annectens.* ❦ Wet to
moist meadows, marshes, lakeshores, streambanks, roadside ditches. ⊕
Common; Minn, Wisc, Mich, ne Ill and nw Ind. Newf to BC, s to Fla,
Tex, Colo, Ariz and Ore.

Carex Section OLIGOCARPAE

One wetland species in Great Lakes region . . . .*C. conoidea*
. . . . PRAIRIE GRAY SEDGE

Carex conoidea Schk.   Oligocarpae
  Prairie gray sedge   FACW+
Clumped perennial. **Stems** 1–7 dm long, much longer than leaves. **Leaves**

⚠
STATUS
Indiana - E

2–4 mm wide. **Spikes** either male or female; male spike on a long stalk
and overtopping female spikes, linear, 1–2 cm long; female spikes 2–4,
widely spaced or upper 2 grouped, short cylindric, 1–2 cm long, on

perigynium

short, rough stalks; bract leaflike with a rough sheath; **female scales** ovate and much shorter than perigynia, with a green midvein prolonged into an awn. **Perigynia** oval, 3–4 mm long and 1–2 mm wide. **Achenes** 3-angled; stigmas 3. May–July. ⚘ Wet meadows and prairies. ⊕ Uncommon in Minn; se Wisc, Mich (s LP, Keweenaw Peninsula in UP), ne Ill and nw Ind. Nfld and Que to Minn, s to NC and Mo.

Carex Section ORTHOCERATES

One wetland species in Great Lakes region ....*C. pauciflora*
.... FEW-FLOWERED BOG SEDGE

Carex pauciflora Lightf.   Orthocerates
Few-flowered bog sedge   OBL
Perennial, from long slender rhizomes. **Stems** single or several togethedm long, longer than leaves. **Leaves** 1–2 mm wide, lower stem leaves reduced to scales; bract absent. **Spike** single, to 1 cm long, with both male and female flowers, the male above the female; **male scales** infolded to form a slender terminal cone; **female scales** lance-shaped, 4–6 mm long, pale brown, soon deciduous. **Perigynia** 1–6, soon turned downward, slender, spongy at base, nearly round in section, straw-colored or pale brown, deciduous when mature, 6–8 mm long. **Achenes** 3-angled, not filling the perigynium; stigmas 3. June–July. ⚘ Open peatlands and floating mats in sphagnum moss, true bogs. ⊕ Occasional in ne and nc Minn and n Wisc, common in Mich UP, occasional in LP. Circumboreal, s to Conn, WVa, Mich, Minn and Wash.

perigynium

Carex deflexa
NORTHERN SEDGE

Carex conoidea
PRAIRIE GRAY SEDGE

Carex pauciflora
FEW-FLOWERED BOG SEDGE

Carex vulpinoidea
BROWN FOX SEDGE

☞ Species
within **Section
Ovales** are
notoriously
difficult to
identify.
Positive
identification
is usually
dependent on
characteristics
of the mature
perigynia.

Carex Section OVALES

▸KEY TO OVALES

1 Bracts leaflike and many times longer than head. . *C. sychnocephala* . . . . MANY-HEAD SEDGE
1 Bracts much shorter and bristlelike, usually less than 2x as long as head **2**

2 Achenes narrow, mostly 0.5–0.8 mm wide; perigynia usually more than 2.5x as long as wide, not oval-shaped or broadest above the middle **3**
2 Achenes wider, 0.9–1.5 mm wide (or if a little narrower, then the perigynium body obovate), perigynia to about 2.5x as long as wide **10**

3 Perigynia 7–10 mm long; plant of se Minn and s LP of Mich . . . . *C. muskingumensis* / SWAMP OVAL SEDGE
3 Perigynia 2–6 mm long **4**

4 Perigynia 2–4 mm long and 1–1.5 mm wide, to 3x as long as wide **5**
4 Perigynia either at least 4 mm long, or more than 3x as long as wide, or both **6**

5 Perigynia beak somewhat spreading, the perigynia often not winged to their base . . . . *C. cristatella* / CRESTED OVAL SEDGE
5 Perigynia with a stiff, upright beak, the perigynia winged to their base . . . . *C. bebbii* / BEBB'S OVAL SEDGE

6 Leaves 1–3 mm wide **7**
6 Leaves 7 mm or more wide **9**

7 Perigynia 1.5–2.5x longer than wide; uncommon in sw LP of Mich . . . . *C. straminea* / AWNED OVAL SEDGE
7 Perigynia 2.5–5x longer than wide; more widespread. **8**

8 Perigynia 3–5 mm long and 1.5–2 mm wide, strongly flattened. . . . . *C. crawfordii* / CRAWFORD'S OVAL SEDGE
8 Perigynia 4–6 mm long and to 1 mm wide, flat on 1 side, convex on other . . . . *C. scoparia* / LANCE-FRUITED OVAL SEDGE

9 Spikes overlapping and crowded, 8–12 mm long, with more than 30 perigynia in each spike . . *C. tribuloides* / AWL-FRUITED OVAL SEDGE
9 Lowermost spikes separate, spikes 5–8 mm long, with 15–30 perigynia in each spike. . . . . *C. projecta* / NECKLACE SEDGE

10 Perigynia less than 4 mm long and less than 2 mm wide **11**
10 Perigynia more than 4 mm long or more than 2 mm wide, or both **14**

11 Perigynia oval and broadest above middle, achene to 1 mm wide **12**
11 Perigynia oval, oblong, or circular; achene often more than 1 mm wide **13**

12 Perigynia beak broad, the winged margins extending to tip of beak; female scales boat-shaped (keeled) and blunt-tipped; plant of s LP of Mich . . . . *C. longii* / ROUND-SHOULDERED OVAL SEDGE
12 Perigynia beak slender, the winged margins not reaching the tip; female scales flat, tapered to a pointed tip; plant of sw Mich . . . . *C. albolutescens* / LONG-FRUITED OVAL SEDGE

13 Heads compact; leaves mostly 2.5–6 mm wide . . . . *C. normalis*
. . . . SPREADING OVAL SEDGE
13 Heads loose, the lower spikelets widely spaced; leaves mostly 1.5–2.5
mm wide . . . . *C. tenera* / NARROW-LEAVED OVAL SEDGE

14 Portion of leaf sheath long-translucent; perigynia oval, widest at
about one-third of total length *C. normalis* / SPREADING OVAL SEDGE
14 Leaf sheath green-veined almost to its top, with only a short translucent area; perigynia round to obovate, widest at or above middle . .
. . . . **15**

15 Female scales lance-shaped, much narrower and somewhat shorter
than perigynia **16**
15 Female scales inconspicuous, blunt-tipped or gradually tapered to a
tip **17**

16 Spikes widely separated . . . . . . *C. straminea* / AWNED OVAL SEDGE
16 Spikes crowded and overlapping . . . *C. alata* / WINGED OVAL SEDGE

17 Perigynia 4–5 mm long and 2–2.6 mm wide, broadest at a third to
two-fifths of its total length. . . . . *C. suberecta*
. . . . WEDGE-FRUITED OVAL SEDGE
17 Perigynia broadest at two-fifths to half its length **18**

18 Perigynia beak broad, its winged margins extending to its tip; female
scales boat-shaped and mostly blunt-tipped, the scale midvein not
reaching the tip . . . . . *C. longii* / ROUND-SHOULDERED OVAL SEDGE
18 Perigynia beak slender, its winged margins not reaching the tip;
female scales flat, gradually tapered to tip, the scale midvein reaching
the tip; plant of sw Mich. *C. albolutescens*
. . . . LONG-FRUITED OVAL SEDGE

Carex alata T. & G.   Ovales
   Winged oval sedge   OBL

STATUS
Illinois - E

perigynium

Clumped perennial. **Stems** 3–10 dm long, longer than leaves. **Leaves** 2–4
mm wide, sheaths green-veined on inner side. **Spikes** 4–8, with both male
and female flowers, female flowers above the few male flowers at base of
spike, silvery green or silvery brown, round to ovate, 8–12 mm long,
grouped into heads 2–4 cm long; **female scales** narrowly ovate, awn-
tipped, translucent but for the narrow green center, shorter than perigynia. **Perigynia** body obovate, very flat, 4–5 mm long and 2–3 mm wide,
several-nerved on both sides, narrowed to a slightly notched beak about
1 mm long. **Achenes** lens-shaped, 1.5–2 mm long; stigmas 2. June–July.
🌿 Swamps, peatlands, marshes, sandy or peaty shores. ⊕ Mostly near
Atlantic coast but inland to c and s LP of Mich and nw Ind. Mass s to
Fla and Tex; inland to NY, Ohio, s Ont, Ind and Mo.

Carex albolutescens Schwein.   Ovales
   Long-fruited oval sedge   FACW

STATUS
Michigan - T

Densely clumped perennial. **Stems** stiff, 3–7 dm long, longer than leaves.
Leaves 2–4 mm wide, sheaths green-veined on inner side. **Spikes** 4–7, terminal spike female, lateral spikes female with few male flowers, 8–12
mm long, densely flowered and clustered into a head or lower spikes
somewhat separate; **female scales** ovate, as long as perigynia but narrower, silvery translucent with a darker midrib extending to scale tip.
Perigynia body obovate, flat on 1 side and slightly convex on other,

perigynium

widest above top of achene, 3–4 mm long and 2–3 mm wide, finely nerved on both sides, abruptly narrowed to a short beak. **Achenes** lens-shaped, 1.5–2 mm long; stigmas 2. June–Aug. Similar to **round-shouldered oval sedge** (*C. longii*). ⚘ Swamps and wet woods, thickets. ⊕ Local in sw Mich and nw Ind. Mass to s Mich, s Ill and Mo, s to Ga, La and Tex.

Carex bebbii (L. H. Bailey) Fernald   Ovales
Bebb's oval sedge   OBL

⚠
STATUS
Indiana - T

Clumped perennial. **Stems** sharply 3-angled, 2–8 dm long. **Leaves** shorter to slightly longer than the stems, 2–5 mm wide; sheaths white, thin and translucent. **Spikes** 5–10, with both male and female flowers, female flowers above male, 5–8 mm long, clustered in an ovate head 1.5–3 cm long; **female scales** tapered to tip, narrower and slightly shorter than the perigynia. **Perigynia** green to brown, flat on 1 side and convex on other, ovate, 2.5–3.5 mm long, finely nerved on back, nerveless on front, wing-margined, with a finely toothed beak 1/3–1/2 the length of the body, shallowly notched at tip. **Achenes** lens-shaped, 1–1.5 mm long; stigmas 2. June–Aug. ⚘ Wet to moist meadows, marshes, streambanks, ditches and other wet places; calcareous fens in s. ⊕ Common northward; Minn (except sw), Wisc, Mich, ne Ill and nw Ind. Newf to BC, s to NJ, Ohio, Ill, Neb and Colo.

perigynium

Carex crawfordii Fernald   Ovales
Crawford's oval sedge   (FAC+)

⚠
STATUS
Illinois - E

Densely clumped perennial. **Stems** 1–8 dm long, stiff. **Leaves** 3–4 on each stem, longer or shorter than the stems, 1–4 mm wide. **Spikes** 3–15, with both male and female flowers, the male below the female, grouped into a narrowly oblong, sometimes drooping head, 1–3 cm long and 4–15 mm wide; **female scales** ovate, light brown with green center, shorter and about as wide as perigynia. **Perigynia** flattened except where enlarged by the achenes, lance-shaped, 3–4 mm long and 0.5–1 mm wide, brown, narrowly winged nearly to the base, finely toothed above the middle, tapered to a long, slender, toothed, notched beak. **Achenes** brown, lens-shaped, 1 mm long; stigmas 2. July–Sept. ⚘ Moist openings and wetland margins, sandy shorelines. ⊕ nc, ne and ec Minn; n Wisc, Mich UP and nw LP; also uncommon in se Wisc and extreme ne Ill. Nfld to BC, s to NJ, Mich, Minn and Wash.

perigynium

Carex cristatella Britton   Ovales
Crested oval sedge   FACW+

Clumped perennial, from short rhizomes. **Stems** sharply 3-angled, 3–10 dm long, slightly shorter to longer than the leaves. **Leaves** 3–7 mm wide; sheaths loose, with fine green lines. **Spikes** with both male and female flowers, female flowers borne above male; spikes 5–12, 4–8 mm long, crowded in an ovate to oblong head 2–3.5 cm long; bracts much reduced; **female scales** tapered to tip, shorter than the perigynia. **Perigynia** widely spreading when mature, green to pale brown, flat on 1 side and convex on other, ovate to lance-shaped, 2.5–4 mm long and 1–2 mm wide, faintly nerved on both sides, strongly winged above the middle, tapered to a finely toothed, notched beak 1–2 mm long. **Achenes** lens-shaped, 1–1.5 mm long; stigmas 2. June–Aug. ⚘ Wet meadows, ditches, floodplains, marshy shores and streambanks. ⊕ Common; Minn (all but ne), Wisc (especially s and c), Mich, ne Ill and nw Ind. NH and w Que to s Man and ND, s to Va, Mo and Neb.

perigynium

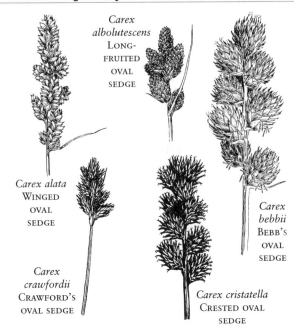

Carex albolutescens
LONG-
FRUITED
OVAL
SEDGE

Carex alata
WINGED
OVAL
SEDGE

Carex bebbii
BEBB'S
OVAL
SEDGE

Carex crawfordii
CRAWFORD'S
OVAL SEDGE

Carex cristatella
CRESTED OVAL
SEDGE

perigynium

Carex longii Mackenzie   Ovales
  Round-shouldered oval sedge   OBL
Densely clumped perennial. **Stems** stiff, 3–12 dm long, longer than the
leaves. **Leaves** 2–3 mm wide, lower stem leaves reduced to scales. **Spikes**
3–10, with both male and female flowers, the male below the female,
stalkless, crowded in a head or the lower separate, 5–15 mm long; lateral spikes mostly female; **female scales** ovate, shorter or nearly as long as
the perigynia. **Perigynia** upright to spreading, obovate, flat on 1 side and
convex on other, 3–5 mm long and 1.5–2.5 mm wide, the body broadest
above the top of enclosed achene, tapered to a beak. **Achenes** lens-
shaped, to 1.5 mm long; stigmas 2. May–Aug. ✾ Open wetlands and
wetland margins, often where sandy. ⊕ s LP of Mich, ne Ill and nw Ind.
Atlantic coast, NS to Fla and Tex, inland to Ill, Mich, Sask, s into Mex.

Carex muskingumensis Schwein.   Ovales
  Swamp oval sedge   OBL
Clumped perennial. **Stems** stout, 5–10 dm long, with many leafy sterile
stems present. **Leaves** 3–5 mm wide. **Spikes** 5–10, with both male and
female flowers, the male below the female, pointed at both ends, 15–25
mm long and 4–6 mm wide, in a dense head 4–8 cm long; **female scales**
lance-shaped, pale brown with translucent margins, half as long as the
perigynia. **Perigynia** upright, lance-shaped, 6–10 mm long, finely nerved
on both sides, tapered to a finely toothed, deeply notched beak half as
long as the body. **Achenes** lens-shaped, 2 mm long; stigmas 2. June–Aug.
✾ Floodplain forests (as along Miss River), wet woods. ⊕ Occasional;
extreme se Minn, Wisc, s LP of Mich, ne Ill and nw Ind. Ohio and Ky n
to s Mich and Minn, Man, w to Okla.

perigynium

Carex normalis Mackenzie   Ovales
  Spreading oval sedge   FACW
Clumped perennial. **Stems** 3–8 dm long, longer than the leaves. **Leaves**
2–6 mm wide, lower stem leaves reduced to scales. **Spikes** 5–10, with

perigynium

both male and female flowers, the male below the female, round in outline, 6–9 mm long, stalkless, loosely grouped in heads 3–5 cm long; **female scales** ovate, translucent, lightly brown-tinged, with green midvein, tapered to a point or blunt-tipped, shorter than the perigynia. **Perigynia** upright, ovate, flat on 1 side and convex on other, green or pale green-brown, 3–4 mm long, finely nerved, tapered to a finely toothed beak. **Achenes** lens-shaped, 2 mm long; stigmas 2. June–Aug. ❦ Moist to wet deciduous woods, floodplain forests, alder thickets, marshes, pond margins. ⊕ c and se Minn, Wisc, s LP of Mich, ne Ill and nw Ind. Maine to Minn and SD, s to NC, Ohio, Mo and Okla.

Carex projecta Mackenzie — Ovales
Necklace sedge — FACW+

Clumped perennial from short rhizomes. **Stems** slender and weak, 3-angled, 4–10 dm long, longer than leaves, upper stems rough. **Leaves** stiff, 3–7 mm wide; sheaths loose. **Spikes** 7–15, with both male and female flowers, female flowers above male in each spike, obovate to nearly round, 5–10 mm long and about as wide, straw-colored, distinct and ± separated (at least the lower spikes) in a somewhat lax and zigzagged inflorescence 3–5 cm long; bracts inconspicuous; **female scales** narrowly ovate, straw-colored, narrower and shorter than the perigynia. **Perigynia** ascending to spreading when mature, lance-shaped, 3–5 mm long and 1–2 mm wide, dull brown, flattened except where filled by the achene, winged on margin, the wing gradually narrowing from middle to base, tapered to a notched, finely toothed beak 1–2 mm long. **Achenes** lens-shaped, 1–2 mm long; stigmas 2. June–Aug. ❦ Floodplain forests, swamps, thickets, wet openings, shaded slopes. ⊕ Occasional to common; ne, nc and ec Minn, Wisc (especially n), Mich, ne Ill and nw Ind. Nfld to Man, s to WVa, Ill and Mo. ☞ Similar to **awl-fruited oval sedge** (*C. tribuloides*) but the perigynia tips spreading rather than erect as in *C. tribuloides*.

perigynium

Carex scoparia Schk. — Ovales
Lance-fruited oval sedge — FACW

Densely clumped perennial, sometimes spreading by surface runners. **Stems** 2–10 dm long, sharply 3-angled, usually longer than the leaves. **Leaves** 1–3 mm wide; sheaths tight, white-translucent. **Spikes** 4–10, with both male and female flowers, female flowers borne above male, ovate to broadest at middle, 6–12 mm long, clustered or separate, in a narrowly ovate head 1–5 cm long; bracts small, the lowest often bristlelike; **female scales** tapered to tip, slightly shorter than perigynia. **Perigynia** green-white, flat, narrowly lance-shaped, 3–7 mm long and 1–2 mm wide, margins narrowly winged, tapered to a finely toothed, slightly notched beak 1–2 mm long. **Achenes** lens-shaped, 1–1.5 mm long; stigmas 2. May–July. ❦ Wet meadows and openings, low prairie, swamps and sandy lakeshores. ⊕ Frequent in n Minn (occasional in s), uncommon in nw and sw Minn; Wisc, Mich, ne Ill and nw Ind. Newf to BC, s to Fla, Ark, Kans, NM and Ore.

perigynium

Carex straminea Willd. — Ovales
Awned oval sedge — OBL

Densely clumped perennial. **Stems** 4–l0 dm long, longer than the leaves. **Leaves** 2–3 mm wide, lower stem leaves reduced to scales. **Spikes** 4–8, stalkless, separated in a head 3–6 cm long, with both male and female flowers, the male in a slender cluster below the female; **female scales** lance-shaped, narrower and shorter than the perigynia, translucent and brown-tinged, with a paler midvein, tapered to a tip or short point.

perigynium

Perigynia flat and thin, tapered to a flattened, finely toothed beak to half as long as the body. **Achenes** lens-shaped, 1.5 mm long; stigmas 2. May–July. *C. richii*. ❦ Marshes and wetland margins. ⊕ Uncommon in sw LP of Mich and nw Ind. Mass s to Va, w to sw Mich and Ind.

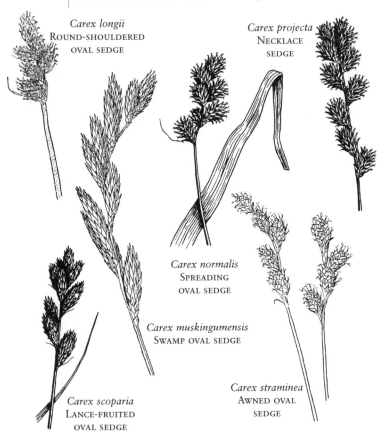

Carex longii
ROUND-SHOULDERED
OVAL SEDGE

Carex projecta
NECKLACE
SEDGE

Carex normalis
SPREADING
OVAL SEDGE

Carex muskingumensis
SWAMP OVAL SEDGE

Carex scoparia
LANCE-FRUITED
OVAL SEDGE

Carex straminea
AWNED OVAL
SEDGE

Carex suberecta (Olney) Britton — Ovales
Wedge-fruited oval sedge — OBL

Clumped perennial. **Stems** 3–7 dm long, shorter or longer than the leaves. **Leaves** 2–3 mm wide, lower stem leaves reduced to scales. **Spikes** 2–5, stalkless, loosely grouped into a head, with both male and female flowers, the male below the female, 7–12 mm long; **female scales** shorter and narrower than the perigynia, yellow-brown with a pale midvein and narrow translucent margins, tapered to a tip. **Perigynia** numerous, conspicuously swollen over the achene, 4–5 mm long, abruptly contracted to the flat, finely toothed beak. **Achenes** lens-shaped, 1.5 mm long; stigmas 2. May–July. ❦ Calcareous swamps, marshes, wet meadows, low prairie, calcareous fens and shores. ⊕ c and s LP of Mich, ne Ill and nw Ind. s Ont s to Va and Mo.

perigynium

Carex sychnocephala Carey — Ovales
Many-head sedge — FACW+

Clumped perennial (sometimes annual), from fibrous roots. **Stems** many and crowded, rounded 3-angled, 0.5–6 dm long. **Leaves** 1.5–4 mm wide; sheaths tight, white-translucent. **Spikes** with both male and female flowers, female flowers borne above male, densely clustered in ovate heads

perigynium

1.5–3 cm long; bracts leaflike, 2–4 per head, the longest bracts much longer than the heads; **female scales** thin and translucent with a green midvein, 2/3 length of perigynia, tapered to a tip or with a short sharp point. **Perigynia** green to straw-colored, flat, lance-shaped, 5–7 mm long and to 1 mm wide, narrowly wing-margined, spongy at base when mature, tapered to a finely toothed, notched beak 3–5 mm long. **Achenes** lens-shaped, 1–1.5 mm long; stigmas 2. June–Aug. ❦ Wet meadows, sandy lake and stream shores, marshes. ⊕ Minn (but uncommon in far ne and se), Wisc, in Mich local in c UP and wc LP. NY and Ont to Alberta, s to Wisc, Iowa, SD and Mont.

perigynium

Carex tenera Dewey   Ovales
    Narrow-leaved oval sedge   FAC+

Clumped perennial, from short rhizomes. **Stems** slender, sharply 3-angled, 3–8 cm long, rough-to-touch above, longer than leaves. **Leaves** 0.5–3 mm wide; sheaths white-translucent on front, mottled green and white on back. **Spikes** 4–8, with both male and female flowers, female flowers borne above male, ovate to round, 4–10 mm long, loose in nodding heads 2.5–5 cm long; bracts small, sometimes bristlelike, longer than the spike; **female scales** tapered to tip, slightly shorter than perigynia. **Perigynia** ovate, flat on 1 side and convex on other, straw-colored when mature, 2.5–4 mm long and 1–2 mm wide, wing-margined, tapered to a notched, finely toothed beak 1–2 mm long. **Achenes** lens-shaped, 1–2 mm long; stigmas 2. June–Aug. ❦ Wet to moist meadows, streambanks, floodplains and moist woods. ⊕ Minn, Wisc, Mich LP, local in UP, ne Ill and nw Ind. Que and Maine to Alberta, s to NC, Ohio, Mo, Neb and Mont.

Carex tribuloides Wahlenb.   Ovales
    Awl-fruited oval sedge   FACW+

Clumped perennial from short rhizomes. **Stems** sharply 3-angled, 3–9 dm long, longer than leaves. **Leaves** stiff, 3–7 mm wide; sheaths loose, with green lines. **Spikes** 5–15, with both male and female flowers, female flowers borne above male, obovate, 6–13 mm long, densely to loosely clustered into an ovate or oblong head 2–5 cm long; bracts inconspicuous; **female scales** tapered to tip, shorter than the perigynia. **Perigynia** light green to pale brown, flattened except where filled by the achenes, lance-shaped, 3–6 mm long and 1–2 mm wide, broadly winged near middle, tapered to a notched, finely toothed beak 1–2 mm long. **Achenes** lens-shaped, 1.5 mm long; stigmas 2. June–July. ❦ Floodplain forests, shady low areas in woods, pond and lake margins, marshes, low prairie. ⊕ ne, c and se Minn (and uncommon in w), s and nc Wisc, Mich, ne Ill and nw Ind. NS to Ont and Minn, s to Fla, La and Okla.

perigynium

Carex Section PALUDOSAE

▶KEY TO PALUDOSAE

1 Perigynia covered with hairs. . . . . *C. trichocarpa*
    . . . . HAIRY-FRUIT LAKE SEDGE
1 Perigynia smooth and hairless **2**

2 Teeth of perigynia beak 1 mm or less in length **3**
2 Teeth of beak 1–3 mm long **4**

3 Lower leaf sheaths red-purple, with network of fibers on inner surface, ligules 12–40 mm long; widespread species . . . . . . *C. lacustris*
    . . . . COMMON LAKESHORE SEDGE

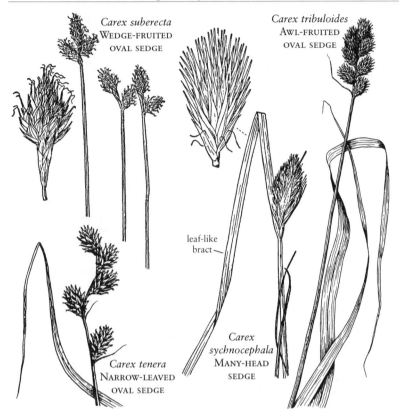

Carex suberecta
WEDGE-FRUITED
OVAL SEDGE

Carex tribuloides
AWL-FRUITED
OVAL SEDGE

leaf-like
bract

Carex
sychnocephala
MANY-HEAD
SEDGE

Carex tenera
NARROW-LEAVED
OVAL SEDGE

3 Lower leaf sheaths pinkish, white or brownish, not becoming fiber-like on inner surface; ligules to 10 mm long; se Mich only . . . .
. . . . *C. hyalinolepis* / SHORELINE SEDGE

4 Sheaths and blades smooth and without hairs; s and w Minn only
. . . . *C. laeviconica* / LONG-TOOTHED LAKE SEDGE
4 Sheaths hairy, underside of blades usually hairy near their base . . .
. . . . *C. atherodes* / SLOUGH SEDGE

Carex atherodes Sprengel
Slough sedge

Paludosae
OBL

⚠
STATUS
Indiana - E

Loosely clumped perennial from long scale-covered rhizomes. **Stems** 3-angled, 5–12 dm long. **Leaves** 3–12 mm wide; sheaths hairy on back, brown to purple-tinged at the mouth, the lower sheaths shredding into narrow strands. **Spikes** either male or female; male spikes 2–6 at ends of stems; female spikes 2–4, widely spaced, cylindrical, 2–11 cm long; bracts leaflike, longer than the stems; **female scales** thin, translucent or pale brown, shorter than the perigynia, tipped with a slender awn. **Perigynia** ovate, 6–11 mm long, long-tapered to a smooth beak, with many distinct nerves, the beak with spreading teeth 1.5–3 mm long. **Achenes** 3-angled, 2–2.5 mm long; stigmas 3. June–Aug. ❀ Marshes, wet meadows, prairie swales, stream and pond margins, usually in shallow water where may form dense colonies. ⊕ Minn (but not far ne and se), se Wisc, Mich (LP and c UP), ne Ill and nw Ind. Circumboreal, in N Amer s to NY, Mo, Neb, Colo, Utah and Ore.

perigynium

perigynium

Carex hyalinolepis Steudel   Paludosae
Shoreline sedge   OBL

Large perennial, from thick, scaly rhizomes. **Stems** stout, 5–15 dm long, with downward-pointing teeth, single or few together; lower leaf sheaths not breaking into fibers. **Leaves** 8–15 mm wide, leaves at base of stem well-developed (not reduced to scales), old leaf-bases persistent around stems; sheaths white or pale brown. **Spikes** either male or female; male spikes 2–4, slender; female spikes 2–4, separate, cylindric, 3–10 cm long and to 1.5 cm wide, upright, densely flowered, stalkless or short-stalked; bracts leaflike and longer than inflorescence. Body of **female scales** ovate, shorter than perigynia, with a green midrib prolonged into an awn to 3 mm long. **Perigynia** 5–8 mm long, very faintly nerved. **Achenes** 3-angled; stigmas 3. May–July. ❀ Wet meadows, marshes and swamps. ⊕ Extreme se Mich. NJ to s Ont and Neb, s to Fla and Tex. ☞ Similar to **common lakeshore sedge** (*C. lacustris*) and sometimes treated as a variety of it (*C. lacustris* var. *laxiflora*).

perigynium

Carex lacustris Willd.   Paludosae
Common lakeshore sedge   OBL

Large clumped perennial, from scaly rhizomes. **Stems** erect, 3-angled, 6–13 dm long, rough-to-touch. **Leaves** equaling or slightly longer than the stem, 6–15 mm wide; sheaths often red-tinged, the lower ones disintegrating into a network of fibers. **Spikes** either male or female, the upper 2–4 male, stalkless, 4–7 cm long; the lower 2–4 spikes female, erect, usually separate, stalkless or short-stalked, cylindric, 3–10 cm long and 3–15 mm wide; bracts leaflike, some or all longer than the head; **female scales** awned or tapered to tip, the body shorter than the perigynia, the sides thin and translucent to pale brown. **Perigynia** olive, flattened to nearly round in section, narrowly ovate, 5–7 mm long, with more than 10 raised nerves, tapered to a smooth beak about 1 mm long. **Achenes** 3-angled, 2.5 mm long; stigmas 3. May–Aug. ❀ Swamps, marshes, kettle wetlands, wetland margins, usually in shallow water; low areas in tamarack swamps. ⊕ Common; Minn (all but sw and se), Wisc, Mich, ne Ill and nw Ind. Que to Sask, s to Fla and Tex.

perigynium

Carex laeviconica Dewey   Paludosae
Long-toothed lake sedge   OBL

Loosely clumped perennial, from scaly rhizomes. **Stems** stout, 3-angled, 3–12 dm long. **Leaves** shorter to longer than the stem, 2–8 mm wide; sheaths smooth, often purple-tinged below and splitting into fibers. **Spikes** either all male or female, the upper 2–6 male, 1–4 cm long; the lower 2–4 spikes female, erect, separate, stalkless or short-stalked, cylindric, 3–10 cm long and 6–10 mm wide; bracts leaflike, equal or longer than the head; **female scales** acute or awn-tipped, the scale body shorter than the perigynium, translucent or brown on the sides. **Perigynia** green-yellow, broadly ovate, inflated, round in section, 4–9 mm long, strongly many-nerved, tapered to a slender beak 1.5–2 mm long. ❀ Wet meadows, marshes, lakeshores and streambanks. ⊕ se, sc, and w Minn, w Wisc, uncommon in ne Ill. Man and Sask, s to Mo, Kans and Mont.

Carex trichocarpa Muhl.   Paludosae
Hairy-fruit lake sedge   OBL

Loosely clumped perennial, with short rhizomes. **Stems** stout, 6–12 dm long, smooth below, rough-to-touch above. **Leaves** 2–6 mm wide, rough-to-touch on margins, upper leaves and bracts often longer than stems. **Spikes** either all male or female, the upper 2–6 spikes male, long-stalked; female spikes 2–4, cylindric, 4–10 cm long, the upper spikes ± stalkless,

perigynium

the lower spikes on slender stalks; **female scales** ovate, with white translucent margins, about half as long as perigynia. **Perigynia** ovate, usually covered with short white hairs, prominently ribbed, gradually tapered to a 2-toothed beak. **Achenes** 3-angled; stigmas 3. May–Aug. ❧ Riverbanks and old river channels, marshes, wet meadows, low prairie. ⊕ nw, c and s Minn; s and c Wisc; s LP of Mich, ne Ill, local in nw Ind. Que to Minn, s to NC, WVa, Ind and Mo. ☞ Similar to **slough sedge** (*C. atherodes*) but sheaths strongly purple-tinged at tip, the leaf blades not hairy on underside, and the perigynia with short white hairs (vs. smooth in *C. atherodes*).

Carex atherodes
SLOUGH SEDGE

Carex lacustris
COMMON
LAKESHORE
SEDGE

Carex hyalinolepis
SHORELINE
SEDGE

Carex laeviconica
LONG-TOOTHED
LAKE SEDGE

Carex trichocarpa
HAIRY-FRUIT
LAKE SEDGE

Carex Section PANICEAE

▶KEY TO PANICAE

1 Perigynia with a distinct beak 1–2 mm long . . . . *C. vaginata*
. . . . SHEATHED SEDGE
1 Perigynia beakless or with a very small beak less than 0.5 mm long
. . . .**2**

2 Plants waxy blue-green; female scales white-translucent on margins
. . . . *C. livida* / LIVID SEDGE
2 Plants green; female scales purple-brown on margins . . . *C. tetanica*
. . . . COMMON STIFF SEDGE

perigynium

achene

Carex livida (Wahlenb.) Willd.　　　　　　　Paniceae
　Livid sedge　　　　　　　　　　　　　　　　　OBL
Perennial forming small clumps, from long slender rhizomes. **Stems** slender, erect, 0.5–6 dm long, shorter or longer than the leaves, light brown at base. **Leaves** 6–12 on lower third of stem, strongly waxy blue-green, channeled, 0.5–4 mm wide, dried leaves of the previous year conspicuous; sheaths very thin. Terminal **spike** male (or rarely with both male and female flowers, the male below the female), linear, 1–3 cm long and 3–4 mm wide; female spikes 1–3, the lowest ± separate, sometimes long-stalked, the upper grouped, stalkless or short-stalked, oblong, 1–2 cm long and 5 mm wide, with 5–15 upright perigynia; bracts leaflike, sometimes longer than the head; **female scales** ovate, rounded to somewhat acute, shorter than the perigynia, light purple with broad green center and white translucent margins. **Perigynia** obovate, slightly flattened and rounded 3-angled, 2–5 mm long and 1–2 mm wide, strongly waxy blue-green, with small dots, two-ribbed and with many fine nerves, tapered to a beakless tip. **Achenes** ovate, 3-angled with prominent ribs, 2.5 mm long, brown-black; stigmas 3. July–Aug. *C. grayana.* ⚘ Wet meadows and fens, especially where calcium-rich. ⊕ Occasional in nc Minn, rare in Wisc, local in Mich UP and n and e LP. Circumboreal, s to NJ, Minn, s Sask and Calif.

perigynium

achene

Carex tetanica Schk.　　　　　　　　　　Paniceae
　Common stiff sedge　　　　　　　　　　　　FACW
Clumped perennial from slender rhizomes. **Stems** 3-angled, 1–6 dm long, rough-to-touch above. **Leaves** 1–5 mm wide; sheaths tight, white or yellow and translucent. **Spikes** either all male or female, terminal spike male, 1–3 cm long; lateral spikes female, usually widely separated, the lower spikes short-cylindric, stalked, 6–30 mm long and 3–5 mm wide, loosely flowered with perigynia in 3 rows; bracts shorter than the head; **female scales** purple-brown on margins, rounded to acute or short-awned, as wide as but shorter than the perigynia. **Perigynia** green, faintly 3-angled, obovate, 2–4 mm long and about 1–2 mm wide, 2-ribbed; beak tiny, bent. **Achenes** 3-angled with concave sides, 2 mm long; stigmas 3. May–July. ⚘ Wet meadows and openings, low prairies, marshy areas. ⊕ nw, wc and s Minn (absent from extreme se), se Wisc, Mich (especially s LP; also w UP), ne Ill and nw Ind. Mass to Alberta, s to NJ, Va, Mo and Neb.

Carex vaginata Tausch　　　　　　　　　Paniceae
　Sheathed sedge　　　　　　　　　　　　　OBL
Perennial, from long rhizomes. **Stems** 2–6 dm long, several together. **Leaves** 2–5 mm wide, leaves not scalelike at base of stem. Terminal **spike**

perigynium

male, 1–2 cm long; female spikes 1–3, sometimes male at tip, loosely spreading, widely separated, the lower stalks long, the upper shorter; bracts with loose sheaths and blades shorter than the spikes; **female scales** shorter and narrower than the perigynia, purple-brown, sometimes with a narrow green center, tapered to a tip. **Perigynia** usually in 2 rows, the lower separate, the upper overlapping, 3–5 mm long, narrowly obovate, with a curved beak 1 mm long. **Achenes** 3-angled, nearly filling the perigynia; stigmas 3. June–Aug. *C. saltuensis*. ※ Swamps and thickets, especially where calcium-rich. ⊕ Occasional; n Minn, n Wisc, Mich (w and e UP, n LP). Circumboreal, s to Maine, NY, n Minn, Sask and BC.

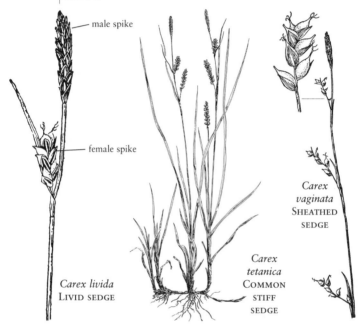

male spike

female spike

Carex vaginata SHEATHED SEDGE

Carex tetanica COMMON STIFF SEDGE

Carex livida LIVID SEDGE

Carex Section PANICULATAE

▸KEY TO PANICULATAE

1 Perigynia with a thin, sunken strip up its middle; inner side of sheaths pale and dotted with red .... *C. diandra* / LESSER PANICLED SEDGE
1 Perigynia without a sunken strip; inner side of upper sheath strongly copper-colored .... *C. prairea* / PRAIRIE SEDGE

Carex diandra Schrank   Paniculatae
  Lesser panicled sedge   OBL

Densely clumped perennial. **Stems** sharply 3-angled, 3–8 dm long, usually longer than leaves. **Leaves** 1–3 mm wide; sheaths white with fine pale lines, translucent on front or slightly copper-colored at mouth. **Spikes** with both male and female flowers, male flowers borne above female, clustered in ovate heads 1–4 cm long; bracts small and inconspicuous, shorter than the spikes; **female scales** brown, tapered to tip or with a short sharp point, about equaling the perigynia. **Perigynia** brown, shiny, unequally convex on both sides, broadly ovate, 2–3 mm long and 1–2 mm wide, beak finely toothed, entire to notched, 1–2 mm long. **Achenes**

perigynium

lens-shaped, 1 mm long; stigmas 2. May–July. ❦ Wet meadows, ditches, peatlands (especially calcareous fens), floating mats. ⊕ n and c Minn, Wisc, Mich, ne Ill, uncommon in nw Ind. Circumboreal, s to NJ, Ill, Mo, Neb, Colo, Utah and Calif.

perigynium

Carex prairea Dewey   Paniculatae
  Prairie sedge   FACW+
Densely clumped perennial, from short rootstocks. **Stems** sharply 3-angled, 5–10 dm long, longer than the leaves. **Leaves** 2–3 mm wide; sheaths translucent, yellow-brown or bronze-colored. **Spikes** with both male and female flowers, male flowers borne above female, ovate, 4–7 mm long, lower spikes usually separate, in linear-oblong heads 3–8 cm long; bracts small; **female scales** red-brown, tapered to tip, as long as and covering most of perigynia. **Perigynia** dull brown, flat on 1 side and convex on other, lance-shaped to ovate, 2–3 mm long and 1–2 mm wide, tapered to a finely toothed, unequally notched beak 1–2 mm long. **Achenes** lens-shaped, 1 mm long; stigmas 2. May–July. ❦ Wet meadows, calcareous fens, marshes, tamarack swamps and peaty lakeshores. ⊕ Locally common in Minn (but not far ne and se), se Wisc, LP and e UP of Mich, ne Ill and nw Ind. NS to BC, s to NJ, Ohio, Iowa and Neb.

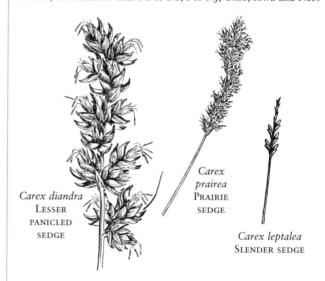

Carex diandra
Lesser
panicled
sedge

*Carex
prairea*
Prairie
sedge

Carex leptalea
Slender sedge

Carex Section POLYTRICHOIDAE

One wetland species in Great Lakes region . . . . *C. leptalea*
. . . . Slender sedge

perigynium

Carex leptalea Wahlenb.   Polytrichoidae
  Slender sedge   OBL
Densely clumped perennial. **Stems** slender, rounded 3-angled, 1–7 dm long, equal or longer than leaves. **Leaves** narrow, 0.5–1.5 mm wide; sheaths tight, white, translucent on front. **Spikes** single on the stems, few-flowered, 5–15 mm long, with both male and female flowers, the male flowers borne above female; bracts absent; **female scales** rounded or with a short sharp point, shorter than the perigynia (or the tip of lowest scale sometimes longer than the perigynium). **Perigynia** yellow-green, nearly round in section to slightly flattened, oblong to oval, 3–5 mm long, fine-

ly many-nerved, beakless or with a short beak. **Achenes** 3-angled, obo-vate, 1–2 mm long; stigmas 3. May–July. ❧ Swamps, alder thickets, open bogs, calcareous fens; usually in partial shade. ⊕ n and c Minn, e and c Wisc, Mich, ne Ill and nw Ind. Labr to Alaska, s to Fla, Mo, ND, Tex, NM and Calif.

Carex Section PSEUDOCYPEREAE

▶ KEY TO PSEUDOCYPEREAE

1 Mature perigynia spreading or upright in spike, thin-textured, ± round in cross-section, abruptly narrowed to the beak . . . . *C. hystericina* / PORCUPINE SEDGE
1 Mature perigynia curved downward, leathery, somewhat three-angled, gradually tapered to the beak **2**

2 Teeth of perigynium beak curved and spreading, 1–2 mm long . . . . *C. comosa* / BRISTLY SEDGE
2 Teeth of perigynium beak nearly straight and parallel, 0.5–1 mm long . . . . *C. pseudocyperus* / FALSE BRISTLY SEDGE

perigynium

Carex comosa F. Boott   Pseudocypereae
Bristly sedge   OBL

Large perennial, often forming large clumps. **Stems** stout, sharply 3-angled, 5–15 dm long. **Leaves** 5–12 mm wide; sheaths translucent on front, with small swollen joints on back. **Spikes** either male or female; terminal spike male, 3–7 cm long; lateral spikes female, 3–5, cylindric, 3–8 cm long and 9–12 mm wide, the lower spikes longer stalked and drooping when mature; bracts leaflike, much longer than the head; **female scales** with translucent margins, tapered into a long, rough awn. **Perigynia** numerous, spreading outward when ripe, flattened 3-angled, lance-shaped, 5–8 mm long, shiny, strongly nerved, gradually tapered to the 2–3 mm long beak, the beak with curved teeth 1–2 mm long. **Achenes** 3-angled, 1.5–2 mm long; stigmas 3. June–Aug. ❧ Marshes, wetland margins, floating mats, ditches. ⊕ nc and e Minn, Wisc, Mich, ne Ill and nw Ind. Que to Minn and SD, s to Fla and Tex; also Wash and n Idaho to Calif.

perigynium

Carex hystericina Muhl.   Pseudocypereae
Porcupine sedge   OBL

Perennial from short rhizomes, often forming large clumps. **Stems** upright or leaning, 3-angled, 2–10 dm long, usually longer than the leaves. **Leaves** yellow-green, 3–8 mm wide; sheaths white, thin and translucent on front, green to yellow or red on back, the lower sheaths breaking into threadlike fibers. **Spikes** either all male or female, the ter-minal spike male, 1–5 cm long, usually short-stalked and often with a bract; lateral spikes female or occasionally with male flowers above female, 1–4, short-cylindric, 1–5 cm long and 1–1.5 cm wide, separate or clustered, the lower spikes usually nodding on slender stalks, the upper spikes short-stalked and upright; **female scales** small, narrow and much shorter than the perigynia, tipped with a rough awn. **Perigynia** spreading or upright, green to straw-colored, ovate, round in section when mature, 5–8 mm long, strongly nerved, abruptly tapered to a slender, toothed beak 3–4 mm long; the beak teeth to 1 mm long. **Achenes** 3-angled with concave sides, 1.5 mm long; stigmas 3. May–July. ❧ Swamps, alder thickets, wet meadows and ditches; calcareous fens in s part of our region. ⊕ Common; Minn, Wisc, Mich, ne Ill and nw Ind. NB to Wash, s to Va, Ky, Ark, Tex, NM and Calif.

Carex pseudocyperus L. Pseudocypereae
False bristly sedge OBL

Large, clumped perennial. **Stems** stout, 3–10 dm long, 3-angled, rough-to-touch. **Leaves** 5–15 mm wide; sheaths translucent, yellow-tinged on back. **Spikes** either all male or female, the terminal spike male, 1.5–7 cm long; lateral spikes female, 2–6, cylindric, 3–8 cm long and 1 cm wide, lower spikes drooping on slender stalks; bracts much longer than the head; **female scales** tipped by an awn, the awn shorter or longer than the perigynia. **Perigynia** spreading, ovate, 3-angled, 4–6 mm long, shiny, strongly nerved, tapered to a toothed beak, the beak teeth 0.5–1 mm long. **Achenes** 3-angled, 1.5 mm long; stigmas 3. June–Aug. ⚘ Marshy lake margins, swamps, fens, wet ditches; Red Lake peatland (Minn) where indicator of calcium-rich fens. ⊕ n and c Minn, Wisc, Mich, reported for nw Ind. Newf to Sask, s to Pa, Ind, Minn and ND.

⚠
STATUS
Indiana - E

perigynium

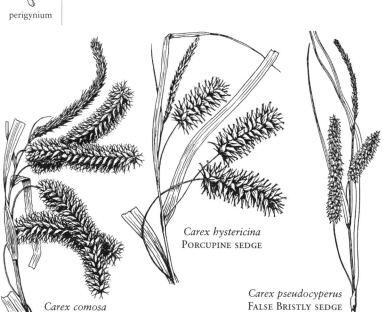

Carex hystericina
Porcupine sedge

Carex pseudocyperus
False Bristly sedge

Carex comosa
Bristly sedge

Carex Section SQUARROSAE

▶KEY TO SQUARROSAE

1 Terminal spike generally male; female scales with an awn as long or longer than the perigynium; uncommon plant of Mich LP . *C. frankii*
. . . . Bristly cat-tail sedge

1 Terminal spike with a few male flowers below the female; female scales unawned or with an awn shorter than perigynium beak . . . **2**

2 Achene slightly less than half as wide as long; style curved near base
. . . . *C. squarrosa* / Narrow-leaved cat-tail sedge

2 Achene half to 3/5 as wide as long; style ± straight . . . . . *C. typhina*
. . . . Common cat-tail sedge

Carex frankii Kunth   Squarrosae
Bristly cat-tail sedge   OBL

Perennial, forming small clumps. **Stems** 2–8 dm long. **Leaves** 6–10 mm wide, lower stem leaves reduced to scales. **Spikes** either all male or female; terminal spike male, short-stalked, 0.5–3 cm long; female spikes 3–6, grouped or separate, cylindric and rounded at each end, 1.5–4 cm long and 1 cm wide, with many flowers; bracts leaflike, longer than head; body of **female scales** small, tapered to a long awn as long or longer than perigynia beak. **Perigynia** oblong, inflated, the body 2–4 mm long, 2-ribbed, very abruptly tapered to a notched beak 1–2 mm long. **Achenes** 3-angled, 2 mm long, with a long, persistent style; stigmas 3. June–Sept. ✤ Low openings in forests. ⊕ Uncommon in s and ne LP of Mich, ne Ill and nw Ind. w NY, s Ont, Mich, e Neb, s to Va, Ga and Tex.

perigynium

Carex squarrosa L.   Squarrosae
Narrow-leaved cat-tail sedge   OBL

Densely clumped perennial. **Stems** 3–9 dm long. **Leaves** 3–6 mm wide, lower stem leaves reduced to scales. **Spikes** 1 (or sometimes 2–3), with both male and female flowers, the male below the female; female portion oval, 1–3 cm long and 1–2 cm wide; lateral spikes (if present) female, on upright stalks; bract of the terminal spike short and narrow; **female scales** tapered to a tip or short-awned, smaller than the perigynia. **Perigynia** numerous and crowded, spreading, obovate, inflated, the body 3–6 mm long, abruptly tapered to a long notched beak 2–3 mm long. **Achenes** 2–3 mm long, with a persistent, strongly bent style; stigmas 3. June–Aug. ✤ Swamps, floodplain forests, alder thickets, forest depressions. ⊕ Uncommon in se Mich, local in ne Ill and nw Ind. Conn s to NC, w to Que, se Mich, Neb and Ark.

perigynium

Carex typhina Michx.   Squarrosae
Common cat-tail sedge   OBL

⚠
STATUS
Michigan - T

Clumped perennial. **Stems** 3–8 dm long and usually shorter than upper leaves. **Leaves** 5–10 mm wide. **Spikes** 1–6, the terminal spike mostly female with a short male base, the female portion cylindric, 2–4 cm long and 1–1.5 cm wide, subtended by a short narrow bract; lateral spikes female, smaller, upright or spreading on short stalks; **female scales** hidden by the perigynia, blunt or tapered to a tip. **Perigynia** obovate, crowded, body 3–5 mm long, abruptly narrowed to a notched beak 2–3 mm long. **Achenes** 2–3 mm long; stigmas 3. June–Sept. ✤ Floodplain forests of large rivers (especially Miss and St. Croix), often occurring with **swamp oval sedge** (*C. muskingumensis*) and **common bur sedge** (*C. grayi*); marshy areas. ⊕ Infrequent in extreme se Minn, Wisc, s LP of Mich, local in ne Ill and nw Ind. Maine and Que to se Minn, s to Ga and La.

perigynium

Carex Section STELLULATAE

▶**KEY TO STELLULATAE**

1   Spike usually single; leaves inrolled; anthers large, 2–4 mm long ..
    . . . . C. exilis / COAST SEDGE
1   Spikes 2 to many; leaves flat or folded like a fan; anthers smaller, 2
    mm or less long **2**

2   Spikes 7–15, crowded into long heads; spikes with 20–40 perigynia
    . . . . C. arcta / NORTHERN CLUSTERED SEDGE
2   Spikes 2–8, often less crowded or with fewer flowers **3**

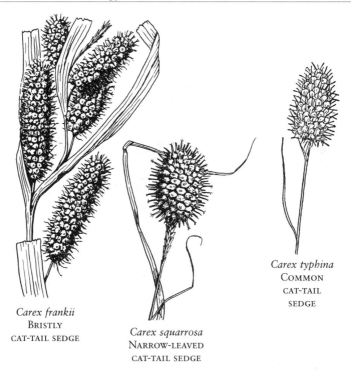

Carex typhina
COMMON
CAT-TAIL
SEDGE

Carex frankii
BRISTLY
CAT-TAIL SEDGE

Carex squarrosa
NARROW-LEAVED
CAT-TAIL SEDGE

3 Plants mostly with male and female flowers on different plants . . .
. . . . *C. sterilis* / FEN STAR SEDGE
3 Plants with male and female flowers on same plant, the terminal spike
with male flowers below female **4**

4 Perigynia beak smooth-margined . . . *C. seorsa* / SWAMP STAR SEDGE
4 Perigynia beak with few to many small, sharp teeth on margin . . **5**

5 Perigynia mostly 2–3 mm wide and 1–1.7x as long as wide . . . . . .
. . . . *C. atlantica* / ATLANTIC STAR SEDGE
5 Perigynia mostly 1–2 mm wide, often more than 1.7x as long as wide
. . . . **6**

6 Leaves wide, the widest leaves 3–5 mm wide . . . . *C. wiegandii*
. . . . WIEGAND'S SEDGE
6 Leaves narrower, the widest leaves less than 3 mm wide **7**

7 Perigynia long and narrow and tipped by a long beak, the body mostly 3–3.5 mm long, 2–3x as long as wide, the beak half to almost as
long as body . . . . *C. echinata* / LARGE-FRUITED STAR-SEDGE
7 Perigynia shorter or relatively wider, and with a shorter beak to half
as long as body **8**

8 Perigynia usually slightly convexly tapered from widest point to beak
and forming a shoulder; beak conspicuously sharp-toothed along its
margin . . . . *C. interior* / INLAND SEDGE
8 Perigynia wedge-shaped with broadest end near tip, concavely
tapered from widest point to beak; beak more sparsely sharp-toothed
. . . . *C. atlantica* / ATLANTIC STAR SEDGE

Carex arcta F. Boott   Stellulatae
Northern clustered sedge   OBL

Loosely to densely clumped perennial from very short, thick rhizomes. **Stems** 2–8 dm long, soft, sharply triangular, very rough-to-touch above, usually shorter than the leaves. **Leaves** clustered near base, light green, flat, 2–4 mm wide, long-tapered to a tip, very rough; sheaths loose, purple-dotted. **Spikes** 5–15, each with both male and female flowers, the male small and below the female; flowers crowded in oblong heads, 1.5–3 cm long, upper spikes densely packed, lower spikes slightly separate; **female scales** ovate, acute, translucent with a brown-tinged center, shorter than the perigynia. **Perigynia** flat on 1 side and convex on other, ovate, 2–3 mm long and 1–1.5 mm wide, green to straw-colored or brown when mature, covered with white dots, widest near the broad base, tapered to a sharp-toothed, notched beak 0.5–1.5 mm long. **Achenes** lens-shaped, brown, 1–2 mm long; stigmas 2. June–Aug. 🌱 Floodplain forests, old river channels, swamps and wetland margins. ⊕ ne and nc Minn, n Wisc, local in w and c UP of Mich. Que to s Yukon, s to NY, Minn and n Calif.

perigynium

Carex atlantica L. H. Bailey   Stellulatae
Atlantic star sedge   FACW

⚠
STATUS
Indiana - E

Densely clumped perennial. **Stems** 3–7 dm long, rough-to-touch on upper stem angles. **Leaves** 0.5–4 mm wide, mostly near base of stem. Terminal **spike** with male flowers at base, 12–15 mm long; lateral spikes female, 8–12 mm long; spikes grouped or separate; **female scales** broadly ovate, shorter than perigynia. **Perigynia** green, ovate to nearly round, 2–3.5 mm long and 1–3 mm wide, several-nerved on both sides, finely toothed on margin and beak; beak sharply notched, 0.5–1 mm long; stigmas 2. June–Aug. *C. howei, C. incomperta.* 🌱 Thickets and swamps, moist sand, sphagnum peat. ⊕ c and e UP and LP of Mich, nw Ind. Atlantic coastal plain, inland to s Ont, Ohio, Mich and n Ind. ☞ Similar to **inland sedge** (*C. interior*) but less common in our region.

perigynium

Carex echinata Murray   Stellulatae
Large-fruited star sedge   OBL

⚠
STATUS
Illinois - E
Indiana - E

Clumped perennial. **Stems** 1–6 dm long, rough above. **Leaves** scalelike at base of stem; leaves with blades 3–6 on lower stem, 1–3 mm wide, shorter to as long as the stems. **Spikes** 3–7, stalkless, few-flowered; terminal spike with a slender male portion near its base; lateral spikes usually all female; bract small; **female scales** ovate, shorter than perigynia, yellow-tinged with green midvein. **Perigynia** 5–15 and crowded in each spike, spreading or curved downward, green or light brown, flat on 1 side and convex on other, narrowly ovate, spongy-thickened at base, 3–4 mm long, tapered to a toothed, notched beak 1–2 mm long. **Achenes** lens-shaped; stigmas 2. July–Sept. *C. angustior, C. cephalantha.* 🌱 Swamp margins, wet sandy lakeshores, hummocks in peatlands (as at Red Lake peatland in Minn). ⊕ Occasional in ne and nc Minn; Wisc, Mich, uncommon in ne Ill and nw Ind. Circumboreal, s to Va, Ind, Iowa, Utah and Calif.

perigynium

Carex exilis Dewey   Stellulatae
Coast sedge   OBL

⚠
STATUS
Wisconsin - T

Densely clumped perennial. **Stems** stiff, 2–7 dm long and longer than the leaves. **Leaves** narrow and rolled inward. **Spike** usually 1, either male or female, or with both male and female flowers, the male below the female, 1–3 cm long; lateral spikes (if present) 1 or 2 and much smaller than terminal spike; lower 2 scales empty and upright; **female scales** ovate, red-

perigynium

brown with translucent margins, about as long as perigynia. **Perigynia** spreading or drooping, ovate, flat on 1 side and convex on other, 3–5 mm long, spongy-thickened at base, tapered to a toothed beak to 2 mm long. **Achenes** lens-shaped; stigmas 2. June–Aug. ❀ Sphagnum moss peatlands, interdunal wetlands near Great Lakes. ⊕ Coastal disjunct; locally common in Minn Red Lake peatland, elsewhere uncommon. nc and ne Minn, n Wisc (Ashland and Door Counties), Mich UP and n LP. Labr, Nfld, Ont and Minn, s to Md, n Mich and n Minn.

perigynium

Carex interior L. Bailey   Stellulatae
  Inland sedge   OBL

Densely clumped perennial. **Stems** slender, sharply 3-angled, 1–6 dm long, equal or longer than the leaves. **Leaves** 1–2 mm wide; sheaths tight, thin and translucent on front. **Spikes** 2–4, the terminal spike with female flowers borne above male (or rarely all male), the lateral spikes female (or rarely with female flowers borne above male), round in outline, about 5 mm wide, ± overlapping in heads 1–2.5 cm long; bracts small or absent; **female scales** blunt-tipped, much shorter than the perigynia. **Perigynia** green-brown to brown, ovate, filled to margins by the achenes, sharp-edged but not wing-margined, 2–3 mm long and 1–2 mm wide, the base spongy so that achene fills upper perigynium body, tapered to a finely toothed beak to 1 mm long; the beak teeth small, not longer than 0.3 mm. **Achenes** lens-shaped, 1–1.5 mm long; stigmas 2. May–Aug. ❀ Swamps, tamarack bogs, alder thickets, wet meadows and wetland margins. ⊕ Common in all but se Minn; Wisc, Mich, ne Ill and nw Ind. Labr and Newf to BC, s to Pa, Ind, Mo, Kans and n Mex.

perigynium

Carex seorsa Howe   Stellulatae
  Swamp star sedge   FACW+

⚠
STATUS
Michigan - T

Densely clumped perennial. **Stems** 2–7 dm long, longer than the leaves. **Leaves** 2–4 on lower third of stem, 1–4 mm wide, lower stem leaves reduced to scales. **Spikes** 4–8, stalkless, with both male and female flowers, the male below the female, or the lateral spikes often all female; **female scales** ovate, much shorter than perigynia. **Perigynia** 5–25, crowded, widely spreading, green, broadly ovate, flat on 1 side and convex on other, spongy-thickened at base, 2–3 mm long and 1–2 mm wide, tapered to a short beak to a third as long as the body. **Achenes** lens-shaped; stigmas 2. May–July. ❀ Moist to wet deciduous woods, swamps and open bogs. ⊕ sw and c LP Mich, nw Ind. Atlantic coastal plain, s NH to Ga, inland to s Ont, Mich, Tenn and nw Ind.

Carex sterilis Willd.   Stellulatae
  Fen star sedge   OBL

⚠
STATUS
Minnesota - T

Clumped perennial. **Stems** stiff, 1–7 dm long, longer than the leaves, rough-to-touch on the upper stem angles. **Leaves** 3–5 from lower part of stem, 1–4 mm wide, rough, lower stem leaves reduced to scales. **Spikes** 3–8, 3–12 mm long, stalkless, clustered or the lower separate; male and female flowers mostly on separate plants; **female scales** red-brown with green midvein and translucent margins, tapered to a tip or short point, about as long as body of perigynia. **Perigynia** 5–25, the lower spreading, red-brown, flat on 1 side and convex on other, broadly ovate, spongy-thickened at base, 2–4 mm long tapered to a finely toothed, notched beak 0.5–1.5 mm long, the beak teeth sharp, to 0.5 mm long. **Achenes** lens-shaped; stigmas 2. April–June. *C. muricata* var. *sterilis*. ❀ Occasional in spring-fed calcareous fens and calcium-rich wet meadows near Great Lakes. ⊕ nw, c, sc and se Minn, Wisc, Mich, ne Ill and nw Ind. Newf to ND, s to NJ and Ill. ☞ Similar to the more common **inland sedge** (*C. interior*).

perigynium

Carex wiegandii Mackenzie

Stellulatae

Wiegand's sedge

(OBL)

perigynium

Clumped perennial. **Stems** 3–6 dm long, longer than leaves, sometimes elongating to 1–2 m. **Leaves** 3–8 on lower stem, fan-folded, 2–5 mm wide, rough-to-touch on upperside, lower stem leaves reduced to scales. **Spikes** 4–6, with both male and female flowers, the male below the female, 4–12 mm long, stalkless, grouped in a cylindric head 1–3 cm long, the 2 lower spikes sometimes separate; **female scales** red-brown with green midvein and translucent margins. **Perigynia** 5–25, the lower ones spreading or turned downward, green to red-brown, flat on 1 side and convex on other, broadly ovate, spongy-thickened at base, 2–4 mm long, tapered to a finely toothed, notched beak about 1 mm long. **Achenes** lens-shaped; stigmas 2. June–Aug. ⚘ Sphagnum moss peatlands, marshes and wet meadows. ⊕ e UP of Mich. Nfld and Labr to Ont and n Mich, s to Mass and n Pa.

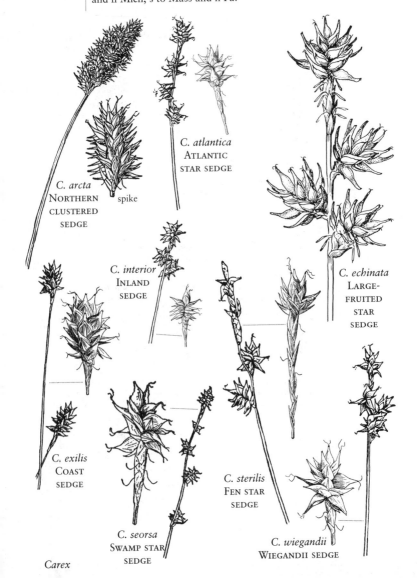

C. arcta
NORTHERN
CLUSTERED
SEDGE

spike

C. atlantica
ATLANTIC
STAR SEDGE

C. interior
INLAND
SEDGE

C. echinata
LARGE-
FRUITED
STAR
SEDGE

C. exilis
COAST
SEDGE

C. sterilis
FEN STAR
SEDGE

C. seorsa
SWAMP STAR
SEDGE

C. wiegandii
WIEGANDII SEDGE

Carex

Carex Section SYLVATICAE

perigynium

Carex castanea Wahl.   Sylvaticae
  Chestnut-color sedge   FACW+

Clumped perennial. **Stems** 3–10 dm long, purple-tinged at base, longer than leaves. **Leaves** 3–6 mm wide, softly hairy. **Spikes** either male or female; the terminal spike male, upright atop a long stalk; lateral spikes female, usually 3, on slender, drooping stalks, short cylindric, 1–2.5 cm long and 6–8 mm wide; **female scales** ovate, brown-tinged, about as long as perigynia. **Perigynia** ovate, 4–6 mm long, somewhat 3-angled, strongly 2-ribbed with several faint nerves, tapered to a notched beak. **Achenes** 3-angled; stigmas 3. June–July. ❦ Swamps, moist openings, wetland margins and ditches. ⊕ ne Minn, n and ne Wisc, Mich (UP and n LP). Nfld to w Ont, s to Conn and Minn.

Carex debilis Michx.   Sylvaticae
  Southern weak sedge   FACW

⚠
STATUS
Indiana - T

Clumped perennial. **Stems** 6–10 dm long, purple-tinged at base. **Leaves** 2–4 mm wide. **Male spike** linear, 2–4 cm long, sometimes with a few female flowers near tip; **female spikes** 2–4, separate along stem, spreading or nodding, 3–6 cm long and 3–5 mm wide, flowers loose in spikes; **female scales** oblong, half the length of perigynia with translucent or brown margins and a green midrib. **Perigynia** lance-shaped, somewhat 3-angled, 2-ribbed, 5–8 mm long, narrowed to a beak. **Achenes** 3-angled; stigmas 3. May–Aug. ❦ Wet woods (usually under conifers), swamp margins, wet sandy ditches. ⊕ Occasional in ec Minn, Wisc, Mich and nw Ind. Nfld to Minn, s to Fla and Tex.

perigynium

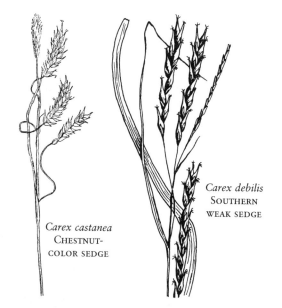

Carex castanea
CHESTNUT-
COLOR SEDGE

Carex debilis
SOUTHERN
WEAK SEDGE

Carex Section VESICARIAE

Carex lurida Wahlenb.   Vesicariae
  Bottlebrush sedge   OBL
Clumped perennial. **Stems** 3–10 dm long, shorter than the leaves, rounded 3-angled and ± smooth, purple-tinged at base. **Leaves** flat, 3–7 mm wide, lower stem leaves reduced to scales. **Spikes** either male or female, terminal spike male, 1–7 cm long; female spikes 1–4 (usually 2), many-flowered, grouped or the lower separate, stalkless and erect or the lower short-stalked and sometimes drooping, 2–7 cm long and 15–20 mm wide; bracts leafy, longer than the head; **male scales** with the midrib prolonged into an awn, **female scales** awned or sharp-pointed. **Perigynia** in many rows, broadly ovate, somewhat inflated, 6–9 mm long, pale, smooth and shining, strongly nerved, tapered to a notched beak half to as long as the body. **Achenes** 3-angled, loosely enclosed in the lower part of the perigynium, the style persistent and twisted; stigmas 3. June–Aug. ❦ River floodplains, swamps, open bogs, fens and wet meadows. ⊕ nc and c Wisc (Wisc and Black River valleys), s and c LP of Mich, ne Ill and nw Ind. NS to Wisc, s to Fla and Mex.

perigynium

Carex oligosperma Michx.
Vesicariae

Running bog sedge
OBL

STATUS
Illinois - E

Perennial, forming colonies from creeping rhizomes. **Stems** slender, 4–10 dm long, purple-tinged at base. **Leaves** stiff, rolled inward, 1–3 mm wide. **Spikes** either all male or female; male spike usually single; female spikes 1 (or 2–3 and widely separated), stalkless or nearly so, ovate to short-cylindric, 1–2 cm long, lowest bract leaflike. **Perigynia** 3–15, ovate, somewhat inflated, compressed, 4–7 mm long, strongly several-nerved, abruptly tapered to a beak 1–2 mm long. **Achenes** 3-angled, 2–3 mm long; stigmas 3. June–Aug. ≉ Open bogs and swamps, floating mats, pioneer mat-former along pond margins. ⊕ Common or dominant sedge in peatlands of n part of region, less common southward. ne, nc and ec Minn, n and se Wisc, Mich, ne Ill and nw Ind. Nfld to NW Terr, s to Conn, Pa, Ind and Minn.

perigynium

Carex retrorsa Schwein.
Vesicariae

Deflexed bottlebrush sedge
OBL

STATUS
Indiana - E

Densely clustered perennial. **Stems** 4–10 dm long. **Leaves** 3–4 dm long and 4–10 mm wide, flat and soft; sheaths dotted with small bumps. **Spikes** either all male or female, or the terminal 1–2 spikes with both male and female flowers, the male above the female, stalkless or lowest spike on a slender stalk; lower spikes 3–8, female, 1.5–5 cm long and 1.5–2 cm wide; **female scales** conspicuous, shorter and narrower than the perigynia. **Perigynia** crowded in rows, spreading or the lowest perigynia angled downward, smooth and shiny, 6–13-nerved, 7–10 mm long, somewhat inflated, tapered to a long, smooth beak 2–4 mm long, the beak teeth short, to 1 mm long. **Achenes** dark brown, 3-angled, 2 mm long, loose in the lower part of the perigynium; stigmas 3. June–Aug. ≉ Floodplain forests, swamps, thickets and marshes. ⊕ Common in n Minn (occasional in s), Wisc, Mich, ne Ill and nw Ind. Que to BC, s to Md, Ind, Iowa and Ore.

perigynium

Carex rostrata J. Stokes
Vesicariae

Beaked sedge
OBL

Perennial with short to long-creeping rhizomes. **Stems** round or bluntly 3-angled, 3–10 dm long, smooth below inflorescence. **Leaves** waxy blue, with many fine bumps on upper surface, to 4 mm wide, inrolled or channeled in section. **Spikes** either male or female, the upper 2–5 male; lower 2–5 spikes female or sometimes 1 or 2 with male flowers above the female, cylindric, 2–10 cm long and 8–12 mm wide. **Perigynia** upright when young, becoming widely spreading when mature, yellow-green to brown, shiny, ovate, nearly round in section, inflated, 2–6 mm long, narrowed to a beak about 1 mm long. **Achenes** 3-angled, 1–2 mm long; stigmas 3. July–Sept. ≉ Peat mats or shallow water. ⊕ Local; ne and nc Minn, n Wisc, UP of Mich. Circumboreal, s to NB, n Mich, n Minn and n Mont. ☞ Similar to C. *utriculata* but much less common in our region, and with the leaves waxy blue and dotted with fine bumps on upper surface, v-shaped in section or inrolled, and only 2–4 mm wide.

perigynium

Carex schweinitzii Dewey
Vesicariae

Schweinitz' sedge
OBL

Loosely clumped perennial. **Stems** 3–7 dm long, single or few together from rhizomes, sharply 3-angled. **Leaves** 4–10 mm wide, rough-to-touch near tip, lower stem leaves reduced to scales. **Spikes** either all male or female; terminal spike male, on a slender stalk and usually with a bract; female spikes 2–5, grouped or the lowest separate, cylindric, 3–8 cm long and to 1.5 cm wide, spikes ascending or spreading; **female scales** translucent or brown-tinged, the midvein prolonged into a finely toothed awn often longer than the perigynium. **Perigynia** spreading or upright, ovate, inflated, round in section, 5–7 mm long, with 7–9 nerves, abruptly tapered to a beak, the beak teeth upright or spreading. **Achenes** 3-angled, loosely enclosed in the perigynia; stigmas 3. May–July. ❦ Shaded streambanks. ⊕ Uncommon in n LP and e UP of Mich. Vt to Mich, s to NC, Tenn and Mo.

perigynium

Carex tuckermanii F. Boott   Vesicariae
Tuckerman's sedge   OBL

Clumped perennial, from short rhizomes. **Stems** 4–8 dm long. **Leaves** 3–6 mm wide and 2–4 dm long, soft and flat. **Spikes** either male or female; male spikes usually 2, separated, raised above female spikes; female spikes 2–4, separated, cylindric, 2–5 cm long. **Perigynia** overlapping and ascending in 6 rows, broadly ovate, 7–10 mm long and 4–7 mm wide, inflated, tapered to a notched beak 2 mm long. **Achenes** 3-angled, obovate, 3–4 mm long, with a deep indentation near the middle of 1 angle; stigmas 3. June–Aug. ❦ Swamps, alder thickets, low areas in forests, pond margins. ⊕ Common northward; ne, nc and ec Minn, Wisc (especially n), Mich; local in ne Ill and nw Ind. NB to Minn, s to NJ, Ohio, and Iowa.

perigynium

Carex utriculata F. Boott   Vesicariae
Beaked sedge   OBL

Large, densely clumped perennial from short rootstocks, also forming turfs from long rhizomes. **Stems** bluntly 3-angled, 3–12 dm long, spongy at base. **Leaves** strongly divided with swollen joints 4–12 mm wide; sheaths white-translucent on front, divided with swollen joints on back. **Spikes** either male or female, the upper 2–5 male, held well above the female spikes, the terminal spike 3–6 cm long; lower 2–5 spikes female or sometimes 1 or 2 with male flowers above the female, usually separate, cylindric, 2–10 cm long and 8–12 mm wide, the upper spikes stalkless or short-stalked, lower spikes stalked, upright; bracts shorter to slightly longer than the head; **female scales** acute to awn-tipped, body of scale shorter than perigynia. **Perigynia** upright at first to widely spreading when mature, in many rows, yellow-green to brown, shiny, ovate, nearly round in section, inflated, 3–8 mm long and 2–4 mm wide, strongly 7-9-nerved, contracted to a toothed beak 1–2 mm long, the teeth mostly straight, 0.5 mm long. **Achenes** 3-angled, 2 mm long; stigmas 3. June–Aug. ❦ Wet meadows, marshes, fens, swamps and lakeshores. ⊕ Common; Minn, Wisc, Mich, occasional in ne Ill and nw Ind. Circumboreal, s to Del, Md, Ind, Iowa, Neb, NM and Calif. ☞ Long confused with *C. rostrata* (a boreal species apparently uncommon in our region) which has waxy blue leaves to only 4 mm wide and with numerous small bumps on upper leaf surface.

perigynium

Carex vesicaria L.   Vesicariae
Inflated sedge   OBL

Clumped perennial, from stout, short rhizomes. **Stems** sharply 3-angled and rough-to-touch below the head, 3–10 dm long, not spongy at base (as in *C. utriculata*). **Leaves** 2–7 mm wide; sheaths white-translucent on front, not conspicuously divided-with small swollen joints on back, the lowest sheaths often shredding into ladderlike fibers. **Spikes** either all

perigynium

male or female, the upper 2–4 male, held well above the female, 2–4 cm long; lower 1–3 spikes female, separate, cylindric, 2–8 cm long and 4–15 mm wide, stalkless or short-stalked, erect; lowest bract usually longer than the head; **female scales** acute to awn-tipped, shorter to as long as perigynia. **Perigynia** upright and overlapping in rows, dull yellow-green to brown, ovate to round, inflated, 3–8 mm long and 3 mm wide, strongly nerved, abruptly tapered to a toothed beak 1–2 mm long, the teeth 0.5–1 mm long. **Achenes** 3-angled, 2–3 mm long; stigmas 3. June–Aug. ❧ Wet meadows, marshes, forest depressions and shores. ⊕ Common; ne, nc and ec Minn, Wisc, Mich, occasional in ne Ill and nw Ind. Circumboreal, from Newf to BC, s to Del, Ind, Mo, SD, NM and Calif.

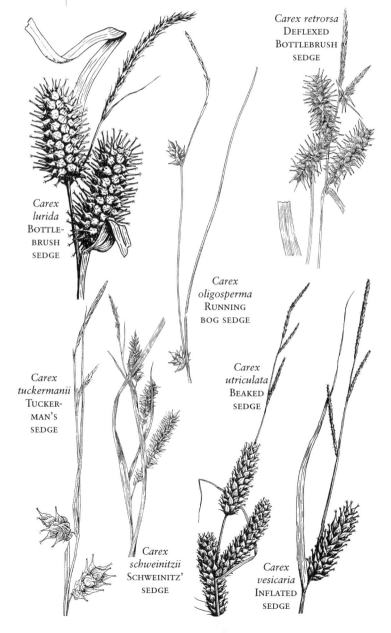

Carex retrorsa
DEFLEXED
BOTTLEBRUSH
SEDGE

Carex lurida
BOTTLE-
BRUSH
SEDGE

Carex oligosperma
RUNNING
BOG SEDGE

Carex utriculata
BEAKED
SEDGE

Carex tuckermanii
TUCKER-
MAN'S
SEDGE

Carex schweinitzii
SCHWEINITZ'
SEDGE

Carex vesicaria
INFLATED
SEDGE

Carex Section VULPINAE

Carex conjuncta Boott   Vulpinae
  Green-headed fox sedge   FACW

⚠
STATUS
Michigan - T
Minnesota - T

Clumped perennial; plants light green. **Stems** slender, 3-angled, 4–9 dm long, as long or longer than leaves, somewhat roughened above. **Leaves** soft, 5–10 mm wide; margins rough; sheaths somewhat cross-wrinkled on inner side. **Spikes** 6–10, either male or female, the male above the female, in a narrow head 2–5 cm long; bract small and bristlelike or absent; **female scales** ovate, about as long as perigynia, tapered to a sharp tip or short awn. **Perigynia** ovate, green or yellow-green, 3–4 mm long and 1–2 mm wide, slightly spongy at base, tapered to a rough, 2-toothed beak. **Achenes** flattened; stigmas 2. June–July. 🌿 Low prairie, stream-banks, wet meadows and thickets. ⊕ Rare in se Minn and s Mich; Wisc, ne Ill and nw Ind. NY to s Minn, s to Va and Kans.

perigynium

Carex crus-corvi Shuttlew.   Vulpinae
  Crowfoot fox sedge   OBL

⚠
STATUS
Michigan - T
Wisconsin - E

Clumped perennial. **Stems** stout, 4–8 dm long, sharply 3-angled, shorter than leaves. **Leaves** 5–10 mm wide; sheaths not cross-wrinkled. **Spikes** in large head, 8–20 cm long, upper spikes grouped, lower spikes separate. **Spikes** with both male and female flowers, male above female; **female scales** triangular-ovate, shorter or equal to perigynia. **Perigynia** ovate, flat on 1 side and convex on other, 5–9 mm long, with a broad, spongy base to 2.5 mm wide, tapered to a notched beak much longer than body. **Achenes** lens-shaped; stigmas 2. June–July. 🌿 Floodplains, marshes, edges of seasonally wet woodland depressions. ⊕ Uncommon in se Minn, s LP of Mich, se Wisc, ne Ill and nw Ind. s Ont, Ind and s Minn, s to Fla and Tex.

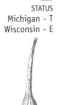
perigynium

Carex laevivaginata (Kük.) Mack.   Vulpinae
  Smooth-sheathed fox sedge   OBL

⚠
STATUS
Minnesota - T

Densely clumped perennial. **Stems** stout, 3-angled, 3–10 dm long. **Leaves** 3–10 mm wide; sheaths not cross-corrugated (as in *C. stipata*). **Spikes** with both male and female flowers, the male above the female, numer-ous, grouped into a dense head 2–5 cm long and 1–1.5 cm wide, green or straw-colored when mature; bracts short or reduced to bristles some-times longer than the spikes; **female scales** shorter than the perigynia, tapered to a tip or short awn. **Perigynia** green or straw-colored, spread-

perigynium

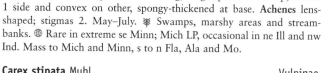

ing, broadly lance-shaped, 5–6 mm long, long-tapered to the tip, flat on 1 side and convex on other, spongy-thickened at base. **Achenes** lens-shaped; stigmas 2. May–July. ⚘ Swamps, marshy areas and stream-banks. ⊕ Rare in extreme se Minn; Mich LP, occasional in ne Ill and nw Ind. Mass to Mich and Minn, s to n Fla, Ala and Mo.

Carex stipata Muhl.   Vulpinae
Common fox sedge   OBL

Densely clumped perennial. **Stems** 3-angled and slightly winged, 2–12 dm long. **Leaves** 4–8 mm wide; sheaths cross-wrinkled on front, divided with small swollen joints on back. **Spikes** with both male and female flowers, male flowers borne above female, clustered or the lowest spikes often separate, in oblong heads 3–10 cm long; bracts small and some-times bristlelike, longer than the spike; **female scales** tapered to a tip or with a short, sharp point, half to 3/4 as long as the perigynia. **Perigynia** yellow-green to dull brown, flat on 1 side and convex on other, narrow-ly ovate, 3–5 mm long and 1–2 mm wide, strongly several-nerved on both sides, tapered to a finely toothed, notched beak 1–3 mm long. **Achenes** lens-shaped, 1.5–2 mm long; stigmas 2. May–July. ⚘ Floodplain forests and swamps, thickets, wet meadows, wetland margins and ditches; usually not in sphagnum bogs. ⊕ Common; Minn, Wisc, Mich, ne Ill and nw Ind. Newf to s Alaska, s to Fla, Tex and Calif.

perigynium

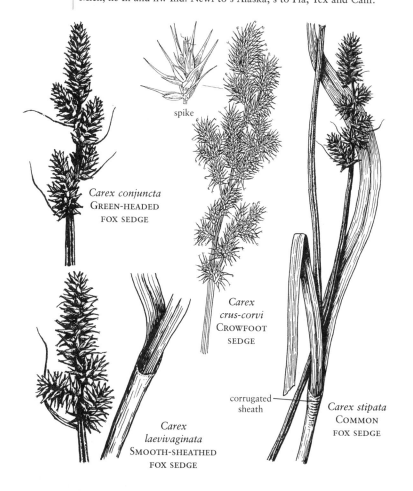

Carex conjuncta
GREEN-HEADED
FOX SEDGE

spike

*Carex
crus-corvi*
CROWFOOT
SEDGE

*Carex
laevivaginata*
SMOOTH-SHEATHED
FOX SEDGE

corrugated
sheath

Carex stipata
COMMON
FOX SEDGE

☞ Another member of this genus, **sawgrass** (*Cladium jamaicensis*), is the dominant plant across large areas of the Florida Everglades.

spikelet

▶**Cladium** P. Browne / Twig-rush

Cladium mariscoides (Muhl.) Torr.
Twig-rush   OBL

Grasslike perennial, spreading by rhizomes and forming colonies. **Stems** single or in small groups, stiff, slender, smooth, 0.3–1 m tall. **Leaves** 1–3 mm wide, upper portion round in section, middle portion flattened. **Flowers** in lance-shaped spikelets, 3–5 mm long, in branched clusters (umbels) at end of stem and also with 1–2 clusters on slender stalks from leaf axils; uppermost flower perfect, the style 3-parted; middle flowers male; lowest scale of each spikelet empty; scales overlapping, ovate, brown; bristles absent. **Achenes** dull brown, 2–3 mm long, pointed at tip; tubercle absent. June–Aug. *Mariscus mariscoides.* ❧ Shallow water, sandy or mucky shores, floating bog mats, calcium-rich wet meadows, seeps, fens and low prairie. ⊕ Minn, Wisc, Mich, ne Ill and nw Ind. NS to Minn, s to w Fla and Ky; e Tex.

▶**Cyperus** L. / Flatsedge

☞ **Toothed flatsedge** (*Cyperus dentatus* Torr.) occurs along several sandy shores and in marshes in nw Ind (⚠ state endangered), widely disjunct from its main range along the Atlantic coast. This obligate wetland species is perennial from scaly rhizomes, with stems 2–4 dm long. The inflorescence is branched, with linear, very flat spikelets. The scales are pale red-brown, tipped with a fine awn which is widely spreading when mature.

Small to medium, annual or perennial, grasslike plants. **Stems** often clumped, unbranched, sharply 3-angled. **Leaves** mostly from base of plants, with 1 or more leaflike bracts near top of stems, the blades flat or folded along midvein. **Flower heads** in umbels at ends of stems; the spikelets many, grouped in 1 to several rounded or cylindric spikes. **Flowers** perfect; bristlelike sepals and petals absent; stamens 1–3; styles 2–3-parted. **Achenes** lens-shaped or 3-angled, beakless.

▶**KEY TO CYPERUS**

1 Achenes lens-shaped; stigmas 2 . . . . **2**
1 Achenes 3-angled; stigmas 3 . . . . **4**

2 Scales straw-colored . . . . *C. flavescens* / YELLOW FLATSEDGE
2 Scales red-purple or deep brown **3**

3 Style cleft to slightly below middle *C. bipartitus* / SHINING FLATSEDGE
3 Style cleft almost to base . . . . . *C. diandrus* / UMBRELLA FLATSEDGE

4 Plants perennial. **5**
4 Plants annual **6**

5 Scales 2–3 mm long, only slightly keeled. . . . . *C. esculentus*
. . . . CHUFA; YELLOW NUTSEDGE
5 Scales 3–5 mm long, keeled . . . . *C. strigosus*
. . . . FALSE NUTSEDGE; STRAW-COLORED CYPERUS

6 Scales curved outward at tip; stamens 1 . . . . **7**
6 Scales not curved outward at tip; stamens 3 . . . . **8**

7 Scales 3-nerved, not awn-tipped . . . . *C. acuminatus*
. . . . SHORT-POINT FLATSEDGE
7 Scales 7–9-nerved, tipped with a short awn . . . . *C. squarrosus*
. . . . AWNED FLATSEDGE

8 Scales to 2 mm long, with 3–5 veins near center of scale. . . . .
. . . . *C. erythrorhizos* / RED-ROOT FLATSEDGE
8 Scales 2–5 mm long, with 7 or more well-spaced veins . *C. odoratus*
. . . . RUSTY FLATSEDGE

Cyperus acuminatus Torr. & Hook.

Short-point flatsedge   OBL

⚠
STATUS
Indiana - E
Minnesota - T

Clumped, grasslike annual. **Stems** 3-angled, 5–30 cm tall. **Leaves** light green, as long as stems or longer, to 2 mm wide; bracts to 3 mm wide, longer than the head. **Spikelets** flat, 3–7 mm long, crowded in 1–5 round clusters (spikes), 1 spike stalkless, the other spikes on stalks 1–3 cm long; **scales** 1–2 mm long, ovate, pale green, becoming tan when mature, strongly 3-nerved; stamens 1; style 3-parted. **Achenes** tan to pale brown, 3-angled, 0.5–1 mm long. Aug–Sept. ❦ Muddy or sandy shores, streambanks and flats. ⊕ Local in sw Minn, uncommon in ne Ill and nw Ind. Ind and n Ill to ND, s to Ga, La and Tex; also the Pacific Coast.

Cyperus bipartitus Torr.

Shining flatsedge   FACW+

☞ Shining flatsedge is very similar to **umbrella flatsedge** (C. *diandrus*), but the scales are shiny and the styles not as deeply divided (vs. dull scales and the styles cleft nearly to base in *C. diandrus*).

Clumped, grasslike annual. **Stems** 3-angled, 1–3 dm tall. **Leaves** usually shorter than stems; leaves and bracts 0.5–2 mm wide, the bracts usually 3, longer than the spikes. **Spikelets** linear, 10–15 mm long and 2–3 mm wide, in clusters (spikes) of 3–10, the spikes stalkless or on stalks to 10 cm long; **scales** overlapping, ovate, shiny, purple-brown on margins; stamens 2 or 3; style 2-parted, lower third not divided. **Achenes** lens-shaped, 1–2 mm long, hidden by the scales. July–Sept. *C. rivularis.* ❦ Wet, sandy, gravelly or muddy shores, streambanks, wet meadows, ditches. ⊕ Fairly common; c and s Minn, Wisc, LP and s UP of Mich, ne Ill and nw Ind. Maine and Que to ND, s to Ga, Tex and S Amer. ☞

Cyperus diandrus Torr.

Umbrella flatsedge   FACW+

Clumped, grasslike annual. **Stems** 3-angled, 5–30 cm tall. **Leaves** about as long as stems, 1–3 mm wide; bracts usually 3, longer than the spikes. **Spikelets** 5–10, linear, 5–20 mm long and 2–3 mm wide; in 1–3 loose, rounded spikes, the spikes on stalks to 6 cm long; **scales** loosely overlapping, ovate, 2–3 mm long, not shiny, purple-brown on margins; stamens 2; style 2-parted, divided nearly to the base, persistent. **Achenes** lens-shaped, pale brown, 1 mm long, visible between the scales. July–Sept. ❦ Sandy or muddy shores, streambanks, wet meadows. ⊕ Occasional; c and s Minn, s Wisc, c and s LP of Mich, ne Ill and nw Ind. Que and Maine to se ND, s to Va, Mo and Kans.

Cyperus erythrorhizos Muhl.

Red-root flatsedge   OBL

Clumped, stout or slender annual, roots red. **Stems** 3-angled, 1–7 dm long. **Leaves** mostly near base of plant, shorter to longer than stems, 2–8 mm wide; bracts 3–7, to 9 mm wide, usually much longer than the spikes. **Spikelets** linear, 2–10 mm long and 1–2 mm wide; grouped in a pinnate manner along a stalk (rachilla), in cylindric clusters, the terminal cluster stalkless, the others on stalks to 8 cm long; **scales** ovate, satiny brown, 1–2 mm long, overlapping; stamens 3; style 3-parted. **Achenes** ivory white, sharply 3-angled, ovate, 0.5–1 mm long. July–Sept. ❦ Sandy or muddy shores, streambanks, exposed mud flats, ditches; often with **rusty flatsedge** (*Cyperus odoratus*). ⊕ Minn (mostly s), s Wisc, s LP of Mich, ne Ill and nw Ind. Widespread in most of temperate N Amer.

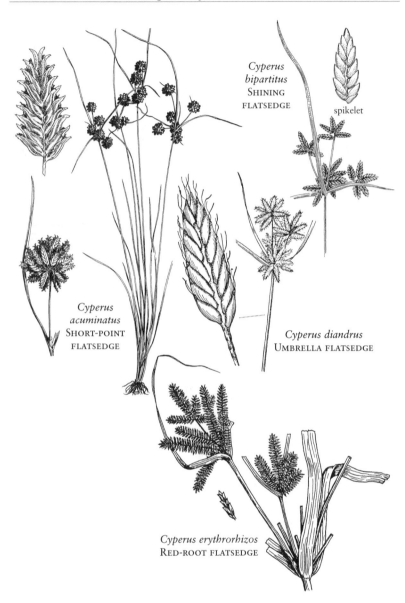

Cyperus bipartitus
SHINING FLATSEDGE

spikelet

Cyperus acuminatus
SHORT-POINT FLATSEDGE

Cyperus diandrus
UMBRELLA FLATSEDGE

Cyperus erythrorhizos
RED-ROOT FLATSEDGE

Cyperus esculentus L.

Chufa; Yellow nutsedge   FACW

☞ True **chufa** (*C. esculentus* var. *sativus*) is grown for its edible tubers in some parts of the world.

Grasslike perennial, with rhizomes ending in small tubers. **Stems** single, 3-angled, erect, 2–7 dm long. **Leaves** light green, mostly from base of plant, about as long as stems, 3–10 mm wide, with a prominent midvein; the bracts 3–6, usually much longer than the spikes. **Spikelets** linear, 3–12 cm long and 1–2 mm wide; pinnately arranged on a stalk, forming loose cylindrical spikes, the spikes to 5 cm long and 1–2 mm wide; **scales** straw-colored, 2–3 mm long, overlapping; stamens 3; style 3-parted. **Achenes** pale brown, 3-angled, 1–2 mm long. July–Sept. ❀ Sandy or muddy shores, streambanks, marshes, ditches and other wet places;

weedy in wet or moist cultivated fields. ⊕ Mostly sc and se Minn, Mich (but local in UP), ne Ill and nw Ind. Maine to ND, s to S Amer, occasional in w USA; common as a lawn weed in se USA.

Cyperus flavescens L.
Yellow flatsedge OBL

Clumped, grasslike annual. **Stems** very slender, 3-angled, 5–30 cm tall. **Leaves** mostly at base of plant, 1–3 mm wide, mostly shorter than the stems; bracts 2–4, much longer than the spikes. **Spikelets** linear, 10–15 cm long and 2–3 mm wide, stalkless or on stalks to 5 cm long; **scales** ovate, straw-colored, 2–3 mm long; stamens mostly 3; style 2-cleft. **Achenes** lens-shaped, black and shiny, 1 mm long. Aug–Sept. ❦ Wet, sandy or mucky shores and wet meadows. ⊕ Local; mostly s LP of Mich, nw Ind. Tropical regions, n to Mass, Mich, nw Ind and Mo.

Cyperus odoratus L.
Rusty flatsedge OBL

Stout, grasslike, fibrous-rooted annual. **Stems** clumped or single, 3-angled, 2–7 dm long. **Leaves** mostly from base of plant, shorter to longer than flowering stems, the blades 2–8 mm wide; the involucral bracts much longer than the spikes. **Spikelets** linear, 1–2 cm long, pinnately arranged along a stalk, forming several to many cylindrical spikes, the spikes stalkless or stalked; **scales** red-brown, 2–3 mm long, overlapping; stamens 3; style 3-parted. **Achenes** brown, 3-angled, 1–2 mm long. July–Sept. *C. engelmannii, C. speciosus, C. ferruginescens*. ❦ Sandy or muddy shores, floating mats, ditches, wet cultivated fields. ⊕ Minn, Wisc, Mich, ne Ill and nw Ind. Tropics, n to Mass Wisc, Minn and ND.

Cyperus squarrosus L.
Awned flatsedge OBL

Small, clumped, sweet-scented, grasslike annual. **Stems** very slender, 3-angled, 3–15 cm long. **Leaves** few, all at base of plant, 1–2 mm wide; bracts 2–3, longer than the spikes. **Spikelets** linear, flattened, 3–10 mm long, in 1–4 dense, rounded spikes, 1 spike stalkless, the other spikes on stalks to 3 cm long; **scales** 1–2 mm long, tipped by an awn to 1 mm long, pale brown; stamens 1; style 3-parted. **Achenes** brown, 3-angled, 0.5–1 mm long. July–Sept. *C. aristatus, C. inflexus*. ❦ Wet, sandy or muddy lakeshores, streambanks, mud and gravel bars, wet meadows. ⊕ Minn, Mich (mostly c and s LP), ne Ill, nw Ind. Throughout most of USA and much of world.

Cyperus strigosus L.
False nutsedge; Straw-colored cyperus FACW

Grasslike perennial, from tuberlike corms. **Stems** single or few, slender, sharply 3-angled, 1–8 dm long. **Leaves** mostly at base of plants, the blades 2–12 mm wide, margins rough-to-touch; the bracts mostly longer than the spikes. **Spikelets** flat, linear, 6–20 mm long and 1–2 mm wide, golden-brown, pinnately arranged and spreading, in several to many cylindric spikes, the spikes often bent downward, on stalks 1–12 cm long, the stalks sometimes branched; **scales** straw-colored, 3–5 mm long; stamens 3; style 3-parted. **Achenes** brown, 3-angled, 1–2 mm long. July–Sept. ❦ Wet, sandy or muddy shores, streambanks, marshes, wet meadows, ditches, cultivated fields. ⊕ Common; ec and s Minn, Wisc, c and s LP of Mich (local in c UP), ne Ill, nw Ind. Que to Minn and SD, s to Fla and Tex; also the Pacific Coast and s into tropical Amer.

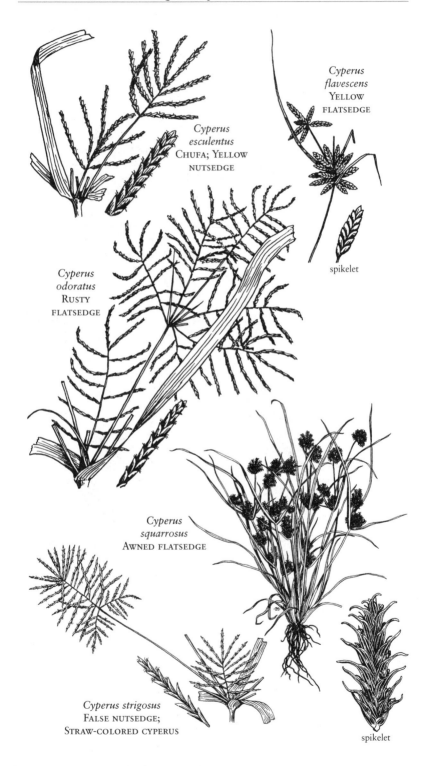

Cyperus esculentus
CHUFA; YELLOW NUTSEDGE

Cyperus flavescens
YELLOW FLATSEDGE

spikelet

Cyperus odoratus
RUSTY FLATSEDGE

Cyperus squarrosus
AWNED FLATSEDGE

Cyperus strigosus
FALSE NUTSEDGE;
STRAW-COLORED CYPERUS

spikelet

Dulichium Pers. / Three-way sedge

Dulichium arundinaceum (L.) Britton

Three-way sedge; Dulichium OBL

Grasslike perennial, spreading by rhizomes and often forming large colonies. **Stems** stout, erect, 3–10 dm long, jointed, hollow, rounded in section. **Leaves** 3-ranked, flat, short, 4–15 cm long and 3–8 mm wide; lower leaves reduced to sheaths. **Flower heads** from leaf axils, in linear clusters of 5–10 spikelets, the clusters 1–2.5 cm long; **scales** lance-shaped, green to brown, 5–8 mm long. **Flowers** perfect; sepals and petals reduced to 6–9 downwardly barbed bristles; stamens 3; style 2-parted. **Achenes** light brown, oblong, 2–4 mm long, beaked by the persistent, slender style. July–Sept. ❦ Shallow marshes, wet meadows, shores, bog margins. ⊕ n and e Minn, Wisc, Mich, ne Ill, nw Ind. Newf to BC s to Fla, Ala, e Tex, Neb, n Idaho and Calif.

*Dulichium
arundinaceum*
Three-way sedge;
Dulichium

▶**Eleocharis** R. Br. / Spike-rush

Small to medium rushlike plants, mostly perennial from rhizomes (annual in several species—*E. caribea, E. microcarpa* and *E. ovata),* often forming large, matlike colonies. **Stems** round, flattened, or angled in section. **Leaves** reduced to sheaths at base of stems. **Flower head** a single spikelet at tip of stem; scales of the spikelets spirally arranged and overlapping. **Flowers** perfect; sepals and petals bristlelike or absent, the bristles usually 6 if present; stamens 3; styles 2–3-parted, the base of style swollen and persistent as a projection (tubercle) atop the achene, or sometimes joined with the achene body. **Achenes** rounded on both sides or 3-angled.

▶**KEY TO ELEOCHARIS**

1 Tubercle joined with achene and not forming a distinct cap **2**
1 Tubercle forming a distinct cap atop the achene **4**

2 Small plants mostly less than 1 dm tall; scales 1–2 mm long; achenes
to 1 mm long . . . . *E. parvula* / SMALL SPIKE-RUSH
2 Plants larger, more than 1 dm tall; scales 3–5 mm long; achenes 2 mm
or more long. **3**

3 Stems 1–4 dm long, not rooting at tips; spikelets with 3–9 flowers .
. . . . *E. pauciflora* / FEW-FLOWER SPIKE-RUSH
3 Stems 4 dm or more long, often rooting at tips; spikelets with 10 or
more flowers . . . . *E. rostellata* / BEAKED SPIKE-RUSH

4 Spikelets slender, about as wide as stems; the scales persistent . . . **5**
4 Spikelets wider than stems; scales deciduous. **7**

5 Stems round in section and divided by cross-walls (appearing jointed)
. . . . *E. equisetoides* / HORSETAIL SPIKE-RUSH
5 Stems 3–4-angled and not divided by cross-walls **6**

6 Stems 3-angled, 1 to 2 mm wide; scales 10 or less. . . . . *E. robbinsii*
. . . . ROBBINS' SPIKE-RUSH
6 Stems 4-angled, 2–6 mm wide; scales 10 or more . *E. quadrangulata*
. . . . SQUARE-STEM SPIKE-RUSH

7 Styles 3-parted; achenes 3-angled to ± round **8**
7 Styles 2-parted; achenes lens-shaped. **15**

8 Body of achene flat across top, tubercle flattened, its base nearly as
wide as top of achene . . *E. melanocarpa* / BLACK-FRUIT SPIKE-RUSH
8 Achene body rounded at top; tubercle long and narrow or constrict-
ed at base **9**

9 Achene round in section, 2x longer than wide **10**
9 Achene 3-angled, nearly as wide as long. **11**

10 Stems ± round in section, less than 0.5 mm wide . . . . . *E. acicularis*
. . . . LEAST SPIKE-RUSH
10 Stems flattened, 1 mm or more wide . *E. wolfii* / WOLF'S SPIKE-RUSH

11 Achenes pitted or rough (use hand lens) **12**
11 Achenes smooth **13**

12 Stems flattened . . . . *E. compressa* / FLAT-STEM SPIKE-RUSH
12 Stems 4–8-angled. . . . . *E. tenuis* / SLENDER SPIKE-RUSH

13 Annual; achenes gray to nearly white; rare plant of nw Ind. . . . .
. . . . *E. microcarpa* / HAIR SPIKE-RUSH
13 Perennial; achenes olive to brown **14**

14 Achene angles not winged; bristles present . . . . *E. intermedia*
. . . . MATTED SPIKE-RUSH
14 Achene angles narrowly winged; bristles absent . . . . . . *E. tricostata*
. . . . THREE-RIBBED SPIKE-RUSH

15 Plants clumped annuals **16**

15 Plants perennials, spreading by short to long rhizomes **17**

16 Achenes black, to 1 mm long. . . . *E. caribea* / Capitate spike-rush
16 Achenes light to dark brown, 1–1.5 mm long. . . . . *E. ovata*
. . . . Blunt spike-rush

17 Plants small, 3–15 cm tall; stems clumped . . . . *E. flavescens*
. . . . Bright green spike-rush
17 Plants larger, 2–10 dm tall; stems scattered and single, or in small
clusters. . . . . *E. palustris* / Creeping spike-rush

---

Eleocharis acicularis (L.) Roemer & Schultes
Least spike-rush   OBL

achene

Small, clumped, mat-forming perennial, from slender rhizomes. **Stems** threadlike, 3–15 cm long and to 0.5 mm wide, somewhat 4-angled and grooved; sheaths membranous, usually red at base. **Spikelets** narrowly ovate, 3–6 mm long and 1–1.5 mm wide; scales with a green midvein and chaffy margins; sepals and petals reduced to 3–4 bristles or absent; style 3-parted. **Achenes** gray, rounded 3-angled, ridged, to 1 mm long; tubercle cone-shaped, constricted at base. May–Sept. ❦ Shallow water, exposed muddy or sandy shores, marshes and streambanks. ⊕ Common; Minn, Wisc, Mich. Circumboreal, s to Fla, La and Mex.

Eleocharis caribaea (Rottb.) S. F. Blake
Capitate spike-rush   FACW

⚠
STATUS
Indiana - T
Michigan - T

achene

Clumped, fibrous-rooted annual. **Stems** stiff, nearly round, 3–20 cm long. **Spikelets** ovate, 2–5 mm long; scales broadly ovate, brown with a green midvein; bristles brown, usually longer than the achene; style 2-parted. **Achenes** lens-shaped, black, shining, to 1 mm long; tubercle pale, very short, flattened and constricted at base. Aug–Sept. *E. capitata, E. geniculata.* ❦ Wet, sandy pond and marsh margins. ⊕ Rare in se Mich and nw Ind. Tropical regions, n to SC and rarely to Ont, Mich and nw Ind.

Eleocharis compressa Sullivant
Flat-stem spike-rush   FACW

⚠
STATUS
Michigan - T

achene

Clumped perennial, from stout black rhizomes. **Stems** flattened and often twisted, 1.5–4 dm long and 0.5–1 mm wide, shallowly grooved; sheaths red or purple at base. **Spikelets** ovate, 4–10 mm long and 3–4 mm wide; lowest scale sterile and encircling the stem; fertile scales with a green midvein, purple-brown on sides, and white translucent margins; sepals and petals absent or reduced to 1–5 bristles; style 3-parted. **Achenes** yellow-brown, covered with small bumps, somewhat 3-angled, 1–1.5 mm long; tubercle small, constricted at base. May–Aug. *E. acuminata.* ❦ Low calcareous prairie, wet meadows, swamps, ditches, dolomite limestone crevices in e UP of Mich. ⊕ Minn, Wisc, rare in LP and e UP of Mich, occasional in ne Ill and nw Ind. Que and NY to Sask, s to Va, Ga, Mo, Tex and Colo.

Eleocharis equisetoides (Elliott) Torr.
Horsetail spike-rush   OBL

⚠
STATUS
Indiana - E

Medium to large perennial, spreading by stout rhizomes. **Stems** round, hollow, to 1 m long and 5 mm wide; sheaths membranous, brown or green. **Spikelets** cylindric, 1.5–3 cm long, not wider than the stem; scales ovate to rounded, with narrow chaffy margins; stamens and petals reduced to 5–6 small bristles; style 3-parted. **Achenes** rounded on sides,

achene

golden-brown, shiny, 2 mm long; tubercle black, flattened, 3-angled, 1 mm long. *E. elliottii, E. interstincta.* ❦ Sandy or mucky lakeshores and pond margins, sometimes in shallow water. ⊕ Local in s LP of Mich and n Ind, formerly from sc Wisc. Mass to Mich, s to Fla, Mo and Tex.

Eleocharis flavescens (Poiret) Urban
Bright green spike-rush   OBL

STATUS
Illinois - E
Minnesota - T

Small, clumped, mat-forming perennial, spreading by slender rhizomes. **Stems** bright green, flattened, 3–15 cm long. **Spikelets** ovate, 2–7 mm long and much wider than stem; scales ovate, red-brown, with a green midvein; sepals and petals reduced to 6–8 barbed bristles; style 2-parted (rarely 3-parted). **Achenes** lens-shaped, brown, 1 mm long; tubercle pale, cone-shaped, constricted at base. *E. olivacea.* ❦ Shallow water, sandy or muddy lakeshores, mud flats; sometimes where calcium-rich. ⊕ Uncommon in nc Minn, Wisc, LP of Mich (especially w), local in ne Ill and nw Ind. NS to Wisc and Minn, s to Fla.

achene

Eleocharis intermedia (Muhl.) Schultes
Matted spike-rush   FACW

achene

Small, densely clumped annual. **Stems** threadlike, grooved, of unequal lengths, 5–20 cm long; sheaths toothed on 1 side. **Spikelets** long-ovate, wider than stem; scales oblong lance-shaped, purple-brown, with a green midvein and white, translucent margins; sepals and petals reduced to barbed bristles or sometimes absent; style 3-parted. **Achenes** light brown to olive, 3-angled, 1 mm long; tubercle cone-shaped, constricted at base. June–Sept. *E. macounii.* ❦ Wet, sandy or mucky shores, streambanks, mud flats. ⊕ nc and ec Minn, Wisc, Mich (local in UP), ne Ill, nw Ind. Que to Minn, s to Pa, WVa, Tenn, Ill and Iowa.

Eleocharis melanocarpa Torr.
Black-fruit spike-rush   FACW+

STATUS
Indiana - T

Densely clumped perennial. **Stems** flattened, wiry, 2–6 dm long; sheaths 1-toothed. **Spikelets** cylindric to narrowly ovate, 5–15 mm long, wider than stem; scales ovate, rounded at tip, brown with a lighter midvein; sepals and petals reduced to 3–4 rough bristles; style 3-parted. **Achenes** oblong pyramid-shaped, rounded 3-angled, dark brown to black, 1 mm long; tubercle light brown, depressed across top of achene and pointed in middle. June–July. ❦ Wet, sandy or mucky lakeshores, moist sandy prairie, mud flats. ⊕ Atlantic coast from Mass to Fla and Tex; disjunct in our area in sw Mich and nw Ind.

achene

Eleocharis microcarpa Torr.
Hair spike-rush   OBL

STATUS
Indiana - E
Michigan - E

Densely clumped annual. **Stems** slender, somewhat 4-angled, to 3 dm long (or longer when underwater). **Spikelets** ovate or oblong, 2–6 mm long, wider than stems; scales ovate, brown-red, with a green midvein and paler margins, all but lowest scale soon deciduous; sepals and petals reduced to 3–6 slender bristles; style 3-parted. **Achenes** pale white, 3-angled, to 1 mm long; tubercle small, pyramid-shaped. July–Aug. *E. torreyana.* ❦ Marshes and wet meadows. ❦ Rare in nw Ind. Atlantic coast from Conn to Fla and Tex; inland in s Mich, Ind and Tenn.

achene

Eleocharis ovata (Roth) Roemer & Schultes
Blunt spike-rush   OBL

Clumped, fibrous-rooted annual. **Stems** slender, round in section, ribbed, 0.5–5 dm long and 1–2 mm wide; sheaths green. **Spikelets** ovate to cylindric, 4–15 mm long and 2–4 mm wide; scales purple-brown, with a green

achene

midvein and pale margins; sepals and petals reduced to 6–7 brown bristles, or absent; styles 2- or 3-parted. **Achenes** lens-shaped, light to dark brown or olive, shiny, 1–1.5 mm long; tubercle flattened-triangular, about as wide as the broad top of achene. June–Sept. *E. engelmannii, E. obtusa.* ✤ Wet, sandy or muddy shores, marshes, ditches, mud flats, temporary ponds. ⊕ Mostly ne and ec Minn, n Wisc, local in w UP and far n LP of Mich. Widespread over much of n N Amer and Eurasia.

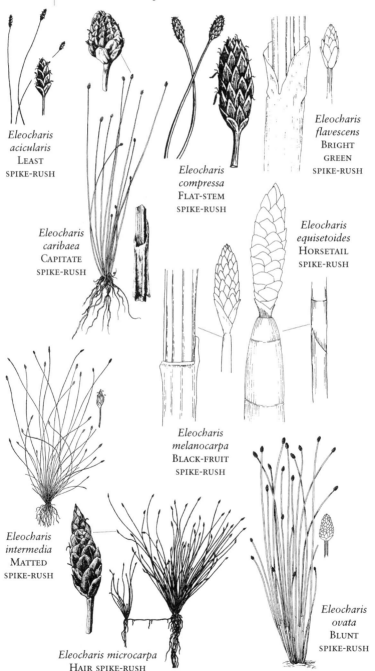

Eleocharis acicularis
LEAST
SPIKE-RUSH

Eleocharis compressa
FLAT-STEM
SPIKE-RUSH

Eleocharis flavescens
BRIGHT
GREEN
SPIKE-RUSH

Eleocharis caribaea
CAPITATE
SPIKE-RUSH

Eleocharis equisetoides
HORSETAIL
SPIKE-RUSH

Eleocharis melanocarpa
BLACK-FRUIT
SPIKE-RUSH

Eleocharis intermedia
MATTED
SPIKE-RUSH

Eleocharis microcarpa
HAIR SPIKE-RUSH

Eleocharis ovata
BLUNT
SPIKE-RUSH

Eleocharis palustris L.
Creeping spike-rush OBL

achene

Perennial, spreading by rhizomes. **Stems** single or in small clusters, slender to stout, round in section, 1–8 dm long and 1–3 mm wide; sheaths red or purple at base. **Spikelets** long-ovate, 5–30 mm long and 2–4 mm wide, wider than stems; lowest scale sterile, encircling the stem; fertile scales lance-shaped to ovate, 2–5 mm long, brown or red-brown, with a green or pale midvein; sepals and petals reduced to usually 4, pale brown, barbed bristles; style 2-parted. **Achenes** lens-shaped, yellow to brown, 1–2 mm long; tubercle flattened-triangular, constricted at base. May–Aug. A variable species known by a number of synonyms including *E. erythropoda, E. macrostachya, E. smallii*. ≋ Shallow water of marshes, wet meadows, muddy shores, bogs, ditches, streambanks and swamps. ⊕ Common; Minn, Wisc, Mich, ne Ill, nw Ind. Circumboreal, s to Va, s to Va, Tenn, n Tex, Colo and NM.

Eleocharis parvula (Roemer & Schultes) Link.
Small spike-rush OBL

⚠ STATUS
Michigan - T

achene

Very small, clumped, perennial, spreading by slender rhizomes and forming dense mats; rhizomes often with tubers. **Stems** threadlike, mostly 2–6 cm long, less than 1 mm wide. **Spikelets** ovate, 2–5 mm long and 1–2 mm wide; scales ovate, green, straw-colored or brown, 1–2 mm long; sepals and petals absent or reduced to small bristles; style 3-parted. **Achenes** pale brown, 3-angled, about 1 mm long; tubercle small, not forming a distinct cap on top of achene body. July–Sept. ≋ Wet saline or alkaline flats and shores. ⊕ Uncommon in far w Minn, Wisc, local in sc LP of Mich. Atlantic and Pacific coasts, uncommon inland.

Eleocharis pauciflora (Lightf.) Link
Few-flower spike-rush OBL

⚠ STATUS
Illinois - E

achene

Small, clumped perennial, spreading by rhizomes. **Stems** threadlike, grooved, 1–3 dm long and less than 1 mm wide. **Spikelets** ovate, 4–8 mm long and 2–3 mm wide; scales ovate, brown, chaffy on margins, 2–5 mm long; sepals and petals reduced to bristles or absent; style 3-parted. **Achenes** gray-brown or brown, 3-angled, 1–3 mm long; tubercle slender, joined to the achene and beaklike. June–Aug. ≋ Wet, sandy or gravelly shores and flats marshes and fens; often where calcium-rich. ⊕ Local in n Minn, mostly near Great Lakes in Mich, ne Ill and nw Ind. Circumboreal, s to NJ, Ill, Minn, Neb, NM and Calif.

Eleocharis quadrangulata (Michx.) Roemer & Schultes
Square-stem spike-rush OBL

⚠ STATUS
Wisconsin - E

achene

Medium to large clumped perennial, spreading by rhizomes. **Stems** stout, sharply 4-angled, to 1 m long and 2–5 mm wide. **Spikelets** cylindric, 2–5 cm long, about as thick as stem; scales in 4 rows, brown, oval to obovate, 5–6 mm long, margins chaffy; sepals and petals reduced to bristles; style 2- or 3-parted. **Achenes** rounded on sides, brown, 2–3 mm long; tubercle dark brown, flattened cone-shape. ≋ Shallow water and wet, sandy or mucky shores; sedge meadows near lakeshores. ⊕ Rare (and possibly no longer present) in e Wisc, mostly s LP of Mich, nw Ind.

Eleocharis robbinsii Oakes
Robbins' spike-rush OBL

Clumped perennial, spreading by rhizomes. **Stems** slender, 3-angled, 2–6 dm long and 1–2 mm wide; when underwater, plants often with numerous sterile stems from base; sheaths brown. **Spikelets** lance-shaped, 1–2 cm long and 2–3 mm wide, barely wider than stems; scales narrowly

achene

ovate, margins chaffy; sepals and petals reduced to 6 barbed bristles; style 3-parted. **Achenes** rounded on both sides, light brown, 2–3 mm long; tubercle flattened and cone-shaped, with a raised ring at base. July–Aug. ❦ Wet, sandy or mucky lake and pond shores, marshes, exposed flats. ⊕ Local in n and c Wisc, Mich (especially sw LP, local in UP) and nw Ind. NB and NS s to Fla; also NY to Mich, nw Ind and Wisc.

Eleocharis rostellata (Torr.) Torr.
Beaked spike-rush   OBL

achene

Clumped perennial, without creeping rhizomes. **Stems** flattened, wiry, 3–10 dm long and 1–2 mm wide; the fertile stems upright, the sterile stems often arching and rooting at tip; sheaths brown. **Spikelets** oblong, tapered at both ends, 5–15 mm long and 2–5 mm wide, wider than the stem; scales ovate, 3–5 mm long, green to brown with a darker midvein and translucent margins; sepals and petals reduced to 4–8 barbed bristles; style 3-parted. **Achenes** olive to brown, rounded 3-angled, 2–3 mm long; tubercle cone-shaped, joined with the achene body and beaklike. June–Aug. ❦ Shores, wet meadows, calcareous fens and mud flats; typically where calcium-rich and often associated with mineral springs. ⊕ Local in nc Minn, se Wisc, LP and far e UP of Mich, ne Ill and nw Ind. NS to BC, s to Fla, Tex and n Mex; S Amer.

Eleocharis tenuis (Willd.) Schultes
Slender spike-rush   FACW

achene

Clumped perennial, spreading by rhizomes. **Stems** slender, 4–8-angled, 2–5 dm long; sheaths red-purple at base. **Spikelets** oblong, 3–10 mm long, wider than stem; scales ovate or obovate, 2–3 mm long, purple-brown to black, with a green midvein and chaffy margins; sepals and petals reduced to 2–4 bristles or absent; style 3-parted. **Achenes** rounded 3-angled, rough, about 1 mm long; tubercle cone-shaped. ❦ Wet sandy or gravelly shores, interdunal pools and flats, swales and ditches, often where calcium-rich. ⊕ Local in ne and ec Minn, LP and e UP of Mich, ne Ill and nw Ind. Nfld to BC, s to SC and Tex.

Eleocharis tricostata Torr.
Three-ribbed spike-rush   OBL

achene

Perennial, spreading by short rhizomes. **Stems** single or in small clusters, slender, somewhat flattened, grooved, 2–6 dm long; sheaths 1-toothed at tip. **Spikelets** cylindric, 5–15 mm long; scales overlapping in many rows, ovate, brown with a green midvein; bristles absent; style 3-parted. **Achenes** brown to olive, 1 mm long, 3-angled, narrowly winged on the angles; tubercle very small, nearly flat, light brown. ❦ Sandy shores. ⊕ Rare in sw LP of Mich. Mass s to Fla; disjunct in sw Mich.

Eleocharis wolfii A. Gray
Wolf's spike-rush   OBL

achene

Clumped perennial, from slender rhizomes. **Stems** flattened, 2-edged, often twisted, 1–3 dm long and 1–2 mm wide; sheaths often purple at base, membranous at tip. **Spikelets** narrowly ovate, 4–10 mm long and 2–3 mm wide, wider than stem; scales green, tinged with purple, narrowly ovate, 2–3 mm long, with chaffy margins; bristles absent; style 3-parted. **Achenes** gray, ± round in section, about 1 mm long; tubercle cone-shaped, constricted at base where joins achene. June–July. ❦ Wet meadows and low prairie. ⊕ Rare in w and sc Minn, sw Wisc, ne Ill and nw Ind. Ind to Alberta, s to Tenn, La and Colo; NY.

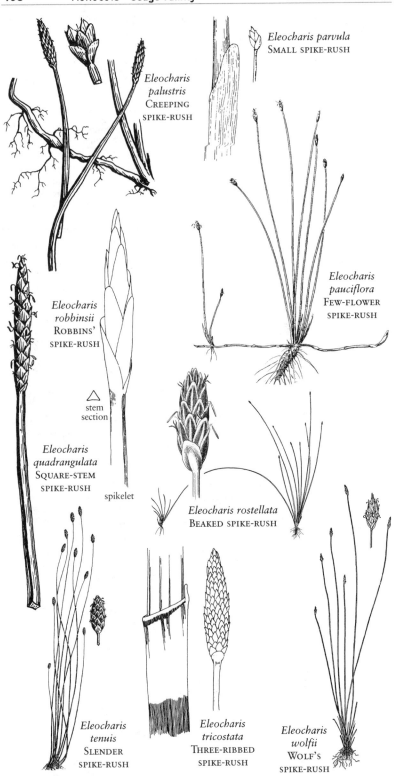

Eleocharis parvula
SMALL SPIKE-RUSH

Eleocharis palustris
CREEPING
SPIKE-RUSH

Eleocharis pauciflora
FEW-FLOWER
SPIKE-RUSH

Eleocharis robbinsii
ROBBINS'
SPIKE-RUSH

△
stem
section

Eleocharis quadrangulata
SQUARE-STEM
SPIKE-RUSH

spikelet

Eleocharis rostellata
BEAKED SPIKE-RUSH

Eleocharis tenuis
SLENDER
SPIKE-RUSH

Eleocharis tricostata
THREE-RIBBED
SPIKE-RUSH

Eleocharis wolfii
WOLF'S
SPIKE-RUSH

▶**Eriophorum** L. / Cotton-grass

☞
Eriophorum
spikelets
resemble
'cottonballs'
when mature;
the cottonballs
are composed
of the bristle-
like sepals
and petals.

Grasslike perennials. **Stems** clumped or single, round to rounded 3-angled in section. **Leaves** mostly at base of plant, the blades flat, folded or inrolled; upper leaves often reduced to bladeless sheaths. **Flower heads** at ends of stems, with 1 or several spikelets; scales many, spirally arranged, chaffy on margins; involucral bracts leaflike in species with several spikelets in the head, or reduced to scales in species with 1 spikelet at end of stems (*E. chamissonis, E. vaginatum*). **Flowers** perfect; sepals and petals numerous, reduced to long, cottony, persistent white to tawny brown bristles; stamens 3; styles 3-parted. **Achenes** brown, ± 3-angled, sometimes with a short beak formed by the persistent style.

▶**KEY TO ERIOPHORUM**

1 Head a single spikelet at end of stem; leaflike bracts absent **2**
1 Head of 2 or more spikelets; leaflike bracts present **3**

2 Plants forming colonies from rhizomes. . . . . *E. chamissonis*
. . . . RUSTY COTTON-GRASS
2 Plants densely clumped, rhizomes absent . . . . *E. vaginatum*
. . . . TUSSOCK COTTON-GRASS

3 Leaves 1–2 mm wide; leaflike bract 1, erect, the head appearing lateral from side of stem. **4**
3 Leaves 3 mm or more wide; leaflike bracts 2 or 3, the head appearing terminal **5**

4 Blade of uppermost stem leaf much shorter than its sheath . . . .
. . . . *E. gracile* / SLENDER COTTON-GRASS
4 Blade as long or longer than its sheath . . . . *E. tenellum*
. . . . CONIFER COTTON-GRASS

5 Scales 3–7-nerved, copper-brown on sides . . . . *E. virginicum*
. . . . TAWNY COTTON-GRASS
5 Scales with 1 nerve, sides olive-green to nearly black **6**

6 Midvein of scale slender, fading before reaching tip of scale. . . . . .
. . . . *E. angustifolium* / THIN-SCALE COTTON-GRASS
6 Midvein of scale widening toward tip of scale and reaching scale tip
. . . . *E. viridicarinatum* / DARK-SCALE COTTON-GRASS

Eriophorum angustifolium Honck.
Thin-scale cotton-grass   OBL
Grasslike perennial, spreading by rhizomes and forming colonies. **Stems** mostly single, 2–8 dm long and 2–3 mm wide, ± round in section, becoming 3-angled below the head. **Leaves** few, flat or folded along midrib, 3–8 mm wide, often dying back from the tips; sheaths sometimes red, dark-banded at tip. **Spikelets** 3–10, clustered in heads 1–3 cm wide when mature, the heads drooping on weak stalks; involucral bracts leaflike, often black at base, the main bract upright and usually longer than the head; scales lance-shaped, brown or purple-green, 4–6 mm long, the midvein not extending to tip of scale; bristles bright white, 2–3 cm long. **Achenes** brown to nearly black, 2–3 mm long. May–July. *E. polystachion.* ❦ Bogs, calcareous fens, wet meadows. ⊕ Minn, Wisc, Mich, occasional in ne Ill and nw Ind. Circumboreal, s to Maine, NY, Mich, n Ill, n Neb, Colo, n NM, Idaho and Ore.

Eriophorum chamissonis C. A. Meyer
Rusty cotton-grass   OBL

Grasslike perennial, spreading by rhizomes and forming colonies. **Stems** single or in small groups, stout, ± round in section, 2–6 dm long and 1–3 mm wide. **Leaves** few, mostly from base of plant and shorter than stems, the uppermost leaves from near middle of stem and often without blades, lower leaves round in section to 3-angled and channeled, 1–2 mm wide. **Spikelets** single, erect at end of stems, clustered in a ± round head 2–3 cm wide; involucral bracts not leaflike, reduced to black scales; flower scales narrowly ovate, black-green, with broad white margins and tips; bristles white to bright red-brown. **Achenes** dark brown, beaked, 2–3 mm long. June–July. ⚘ Bogs. ⊕ n and c Minn. Circumboreal, s to NB, Minn, nw Wyo and Ore.

Eriophorum gracile Koch
Slender cotton-grass   OBL

STATUS
Indiana - T

Grasslike perennial, spreading from rhizomes. **Stems** single, spreading or reclining, slender, ± round in section, 2–6 dm long and 1–2 mm wide. **Leaves** few, channeled on upper side, 1–2 mm wide, the basal leaves often withered by flowering time, blades of uppermost leaves small. **Spikelets** in clusters of 2–5 at ends of stems, on spreading to nodding stalks 2–3 cm long; involucral bract leaflike and erect, shorter than spikelet cluster; scales ovate, pale to black-brown with a prominent midvein; bristles bright white. **Achenes** light brown, 3–4 mm long. May–July. ⚘ Fens and bogs. ⊕ Minn, Wisc, Mich and uncommon in nw Ind. Circumboreal, s to Pa, n Ind, Iowa, Neb, Colo, Idaho and Calif.

Eriophorum tenellum Nutt.
Conifer cotton-grass   OBL

Grasslike perennial, with rhizomes and forming colonies. **Stems** single, slender, erect, 3–8 dm long, rounded 3-angled, rough-to-touch on upper angles. **Leaves** linear, 1–2 mm wide, channeled, not reduced and bladeless on upper stem. **Spikelets** 3–6, in short-stalked clusters at ends of stems, or with 1–2 rough, drooping stalks to 5 cm long; involucral bract leaflike, stiff and erect, usually shorter than the spikelet cluster; scales ovate, straw-colored to red-brown; bristles white. **Achenes** brown, 2–3 mm long. ⚘ Bogs and conifer swamps. ⊕ nc and ne Minn, Wisc, UP of Mich (local in LP). Nfld to Minn, s to NJ, Pa.

Eriophorum vaginatum L.
Tussock cotton-grass   OBL

Densely clumped, grasslike perennial, forming large hummocks. **Stems** stiff, rounded 3-angled, 2–7 dm long. **Leaves** at base of stems, mostly shorter than stems, only 1 mm wide, with 1–3 inflated, bladeless sheaths on stem. **Spikelets** clustered in a single head at end of stems; involucral bracts absent; scales narrowly ovate, purple-brown to black, with white margins, spreading when mature; bristles usually white (rarely red-brown). **Achenes** obovate, 3–4 mm long. June. *E. callithrix, E. spissum.* ⚘ Sphagnum bogs and tamarack swamps. ⊕ Common in n parts of our region. nc, ne and ec Minn, n and e Wisc (local in se), Mich. Circumboreal, s to NJ, Pa, n Ind and Alberta.

Eriophorum virginicum L.
Tawny cotton-grass   OBL

STATUS
Illinois - E

Large grasslike perennial, with slender rhizomes. **Stems** single or in small groups, stiff, erect, to 1 m long, leafy, mostly smooth. **Leaves** flat, 2–4 mm wide, the uppermost often longer than the head. **Spikelets** in dense

☞ The widely spreading, leaflike involucral bracts and copper-colored, cottony bristles are diistinctive.

clusters of several to many at ends of stems, on short stalks of ± equal lengths, the clusters wider than long; involucral bracts 2–3, leaflike, spreading or bent downward, unequal, much longer than the head; scales ovate, thick, copper-brown with a green center; bristles tawny or copper-brown. **Achenes** light brown, 3–4 mm long. July–Aug. ❧ Sphagnum moss peatlands. ⊕ Common in ne and ec Minn, Wisc and Mich; uncommon in ne Ill and nw Ind. Nfld and Que to Minn and Man, s to Fla and Ky.

Eriophorum viridicarinatum (Engelm.) Fernald
Dark-scale cotton-grass　　　　　　　　　　　　　　　　　OBL

⚠
STATUS
Illinois - E

Grasslike perennial, forming colonies from spreading rhizomes. **Stems** mostly single, ± round in section, 3–7 dm long. **Leaves** flat except at tip, the uppermost leaves 10–15 cm long; sheaths green. **Spikelets** usually 20–30, clustered in heads at ends of stems, on short to long, finely hairy stalks; involucral bracts 2–4, not black at base, longer or equal to head; scales narrowly ovate, black-green, the midvein pale, extending to tip of scale; bristles white. **Achenes** brown, 3–4 mm long. May–July. ❧ Bogs and open conifer swamps. ⊕ Common across most of our range; n and ec Minn, Wisc, Mich, rare in ne Ill. Newf to Alaska, s to NY, Ohio, n Ind, Minn, ne ND, Colo, and n Idaho. ☞ Similar to **thin-scale cotton-grass** (*E. angustifolium*), but usually with more spikelets, the scale midvein extending to the tip of scale, and the leaf sheaths not dark-banded at tip.

▸Fimbristylis Vahl / Fimbry

Annual or perennial grasslike plants. **Stems** slender, clumped or single. **Leaves** mostly at base of plants, narrowly linear, flat to inrolled. **Spikelets** many-flowered, in umbel-like clusters at ends of stems; involucral bracts 2–3, short and leaflike; scales spirally arranged and overlapping. **Flowers** perfect, sepals and petals absent, stamens 1–3; styles 2–3-parted, swollen at base, deciduous when mature. **Achenes** lens-shaped or 3-angled.

▸KEY TO FIMBRISTYLIS

1 Plants annual; achenes 3-angled; styles 3-parted . . . . . *F. autumnalis*
. . . . Autumn sedge
1 Plants perennial; achenes lens-shaped; styles 2-parted. . . *F. puberula*
. . . . Chestnut sedge

Fimbristylis autumnalis (L.) Roemer & Schultes
Autumn sedge　　　　　　　　　　　　　　　　　　　　FACW+

Clumped, grasslike annual, with shallow fibrous roots. **Stems** flattened, slender, sharp-edged, 0.5–3 dm long. **Leaves** shorter than the stems, flat, 1–2 mm wide. **Spikelets** usually many in an open umbel-like cluster, the spikelets lance-shaped, 3–8 mm long, single or several at ends of thread-like, spreading stalks; involucral bracts 2–3, leaflike, usually shorter than the head; scales ovate, golden-brown with a prominent green midvein, 1–2 mm long; style 3-parted. **Achenes** ivory to tan, 3-angled and ribbed on the angles, to 0.5 mm long. July–Sept. ❧ Sandy or mucky shores (especially where seasonally flooded and then later drying), streambanks, wet meadows, ditches. ⊕ Uncommon in ne and ec Minn; Wisc, LP of Mich, ne Ill and nw Ind. Maine and Que to Minn and SD, s to Fla and Tex; Mex, c and S Amer.

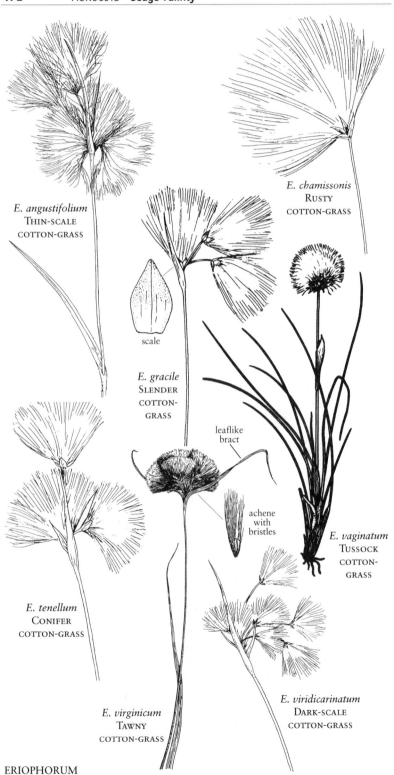

E. angustifolium
THIN-SCALE
COTTON-GRASS

E. chamissonis
RUSTY
COTTON-GRASS

scale

E. gracile
SLENDER
COTTON-
GRASS

leaflike
bract

achene
with
bristles

E. vaginatum
TUSSOCK
COTTON-
GRASS

E. tenellum
CONIFER
COTTON-GRASS

E. virginicum
TAWNY
COTTON-GRASS

E. viridicarinatum
DARK-SCALE
COTTON-GRASS

ERIOPHORUM

Fimbristylis puberula (Michx.) Vahl
Chestnut sedge OBL

Grasslike perennial, with short rhizomes. **Stems** single or in small clumps, slender, stiff, 2–7 dm long, round to oval in section, sometimes swollen at base. **Leaves** shorter than the stems, usually inrolled, 1–3 mm wide, often hairy. **Spikelets** few to many in an umbel-like cluster; the spikelets ovate, 5–10 mm long, the central spikelet stalkless, the others on slender stalks; involucral bracts 2–3, leaflike, the longest equal or longer than the head; scales ovate, brown with a lighter midvein, 3–4 mm long, usually finely hairy, often tipped with a short awn; style 2-parted, the style branches finely hairy. **Achenes** light brown, lens-shaped, 1–2 mm long. June–Sept. ❦ Wet meadows, shores, and low prairie, often where sandy and calcium-rich; also in drier prairies. ⊕ Rare in wc Minn and se Wisc, once known from several locations in s LP of Mich, local in ne Ill and nw Ind. NJ to s Wisc and Neb, s to Fla, Tex and NM.

▶ Fuirena Rottb. / Umbrella-sedge

Fuirena pumila (Torr.) Sprengel
Umbrella-sedge OBL

Clumped, grasslike annual. **Stems** smooth, 1–6 dm long. **Leaves** flat, to 10 cm long and 5 mm wide, the margins hairy; lower sheaths hairy. **Spikelets** stalkless, in clusters of mostly 1–3, the spikelets ovate, 6–15 mm long; scales ovate, brown, 2–4 mm long, hairy, 3-nerved, tipped with a spreading awn almost as long as scale; bristles 3, downwardly barbed. **Achenes** smooth, 3-angled. July–Sept. *F. squarrosa.* ❦ Sandy or mucky shores, especially where seasonally flooded; floating sedge mats. ⊕ c Wisc, sw LP of Mich and nw Ind. Mass s to Fla and Tex; disjunct in Great Lakes region.

▶ Hemicarpha Nees / Dwarf-bulrush

Hemicarpha micrantha (Vahl) Pax
Dwarf-bulrush OBL

Small, densely clumped grasslike annual. **Stems** compressed, 3–15 cm long. **Leaves** slender, 2 per stem, to 10 cm long and 0.5 mm wide, mostly shorter than the stems. **Spikelets** in stalkless clusters of 1–3; the spikelets many-flowered, ovate, 2–5 mm long; involucral bracts 2–3, leaflike, the main bract upright and longer than the spikelets (the head appearing lateral); scales brown with a green midvein, 1–2 mm long, tipped with an awn; bristles absent; style 2-parted, not swollen at base. **Achenes** brown, oblong, to 1 mm long. Aug–Sept. *Lipocarpa micrantha.* ❦ Sandy or muddy shores and streambanks, usually where seasonally flooded. ⊕ Mostly ec Minn, local in wc and sw LP of Mich, ne Ill and nw Ind. Maine to Ont and Minn, s to Fla, Tex, NM, Ariz and the Pacific states; Mex, c and S Amer and W Indies.

▶ Rhynchospora Vahl / Beak-rush

Grasslike perennials (annual in *R. scirpoides* and sometimes in *R. macrostachya*), clumped or spreading by rhizomes. **Stems** erect, leafy, usually 3-angled or sometimes round. **Leaves** flat or rolled inward. **Spikelets** clustered in dense heads, the heads open to crowded; scales

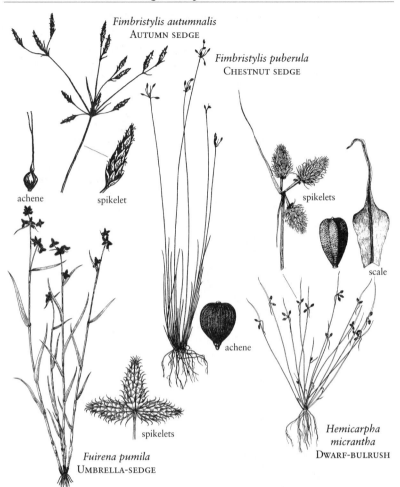

Fimbristylis autumnalis
AUTUMN SEDGE

Fimbristylis puberula
CHESTNUT SEDGE

achene

spikelet

spikelets

scale

achene

Fuirena pumila
UMBRELLA-SEDGE

spikelets

spikelets

Hemicarpha micrantha
DWARF-BULRUSH

overlapping in a spiral. **Flowers** perfect, or sometimes upper flowers male only; sepals and petals reduced to usually 6 (1–20) bristles or sometimes absent; stamens usually 3; styles 2-parted, swollen at base and persistent on the achene as a tubercle. **Achenes** lens-shaped.

▶**KEY TO RHYNCHOSPORA**

1 Plants annual; spikelets with many perfect flowers, scales not empty; bristles subtending the achene absent . . . . *R. scirpoides*
. . . . LONG-BEAKED BEAK-RUSH
1 Plants mostly perennial; spikelets few-flowered, the lower scales empty; bristles present. **2**

2 Leaves 5 mm or more wide; achenes flattened, with a tubercle more than 10 mm long; annual or short-lived perennial . *R. macrostachya*
. . . . TALL BEAK-RUSH
2 Leaves 1–4 mm wide; achenes rounded or lens-shaped, tubercle less than 3 mm long; perennials **3**

3 Surface of achene covered with conspicuous ridges or wrinkles; bristles subtending achene much shorter than achene . . . . *R. globularis*
. . . . GRASS BEAK-RUSH

3 Surface of achene smooth or only slightly wrinkled; bristles longer than achene. **4**

4 Spikelets white to tan; bristles 8 or more *R. alba* / WHITE BEAK-RUSH
4 Spikelets brown, dark olive-green or nearly black; bristles 5–6 . . . **5**

5 Scales dark olive-green to black; bristles with upward-pointing barbs, at least some of the bristles longer than the tubercle . . . . . . *R. fusca* . . . . GRAY BEAK-RUSH
5 Scales brown; bristles with downward pointing barbs (rarely smooth), the bristles shorter to as long as the tubercle. **6**

6 Stems narrow and threadlike; achene margins not translucent, achene body less than half as wide as long *R. capillacea* / NEEDLE BEAK-RUSH
6 Stems stout; achene with translucent margins, body more than half as wide as long. . . . . *R. capitellata* / BROWN BEAK-RUSH

Rhynchospora alba (L.) Vahl
White beak-rush   OBL

Clumped, grasslike perennial. **Stems** slender, erect, 1–6 dm long. **Leaves** bristlelike, 0.5–3 mm wide, shorter than the stems. **Spikelets** in 1–3 rounded heads, 5–20 mm wide, at or near ends of stems, the lateral heads usually long-stalked; the spikelets oblong, narrowed at each end, 4–5 mm long, white, becoming pale brown; bristles 8–15, downwardly barbed, about equaling the tubercle. **Achenes** lens-shaped, brown-green, 1–2 mm long; tubercle triangular, about half as long as achene. June–Sept. ⚘ Bogs, fens, open conifer swamps of black spruce and tamarack. ⊕ n and e Minn, Wisc, Mich, ne Ill and nw Ind. Circumboreal, s to NC, Ohio, n Ind, n Ill, Minn and Calif.

Rhynchospora capillacea Torr.
Needle beak-rush   OBL

Small, clumped, grasslike perennial. **Stems** slender, 0.5–4 dm long. **Leaves** threadlike, rolled inward, to only 0.5 mm wide, much shorter than the stem. **Spikelets** in 1–2 small, separated clusters, each cluster subtended by 1 to several short, bristlelike bracts; the spikelets ovate, 3–7 mm long; scales overlapping, ovate, brown with a paler, sharp-tipped midvein; bristles 6, downwardly barbed, longer than the achenes; style 2-parted. **Achenes** lens-shaped, satiny yellow-brown, 2 mm long; tubercle dull brown, narrowly triangular, about 1 mm long. June–Aug. ⚘ Calcareous fens, interdunal flats, wet sandy or gravelly shores, seeps; usually where calcium-rich. ⊕ Uncommon in nw and s Minn; Wisc, Mich (but uncommon in w UP), ne Ill and nw Ind. Newf to Alberta, s to Va, Tenn, Ohio, Ind, Mo and SD.

Rhynchospora capitellata (Michx.) Vahl
Brown beak-rush   OBL

Clumped, grasslike perennial. **Stems** erect, 3-angled, 3–8 dm long. **Leaves** flat, 2–4 mm wide, rough on margins, shorter than stems. **Spikelets** 3–5 mm long, several to many in 2–7 rounded, ± loose clusters 1–1.5 cm wide, the lateral clusters often in pairs on slender stalks; bristles 6, 2–3 mm long, usually downwardly barbed, about equaling the achene; style 2-parted. **Achenes** lens-shaped, dark brown, 1–2 mm long; tubercle triangular, about as long as achene. June–Sept. *R. glomerata.* ⚘ Wet sandy or mucky shores and flats, wet meadows, bogs, calcareous fens, ditches. ⊕ Mostly c and s LP of Mich, ne Ill and nw Ind. NS to Ont, Mich, n Ill and Mo, s to Fla and Tex; Pacific coast.

Rhynchospora fusca (L.) Aiton f.
Gray beak-rush   OBL

Clumped, grasslike perennial, spreading by short rhizomes and forming colonies. **Stems** slender, 3-angled, l–3 dm long. **Leaves** very slender, rolled inward, mostly shorter than the stems. **Spikelets** spindle-shaped, dark brown, 4–6 mm long, in 1–4 loose clusters, the lower clusters on long stalks, each cluster subtended by an erect, leafy bract, the bract longer than the cluster; bristles 6, upwardly barbed; style 2-parted. **Achenes** light brown, 1–1.5 mm long; tubercle flattened-triangular, nearly as long as achene. ⚘ Wet, sandy shores, interdunal wetlands, sedge meadows, bog mats. ⊕ Red Lake peatland in nc Minn, local in ne Minn; Wisc, UP and mostly n LP of Mich (plus rare in extreme sw Mich). Nfld and Que to Sask, s to Md, NY, Mich and Minn; Europe.

Rhynchospora globularis (Chapman) Small
Grass beak-rush   FACW

Clumped, grasslike perennial. **Stems** sharply 3-angled, 3–8 dm long. **Leaves** flat, 2–4 mm wide, the uppermost sometimes longer than stems. **Spikelets** 2–4 mm long, in 1–4 clusters at ends of stems and on stalks from upper leaf axils; bracts as long or longer than head; scales broadly ovate, dark brown; bristles 6, upwardly barbed, shorter than achenes; style 2-parted. **Achenes** brown, lens-shaped, 1–1.5 mm long; tubercle cone-shaped. June. ⚘ Sand flats, low prairie and sedge meadows. ⊕ Uncommon in ne Ill, nw Ind and possibly sw LP of Mich. Atlantic coast from NJ to SC, inland in s USA and Ohio, n Ill and Mo.

Rhynchospora macrostachya Torr.
Tall beak-rush   OBL

Large grasslike annual (or sometimes a short-lived perennial), rhizomes absent. **Stems** single or few, 3-angled, 0.5–2 m long. **Leaves** flat, to 1 cm wide. **Spikelets** 15–20 mm long, in a single, loose cluster at end of stem; scales lance-shaped, light brown; bristles 6 (3 on each side of achene), about 1 cm long; style 2-parted. **Achenes** flattened, dark brown, 4–6 mm long; tubercle long and beaklike, 15–20 mm long. ⚘ Sandy or mucky shores, especially on wet, exposed flats. ⊕ Local in sw LP of Mich and nw Ind. Mass to s Mich, s to Fla, Mo and Tex.

Rhynchospora scirpoides (Vahl) Griseb.
Long-beaked beak-rush   OBL

Clumped, grasslike annual. **Stems** 1–5 dm long. **Leaves** 1–3 mm wide, sometimes longer than stems. **Spikelets** ovate, 3–6 mm long, in open clusters at ends of stems; scales overlapping, ovate, brown, 2–3 mm long; bristles absent; style 2-parted. **Achenes** lens-shaped, dark brown, to 1 mm long and about as wide; tubercle flattened-triangular, about as long as achene. Aug–Sept. *Psilocarya scirpoides*. ⚘ Wet sandy or mucky shores and mudflats. ⊕ Rare in c Wisc, LP of Mich (especially sw), and nw Ind. RI and Mass to Wisc and nw Ind, s to Va and e NC.

▶Scirpus L. / Bulrush

Stout, rushlike perennials, mostly spreading by rhizomes. **Stems** unbranched, 3-angled or round in section, solid or pithy. **Leaves** broad and flat, to narrow and often folded near tip, or reduced to sheaths at base of stems; involucral bracts several and leaflike, or single and appearing like a continuation of the stem. **Spikelets** single, or in paniclelike or umbel-like clusters at ends of stems, or appearing lateral from the stem;

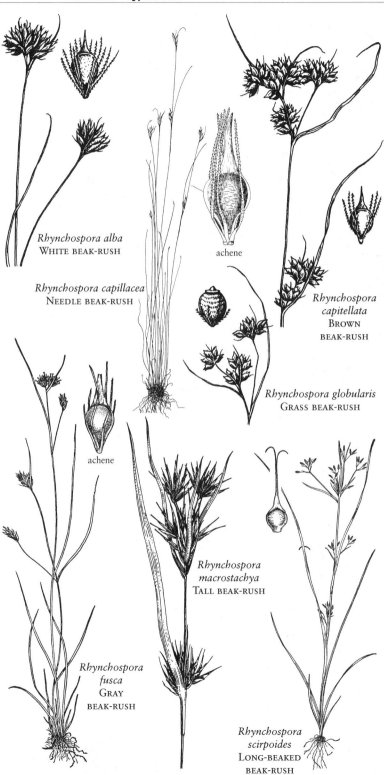

Rhynchospora alba
WHITE BEAK-RUSH

Rhynchospora capillacea
NEEDLE BEAK-RUSH

achene

Rhynchospora capitellata
BROWN
BEAK-RUSH

Rhynchospora globularis
GRASS BEAK-RUSH

achene

Rhynchospora fusca
GRAY
BEAK-RUSH

Rhynchospora macrostachya
TALL BEAK-RUSH

Rhynchospora scirpoides
LONG-BEAKED
BEAK-RUSH

☞ Some members of the genus Scirpus have been renamed in a forthcoming edition of the *Flora of North America*. The traditional treatment of the genus is presented here, with proposed new names in parentheses after the botanical name.

the spikelets stalked or stalkless; scales overlapping in a spiral. **Flowers** perfect; sepals and petals reduced to 1–6 smooth or downwardly barbed bristles, or sometimes absent; stamens 2 or 3; styles 2–3-parted. **Achenes** lens-shaped, flat on 1 side and convex on other, or 3-angled, usually tipped with a beak.

▶**KEY TO SCIRPUS**

1 Spikelets single at end of slender stems; bracts below head absent or very short **2**
1 Spikelets mostly more than 1; bracts conspicuous, leaflike or appearing to be a continuation of stem. **4**

2 Plants usually underwater, the leaves limp and floating; not clumped, spreading by rhizomes or stolons *S. subterminalis* / WATER-BULRUSH
2 Plants of peatlands, usually forming dense clumps **3**

3 Stems ± round in section, smooth *S. cespitosus* / CLUMPED BULRUSH
3 Stems 3-angled, rough on angles . . . . *S. hudsonianus*
. . . . ALPINE COTTON-GRASS

4 Bract single, erect, similar to stem and appearing to be a continuation of it **5**
4 Bracts 2 or more, flat and leaflike, usually spreading, appearing different than the stem. **11**

5 Stems sharply 3-angled **6**
5 Stems round in section or rounded 3-angled **7**

6 Leaves short, less than half length of stem; stigmas 2; achenes flat on 1 side, convex on other . . . . . *S. pungens* / COMMON THREESQUARE
6 Leaves often longer than stem; stigmas 3; achenes 3-angled. . . . . . .
. . . . *S. torreyi* / TORREY'S THREESQUARE

7 Stems to 5 dm long; spikelets less than 10 . . . . **8**
7 Stems more than 5 dm long; spikelets mostly more than 10 . . . . . **9**

8 Scales tipped with a short black awn about 0.2 mm long . . . .
. . . . *S. supinus* / SHARPSCALE-BULRUSH
8 Scales blunt-tipped or with a very short point less than 0.1 mm long
. . . . *S. smithii* / Bluntscale-bulrush

9 Scales pale brown, smooth; achenes 3-angled; stigmas 3; panicle branches flexible . . . . *S. heterochaetus* / SLENDER BULRUSH
9 Scales red-brown, hairy; achenes flat on 1 side and convex on other; stigmas 2; panicle branches stiff. **10**

10 Stems firm, difficult to compress between fingers; spikelets oblong to cylindric, more than 10 mm long when mature . . . . *S. acutus*
. . . . HARDSTEM-BULRUSH
10 Stems spongy, easily compressed; spikelets ovate, mostly less than 10 mm long . . . . *S. validus* / SOFTSTEM-BULRUSH

11 Stems sharply 3-angled **12**
11 Stems round in section or upper stem rounded 3-angled **13**
. . . .
12 Styles 3-parted; achenes 3-angled; leaf sheaths convex at tip . . . . . .
. . . . *S. fluviatilis* / RIVER-BULRUSH

12 Styles 2-parted; achenes lens-shaped; leaf sheaths straight or concave at tip . . . . *Scirpus maritimus* / ALKALI-BULRUSH

13 Lower sheaths red-tinged **14**
13 Sheaths green or brown **15**

14 Achenes 3-angled; stigmas 3; bristles usually 6 . . . . *S. expansus*
. . . . WOODLAND BULRUSH
14 Achenes lens-shaped; stigmas 2; bristles usually 4 . . . .
. . . . *S. microcarpus* / SMALL-FRUIT BULRUSH

15 Spikelets many in dense, ± round heads; bristles about as long as achene or shorter . . . . *S. atrovirens* / BLACK BULRUSH
15 Spikelets few in open clusters; bristles much longer than achene . **16**

16 Mature bristles longer than scales, giving spikelets woollyappearance
. . . . *S. cyperinus* / WOOL-GRASS
16 Mature bristles equal or only slightly longer than scales, spikelets not woolly . . . . *S. pendulus* / DROOPING BULRUSH

Scirpus acutus Muhl. (*Schoenoplectus acutus*)

Hardstem-bulrush   OBL

☞ **Hardstem-bulrush** stems are difficult to flatten between fingers in contrast to the otherwise similar **softstem-bulrush** (*S. validus*), in which the stems are easily compressed.

Perennial, from stout rhizomes and often forming large colonies. **Stems** round in section, 1–3 m long. **Leaves** reduced to 3–5 sheaths near base of stem, blades absent, or upper leaves with blades to 25 cm long; main bract erect, appearing as a continuation of stem, 2–10 cm long, eventually turning brown. **Spikelets** 5–15 mm long and 3–5 mm wide, in clusters of mostly 3–7, the clusters grouped into a branched head of up to 60 spikelets, the head appearing lateral from side of stem, the branches stiff and spreading; scales chaffy, mostly translucent, 3–4 mm long, often with red-brown spots, usually tipped with an awn to 1 mm long; bristles 6, unequal, usually shorter than achene; style 2-parted (rarely 3-parted). **Achenes** light green to dull brown, flat on 1 side and convex on other, 2–3 mm long, the style beak small, to 0.5 mm long. May–Aug. ⚘ Usually emergent in shallow to deep water (1–2 m deep) of marshes, ditches, ponds and lakes; sometimes where brackish. ⊕ Common; Minn, n and e Wisc, Mich, ne Ill and nw Ind. NS to BC, s to NC, Tex and Calif.

Scirpus atrovirens Willd.

Black bulrush   OBL

Loosely clumped perennial, with short rhizomes. **Stems** 3-angled, leafy, 0.5–1.5 m long. **Leaves** mostly on lower half of stem, blades ascending, usually shorter than the head, 6–18 mm wide; bracts 3–4, leaflike, to 15 cm long, mostly longer than the head. **Spikelets** many, 2–8 mm long and 1–3 mm wide, crowded in rounded heads at end of stems, the heads on stalks to 12 cm long; scales brown–black, translucent except for the broad green midvein, 1–2 mm long, tipped by an awn to 0.5 mm long; bristles 6, white or tan, shorter or equal to the achene; style 3-parted. **Achenes** tan to nearly white, compressed 3-angled, about 1 mm long, with a short beak 0.2 mm long. June–Aug. *S. atrovirens* var. *pallidus*. *S. hattorianus, S. pallidus*. ⚘ Wet meadows, shores, ditches, streambanks, swamps, springs and other wet places. ⊕ Common; Minn, Wisc, Mich, ne Ill and nw Ind. Ont to Alberta and Wash s to Mo, Tex, NM and Ariz.

Scirpus cespitosus L. (*Trichophorum caespitosum*)
Tufted bulrush   OBL

Densely clumped perennial, rhizomes short. **Stems** slender, smooth, ± round in section, 1–4 dm long. **Leaves** light brown and scalelike at base of stems, and also usually 1 leaf upward on stem, the blade narrow, short, to 6 mm long. **Spikelets** 1 at end of stems, brown, 4–6 mm long, several-flowered; scales yellow-brown, deciduous, the lowest scale about as long as spikelet; bristles 6, usually slightly longer than achene; style 3-parted. **Achenes** brown, 3-angled, 1.5 mm long. ❦ Open bogs, cedar swamps, calcareous fens, wet swales between dunes; also Lake Superior rocky shores. ⊕ Mostly n Minn, e half of Wisc, UP of Mich (and uncommon in n LP), rare in ne Ill. Circumboreal, where an important plant of the arctic tundra; s to New Eng, NY, n Ill, Minn, Utah and Ore; disjunct in mts of NC and Tenn.

Scirpus cyperinus (L.) Kunth
Wool-grass   OBL

Coarse, densely clumped perennial, rhizomes short. **Stems** leafy, to 2 m tall, rounded 3-angled to nearly round in section. **Leaves** flat, 3–10 mm wide, rough-to-touch on margins; sheaths brown; bracts 2–4, leaflike, spreading, usually drooping at tip, often red-brown at base. **Spikelets** numerous, ovate, 3–8 mm long and 2–3 mm wide, appearing woolly due to the long bristles, in clusters of 1 to several spikelets; the spikelet clusters grouped into large, spreading, branched heads at ends of stems; scales ovate, 1–2 mm long; bristles 6, smooth, brown, much longer than achene and scale; styles 3-parted. **Achenes** white to tan, flattened 3-angled, 0.5–1 mm long, with a short beak. July–Sept. *S. atrocinctus, S. pedicellatus.* ❦ Wet meadows, marshes, swamps, ditches, bog margins, thickets; where wet or in very shallow standing water. ⊕ Common to abundant; Minn, Wisc, Mich, n Ill and n Ind. Newf to s BC, s to Fla, e Tex and SD.

Scirpus expansus Fernald
Woodland bulrush   OBL

Perennial, with long red rhizomes. **Stems** single, stout, to 2 m long, 3-angled. **Leaves** flat, 1–2 cm wide, margins rough-to-touch; lower sheaths red at base; bracts leaflike, the largest 30 cm or more long. **Spikelets** ovate, 3–5 mm long, clustered in small heads; the heads 2–3x branched; scales 1–2 mm long, oval, brown with a green midvein; bristles 6, light brown, about as long as achene, downwardly barbed, deciduous; style 3-parted. **Achenes** compressed 3-angled, dull brown to purple-brown, 1–2 mm long, with a short beak. June–July. ❦ Marshes, streambanks, shores and ditches. ⊕ w LP of Mich. Maine s to Ga, occasionally w to Ohio and sw Mich.

Scirpus fluviatilis (Torr.) A. Gray (*Schoenoplectus fluviatilis*)
River-bulrush   OBL

Perennial, spreading by rhizomes and often forming large colonies. **Stems** stout, erect, 6–15 dm long, sharply 3-angled, the sides ± flat. **Leaves** several on stem, smooth, 6–15 mm wide, upper leaves often longer than the head; bracts 3–5, leaflike, erect to spreading, to 3–4 dm long. **Spikelets** 1–3 cm long and 6–12 mm wide, clustered in an umbel with 10–20 spikelets at end of stem, several of the spikelets nearly stalkless in 1–2 clusters, others single or in groups of 2–5 at ends of spreading or drooping stalks to 8 cm long; scales gold-brown, short-hairy on back, 6–10 mm long, the midvein extended into a curved awn 1–3 mm long; bristles 6, unequal, white to copper-brown, downwardly barbed, persistent, about as long as body of achene; style yellow, 3-parted. **Achenes** 3-angled, dull, tan to gray-green, 3–5 mm long, with a beak to 0.5 mm long. June–Aug. ❧ Usually in shallow water of streams, ditches, marshes, lakes and ponds; sometimes where brackish. ⊕ Occasional; Minn, Wisc (all but nc), mostly c and s LP of Mich (local in UP), common in ne Ill and nw Ind. Que to Wash, s to Va, Mo, Kans and Calif.

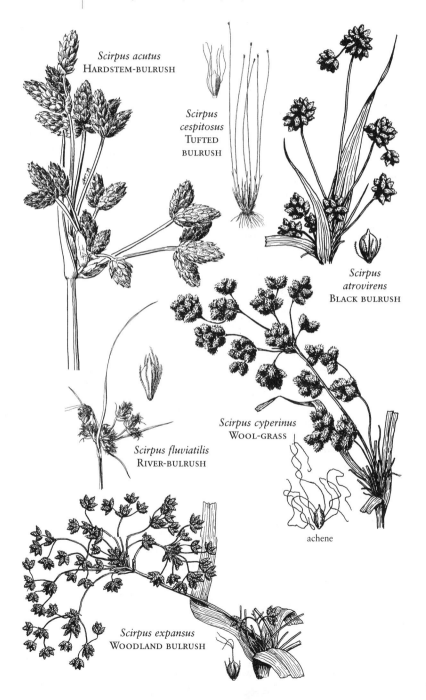

Scirpus acutus
HARDSTEM-BULRUSH

Scirpus cespitosus
TUFTED
BULRUSH

Scirpus atrovirens
BLACK BULRUSH

Scirpus cyperinus
WOOL-GRASS

Scirpus fluviatilis
RIVER-BULRUSH

achene

Scirpus expansus
WOODLAND BULRUSH

Scirpus heterochaetus Chase (*Schoenoplectus heterochaetus*)
Slender bulrush   OBL

☞ Slender bulrush is similar to **hardstem-bulrush** (*S. acutus*) but much less common; slender bulrush is more slender, the head is more open, and the achene is 3-angled.

Perennial, spreading by stout rhizomes. **Stems** slender, round in section, 1–2 m long. **Leaves** reduced to 3–4 sheaths at base of stem, upper sheaths with blades 6–8 cm long; main bract erect, 1–10 cm long, shorter than head. **Spikelets** mostly single at ends of stalks, the spikelets 5–15 mm long and 3–6 mm wide, in open, lax heads; scales chaffy, brown, 3–4 mm long, tipped with an awn to 2 mm long; bristles 2–4, unequal, about as long as achene; style 3-parted. **Achenes** 3-angled, light green to brown, 2–3 mm long, with a beak about 0.5 mm long. June–Aug. ⚘ Emergent in shallow to deep water (1–2 m deep) of marshes, ponds and lakes, ditches. ⊕ s and far n Minn, s Wisc, possibly sc Mich (rare), rare in ne Ill. Que and Mass to ND, s to Va, Mo, n Tex; occasional w to Wash and Calif.

Scirpus hudsonianus (Michx.) Fern. (*Trichophorum alpinum*)
Alpine cotton-grass   OBL

☞ Scirpus hudsonianus is similar to the **cottongrasses** (*Eriophorum*) and is sometimes placed in that genus as *Eriophorum alpinum* or within a new genus as *Trichophorum alpinum*.

Perennial, from short rhizomes. **Stems** single to clustered, slender, 1–4 dm long, sharply 3-angled, rough-to-touch on the angles. **Leaves** reduced to scales at base of stem, with 1–2 leaves upward on stem, these with short narrow blades 5–15 mm long. **Spikelets** single at ends of stems, brown, 5–7 mm long, with 10–20 flowers, involucral bract awl-shaped, shorter than spikelet, sometimes absent; scales ovate, blunt-tipped, yellow-brown; bristles 6, white, flattened, longer than the scales, when mature forming a white tuft 1–2 cm longer than the spikelet. **Achenes** 3-angled, dull brown, 1–4 mm long. *Eriophorum alpinum.* ⚘ Open bogs, conifer swamps, wet meadows, wet sandy shores; sometimes where calcium-rich. ⊕ n Minn, e Wisc, UP and n LP of Mich. Circumboreal, s to Conn, NY, Mich, Minn and BC.

Scirpus maritimus L. (*Schoenoplectus maritimus*)
Alkali-bulrush   (OBL)

⚠ STATUS Illinois - E

Perennial, from tuber-bearing rhizomes. **Stems** single, sharply 3-angled, 5–15 dm long. **Leaves** several on stem, smooth, to 1 cm wide; bracts 3–5, the longest bract sometimes erect, to 30 cm long. **Spikelets** cylindric, 10–25 mm long and 6–9 mm wide, in clusters of 3–20 in a dense, stalkless head, or some spikelets single or in groups of 2–4 on stalks to 4 cm long; scales ovate, notched at tip, pale brown, 5–7 mm long, with an awn to 2 mm long; bristles 2–6, coppery, about half as long as achene; style 2-parted. **Achenes** lens-shaped, brown to black, 3–4 mm long, the beak small, to 0.3 mm long. June–Aug. *S. paludosus.* ⚘ Marshes, shores, ditches; especially where brackish. ⊕ w Minn, possibly c Mich, ne Ill (uncommon but likely spreading along salted highways). Nearly circumboreal; s along Atlantic coast, inland s to ne Ill, Minn and w USA.

Scirpus microcarpus C. Presl
Small-fruit bulrush   OBL

Perennial, from stout rhizomes. **Stems** single or few together, 5–15 dm long, weakly 3-angled. **Leaves** several along stem, flat, ascending, 7–15 mm wide, the upper leaves longer than the head, margins rough-to-touch; sheaths often red-tinged; bracts 3–4, leaflike, to 2–3 dm long. **Spikelets** numerous, 3–6 mm long and 1–2 mm wide; in a loose, spreading, umbel-like head, the head formed of clusters of 4–20 or more spikelets on stalks to 15 cm long; scales 1–2 mm long, brown and translucent except for green midvein; bristles 4–6, white to tan, downwardly barbed, longer than achene; style 2-parted. **Achenes** lens-shaped, pale tan to nearly white, about 1 mm long, the beak tiny. June–July. *S.*

rubrotinctus. ❦ Streambanks, wet meadows, marshes, wet shores, thickets, swamps, springs; not in dense shade. ⊕ n, c and se Minn, n and e Wisc, UP and nc LP of Mich, possibly extreme ne Ill. Newf to BC, s to WVa, Iowa, Neb, NM and Calif.

Scirpus pendulus Muhl.
Drooping bulrush — OBL

Loosely clumped perennial, from short, thick rhizomes. **Stems** upright, rounded 3-angled, to 1.5 m long, lower stem covered by old leaf bases. **Leaves** several on stem, flat, 4–10 mm wide, shorter than head; bracts leaflike, 3 or more, shorter than the head, pale brown at base. **Spikelets** many, cylindric, 4–10 mm long and 2–4 mm wide; in an open, umbel-like head at end of stem, the spikelets drooping and clustered in groups of 1 stalkless and several stalked spikelets; scales about 2 mm long, red-brown with a green midvein; bristles 6, brown, smooth, longer than achene and about as long as scale; style 3-parted. **Achenes** compressed 3-angled, light brown, about 1 mm long, with a short, slender beak. June–Aug. *S. lineatus.* ❦ Marshes, wet meadows, streambanks, swamp openings and ditches. ⊕ Common; ec and se Wisc, LP of Mich (uncommon in UP), ne Ill and nw Ind. Maine to Minn and SD, s to Fla, Tex, NM and n Mex.

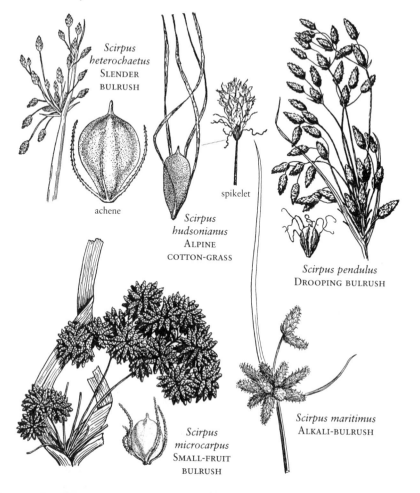

Scirpus heterochaetus
SLENDER BULRUSH

achene

spikelet

Scirpus hudsonianus
ALPINE COTTON-GRASS

Scirpus pendulus
DROOPING BULRUSH

Scirpus microcarpus
SMALL-FRUIT BULRUSH

Scirpus maritimus
ALKALI-BULRUSH

Scirpus pungens Vahl (*Schoenoplectus pungens*)
Common threesquare
OBL

Perennial, from slender rhizomes and forming colonies. **Stems** erect to somewhat curved, 2–12 dm long, 3-angled, the sides concave to slightly convex. **Leaves** mostly 1–3 near base of stem, usually folded, or channeled near tip, reaching to about middle of stem and 1–3 mm wide; main bract erect, sharp-tipped, resembling a continuation of the stem, 2–15 cm long. **Spikelets** 5–20 mm long and 3–5 mm wide, clustered in heads of 1–6 stalkless spikelets, the head appearing lateral; scales brown and translucent, 3–5 mm long, notched at tip, with a midvein extended into a short awn 1–2 mm long; bristles 4–6, unequal, shorter than achene; style 2–3-parted. **Achenes** light green or tan to dark brown, 3-angled or flat on 1 side and convex on other, 2–3 mm long, the beak to 0.5 mm long. May–Sept. Includes *S. americanus* and *S. olneyi*. ❧ Shallow water, wet sandy, gravelly or mucky shores, streambanks, wet meadows, ditches, seeps and other wet places. ⊕ Fairly common; Minn, nw and e Wisc, Mich LP (occasional in UP), common in ne Ill and nw Ind. s Can, s to S Amer; Europe, Australia and New Zealand.

Scirpus smithii A. Gray (*Schoenoplectus smithii*)
Bluntscale-bulrush
OBL

⚠
STATUS
Illinois - E
Indiana - E

Clumped annual. **Stems** slender, smooth, round or rounded 3-angled, to 6 dm long. **Leaves** reduced to sheaths, or some with short blades; bract narrow, upright, 2–10 cm long, appearing to be a continuation of stem. **Spikelets** ovate, 5–10 mm long, in a single cluster of 1–12 spikelets; scales yellow-brown with a green midvein; bristles 4–6, barbed or smooth, longer than achene, sometimes smaller or absent; style 2-parted. **Achenes** lens-shaped or flat on 1 side and convex on other, glossy brown to black, 1–2 mm long. July–Aug. *S. purshianus*. ❧ Sandy, gravelly or mucky shores, floating mats, bogs. ⊕ c and se Minn, s Wisc, LP of Mich (local in w UP), rare in ne Ill and nw Ind. Que to Minn, s to Ga and Tenn.

Scirpus subterminalis Torr. (*Schoenoplectus subterminalis*)
Water-bulrush
OBL

Aquatic perennial, spreading by rhizomes. **Stems** slender, weak, round in section, to 1 m or more long, floating or slightly emergent from water surface near tip. **Leaves** many, threadlike, channeled, from near base of stem and extending to just below water surface; bract 1–6 cm long, appearing to be a continuation of stem. **Spikelets** single at ends of stems, with several flowers, light brown, narrowly ovate, tapered at each end, 7–12 mm long; scales thin, 4–6 mm long, light brown with a green midvein; bristles shorter to about as long as achene, downwardly barbed; style 3-parted. **Achenes** 3-angled, brown, 2–4 mm long, tipped with a slender beak to 0.5 mm long. July–Aug. ❧ In water to about 1 m deep of lakes, ponds and bog margins. ⊕ ne and c Minn, Wisc, Mich (local in w UP) and uncommon in nw Ind. Nfld to Alaska, s to SC, Ga, Mo, Utah and Calif.

Scirpus supinus L. (*Schoenoplectus hallii*)
Sharpscale-bulrush
OBL

⚠
STATUS
Illinois - E
Indiana - E
Michigan - T

Small, clumped annual. **Stems** slender, 1–3 dm long, rounded 3-angled, finely grooved. **Leaves** 1 to several near base of stem, reduced to sheaths or upper leaves with a narrow blade to 10 cm long; main bract erect, 2–10 cm long, resembling a continuation of stem. **Spikelets** cylindric, 4–12 mm long and 2–3 mm wide, in heads of 3–8 spikelets, ± stalkless, or some spikelets in clusters of 2–3 on stalks to 1 cm long, the head appearing lateral from side of stem; scales 2–3 mm long, light brown with a green midvein, tipped by an awn to 1 mm long; bristles several or absent; style 3-parted. **Achenes** 3-angled, light to dark brown, 1–2 mm long, cross-ridged (under 10x magnification), tipped with a short beak. July–Sept. *S. hallii* var. *supinus, S. saxmontanus.* ❧ Sandy and muddy shores and flats, often where seasonally flooded. ⊕ Uncommon in wc LP of Mich (near Lake Mich), ne Ill and nw Ind. Mass to s Mich, n Ill, Iowa and SD, s to Mo, Tex and n Mex; Eurasia.

Scirpus torreyi Olney (*Schoenoplectus torreyi*)
Torrey's threesquare · OBL

⚠️ **STATUS** Indiana - E

Perennial, spreading by rhizomes and often forming colonies. **Stems** erect, sharply 3-angled, 5–10 dm long. **Leaves** several, narrow, often longer than the stem; bract erect, 5–15 cm long, appearing to be a continuation of stem. **Spikelets** ovate, light brown, 8–15 mm long, in a single head of 1–4 spikelets, the head appearing lateral from side of stem; scales ovate, shiny brown, with a greenish midvein sometimes extended as a short awn to 0.5 mm long; bristles about 6, downwardly barbed, longer than achene; style 3-parted. **Achenes** compressed 3-angled, shiny, light brown, 3–4 mm long, tipped by a slender beak to 0.5 mm long. June–Aug. ❧ Shallow water, wet sandy or mucky shores. ⊕ ne and ec Minn, Wisc, local in LP of Mich (mostly sc) and reported from Keweenaw Peninsula in UP, historic records from ne Ill; rare in nw Ind. NB to Man, s to NJ, Va, Pa, nw Ind, Mo and Neb.

Scirpus validus Vahl (*Schoenoplectus tabernaemontani*)
Softstem-bulrush · OBL

☞ Similar to **hardstem bulrush** (*S. acutus*) but the stems of softstem-bulrush are easily crushed between the fingers. Softstem bulrush is also generally a smaller, more slender plant, with a more open head.

Perennial, spreading by rhizomes and sometimes forming large colonies. **Stems** stout, smooth, erect, 1–3 m long, round in section. **Leaves** reduced to 4–5 sheaths at base of stem, or upper leaves with a blade to 7 cm long; main bract erect, 1–10 cm long, shorter than the head. **Spikelets** red-brown, 4–12 mm long and 3–4 mm wide, single or in clusters of 2–5 at ends of stalks, the stalks spreading or drooping, the clusters in paniclelike heads; scales ovate, light to dark brown, 2–3 mm long, the midvein usually extended into a short awn to 0.5 mm long; bristles 4–6, downwardly barbed, equal or longer than achene; style 2-parted. **Achenes** flat on 1 side and convex on other, brown to black, about 2 mm long, tapered to a very small beak to 0.2 mm long. June–Aug. ❧ Shallow water and shores of lakes, ponds, marshes, streams, and ditches. ⊕ Common; Minn, Wisc, Mich, ne Ill and nw Ind. Newf to s Alaska, s to S Amer.

Scleria Bergius / Nut-rush; Stone-rush

Annual or sometimes perennial sedgelike herbs, tufted or spreading by short rhizomes. **Stems** slender, 3-angled. **Leaves** narrow, shorter than the stem. **Flowers** either male or female, borne in separate spikelets on the same plant; male spikelets few-flowered; female spikelets with uppermost flower fertile, the lower scales empty. Flowers in clusters at ends of stems, or with both terminal clusters and clusters from upper leaf axils; sepals and petals absent; stamens 1–3; style 3-parted. **Fruit** a hard, white achene.

▸**KEY TO SCLERIA**

1 Flowers in clusters at ends of stems or from leaf axils. . *S. reticularis*
· RETICULATED NUT-RUSH
1 Flowers 1 to few in stalkless heads along a spike. · · · · · *S. verticillata*
· LOW NUT-RUSH

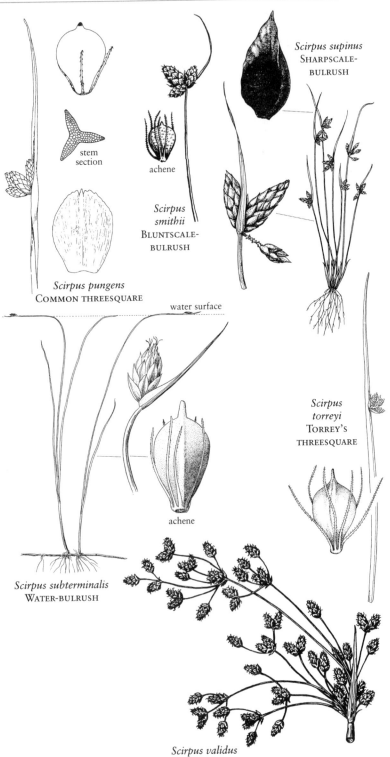

stem section

achene

Scirpus pungens
COMMON THREESQUARE

Scirpus supinus
SHARPSCALE-
BULRUSH

Scirpus smithii
BLUNTSCALE-
BULRUSH

water surface

Scirpus torreyi
TORREY'S
THREESQUARE

achene

Scirpus subterminalis
WATER-BULRUSH

Scirpus validus
SOFTSTEM-BULRUSH

Scleria reticularis Michx.

Reticulated nut-rush   OBL

⚠

Annual or perennial, from short, slender rhizomes. **Stems** slender, 3-angled, to 8 dm long. **Leaves** linear, smooth or sometimes hairy, 2–4 mm wide, shorter than the stem. **Spikelets** in a cluster at end of stem and in 1–3 short-stalked clusters from upper leaf axils; scales lance-shaped to ovate. **Achenes** round, dull white or gray, 1–2 mm wide, covered with a fine cross-hatch of small ridges, tipped with a small sharp point. July–Sept. ⚘ Sandy marshes, wet sand flats. ⊕ Tropical Amer, n along Atlantic coast to Mass, inland to extreme sw Mich, ne Ill, nw Ind, sc Wisc and Mo.

Scleria verticillata Muhl.

Low nut-rush   OBL

⚠

Clumped annual, roots fibrous. **Stems** slender, smooth, 3-angled, 2–6 dm long. **Leaves** erect, linear, 1 mm wide, shorter than the stems; sheaths often hairy. **Spikelets** in 2–8 separated heads, each head stalkless, 2–4 mm long, subtended by a small, bristlelike bract 4–6 mm long; scales lance-shaped. **Achenes** ± round, white, 1 mm wide, covered with horizontal ridges, tipped with a short, sharp point. July–Sept. ⚘ Sandy or gravelly shores, interdunal flats, wet meadows, marshes. ⊕ wc and s Minn, s Wisc, LP of Mich (especially s), ne Ill and nw Ind. Tropical Amer, n to Conn, Mich, Wisc and Minn.

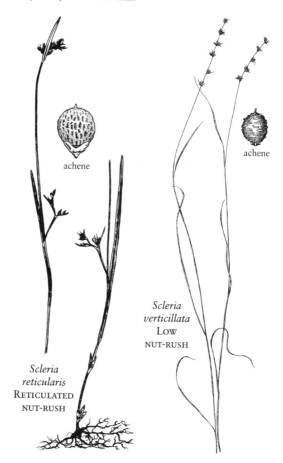

achene

achene

*Scleria
verticillata*
Low
NUT-RUSH

*Scleria
reticularis*
RETICULATED
NUT-RUSH

Carex michauxiana
(Michaux's sedge), Cyperaceae

Eriophorum virginicum (Tawny cotton-grass)
Cyperaceae

Scirpus cyperinus (Wool-grass)
Cyperaceae

Scirpus hudsonianus (Alpine cotton-grass)
Cyperaceae

Eriocaulaceae
Pipewort Family

▶**Eriocaulon** L. / Pipewort

Eriocaulon aquaticum (Hill.) Druce
Pipewort OBL

⚠
STATUS
Indiana - E

Perennial, spongy at base, with fleshy roots. **Stems** usually single, leafless, slightly twisted, 5–7-ridged, 5–20 cm long (or reaching 2–3 m long when in deep water). **Leaves** grasslike, in a rosette at base of plant, thin and often translucent, 2–10 cm long and 2–5 mm wide, 3–9-nerved with conspicuous cross-veins. **Flowers** either male or female, grouped together in a single, ± round head at end of stem, the heads white-woolly, 4–6 mm wide. **Fruit** a 2–3-seeded capsule. July–Sept. *E. septangulare.* ≉ Shallow water, sandy or peaty shores. ⊕ ne and ec Minn, Wisc, Mich and rare in n Ind. Nfld to Minn, s to NC and n Ind.

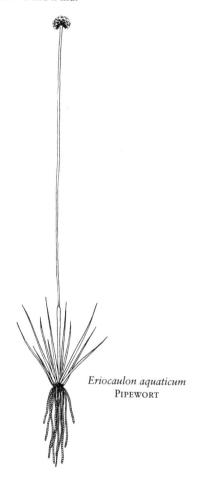

Eriocaulon aquaticum
PIPEWORT

Hydrocharitaceae
Frog's-Bit Family

Aquatic, perennial herbs. **Stems** leafy, the leaves usually whorled (*Elodea*), or plants stemless with clusters of long, linear, ribbonlike leaves (*Vallisneria*). **Flowers** usually either male or female and borne on separate plants, small and stalkless, or in a spathe at end of a stalk; sepals 3; petals 3 or absent; male flowers with 3 or more stamens; stigmas 3. **Fruit** several-seeded, maturing underwater.

▸**KEY TO HYDROCHARITACEAE**

1 Plants leafy-stemmed, the leaves short and whorled, to 3 cm long . . . . *Elodea* / WATER-WEED
1 Leaves all from base of plant, long and ribbonlike, to 1 m long . . . . *Vallisneria americana* / TAPE-GRASS; EEL-GRASS; WATER-CELERY

▸**Elodea** Michx. / Water-weed

Aquatic perennial herbs, rooting from lower nodes or free-floating. **Stems** slender, leafy, branched. **Leaves** crowded near tip of stem, mostly in whorls of 3–4, or opposite, stalkless; margins finely sharp-toothed. **Flowers** either male or female and on separate plants, tiny, single from upper leaf axils, subtended by a 2-parted spathe, usually extended to the water surface by a long, threadlike hypanthium, or stalkless and breaking free to float to water surface in male flowers of *E. nuttallii*; sepals 3; petals 3 or absent, white or purple; male flowers with 9 stamens; female flowers with 3 stigmas, the stigmas entire or 2-parted. **Fruit** a capsule, ripening underwater. *Anacharis* or *Philotria* in older floras.

▸**KEY TO ELODEA**

1 Leaves mostly 2 mm or more wide; male flowers long-stalked in a spathe, the spathe more than 7 mm long, extended to water surface by a long, threadlike hypanthium. . . . . *E. canadensis* . . . . COMMON WATER-WEED
1 Leaves to 1.5 mm wide; male flowers stalkless in a spathe, the spathe 2–4 mm long, breaking free to float to water surface at flowering time . . . . *E. nuttallii* / FREE-FLOWERED WATER-WEED

Elodea canadensis Michx.
Common water-weed   OBL

Submerged perennial herb. **Stems** round in section, usually branched, 2–10 dm long. **Leaves** bright green, firm; lower leaves opposite, reduced in size, ovate or lance-shaped; upper leaves in whorls of 3, the uppermost crowded and overlapping, lance-shaped, 5–15 mm long and about 2 mm wide, rounded at tip. **Flowers** either male of female and on separate plants, at ends of threadlike stalks, 2–30 cm long; **male flowers** in spathes from upper leaf axils, the spathes about 10 mm long and to 4 mm wide; sepals green, 3–5 mm long; petals white, 5 mm long; stamens 9. **Female flowers** in spathes from upper leaf axils, the spathes 10–20 mm long, extended to water surface by a threadlike hypanthium; sepals 2–3 mm long; petals white, 2–3 mm long. **Fruit** a capsule, 5–6 mm long, tapered to a beak 4–5 mm long. June–Aug. *Anacharis canadensis.* ❦ Shallow to deep water of lakes (including Great Lakes), streams and ditches. ⊕ Common; Minn, Wisc, Mich, ne Ill and nw Ind. Que to BC, s to NC, Ala, Ark, Okla, Colo, Utah, Nev and Calif.

Elodea nuttallii (Planchon) St. John
Free-flowered water-weed   OBL

☞ Elodea nuttallii is similar to common water-weed (E. canadensis) but is less common, and plants are smaller, with leaves narrower, paler green, and not closely overlapping at stem tips, and the male flowers not elevated on a long slender stalk.

Submerged perennial herb. **Stems** slender, round in section, usually branched, 3–10 dm long. **Lower leaves** opposite, reduced in size, ovate to lance-shaped; **upper leaves** in whorls of 3 (or sometimes 4), not densely overlapping at tip, linear to lance-shaped, 6–13 mm long and 0.5–1.5 mm wide, tapered to a pointed tip. **Flowers** either male or female and on separate plants; **male flowers** in stalkless spathes from middle leaf axils, the spathes ovate, 2–3 mm long, the flowers single and stalkless in the spathe, breaking free and floating to water surface and then opening; sepals green or sometimes red, 2 mm long; petals absent or very short (to 0.5 mm long); stamens 9. **Female flowers** in cylindric spathes from upper leaf axils, the spathes 1–2.5 cm long, extended to water surface by a threadlike stalk to 10 cm long; sepals green, about 1 mm long; petals white, longer than sepals. **Fruit** a capsule, 5–7 mm long. June–Aug. *Anacharis nuttallii, A. occidentalis, Philotria nuttallii.* ❦ Shallow to deep water of lakes, streams and ditches. ⊕ Minn (mostly e), Mich, ne Ill and nw Ind. Que to Minn and Neb, s to NC, Mo, Okla and NM.

Vallisneria L. / Tape-grass

Vallisneria americana Michx.
Tape-grass; Eel-grass; Water-celery   OBL
Submerged perennial herb, fibrous rooted, spreading by stolons and often forming large colonies. **Stems** absent. **Leaves** long and ribbonlike, in tufts from a small crown, to 1 m or more long and 3–10 mm wide, rounded at tip, margins smooth. **Flowers** either male or female and on separate plants; **male flowers** small, about 1 mm wide, in a many-flowered head, the head within a stalked spathe from base of plant, the stalk 3–15 cm long; sepals 3, petals 1, stamens 2; the male flowers released singly from the spathe and floating to water surface where they open. **Female flowers** single in a spathe, on long slender stalks that extend to water surface, the stalk contracting and coiling after flowering to draw the fruit underwater; sepals 3, petals small, 3; stigmas 3. **Fruit** a cylindric, curved capsule, 4–10 cm long. July–Sept. ❦ Shallow (sometimes deep) water of lakes and streams. ⊕ Minn (mostly e), Wisc, Mich, ne Ill and nw Ind. NS to Minn and SD, s to Fla, Tex, NM and Ariz.

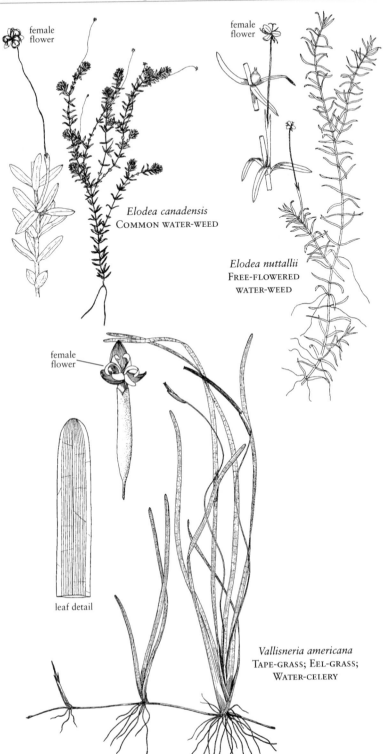

female
flower

Elodea canadensis
COMMON WATER-WEED

female
flower

Elodea nuttallii
FREE-FLOWERED
WATER-WEED

female
flower

leaf detail

Vallisneria americana
TAPE-GRASS; EEL-GRASS;
WATER-CELERY

Iridaceae
Iris Family

Perennial herbs with rhizomes, bulbs, or fibrous roots. **Leaves** parallel-veined, narrow, 2-ranked, the margins joined to form an edge facing the stem (equitant). **Flowers** perfect, with 6 petal-like segments, single or in clusters at ends of stem, stamens 3, style 3-parted. **Fruit** a 3-chambered capsule.

▶**KEY TO IRIDACEAE**

1 Flowers more than 2 cm wide; stems not winged; leaves more than 6 mm wide . . . . *Iris* / IRIS; FLAG
1 Flowers to 2 cm wide; stems winged; leaves to 6 mm wide . . . . *Sisyrinchium* / BLUE-EYED-GRASS

▶**Iris** L. / Iris; Flag

Perennial herbs, spreading by thick rhizomes. **Stems** erect. **Leaves** sword-like, erect or upright, the margins joined to form an edge facing the stem. **Flowers** 1 or several at ends of stems; yellow or blue-violet; sepals 3, spreading or bent downward, longer and wider than the petals; petals 3, erect or arching; stamens 3; styles 3-parted, the divisions petal-like and arching over the stamens. **Fruit** an oblong capsule.

▶**KEY TO IRIS**

1 Flowers yellow. . . . . *I. pseudacorus* / YELLOW FLAG
1 Flowers blue or violet **2**

2 Stems as long or longer than leaves; base of plant often purple-tinged; sepal base unspotted, or with a with a hairless, green-yellow spot . . . . *I. versicolor* / NORTHERN BLUE FLAG
2 Stems shorter than leaves; base of plant usually brown; sepal base with a hairy, bright yellow spot . *I. virginica* / SOUTHERN BLUE FLAG

Iris pseudacorus L.
Yellow flag   OBL
Perennial herb, from thick rhizomes. **Stems** 0.5–1 m long, shorter or equal to the leaves. **Leaves** sword-shaped, stiff and erect, waxy, 1–2 cm wide. **Flowers** several at end of stems, yellow, 7–9 cm wide, sepals spreading, upper portion marked with brown; petals erect, narrowed in middle, 1–2.5 cm long. **Fruit** a 6-angled, oblong capsule, 5–9 cm long. May–June. ❀ Lakeshores, streambanks, marshes, ditches. ⊕ Minn, Wisc, Mich, ne Ill and nw Ind. Introduced from Europe and occasional throughout e USA and s Can.

Iris versicolor L.
Northern blue flag   OBL
Perennial herb, from thick, fleshy rhizomes and forming colonies. **Stems** ± round in section, often branched above, 4–9 dm long. **Leaves** sword-shaped, erect or arching, somewhat waxy, 2–3 cm wide, usually shorter

☞ *Iris versi-color* is similar to **southern blue flag** (*Iris virginica*), which is sometimes considered a variety of this species, but *I. versicolor* has a more northerly distribution.

than stem. **Flowers** several on short stalks at ends of stems, blue-violet, 6–8 cm wide; sepals spreading, unspotted, or with a green-yellow spot near base, surrounded by white streaks and purple veins; petals erect, about half as long as sepals. **Fruit** an oblong capsule, 3–6 cm long. June–July. ❧ Marshes, shores, wet meadows, open bogs, swamps, thickets, forest depressions; often in shallow water. ⊕ Minn (all but se), n and c Wisc, UP and n LP of Mich. Nfld and Labr to Man, s to Va, Wisc and Minn.

Iris virginica L.
Southern blue flag   OBL

Perennial herb, from thick rhizomes, often forming large colonies. **Stems** ± round in section, to 1 m long. **Leaves** sword-shaped, erect or arching, 2–3 cm wide, usually longer than stems. **Flowers** several on short-stalks at ends of stems, blue-violet, often with darker veins, 6–8 cm wide; sepals spreading, curved backward at tip, with a hairy, bright yellow spot near base; petals shorter than sepals. **Fruit** an ovate to oval capsule, 4–7 cm long. May–July. *I. shrevei.* ❧ Swamps, thickets, shores, streambanks, marshes, ditches. ⊕ Common; s Minn, c and s Wisc, LP of Mich, ne Ill and nw Ind. Atlantic coast from Md to Tex, inland to Ont, Minn and Okla.

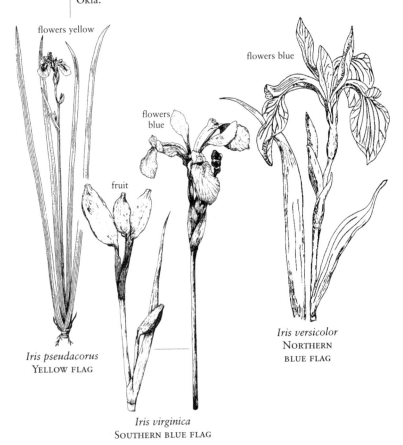

flowers yellow

flowers blue

flowers blue

fruit

Iris pseudacorus
YELLOW FLAG

Iris versicolor
NORTHERN
BLUE FLAG

Iris virginica
SOUTHERN BLUE FLAG

Sisyrinchium L. / Blue-eyed-grass

Clumped perennial herbs, from fibrous roots. **Stems** slender, leafless, flattened or winged. **Leaves** narrow and linear, from base of plant, the margins joined and turned to form an edge facing the stem. **Flowers** in an umbel at end of stem, above a pair of erect green bracts (spathe), blue-violet (our species), with 6 spreading segments, the segments joined only at base, the tips rounded but with an small bristle. **Fruit** a rounded capsule; seeds round, black.

▶**KEY TO SISYRINCHIUM**

1 Spathes stalked from axils of leafy bracts, upper stem appearing branched . . . . *S. atlanticum* / EASTERN BLUE-EYED-GRASS
1 Spathes stalkless at end of unbranched stem, upper stem not appearing branched **2**

2 Stems flattened and winged, 2–4 mm wide; larger leaves 2–3 mm wide
. . . . *S. montanum* / MOUNTAIN BLUE-EYED-GRASS
2 Stem slender, barely winged, to 1 mm wide; larger leaves to 1.5 mm wide . . . . *S. mucronatum* / MICHAUX'S BLUE-EYED-GRASS

Sisyrinchium atlanticum E. Bickn.
Eastern blue-eyed-grass   FACW

STATUS
Illinois - E
Michigan - T

Perennial herb, spreading and forming small clumps; plants pale green and waxy. **Stems** slender, 0.5–2 mm wide, often angled at the upper nodes, the margins smooth and narrowly winged. **Leaves** mostly from base of plant, shorter than stems, 1–3 mm wide. **Flowers** single in 2–3 spathes, the spathes of 2 bracts, 1–2 cm long, often purple-tinged, stalked from the axils of leaflike bracts; flower segments (tepals) blue-violet, 8–12 mm long, bristle-tipped. **Fruit** a stalked, oval capsule, 3–5 mm long. June–July. ⚘ Wet sandy shores. ⊕ Rare in c and sw LP of Mich and ne Ill, nw Ind. NS and Maine s to Fla and Miss, occasionally inland to Mich, n Ind and Mo.

Sisyrinchium montanum Greene
Mountain blue-eyed-grass   FACW-

STATUS
Illinois - E
Indiana - E

Clumped perennial, from fibrous roots; plants pale-green and waxy. **Stems** stiff and erect, leafless, flattened and winged, 1–5 dm tall and 2–4 mm wide. **Leaves** mostly from base of plant, narrow and grasslike, about half as long as stem, 1–3 mm wide. **Flowers** in head of 1 to several flowers at end of stem, subtended by a spathe, the spathe of 2 bracts, the outer bract 3–7 cm long, the inner bract about half as long; the flower segments (tepals) blue-violet with a yellow center, 5–15 mm long, with a short, slender tip. **Fruit** a ± round, pale brown capsule, 4–7 mm wide, on an erect stalk shorter than the inner bract. May–July. *S. angustifolium.* ⚘ Wet meadows, shores, thickets, ditches, swales; also in drier woods and fields. ⊕ Minn (all but far se), local in se Wisc, LP of Mich (local in UP), uncommon in ne Ill and nw Ind. Que to Alaska, s to NY, Ind, Iowa, Kans and Colo.

Sisyrinchium mucronatum Michx.
Michaux's blue-eyed-grass   FACW-

Clumped perennial herb; plants dark green. **Stems** very slender, to 1 mm wide, leafless, margins not or barely winged. **Leaves** from near base of plant, narrow and linear, to 1.5 mm wide. **Flowers** in a single head at end of stem, subtended by a spathe, the spathe of 2 bracts, the bracts often purple-tinged, the outer bract 2–3 cm long, the inner bract shorter, 1–2 cm long; the segments (tepals) deep violet-blue, 8–10 mm long, tipped with a sharp point. **Fruit** a ± round, pale brown capsule, 2–4 mm long, on spreading stalks. May–June. ❦ Wet meadows, calcareous fens. ⊕ Minn, occasional in e UP and e LP of Mich. Maine and Mass to Ont and Man, s to NC, Mich and Minn.

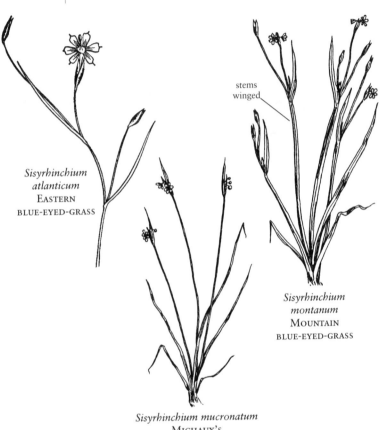

Sisyrhinchium atlanticum
EASTERN
BLUE-EYED-GRASS

stems winged

Sisyrhinchium montanum
MOUNTAIN
BLUE-EYED-GRASS

Sisyrhinchium mucronatum
MICHAUX'S
BLUE-EYED-GRASS

Juncaceae
Rush Family

▸**Juncus** L. / Rush

Clumped or rhizomatous rushes, mostly perennial (annual in *J. bufonius*). **Stems** erect and unbranched. **Leaves** from base of plant or along stem, alternate, round in section, or flat to rolled inward, or reduced to sheaths at base of stem; leaves in some species with cross-partitions at intervals (septate). **Flowers** perfect, regular, in compact to open clusters of few to many flowers, subtended by 1 or several leaflike involucral bracts; sepals and petals of 6 chaffy, scalelike, green to brown tepals; stamens 6 or 3; stigmas 3, ovary superior, 1 or 3-chambered. **Fruit** a many-seeded capsule; seeds with a short slender tip or with a tail-like appendage at each end.

☞ Juncus is distinguished from the **bulrushes** (*Scirpus*) by the fruit being a capsule rather than an achene as in *Scirpus*. Correctly identifying species within the genus *Juncus* is difficult (apart from distinctive species such as *J. effusus*), and based in part on characteristics of the small seeds within the capsule. The key is largely based on the key in *Flora of North America*, Vol. 22 (2000).

▸**KEY TO JUNCUS GROUPS (SUBGENERA)**

1 Flowers borne singly (each flower atop a stalk); bractlets present (except in *J. pelocarpus*) **2**
1 Flowers borne in heads (flowers ± stalkless); bractlets absent **4**

2 Inflorescences appearing lateral; inflorescence bract round in section, erect, appearing to be continuation of stem; basal leaves without blades, stem leaves absent . . . . **GROUP 1 (Subgenus Genuini)**
2 Inflorescences appearing terminal; inflorescence bract erect or upright, flat, involute or round in section; basal leaves (at least some) usually with blade, stem leaves present or absent **3**

3 Leaves round in section, with cross-partitions at intervals (septate); capsules beaked . . . . **GROUP 2 (Subgenus Septati)**
3 Leaves flat, involute, or round in section, not septate; capsules not beaked. . . . . **GROUP 3 (SUBGENUS POIOPHYLLI)**

4 Leaves flat or ensiform (sword-shaped) **5**
4 Leaves round in section or compressed. **6**

5 Leaves ensiform, imperfectly septate . **GROUP 4 (Subgenus Ensifolii)**
5 Leaves flat, not septate. . . . . **GROUP 5 (Subgenus Graminifolii)**

6 Capsules large; seeds large, long tailed; leaves not noticeably septate . . . . **GROUP 6 (Subgenus Alpini)**
6 Capsules smaller; seeds not tailed or if tailed not long; leaves septate or not. . . . . **GROUP 2 (Subgenus Septati)**

▸**KEY TO JUNCUS GROUP 1 (SUBGENUS GENUINI)**

1 Stems densely clumped; stamens 3. . . . . *J. effusus* / Soft rush
1 Stems single from rhizomes, the stems often in rows; stamens 6 . . **2**

2 Tepals dark brown; capsules red-brown; anthers equal to or longer than filaments . . . . *J. arcticus* / Baltic rush; Wire-rush
2 Tepals greenish; capsules green to light brown; anthers shorter than filaments . . . . *J. filiformis* / Thread rush

▶**KEY TO JUNCUS GROUP 2 (SUBGENUS SEPTATI)**

1 Seeds tailed, 0.7–2.6 mm long (including tails); seed body with a whitish translucent covering. **2**
1 Seeds not tailed, 0.3–0.7 mm long; seed body clear yellow-brown . **4**

2 Seeds 1.1–1.9 mm long; heads ovate, 5–50-flowered; inflorescence branches erect to ascending . . . . *J. canadensis* / CANADA RUSH
2 Seeds 0.7–1.2 mm; heads 2–8-flowered; inflorescence branches erect to spreading **3**

3 Outer tepals obtuse to nearly acute . . . . *J. brachycephalus*
. . . . SMALL-HEAD RUSH
3 Outer tepals acuminate to acute. . . . . *J. brevicaudatus*
. . . . NARROW-PANICLE RUSH

4 Flowers 1–2(–4) at each node, not in heads; capsules fertile only below middle. . . . . *J. pelocarpus* / BROWN-FRUIT RUSH
4 Flowers in heads of 3–60; capsules fertile throughout or only below middle **5**

5 Heads sphere-shaped or nearly so, 15–60-flowered. **6**
5 Heads obconic to hemispheric, 3–15-flowered **11**

6 Stamens 3 . . . . **7**
6 Stamens 6 . . . . **10**

7 Plants clumped; tepals lance-shaped *J. acuminatus* / TAPER-TIP RUSH
7 Plants rhizomatous; tepals narrowly lance-shaped. **8**

8 Capsules shorter than (and hidden by) tepals. . . . . . *J. brachycarpus*
. . . . WHITE-ROOT RUSH
8 Capsule longer to slightly shorter than tepals **9**

9 Capsules remaining joined at tip when mature . . . . . . *J. scirpoides* /
. . . . ROUND-HEADED RUSH
9 Capsule valves separating at tip as seeds mature . . . . *J. nodosus*
. . . . KNOTTED RUSH

10 Outer tepals 2.4–4.1 mm long, equaling inner tepals; auricles 0.5–1.7 mm . . . . *J. nodosus* / KNOTTED RUSH
10 Outer tepals 4–6 mm, outer and inner tepals unequal in length; auricles 1–4 mm. *J. torreyi* / TORREY'S RUSH

11 Stamens 3 . . . . **12**
11 Stamens 6 . . . . **13**

12 Heads 5–50; tepals 2.6–3.5 mm long, nearly equal; capsules 2.8–3.5 mm long . . . . *J. acuminatus* / TAPER-TIP RUSH
12 Heads 30–250; tepals 1.7–2.9 mm long, inner tepals shorter than outer tepals; capsules 1.9–2.9 mm . . . . *J. nodosus* / KNOTTED RUSH

13 Stems sometimes creeping or floating; submersed leaves may be threadlike and formed before flowering; inflorescences with 1–9 heads. . . . . *J. articulatus* / JOINTED RUSH
13 Stems erect; threadlike submersed leaves not formed except in *J. militaris*; heads 1–60 or more **14**

☞ **Stout rush** (*Juncus nodatus* Cov., subgenus Septati) is an obligate wetland species of sandy areas known from several counties in nw Ind (ranging from n Ind to Kans, s to Miss and Tex). Plants are large (to 1 m tall), with leaves round in section and conspicuously cross-divided. The inflorescence is terminal, with several hundred heads, each head with 2–10 flowers.

14 Lower stem leaves overtopping inflorescence, uppermost stem leaf usually reduced to an inflated, bladeless sheath . . . . *J. militaris*
. . . . BAYONET RUSH
14 Lower stem leaves shorter than inflorescence, uppermost stem leaf usually with a blade, its sheath not inflated **15**

15 Inner tepals blunt-tipped; inflorescence stiffly erect . . . .
. . . . *J. alpinoarticulatus* / ALPINE RUSH
15 Inner tepals tapered to a sharp tip; inflorescence spreading . . . .
. . . . *J. articulatus* / JOINTED RUSH

▶**KEY TO JUNCUS GROUP 3 (SUBGENUS POIOPHYLLI)**

1 Plants annual, to 10 cm tall . . . . *J. bufonius* / TOAD-RUSH
1 Plants perennial, more than 10 cm tall **2**

2 Auricles at summit of leaf sheath 3–6 mm long, membranous, transparent . . . . *J. tenuis* / PATH-RUSH
2 Auricles absent or very short membranous or hardened projections less than 2 mm long **3**

3 Leaf blade flat . . . . *J. compressus* / BLACK GRASS
3 Leaf blade round in cross-section or channeled and closed for ± entire length . . . . *J. vaseyi* / VASEY'S RUSH

▶**KEY TO JUNCUS GROUP 4 (SUBGENUS ENSIFOLII)**

One species in subgenus in Great Lakes region; leaves folded and joined near tip, with one edge facing the stem (similar to *Iris*); rare in nw Wisc only . . . . *J. ensifolius* / DAGGER-LEAF RUSH

▶**KEY TO JUNCUS GROUP 5 (SUBGENUS GRAMINIFOLII)**

1 Stems single from long rhizomes; stamens 6, pale yellow; nw Minn only . . . . *J. longistylis* / LONG-STYLE RUSH
1 Stems single or in small clumps from short rhizomes; stamens 3, red-brown; occasional across Great Lakes region . . . . *J. marginatus*
. . . . GRASS-LEAF RUSH

▶**KEY TO JUNCUS GROUP 6 (SUBGENUS ALPINI)**

One species in subgenus in northern portions of Great Lakes region; leaf blades without cross-partitions at regular intervals . . . *J. stygius*
. . . . MOOR RUSH

Juncus acuminatus Michx.

Taper-tip rush   OBL

Clumped perennial rush. **Stems** erect, slender, 2–8 dm tall, with 1–2 leaves. **Leaves** from stem and at base of plant, round to compressed in section, 5–40 cm long and 1–3 mm wide; auricles rounded, 1–2 mm long; bract erect, round, 1–4 cm long, shorter than the head. **Flowers** in an open, pyramid-shaped inflorescence, 5–12 cm long and less than half as wide, composed of 5–50 rounded heads 6–10 mm wide, each head with 5–30 flowers, the branches spreading, 1–10 cm long; tepals lance-shaped, green or straw-colored, 3–4 mm long; stamens 3, shorter than the tepals. **Capsules** oval, straw-colored to light brown, 3–4 mm long, about as long as the tepals, tipped with a short, blunt point. June–Aug. ❀ Wet sandy shores, streambanks and ditches; not in open bogs. ⊕ Wisc, c and s LP of Mich, ne Ill and nw Ind. NS and Maine to Wisc, s to Fla and Mex; BC to Ore.

Juncus alpinoarticulatus Chaix.

Alpine rush OBL

⚠
STATUS
Illinois - E

Perennial rush, spreading by rhizomes. **Stems** in small clumps, 1.5–4 dm long. **Leaves** mostly from base of plant and with 1–2 stem leaves, round in section, hollow, with small swollen joints, 2–12 cm long and 0.5–1 mm wide; sheaths green to red, auricles rounded, 0.5–1 mm long; bract round in section, 2–6 cm long and shorter than the head. **Flowers** in an open panicle of 5–25 heads, 2–15 cm long and 1–5 cm wide, the heads oblong pyramid-shaped, 2–6 mm wide, mostly 2–5-flowered, the branches upright, 1–7 cm long; tepals green to brown, 2–3 mm long, the inner tepals shorter, the margins chaffy; stamens 6. **Capsules** oblong, 3-angled, straw-colored to chestnut brown, satiny, 2–3 mm long, slightly longer than the tepals, tapered to a rounded tip. June–Sept. *J. alpinus*. ❀ Sandy or gravelly shores, streambanks, fens; often where calcium-rich. ⊕ n and c Minn, Wisc, Mich, ne Ill and nw Ind. Circumboreal, s to Pa, Ind, Mo, Neb, Colo, Utah, Idaho and Wash.

Juncus arcticus Willd.

Baltic rush; Wire-rush OBL

Perennial rush, spreading by stout, brown to black rhizomes. **Stems** slender and tough, dark green, 3–9 dm long, in rows from the rhizomes. **Leaves** reduced to red-brown sheaths at base of stem; bract erect, round in section, 1–2 dm long, longer than the head and resembling a continuation of stem. **Flowers** single on stalks, in dense to spreading heads, the heads appearing lateral, extending outward from stem 1–7 cm; tepals lance-shaped, dark brown, 3–5 mm long, margins chaffy; stamens 6. **Capsules** ovate, somewhat 3-angled, red-brown, 3–4 mm long, shorter to slightly longer than the tepals, tapered to a sharp point. May–Aug. Also known as *J. balticus*. ❀ Wet sandy or gravelly shores, interdunal wetlands near Great Lakes, meadows, ditches, marshes, seeps. ⊕ Common (especially near Lake Michigan); all but se Minn, e Wisc, Mich, ne Ill and nw Ind. Circumboreal, s to NY, Pa, Ohio, Ill, Mo, n Tex, NM and Calif; S Amer.

Juncus articulatus L.

Jointed rush OBL

⚠
STATUS
Indiana - E

Perennial rush, with coarse white rhizomes. **Stems** usually clumped, 2–6 dm long. **Leaves** from stem and at base of plant, ± round in section, hollow, with small swollen joints, 4–12 cm long and 1–3 mm wide; sheaths green or sometimes red, auricles rounded, about 1 mm long; bract erect, round in section, 1–4 cm long, shorter than the head. **Flowers** in open panicles, 4–10 cm long and 3–6 cm wide, composed of 3–30 heads, the heads rounded, 6–8 mm wide, 3–10-flowered, panicle branches erect to widely spreading, 1–4 cm long; tepals green to dark brown, 2–3 mm long; stamens 6. **Capsules** oval, dark brown, shiny, 3–4 mm long, longer than the tepals, tapered to a tip. July–Sept. ❀ Sandy, gravelly or mucky shores, streambanks and springs. ⊕ Rare in ec Minn; Mich, local in ne Ill and nw Ind. Newf to BC, s to WVa, Ohio, Ind, Minn, SD, Ariz and Calif.

Juncus brachycarpus Engelm.
White-root rush   FACW

Perennial rush, spreading by stout white rhizomes. **Stems** erect, round in section, 3–8 dm long. **Leaves** from stem and base of plant, round in section, 3–50 cm long and 1–2 mm wide, cross-divided; auricles rounded, 0.5–2 mm long; bract erect, channeled, 1–3 cm long, shorter than the head. **Flowers** in an open or crowded raceme or panicle of 3–10 or more heads, 2–8 cm long and 1–3 cm wide, the heads round, 8–10 mm wide, with 30 or more flowers, the branches upright, 1–4 cm long; tepals narrowly lance-shaped, straw-colored, 2–4 mm long; stamens 3, shorter than the tepals. **Capsules** ovate, brown, 2–3 mm long, shorter than the tepals, abruptly tapered to a small point. June–Aug. ⚘ Wetland margins, sandy swales and prairies. ⊕ Uncommon in sc Minn, extreme se Mich, occasional in ne Ill and nw Ind. Mass to s Ont, s Minn and Kans, s to Ga and Tex.

Juncus brachycephalus (Engelm.) Buchenau
Small-head rush   OBL

Densely clumped perennial rush. **Stems** erect, round in section, 3–7 dm long. **Leaves** from stem and base of plant, round in section, 2–20 cm long and 1–2 mm wide, often spreading; auricles rounded, to 1 mm long; bract erect, round in section, 1–5 cm long, shorter than the head. **Flowers** in an open raceme or panicle of 10–80 heads, 5–25 cm long and 2–12 cm wide, the heads oval, 2–5 mm wide, 2-6-flowered, branches upright to spreading, 1–5 cm long; tepals lance-shaped, green to light brown, 3-nerved, 2–3 mm long, margins chaffy; stamens 3 or sometimes 6. **Capsules** ovate, ± 3-angled, light brown, 3–4 mm long, longer than the tepals, abruptly narrowed to a short beak. June–Sept. ⚘ Sandy or gravelly shores, streambanks, open bogs, calcium-rich springs. ⊕ Wisc, Mich (most common in LP), ne Ill and nw Ind. Maine to Ont and Wisc, s to Pa, Ind, and Ill.

Juncus brevicaudatus (Engelm.) Fernald
Narrow-panicle rush   OBL

Densely clumped perennial rush. **Stems** erect, round in section, 1.5–5 dm long. **Leaves** from stem and base of plant, round in section, hollow, with small swollen joints, 3–20 cm long and 1–2 mm wide; sheaths green or sometimes red, auricles rounded, 1–2 mm long; bract erect, round in section, 2–7 cm long, shorter to longer than the head. **Flowers** in a raceme or panicle of 3–35 heads, 3–12 cm long and 1–4 cm wide, the heads oval, 2–6 mm wide, 2-7-flowered, branches upright, 0.5–3.5 cm long; tepals green to light brown, often red-tinged near tip, 3-nerved, 3–4 mm long, margins chaffy; stamens 3. **Capsules** oval, 3-angled, dark brown, 3–5 mm long, longer than the tepals, tapered to a sharp point. Aug–Sept. ⚘ Wet meadows, marshes, fens, sandy lakeshores, streambanks, rocks along Lake Superior. ⊕ n and ec Minn, n Wisc, UP, n and c LP of Mich. Que and NS to n Alberta, s to Mass, WVa, Pa, Minn and ND.

Juncus bufonius L.
Toad-rush   FACW+

Small annual rush. **Stems** clumped, erect to spreading, 5–20 cm long. **Leaves** from stem and at base of plant, flat or channeled, 1–7 cm long and to 1 mm wide, usually shorter than stem; sheaths green to red or brown, auricles absent; bract erect, 1–10 cm long, shorter than the head. **Flowers** single, mostly stalkless, with 1–7 flowers along each branch of the inflorescence, the inflorescence comprising half or more of the entire length of plant; tepals lance-shaped, green to straw-colored, 4–6 mm

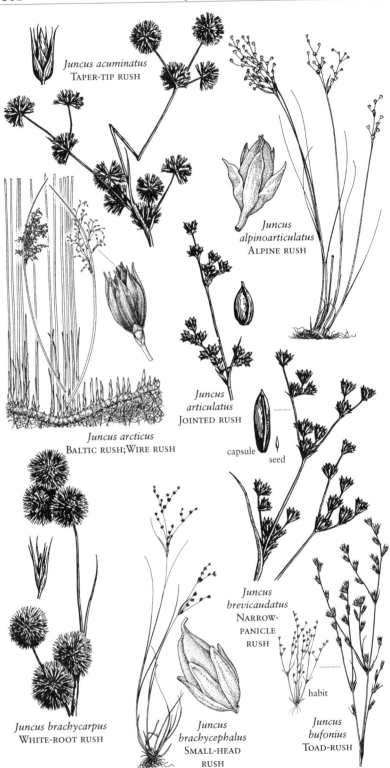

Juncus acuminatus
TAPER-TIP RUSH

Juncus alpinoarticulatus
ALPINE RUSH

Juncus arcticus
BALTIC RUSH; WIRE RUSH

Juncus articulatus
JOINTED RUSH

capsule   seed

Juncus brevicaudatus
NARROW-PANICLE RUSH

Juncus brachycarpus
WHITE-ROOT RUSH

Juncus brachycephalus
SMALL-HEAD RUSH

habit

Juncus bufonius
TOAD-RUSH

long, margins chaffy; stamens 6. **Capsules** ovate, brown or green, 3–4 mm long, rounded at tip, shorter than the tepals. June–Aug. ⚘ Sandy or silty shores, mud flats, streambanks, wet compacted soil of trails and wheel ruts. ⊕ n and c Minn, Wisc, Mich, ne Ill and nw Ind. Throughout most of N Amer; Eurasia.

Juncus canadensis J. Gay
Canada rush — OBL

Clumped perennial rush. **Stems** erect, rigid, round in section, 3–9 dm long. **Leaves** from stem and at base of plant, round in section, hollow, with small swollen joints, 3–20 cm long and 1–3 mm wide; sheaths green to red, auricles rounded, 1–2 mm long; bract erect, round in section, 3–7 cm long and shorter than the head. **Flowers** in an open or crowded raceme or panicle of few to many heads, 2–20 cm long and 1–10 cm wide, the heads ± round, 3–8 mm wide, with 5–40 or more flowers, the branches upright, 1–10 cm long; tepals narrowly lance-shaped, green to brown, 3–5 mm long; stamens 3. **Capsules** ovate, 3-angled, light to dark brown, 3–5 mm long, equal or longer than the tepals, rounded to a short tip. July–Sept. ⚘ Sandy, muddy or mucky shores, marshes, streambanks, thickets, ditches. ⊕ n and ec Minn, Wisc, Mich, ne Ill and nw Ind. Newf and Que to Minn, s to Ga, Tenn, La and Neb.

Juncus compressus Jacq.
Black grass — OBL

☞ Reports of Juncus gerardii from our region are probably best considered *J. compressus* [see *Plants of the Chicago Region* (1994) by Swink and Wilhelm].

Clumped, perennial rush. **Stems** erect, flattened, 2–7 dm long. **Leaves** from plant base and 1 or 2 along stem, flat or channeled, 5–20 cm long and to 1.5 mm wide; auricles rounded, to 1 mm long; bract erect, somewhat bent, flat or folded, 2–8 cm long, often longer than head. **Flowers** on short stalks 1–5 mm long, with 1–2 flowers along each branch of the inflorescence, the inflorescence 3–7 cm long and 1–3 cm wide, branches upright; tepals ovate, light to dark brown, 1–3 mm long, margins translucent; stamens 6. **Capsules** nearly round, light brown, 2–3 mm long, longer than tepals. June–Aug. ⚘ Wet meadows, disturbed wet areas, ditches along highways where forming dark green colonies; often where salty. ⊕ Uncommon in s Minn, s Wisc, ne Ill and nw Ind; once known from se Mich. Introduced from Eurasia, naturalized in N Amer; ± circumboreal, s in salt marshes along Atlantic Coast to Va, s along Pacific Coast to Wash, occasional inland.

Juncus effusus L.
Soft rush — OBL

Densely clumped perennial rush. **Stems** erect, round in section, to about 1 m long. **Leaves** reduced to bladeless sheaths at base of stem, the sheaths to 2 dm long, mostly red-brown; bract round in section, 10–30 cm long, appearing like a continuation of stem, longer than the head. **Flowers** in a many-flowered inflorescence, with 2–4 flowers along each branch of the inflorescence, the inflorescence appearing lateral, the branches upright to spreading or bent downward, 2–6 cm long; tepals lance-shaped, green to straw-colored, 2–3 mm long; stamens 3. **Capsules** broadly ovate, olive-green to brown, 2–3 mm long, about as long as tepals, sometimes tipped with a short point. June–July. ⚘ Marshes, shores, thickets, streambanks, bog margins, wet meadows. ⊕ Common; e and c Minn, Wisc, Mich, ne Ill and nw Ind. Throughout e USA and se Can.

Juncus ensifolius Wikström
Dagger-leaf rush
NI

Perennial rush, spreading by rhizomes. **Stems** single or in loose clumps, erect, flattened and narrowly winged, 2–6 dm long. **Leaves** from stem and at base of plant, the blade folded along midrib, the margins joined, with one edge turned toward the stem, 5–12 cm long and 2–6 mm wide; sheaths green or red, with broad chaffy margins, auricles absent; bract erect, 1–4 cm long, shorter than the head. **Flowers** in an open panicle of 3–11 heads, 4–7 cm long and 3–5 cm wide, the heads ± round, 8–10 mm wide, with 15 or more flowers, the branches upright, 1–10 cm long; tepals lance-shaped, straw-colored to red-brown, 3–4 mm long; stamens 3 (or 6). **Capsules** oval, dark brown, 3–4 mm long, tapered to a short beak, shorter to longer than the tepals. July–Sept. ≋ Margins of streams, ponds and springs. ⊕ Disjunct from main range of w USA in Ashland Co., Wisc, where probably introduced. SD and Mont to Alaska, s to NM, Ariz and Calif; Que, Ont, n Wisc.

Juncus filiformis L.
Thread rush
FACW

Perennial rush, with short or long rhizomes. **Stems** clumped or in rows from the rhizomes, erect, round in section, 1–5 dm long. **Leaves** reduced to bladeless sheaths at base of stem, the sheaths pale brown, to 6 cm long; bract erect, round in section, 6–20 cm long, appearing to be a continuation of stem, longer than the head. **Flowers** in an branched inflorescence, 1–3 cm long, with 1–3 flowers along each branch of the inflorescence, the inflorescence appearing lateral, the branches erect to spreading, to 1 cm long; tepals lance-shaped, green to straw-colored, 2–3 mm long, margins chaffy; stamens 6. **Capsules** broadly ovate, light brown, 2–3 mm long, slightly longer than the tepals, tipped by a short beak. ≋ Sandy, mucky, or gravelly shores, streambanks, thickets. ⊕ ne Minn, n Wisc and UP of Mich. Circumboreal, s in mts to NY and WVa, n Mich, n Minn.

Juncus longistylis Torr.
Long-style rush
FACW

Perennial rush, spreading by rhizomes. **Stems** 3–7 dm long. **Leaves** mostly at base of plant, flat and grasslike, 4–15 cm long and 1–3 mm wide, smaller upward; sheaths green, with broad membranous margins, auricles rounded, 1–2 mm long. **Flowers** in an inflorescence of 2–6 stalked, rounded heads, 5–7 cm long and 2–4 cm wide, the heads rounded, satiny chestnut brown, 1–2 cm wide, with 3–10 flowers, the branches erect, 1–4 cm long; tepals lance-shaped, green to brown, 4–6 mm long, margins translucent; stamens 6. **Capsules** oblong, brown, 2–3 mm long, slightly shorter than the tepals, rounded at tip, with a short beak. June–Aug. ≋ Shores, wet meadows, springs. ⊕ nw Minn. Newf and w Ont to BC, s to Minn, Neb, Colo, NM and Calif.

Juncus marginatus Rostk.
Grass-leaf rush
FACW

Perennial rush, spreading by rhizomes. **Stems** single or in small clumps, erect, compressed, 2–5 dm long, bulblike at base. **Leaves** from base of plant and on stem, flat, grasslike, 2–30 cm long and 1–3 mm wide; sheaths green, membranous on margins, auricles rounded, to 0.5 mm long; bract erect to spreading, flat, 1–8 cm long, shorter to slightly longer than the head. **Flowers** in an open panicle, 2–8 cm long and 1–6 cm wide, composed of 5–15 heads, the heads rounded, 3–6 mm wide, 6–20-flowered, branches upright, 0.5–2.5 cm long; tepals lance-shaped, green with

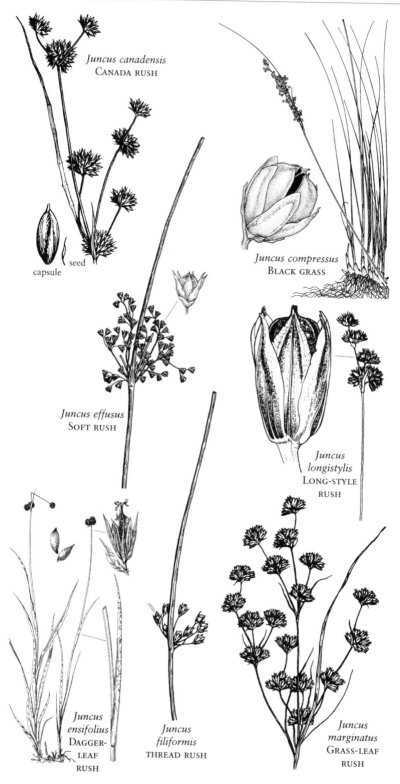

Juncus canadensis
CANADA RUSH

capsule   seed

Juncus compressus
BLACK GRASS

Juncus effusus
SOFT RUSH

Juncus longistylis
LONG-STYLE
RUSH

Juncus ensifolius
DAGGER-
LEAF
RUSH

Juncus filiformis
THREAD RUSH

Juncus marginatus
GRASS-LEAF
RUSH

red spots, 2–3 mm long, margins chaffy; stamens 3. **Capsules** ± round, brown with red spots, 2–3 mm long, slightly longer than the tepals, rounded at tip. June–Aug. *J. marginatus* var. *marginatus;* includes *J. biflorus.* ❦ Sandy shores and streambanks, wet meadows, marshes, low prairie, springs. ⊕ Uncommon in ec Minn, Wisc, local in c and s LP of Mich, ne Ill and nw Ind. Newf to Mich and SD, s to Fla, Tex and Ariz.

Juncus militaris Bigelow
Bayonet rush   OBL

Perennial rush, spreading by rhizomes, the rhizomes when underwater often producing long threadlike leaves 3–4 dm long. **Stems** stout, erect, round in section, 3–12 dm long. **Leaves** mostly 2 from near middle of stem, round in section, 5–7 dm long and about 5 mm wide, longer than the head, upper leaf often reduced to a sheath; sheaths often inflated, auricles rounded, only to 0.2 mm long; bract an inflated sheath with or without a blade, the blade (if present) round in section, 1–2 cm long, shorter than the head. **Flowers** in an open panicle of 50 or more heads, 4–15 cm long and 4–10 cm wide, the heads oblong pyramid-shaped, 3–6 mm wide, with 5–15 flowers, the branches upright, 1–7 cm long; tepals lance-shaped, straw-colored to red-brown, 2–3 mm long, margins chaffy; stamens 6. **Capsules** narrowly ovate, 3-angled, straw-colored to brown, satiny, 2–4 mm long, about equal to the tepals, tapered to a conspicuous beak. ❦ Lakeshores, marshes, open bogs. ⊕ Uncommon in n LP of Mich. Nfld s to Del along Atlantic coast, occasional inland in NY, Ont and Mich.

Juncus nodosus L.
Knotted rush   OBL

Perennial rush, spreading by rhizomes. **Stems** erect, slender, round in section, 1.5–6 dm long. **Leaves** on stem and one at base of plant, round in section, hollow, with small swollen joints, 3–30 cm long and 1–2 mm wide, upper leaves usually longer than the head; sheaths green, their margins green, becoming yellow and membranous toward tip, auricles rounded, yellow, 0.5–1 mm long; bract erect to spreading, round in section, 2–12 cm long, usually much longer than head. **Flowers** in a raceme or panicle of several heads, 1–6 cm long and 1–3 cm wide, the heads ± round, 6–10 mm wide, 6–20-flowered, the branches erect to spreading, 0.5–3 cm long; tepals narrowly lance-shaped, green to light brown, 3–4 mm long; the margins narrowly translucent; stamens 6. **Capsules** awl-shaped, brown, 4–5 mm long, longer than the tepals, tapered to a sometimes curved beak. July–Sept. ❦ Sandy, gravelly or clayey shores and streambanks, wet meadows, fens, ditches, springs; often where calcium-rich. ⊕ Minn, Wisc, Mich, ne Ill and nw Ind. Newf and NS to NW Terr and BC, s to Va, Ohio, Ind, Iowa, Neb, Colo, NM and Calif.

Juncus pelocarpus E. Meyer
Brown-fruit rush   OBL

Perennial rush, spreading by rhizomes and forming colonies. **Stems** erect, round in section, 1–4 dm long. **Leaves** from stem and at base of plant, round in section, very slender, 2–10 cm long and about 1 mm wide; auricles absent or short and straw-colored; bract erect, round in section, 2–4 cm long, shorter than the head. **Flowers** single or paired in a much-branched inflorescence, 5–15 cm long and 4–10 cm wide, the flowers on mostly 1 side of each branch, the branches upright to widely spreading, 1–4 cm long, with at least some of the flowers usually replaced by clusters of awl-shaped leaves; tepals ovate, dark brown, about 2 mm long, margins chaffy; stamens 6. **Capsules** narrowly ovate, dark brown, satiny,

2–3 mm long, equal or slightly longer than tepals, tapered to a slender beak. July–Aug. ⚘ Shallow water, sandy or mucky shores, bog margins. ⊕ Minn, Wisc, Mich and nw Ind. Labr, Nfld and Que to Minn, s to Md and n Ind.

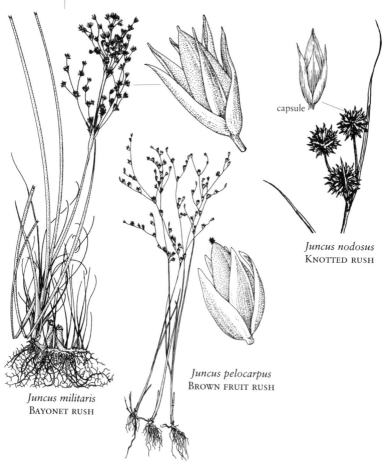

capsule

Juncus nodosus
KNOTTED RUSH

Juncus pelocarpus
BROWN FRUIT RUSH

Juncus militaris
BAYONET RUSH

Juncus scirpoides Lam.
Round-headed rush   FACW+

Perennial rush, from coarse, pale rhizomes. **Stems** single or clumped, erect, round in section, 1–7 dm long. **Leaves** mostly 2–3 per stem, basal leaves absent or single, blades round in section, hollow, with small swollen joints, 2–20 cm long and 1–2 mm wide, uppermost leaf shorter than the head; sheaths green or the lower red, membranous on upper margins, auricles pointed, 1–2 mm long; bract erect, round in section, 1–6 cm long, shorter to slightly longer than head. **Flowers** in an open to crowded raceme or panicle of 2–15 heads, 3–12 cm long and 1–5 cm wide, the heads round 5–10 mm wide, with 20–60 flowers, branches upright, 1–7 cm long; tepals lance-shaped, green to brown, 2–3 mm long; stamens 3. **Capsules** awl-shaped, 3-angled, straw-colored to brown, 3–4 mm long, equaling to slightly longer than the tepals. June–Sept. ⚘ Wet sandy shores, wet meadows, and streambanks. ⊕ Local in sw LP of Mich and nw Ind. Atlantic coast from NY to Fla and Tex, n to Ky, Mo, Okla; s Mich and n Ind.

Juncus stygius L.

Moor rush   OBL

Perennial rush, from slender rhizomes. **Stems** single or few together, erect, round in section, 1–4 dm long. **Leaves** 1–3 from near base of plant, with 1 leaf above middle of stem, round in section or somewhat flattened, 3–15 cm long and 0.5–2 mm wide; auricles short and rounded or absent; bract erect, round in section, 1–2 cm long, shorter than the head. **Flowers** in an inflorescence of 1–3 heads, the heads obovate, 5–10 mm wide, 1–4-flowered, branches erect, to 1 cm long; tepals lance-shaped, straw-colored to red-brown, 4–5 mm long, margins chaffy; stamens 6, nearly as long as the tepals. **Capsules** oval, 3-angled, green-brown, 6–8 mm long, longer than the tepals, tipped with a distinct point. ❧ Open bogs, marshes, and shallow water. ⊕ ne Minn, n Wisc, and Isle Royale and Mich UP near Marquette. Nearly circumboreal, s to New Eng, NY, n Mich and n Minn.

Juncus tenuis Willd.

Path-rush   FAC

Clumped, perennial rush. **Stems** erect, round in section to slightly flattened, 1–6 dm long. **Leaves** near base of stem, flat to broadly channeled, 10–15 cm long and to 1 mm wide; sheaths green, the margins yellow and glossy, auricles triangular, 1–3 mm long; bracts 1–3 (usually 2), the lowest erect, flat, 6–10 cm long, longer than the head. **Flowers** stalkless or on short stalks to 3 mm long, on branches with 1–7 flowers, in a crowded to spreading head 2–5 cm long; tepals lance-shaped, green to straw-colored or light brown, 3–5 mm long, margins narrowly translucent; stamens 6. **Capsules** ovate, green to straw-colored, 2–5 mm long, shorter or equaling the tepals, rounded at tip. June–July. ❧ Wet meadows, shores, streambanks, springs, common in disturbed places (often where soils compacted) such as trails, roadsides and ditches; also in drier woods and meadows. ⊕ Common; Minn, Wisc, Mich, ne Ill and nw Ind. Newf to Alberta and Wash, s to Md, Tenn, Tex and Colo; Mex, c and S Amer.

Juncus torreyi Coville

Torrey's rush   FACW

Perennial rush, from tuber-bearing rhizomes. **Stems** single, erect, round in section, 4–8 dm long. **Leaves** from stem and base of plant, round in section, hollow, with small swollen joints, 15–30 cm long and 1–2 mm wide, the upper leaves often longer than the head; sheaths green, the margins white and translucent, auricles 1–3 mm long; bract erect or spreading, round in section, 4–12 cm long, longer than the head. **Flowers** in a crowded, rounded raceme or panicle of 3–23 heads, 2–5 cm long and as wide, the heads round, 10–15 mm wide, with 25 to many flowers, branches erect to spreading 1–4 cm long; tepals narrowly lance-shaped, green to brown, 3–5 mm long, margins narrowly translucent; stamens 6. **Capsules** awl-shaped, brown, 4–6 mm long, equal or longer than the tepals, tapered to a short beak. June–Sept. ❧ Sandy shores, streambanks, wet meadows, marsh borders, springs, ditches. ⊕ Mostly nw, c and s Minn, Wisc, LP and local in e UP of Mich, ne Ill and nw Ind. Maine to BC, s to Ky, Ala, Tex, Colo and Calif.

Juncus vaseyi Engelm.

Vasey's rush   FACW

Clumped perennial rush. **Stems** erect, 2–6 dm long. **Leaves** all at base of plant, round in section, solid, narrowly channeled on upper surface, to 3 dm long and to 1 mm wide, usually shorter than stem; sheaths green or red, the margins membranous, auricles short or absent; bract upright, usually shorter than the head. **Flowers** single, stalkless or on short stalks, in a crowded inflorescence, 1–4 cm long; tepals lance-shaped, green to light brown, 4–6 mm long, margins narrowly translucent; stamens 6. **Capsules** cylindric, 1–2 mm long, equal or slightly longer than the tepals, blunt-tipped. July–Aug. ❧ Wet meadows, sandy shores. ⊕ n and e Minn, uncommon in e UP and n LP of Mich and ne Ill. NS to BC, s to NY, Ill, Iowa, ND, Colo and Idaho.

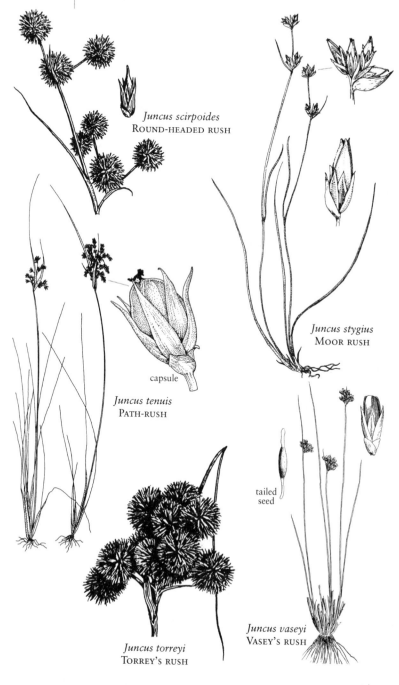

Juncus scirpoides
Round-headed rush

Juncus stygius
Moor rush

capsule

Juncus tenuis
Path-rush

tailed
seed

Juncus torreyi
Torrey's rush

Juncus vaseyi
Vasey's rush

Juncaginaceae
Arrow-Grass Family

▶**Triglochin** L. / Arrow-grass

Grasslike perennial herbs, clumped from creeping rhizomes, often in brackish habitats. **Stems** slender, leafless. **Leaves** all from base of plant, slender, linear, round or somewhat flattened in section, sheathing at base. **Flowers** perfect, regular, on short stalks in a spikelike raceme at end of stem; flower segments (tepals) 6; stigmas 3 or 6, styles short or absent; stamens 6, anthers stalkless, nearly as large as tepals. **Fruit** of 3 or 6 carpels, these splitting when mature into 1-seeded segments.

▶**KEY TO TRIGLOCHIN**

1 Plants generally small and slender; stigmas 3; fruits linear, clublike toward tip . . . . *T. palustre* / MARSH ARROW-GRASS
1 Plants larger, usually 3 dm or more tall; stigmas 6; fruits short-cylindric . . . . *T. maritimum* / COMMON OR SEASIDE ARROW-GRASS

Triglochin maritimum L.
  Common or Seaside arrow-grass   OBL

Clumped perennial herb, from a thick crown and spreading by rhizomes. **Stems** 2–8 dm long. **Leaves** upright to spreading, somewhat flattened, to 5 dm long and 1–3 mm wide. **Flowers** 2–3 mm wide, in densely flowered, spikelike racemes 1–4 dm long; the flowers on upright stalks 4–6 mm long, the stalks extending downward on the stem as a wing; tepals 6, 1–2 mm long; stigmas 6; stamens 6. **Fruit** of 6 ovate carpels, 2–5 mm long and 1–3 mm wide, the carpel tips curved outward. June–Aug. ❧ Sandy, gravelly, or marly lakeshores and streambanks; marshes, brackish wetlands. ⊕ Mostly n and c Minn, occasional in most of Wisc (especially se), Mich, ne Ill and nw Ind. Circumboreal, s to Pa, Ind, Ill, Iowa, Neb, Colo, Mex and Baja Calif; S Amer.

Triglochin palustre L.
  Marsh arrow-grass   OBL

Small, clumped perennial herb. **Stems** slender, 2–4 dm long. **Leaves** erect, round in section, to 3 dm long and 1–2 mm wide. **Flowers** small, 1–2 mm wide, in loosely flowered racemes, 10–25 cm long; the flowers on erect stalks, 2–5 mm long; tepals 6, 1–2 mm long; stigmas 3; stamens 6. **Fruit** of 3 narrow, clublike carpels, 5–8 mm long and 1 mm wide, splitting upward from base into 3 segments. June–Sept. ❧ Sandy, gravelly, or marly lakeshores and streambanks, calcareous fens, marshes, interdunal swales; often where calcium-rich. ⊕ Minn (mostly nw and s), Wisc, Mich, ne Ill and nw Ind. Circumboreal, s to Maine, Pa, Ill, Iowa, Neb, Colo, Idaho and Calif; S Amer.

Lemnaceae
Duckweed Family

Small perennial herbs, floating at or near water surface, single or forming colonies. Plants thalluslike (not differentiated into stems and leaves), the **thallus** (or frond) flat or thickened; the roots, if present, unbranched, 1 or several from near center of leaf underside; reproducing vegetatively by buds from 1–2 pouches on the sides, the parent and budded plants often joined in small groups. **Flowers** rare, either male or female, in tiny reproductive pouches on margins (*Lemna, Spirodela*) or upper surface (*Wolffia*) of the leaves, subtended by a small spathe within the pouch; sepals and petals absent; male flowers 1–2, consisting of 1 anther on a short filament; female flower 1 (a single ovary), in same pouch as male flowers. **Fruit** a utricle with 1 to several seeds.

▶**KEY TO LEMNACEAE**

1 Roots absent; leaves thickened, less than 1.5 mm long . . . . . *Wolffia*
. . . . WATER-MEAL
1 One to several roots present on leaf underside; leaves flat, mostly more than 1.5 mm long 2

2 Each leaf with 1 root; leaf underside green or purple-tinged . *Lemna*
. . . . DUCKWEED
2 Each leaf with 3 or more roots; leaf underside solid purple . . . . . .
. . . . *Spirodela polyrhiza* / GREATER DUCKWEED

▶**Lemna** L. / Duckweed

☞ Newer floras define several new species of Lemna. The treatment of Crow and Hellquist (2000) is followed here. Several species of *Lemna* will often occur intermixed in the same quiet water habitats.

Small perennial floating herbs, with 1 root per frond (or roots sometimes absent on oldest and youngest leaves). **Fronds** single or 2 to several and joined in small colonies, floating on water surface or underwater (star-duckweed, *L. trisulca*), varying from round, ovate, to obovate or oblong, tapered to a long point (stipe) in star-duckweed; green or often red-tinged; upper surface flat to slightly convex, underside flat or convex. Reproductive pouches 2, on margins of frond. **Flowers** uncommon, consisting of 2 stamens (male flowers) and a single pistil (female flower) in each pouch. **Fruit** an utricle with 1 to several seeds. Reproduction mostly by budding of new leaves from the reproductive pouches.

▶**KEY TO LEMNA**

1 Frond tapered to a petiole-like base; lateral fronds usually attached to parent frond; plants typically forming tangled mats and floating below water surface . . . . *L. trisulca* / STAR-DUCKWEED
1 Fronds sessile, ± round, floating on water surface 2

2 Fronds elliptic, 0.5–1.5 mm wide, faintly 1-nerved, sides of frond ± parallel and rounded at ends . . *Lemna valdiviana* / PALE DUCKWEED
2 Fronds nearly round to obovate, 1–3 mm wide, faintly 3-nerved, sides of frond curved 3

3 Fronds with conspicuous (under magnification) small bumps (papilla) on surface; root sheath with lateral wings. . . . . . . *Lemna perpusilla* . . . . MINUTE DUCKWEED

3 Fronds without conspicuous papilla; root sheath without lateral wings . . . . *Lemna minor* / LESSER DUCKWEED

Lemna minor L.

Lesser duckweed   OBL

Perennial floating herb, with 1 root from middle of underside of frond. **Fronds** ± round to oval, 2–4 mm long, often in groups of 2–5, underside often red-tinged; both sides flat or slightly convex. **Fruit** a 1-seeded utricle. July–Sept. ❦ Quiet or stagnant water of ponds, oxbows, shores, slow-moving rivers, ditches. ⊕ Common; Minn, Wisc, Mich, ne Ill and nw Ind. Temperate N Amer, Europe, Africa, Australia and most of Asia; absent from S Amer.

Lemna perpusilla Torr.

Minute duckweed   OBL

Perennial floating herb; roots single from underside of frond or absent. **Fronds** single or several together, obovate to elliptic, asymmetrical at base, 2–3 mm long, upper surface convex or keeled, with small bumps (papilla) near center and tip of frond. **Fruit** a 1-seeded utricle. ❦ Quiet water of ponds, ditches. ⊕ Minn, Wisc, Ill; once present in Ind. s Que and Mass, to Ohio, Ill, Minn and ND, s to Ga, Tex and NM.

Lemna trisulca L.

Star-duckweed   OBL

Perennial floating herb, forming tangled colonies just below water surface, floating at surface only when flowering; roots single from underside of frond or absent. **Fronds** several to many, joined to form star–shaped colonies; fronds oblong lance-shaped, 5–20 mm long, tapered to a slender base (stipe), flat on both sides. **Fruit** a 1-seeded utricle. ❦ Ponds, streams, ditches. ⊕ Occasional to common; Minn, Wisc, Mich, ne Ill and nw Ind. Temperate zones of the N Hemisphere.

Lemna valdiviana Phil.

Pale duckweed   OBL

Perennial floating herb; roots single from underside of frond or absent. **Fronds** pale green, usually in tangled groups of 2–5; fronds oblong, narrowly elliptic, or somewhat sickle-shaped, 1–4.5 mm long, upper surface flat or slightly convex. **Fruit** a 1-seeded utricle. ❦ Quiet water. ⊕ Ill; historic records from Mich and Ind. NH and Mass to Ill, Colo and Ore, s to Fla, Tex and Calif.

▶Spirodela Schleiden / Greater duckweed

Spirodela polyrhiza (L.) Schleiden

Greater duckweed   OBL

Perennial herb, floating on water surface; roots 5–12 per frond. **Fronds** usually in clusters of 2–5, flat, round to obovate, 3–6 mm long, upper surface green, underside red-purple. **Flowers** uncommon, comprised of 2–3 stamens (male flowers) and 1 pistil (female flower) in each pouch. **Fruit** a 1–2-seeded utricle. Reproduction mainly by budding of new leaves from reproductive pouches (1 pouch on each margin of frond). ❦ Stagnant or slow-moving water of lakes, ponds, marshes and ditches,

☞ **Greater duckweed** is similar to *Lemna* but in *Spirodela*, the fronds are larger and purple on their underside.

often with lesser duckweed (*Lemna minor*). ⊕ Minn, Wisc, Mich, ne Ill and nw Ind. Cosmopolitan.

▶**Wolffia** Horkel / Water-meal

☞ Wolfiella floridana is a floating, aquatic species reported from Cook Co. in ne Ill. The species lacks roots and has thin, linear leaves to 1 cm long, in contrast to *Wolfia*, which has much smaller, thickened leaves less than 2 mm long.

Tiny perennial herbs, without roots, floating at or just below water surface, sometimes abundant and forming a granular scum across surface, usually mixed with other members of Duckweed Family. **Fronds** single or often paired, globe-shaped or ovate, flat or rounded on upper surface. **Flowers** uncommon, consisting of 1 stamen (male flower) and 1 pistil (female flower) in the pouch. **Fruit** a round, 1-seeded utricle. Reproduction mainly by budding from the single pouch near base of frond. ☞ Water-meals are the world's smallest flowering plants. The fronds feel granular or mealy and tend to stick to skin. The 3 species in our region often occur together, usually in stagnant and/or polluted water.

▶**KEY TO WOLFFIA**

1 Leaves rounded on upper surface, not brown-dotted *W. columbiana* . . . . COLUMBIA WOLFFIA
1 Leaves flattened on upper surface, brown-dotted (under 10x) **2**

2 Leaves rounded at tip, with a wartlike bump in center of upper surface. *W. papulifera* / POINTED DUCKWEED
2 Leaves with an upturned point at tip, wartlike bump absent . . . . *W. punctata* / DOTTED WOLFFIA

Wolffia columbiana Karsten
Columbia wolffia   OBL
Small perennial floating herb. **Fronds** float low in water, only small upper surface exposed, round to broadly ovate and 1–1.5 mm long when viewed from above; nearly round when viewed from side, not raised and pointed at tip; green, not brown-dotted. ⚘ Stagnant water of ponds and marshes. ⊕ Local in c and se Minn; Wisc, LP and e UP of Mich, ne Ill and nw Ind. Maine to Ont and ND, s through the e and c USA; Calif, Mex, n S Amer.

Wolffia papulifera C. Thompson
Pointed duckweed   OBL

⚠ STATUS Michigan - T

Small perennial floating herb. **Fronds** broadly ovate, 0.5–1.5 mm long and 0.5–1 mm wide, rounded at tip, brown-dotted; upper surface floating just above water surface, with a wartlike bump near center. Aug–Sept. *Wolffia brasiliensis*. ⚘ Quiet water of ponds, often occurring with other species of *Wolffia*. ⊕ Mich, ne Ill and nw Ind. NJ to Mich, Ill and Kans, s to Fla and Tex; S Amer.

Wolffia punctata Griseb.
Dotted wolffia   OBL
Small perennial floating herb. **Fronds** oval to oblong when viewed from above, 0.1–1 mm long and to 0.5 mm wide, with a raised pointed tip, usually brown-dotted; upper surface floating just above water surface, bright green, underside paler. *W. borealis*. ⚘ Quiet water of ponds, marshes and ditches, often with other species of *Wolffia* and *Lemna*. ⊕ Uncommon in c and se Minn; Wisc, c and s LP of Mich, ne Ill and nw Ind. NH to Ont, Minn and SD, s to Fla, Tex and Colo; Wash, Ore; W Indies.

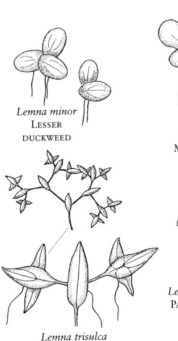

Lemna minor
LESSER
DUCKWEED

Lemna perpusilla
MINUTE DUCKWEED

Lemna valdiviana
PALE DUCKWEED

Lemna trisulca
STAR-DUCKWEED

Wolfia columbiana
COLUMBIA WOLFIA

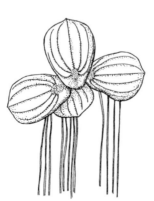

Wolfia papulifera
POINTED DUCKWEED

Spirodela polyrhiza
GREATER DUCKWEED

Wolfia punctata
DOTTED WOLFIA

Liliaceae
Lily Family

Perennial herbs, from corms, bulbs or rhizomes. **Stems** leafy or leafless. **Leaves** linear to ovate, usually from base of plant, sometimes along stem, alternate to opposite or whorled. **Flowers** perfect (with both male and female parts), regular; sepals and petals of 6 petal-like tepals in 2 series of 3; stamens 6; ovary superior or inferior, 3-chambered. **Fruit** a capsule or round berry.

▶**KEY TO LILIACEAE**

1 Leaves from stem **2**
1 Leaves all from base of plant; flowers at ends of leafless stalks (scapes)**4**

2 Plants large, 3–8 dm tall; flowers showy, orange. . . . .
. . . . *Lilium philadelphicum* / WOOD-LILY
2 Plants smaller, mostly 0.5–4 dm tall; flowers small, white **3**

3 Tepals 4; leaves usually 2. . . . . *Maianthemum canadense*
. . . . CANADA MAYFLOWER; WILD LILY-OF-THE-VALLEY
3 Tepals 6; leaves usually 3 . . *Smilacina trifolia* / FALSE SOLOMON'S SEAL

4 Flowers yellow; ovary inferior *Hypoxis hirsuta* / YELLOW STAR-GRASS
4 Flowers white or greenish; ovary superior **5**

5 Stems sticky-hairy . . . . *Tofieldia glutinosa* / FALSE ASPHODEL
5 Stems smooth and waxy, not sticky-hairy . . . . . . *Zigadenus elegans*
. . . . WHITE CAMAS

▶**Hypoxis** L. / Star-grass

Hypoxis hirsuta (L.) Cov.
Yellow star-grass   FAC

☞ Hypoxis is sometimes placed in the Amaryllis Family (Amaryllidaceae).

Low perennial herb, from a small, shallow corm. **Stems** leafless, lax, 1 to several, silky-hairy in upper part, shorter than leaves when flowering, to 4 dm long when mature. **Leaves** from base of plant, linear, hairy, to 6 dm long and 2–10 mm wide. **Flowers** 1–6 (usually 2), yellow, 1–2.5 cm wide, in racemes at ends of stems, tepals hairy on outside, 5–12 mm long, spreading in flower, closing and turning green after flowering, persistent. **Capsule** oval, 3–6 mm long; seeds black. May–July. ❦ Wet meadows, shores, moist prairie; often where calcium-rich. ⊕ w and s Minn, Wisc, c to s LP of Mich, ne Ill and nw Ind. Maine to Man, s to Ga and Tex.

Lilium L. / Lily

☞ **Michigan lily** (*Lilium michiganense*, FACW) occurs in wet meadows, along streams, and in floodplain forests of the Gt Lakes region. The orange flower is nodding instead of upright as in *L. philadelphicum*.

Lilium philadelphicum L.
  Wood-lily   FAC-
Perennial herb from a scaly bulb. **Stems** erect, 3–8 dm long. **Leaves** all from stem, narrowly lance-shaped, 4–10 cm long and 3–9 mm wide, parallel-veined; lower leaves alternate, upper leaves opposite or whorled; petioles absent. **Flowers** 1–5, erect, large and showy, on stalks 1–8 cm long at ends of stem; tepals orange-red, yellow and dark-spotted toward base, lance-shaped, 4–8 cm long and 0.8–2.8 cm wide, stamens and pistil about as long as tepals; stigma 3-parted; ovary superior. **Capsule** oblong, 2.5–4 cm long; seeds flat. June–July. ❀ Wet meadows, low prairie, fens and open bogs, seeps, ditches; also in drier meadows, prairies and woods. ⊕ Minn, Wisc, Mich, ne Ill and nw Ind. NH to BC, s to NC, Ky, Iowa, Neb and NM.

▸Maianthemum Wiggers / Wild lily-of-the-valley

Maianthemum canadense Desf.
  Canada Mayflower; Wild lily-of-the-valley UPL
Small perennial herb, spreading by rhizomes. **Stems** erect, 5–20 cm long. **Leaves** usually 2 along stem, ovate, heart-shaped at base, 3–10 cm long; petioles short or absent. **Flowers** small, white, 4–6 mm wide, stalked, in a short raceme at end of stem, the raceme 3–6 cm long; tepals 4, spreading; stamens 4; style 2-lobed. **Fruit** a pale red berry, 3–4 mm wide; seeds 1–2. May–July. ❀ On hummocks in swamps, open bogs and thickets; also common in moist to dry woods. ⊕ Very common across most of our region. Minn, Wisc, Mich, ne Ill and nw Ind. Labr and Nfld to NW Terr, s to NC, Ky, Ill and SD.

Smilacina Desf. / False Solomon's seal

Smilacina trifolia (L.) Desf.
  False Solomon's seal   OBL
Perennial herb, from long rhizomes. **Stems** erect, 1–5 dm long at flowering time. **Leaves** alternate, smooth, usually 3 (2–4), oval or oblong lance-shaped, 6–12 cm long and 1–4 cm wide; petioles absent. **Flowers** small, white, 8 mm wide, stalked, 3–8 in a raceme; tepals 6, spreading; stamens 6. **Fruit** a dark red berry, 3–5 mm wide; seeds 1–2. May–June. ❀ Open bogs, conifer swamps, thickets. ⊕ n and ec Minn, n and c and Wisc (plus uncommon in se), Mich. Nfld to NW Terr and BC, s to NJ, Ohio, s Wisc and Minn; n Asia.

Tofieldia Hudson / False asphodel

⚠ STATUS
Wisconsin - T
Illinois - T

Tofieldia glutinosa (Michx.) Pers.
  False asphodel   OBL
Perennial herb, from a bulb. **Stems** erect, nearly leafless, 2–5 dm long, covered with sticky hairs. **Leaves** 2–4 from base of plant, linear, hairy,

8–20 cm long and to 8 mm wide, sometimes with 1 bractlike leaf near middle of stem. **Flowers** white, on sticky-hairy stalks 3–6 mm long, in a raceme 2–5 cm long when in flower, becoming longer when fruiting, 2–3 at each node of the raceme, upper flowers opening first; tepals 6, oblong lance-shaped, 4 mm long; stamens 6. **Fruit** an oblong capsule, 5–6 mm long; seeds about 1 mm long, with a slender tail at each end. June–Aug. ❦ Sandy or gravelly shores, interdunal wetlands, calcareous fens, rocky shores of Lake Superior. ⊕ nw and c Minn, uncommon in e Wisc (especially se), Mich (but local in c LP), local in ne Ill and ne Ind. Nfld to Alaska, s to NC, WVa, n Ind, n Ill, n Rocky Mts and Calif.

▶**Zigadenus** Michx. / Death camas

Zigadenus elegans Pursh
White camas   FACW

⚠
STATUS
Illinois - E

Perennial herb, from an ovate bulb; plants waxy, especially when young. **Stems** erect, 2–6 dm long. **Leaves** mostly from base of plant, linear, 2–4 dm long and 4–12 mm wide; stem leaves much smaller. **Flowers** green-yellow or white, in a raceme or panicle, 1–3 dm long, the branches upright, subtended by large, lance-shaped, green or purplish bracts; tepals 6, obovate, 7–12 mm long, usually purple-tinged near base; stamens 6. **Fruit** an ovate capsule, 10–15 mm long; seeds 3 mm long. July–Aug. *Z. glaucus*. ❦ Sandy or rocky shores of Great Lakes, open bogs, calcareous fens. ⊕ w and s Minn, local in c and s Wisc, LP of Mich (local in c and e UP), rare in ne Ill and nw Ind. Que to BC and Alaska, across n USA and s in Rocky Mts to n Mex; disjunct in s Appalachian and Ozark Mts.

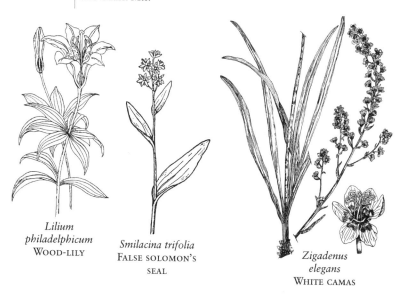

Lilium philadelphicum
WOOD-LILY

Smilacina trifolia
FALSE SOLOMON'S
SEAL

Zigadenus elegans
WHITE CAMAS

Najadaceae
Water-Nymph Family

▶**Najas** L. / Naiad; Water-nymph

Aquatic annual herbs, roots fibrous, rhizomes absent. **Stems** wavy, with slender branches. **Leaves** simple, opposite or in crowded whorls, stalkless, abruptly widened at base to sheath the stem; margins toothed to nearly entire, the teeth sometimes spine-tipped. **Flowers** either male or female, separate on same plant or on different plants, tiny, single and stalkless in leaf axils, enclosed by the sheathing leaf bases; **male flowers** a single anther within a membranous envelope (spathe), this surrounded by perianth scales, the scales sometimes joined into a tube; **female flowers** surrounded by 1–2 spathes, pistils 1, stigmas 2–4, style usually persistent. **Fruit** a 1-seeded achene.

▶**KEY TO NAJAS**

1 Leaves coarsely toothed and spine-tipped (spines visible without a lens), bright green; midvein of leaf underside and stems between nodes often prickly . . . . *N. marina* / ALKALINE WATER-NYMPH
1 Leaves nearly entire or toothed (if spine-tipped, the spines, except in *N. minor,* not visible without a lens), often olive green; leaf surface and stems between leaves smooth. **2**

2 Base of leaves lobed or clasping stem **3**
2 Leaves tapered to base, not lobed or clasping stem **4**

3 Leaves somewhat stiff, curved downward near tip; base of leaf lobed; seed coat pitted, the pits wider than long and arranged in regular, ladderlike rows . . . . *N. minor* / EUTROPHIC WATER-NYMPH
3 Leaves slender, not stiff, not curved downward near tip; base of leaf clasping; seed coat pitted, the pits longer than wide . . *N. gracillima* . . . . SLENDER WATER-NYMPH

4 Achenes smooth and glossy, widest above middle. . . . . . . *N. flexilis* . . . . NORTHERN WATER-NYMPH
4 Achenes rough and pitted, widest at middle and tapered to ends. . . . . *N. guadalupensis* / SOUTHERN WATER-NYMPH

Najas flexilis (Willd.) Rostkov & Schmidt
Northern water-nymph   OBL
Annual aquatic herb. **Stems** branched, 5–40 cm long. **Leaves** densely clustered at tips of stems, linear, tapered to a long slender point, spreading or ascending, 1–4 cm long and to 0.5 mm wide; margins with tiny sharp teeth. **Flowers** either male and female, separate on same plant. **Achenes** oval, olive-green to red, the beak 1 mm or more long; seeds straw-colored, shiny, 2–4 mm long. July–Sept. ❧ Ponds, lakes and streams. ⊕ Common; Minn (all but sw), Wisc, Mich, ne Ill and nw Ind. Newf and Que to s Man, s to Md, Ind, Iowa and Neb; also BC and n Alberta, s to Idaho and Calif.

Najas gracillima (A. Braun) Magnus
Slender water-nymph   OBL

Annual aquatic herb; plants light green. **Stems** very slender, branched, 0.5–5 dm long. **Leaves** opposite or in groups of 3 or more, bristlelike, 0.5–3 cm long and to 0.5 mm wide, spreading or ascending; margins with very small teeth. **Flowers** either male or female and on the same plant. **Achenes** cylindric, narrowed at ends; seeds light brown, 2–3 mm long. ⚘ Shallow water of lakes, usually in muck; intolerant of polluted water. ⊕ Uncommon in ne and c Minn, n Wisc, local in w UP and s LP of Mich, Ind. NS to Minn, s to Ala and Iowa.

Najas guadalupensis (Sprengel) Magnus
Southern water-nymph   OBL

Annual aquatic herb. **Stems** much branched, 1–6 dm long. **Leaves** numerous, linear, spreading and often curved downward at tip, 1–3 cm long and 0.5–2 mm wide; groups of smaller leaves also present in leaf axils; margins with very small teeth. **Flowers** either male or female, separate on same plant. **Achenes** cylindric, the beak to 0.5 mm long; seeds brown or purple, 1–3 mm long. July–Sept. ⚘ Shallow to deep water of lakes, ponds and sometimes rivers; often with **northern water-nymph** (*Najas flexilis*) but less common. ⊕ s Minn, s Wisc, mostly c and s LP of Mich, ne Ill and nw Ind. Mass and s Que to Minn, ND, Wyo and Ore, s to Mex and S Amer.

Najas marina L.
Alkaline water-nymph   OBL

Annual aquatic herb. **Stems** stout, 1–5 dm long and 1–4 mm wide, compressed, branched, prickly. **Leaves** opposite or whorled, linear, 0.5–4 cm long and 1–4 mm wide, sometimes with spines on underside; margins coarsely toothed, the teeth 1–4 mm apart and spine-tipped. **Flowers** either male or female and on different plants. **Achenes** olive-green, the beak about 1 mm long; seeds dull, 2–5 mm long. July–Sept. ⚘ Shallow water (to 1 m deep) of lakes and marshes. ⊕ Uncommon in wc Minn, Wisc, local in c and se LP of Mich. Nearly cosmopolitan, but local in N Amer: NY, Fla, Tex, Utah, Ariz, and Calif.

Najas minor Allioni
Eutrophic water-nymph   OBL

Annual aquatic herb; plants dark green. **Stems** slender, branched, 1–2 dm long. **Leaves** opposite or whorled, linear, 0.5–3.5 cm long and to 0.2 mm wide, curved downward at tip; margins sharp-toothed, with 7–15 teeth on each side. **Flowers** either male and female, separate on the same plant. **Achenes** oval, the beak about 1 mm long; seeds 2–3 mm long, purple-tinged. ⚘ Marshes, lakes, ponds. ⊕ Introduced; local in se Wisc, extreme se Mich, ne Ill and nw Ind.

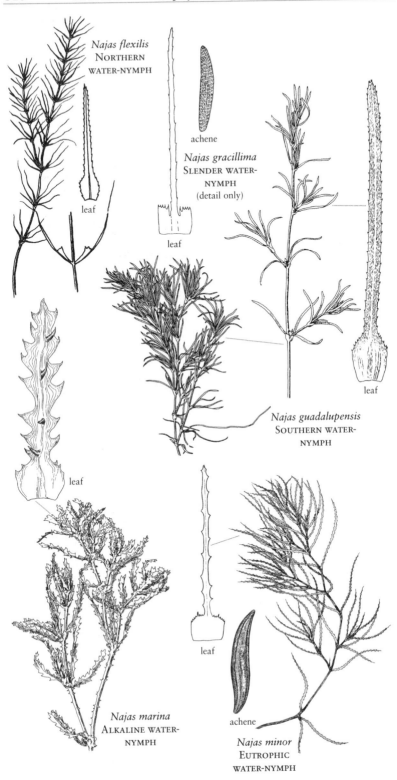

Najas flexilis
NORTHERN
WATER-NYMPH

leaf

achene

Najas gracillima
SLENDER WATER-
NYMPH
(detail only)

leaf

leaf

leaf

Najas guadalupensis
SOUTHERN WATER-
NYMPH

leaf

leaf

Najas marina
ALKALINE WATER-
NYMPH

achene

Najas minor
EUTROPHIC
WATER-NYMPH

Orchidaceae
Orchid Family

Perennial herbs, from fleshy or tuberous roots, corms or bulbs. **Leaves** simple, along the stem and alternate, or mostly at base of plant, stalkless and usually sheathing the stem, parallel-veined, often somewhat fleshy. **Flowers** perfect (with both male and female parts), irregular, showy in many species, in heads of 1 or 2 flowers at ends of stems, or with several to many flowers in a spike, raceme or panicle, each flower usually subtended by a bract; sepals 3, green or colored, sometimes resembling the lateral petals, the lateral sepals free, or joined to form an appendage below the lip (as in *Cypripedium*), or joined with the lateral petals to form a hood over the lip (*Spiranthes*); petals 3, white or colored, the 2 lateral petals alike, the lowest petal different and called the lip; stamens 1–2, attached to the style and forming a stout column; ovary inferior. **Fruit** a many-seeded capsule, opening by 3 or sometimes 6 longitudinal slits, but remaining closed at tip and base; seeds miniscule.

▶**KEY TO ORCHIDACEAE**

1 Plants without leaves; stems yellowish (chlorophyll absent) . . . . . .
. . . . *Corallorhiza trifida* / YELLOW CORALROOT
1 Plants with 1 or more leaves; stems green **2**

2 Leaves whorled . . . *Isotria verticillata* / LARGER WHORLED POGONIA
2 Leaves various, not whorled **3**

3 Lip of flower inflated and pouchlike **4**
3 Lip not inflated or pouchlike **5**

4 Leaf 1, lip hair-covered; rare plant of n Minn, nw Wisc, n Mich . .
. . . . *Calypso bulbosa* / CALYPSO; FAIRY SLIPPER
4 Leaves 2 or more, lip hairless; plants more widespread . . . .
. . . . *Cypripedium* / LADY'S-SLIPPER

5 Base of lip extended downward as a spur **6**
5 Spur absent **7**

6 Flowers showy, lip of flower white with purple spots; rare plant in n portions of region . . . . *Amerorchis rotundifolia*
. . . . ROUND-LEAF ORCHID
6 Flowers white or yellow-green; most species widespread . . . .
. . . . *Platanthera* / REIN-ORCHID

7 Lip above other flower parts **8**
7 Lip below other flower parts **9**

8 Flowers large and rose-purple; leaf 1 . . . . *Calopogon tuberosus*
. . . . GRASS-PINK
8 Flowers small and yellow-green or cream-colored; leaves 1–5 . . . . .
. . . . *Malaxis paludosa* / BOG ADDER'S MOUTH

9 Lip of flower bearded **10**
9 Lip of flower not bearded **11**

10 Leaf flat, present at flowering time . . . . . . *Pogonia ophioglossoides*
. . . . ROSE POGONIA; SNAKE-MOUTH
10 Leaf folded, absent at flowering (developing later) *Arethusa bulbosa*
. . . . SWAMP-PINK; DRAGON'S MOUTH

11 Leaves in an opposite pair on stem. **12**
11 Leaves not opposite **13**

12 Leaves near middle of stem, lip of flower lobed at tip . . . . . . *Listera*
. . . . TWAYBLADE
12 Leaves basal, lip of flower not lobed at tip . . . . *Liparis loeselii*
. . . . FEN-ORCHID; LOESEL'S TWAYBLADE

13 Upper stem leafless . . . . *Malaxis* / ADDER'S MOUTH
13 Upper stem with small, scalelike leaves *Spiranthes* / LADIES' TRESSES

▶Amerorchis Hultén / Orchis

Amerorchis rotundifolia (Banks ex Pursh) Hultén
Round-leaf orchid   OBL

⚠
STATUS
Michigan - E
Wisconsin - T

Perennial herb, roots few from a slender rhizome. **Stems** leafless, smooth, 15–30 cm long. **Leaves** single from near base of plant, oval, 4–15 cm long and 2–8 cm wide; usually with 1–2 bladeless sheaths below. **Flowers** 4 or more, in a raceme 3–8 cm long; sepals white to pale pink; petals white to pink or purple-tinged, the 2 lateral petals joined with the upper sepal to form somewhat of a hood over the column; lip white, with purple spots, 6–10 mm long and 4–7 mm wide, 3–lobed, the terminal lobe largest and notched at tip; spur about 5 mm long, shorter than lip. June–July. *Orchis rotundifolia.* ≋ Conifer swamps (on moss under cedar, tamarack, or black spruce); s in region in cold conifer swamps of balsam fir, black spruce and cedar; usually found over limestone and where sphagnum mosses not predominant. ⊕ w and nc Minn (where locally common in suitable habitats), local in n and e Wisc (mostly near Lake Mich, uncommon in c and e UP and n LP of Mich. Greenland to Alaska, s to Que, NY, n Great Lakes, Mont and BC.

▶Arethusa L. / Dragon's mouth

Arethusa bulbosa L.
Swamp-pink; Dragon's mouth   OBL
Perennial herb; roots few, fibrous, from a corm. **Stems** leafless, smooth, 1–4 dm long. **Leaves** 1, linear, small and bractlike at flowering time, later expanding to 2 dm long and 3–8 mm wide; lower stem with 2–4 bladeless sheaths. **Flowers** single at ends of stems, sepals rose-purple, oblong, 2.5–5 cm long; petals joined and ± hoodlike over the column, lip pink, streaked with rose-purple, 2.5–4 cm long, curved downward near middle. June–July. ≋ Open bogs and conifer swamps (in sphagnum moss), floating mats around bog lakes, calcareous fens; often with **grass-pink** (*Calopogon tuberosus*) and **rose pogonia** (*Pogonia ophioglossoides*). ⊕

nc and ne Minn, Wisc and Mich; once known from nw Ill and ne Ind but probably now absent. Nfld to Minn, s to NJ (and in mts to SC) and s Wisc.

Calopogon R. Br. / Grass-pink

⚠️
STATUS
Illinois - E

☞ Grass-pink is distinguished from **swamp-pink** (*Arethusa bulbosa*) and **rose pogonia** (*Pogonia ophioglossoides*) by having a raceme of several flowers vs. single flowers in *Arethusa* and *Pogonia*.

Calopogon tuberosus (L.) BSP.
 Grass-pink   OBL
Perennial herb, from a corm. **Stems** leafless, smooth, 2–7 dm long. **Leaves** 1 near base of plant, linear, 1–4 dm long and 2–15 mm wide. **Flowers** pink to purple, 2–15 in a loose raceme, 3–12 cm long; sepals ovate, 1–2.5 cm long; petals oblong, 1–2.5 cm long, the lip located above the lateral petals, 1–2 cm long, bearded on inside with yellow-tipped bristles. *C. pulchellus.* ⚘ Open bogs and floating mats, openings in conifer swamps, calcareous fens near Great Lakes shoreline. ⊕ Minn, Wisc, Mich, ne Ill and nw Ind. Nfld to Minn and se Man, s to Fla and Tex; Cuba.

▶ Calypso Salisb. / Calypso

⚠️
STATUS
Michigan - T
Wisconsin - T

Calypso bulbosa (L.) Oakes
 Calypso; Fairy slipper   FACW
Perennial herb, from a corm. **Stems** 0.5–2 dm long, with 2–3 bladeless sheaths on lower portion. **Leaves** single from the corm, ovate, 3–5 cm long and 2–3 cm wide, petioles 1–5 cm long. **Flowers** 1, nodding at end of stem; sepals and lateral petals similar, pale purple to pink, lance-shaped, 1–2 cm long and 3–5 mm wide, lip white to pink, streaked with purple, 1.5–2 cm long and 5–10 mm wide, the lip extended to form a white "apron" with several rows of yellow bristles. May–June. ⚘ Mature conifer forests or mixed forests of conifers and deciduous trees (such as balsam fir, hemlock, and paper birch), usually in shade; soils rich in woody humus. ⊕ Minn, uncommon in n Wisc, local in UP (and on Isle Royale) and n LP of Mich. Circumboreal, s to NY, Mich and Minn; s in Rocky Mts to NM and Ariz; Calif. ☞ The single leaf of calypso appears in late August or September, persists through the winter, and withers after flowering in spring. Between fruiting in June and July and the emergence of the new leaf in late summer of fall, no aboveground portions of the plant may be visible.

▶ Corallorhiza Gagnebin / Coralroot

☞ **Yellow coralroot** flowers earlier than our other species of coralroot (which are typically found in moist to dry forests).

Corallorhiza trifida Chat.
 Yellow coralroot   FACW-
Perennial saprophytic herb, roots absent. **Stems** yellow-green, smooth, 1–3 dm long, single or in clusters from the coral-like rhizome. **Leaves** reduced to 2–3 overlapping sheaths on lower stem. **Flowers** yellow-green, 5–15 in a raceme 3–8 cm long; sepals and lateral petals yellow-green, linear, 3–5 mm long, lip white, sometimes with purple-spots, obovate, 3–5 mm long and 2–3 mm wide. **Capsules** drooping, 1–1.5 cm long and 3–7 mm wide. May–June. ⚘ Moist to wet, mostly conifer woods, swamps (often under cedar) and thickets; usually where shaded. ⊕ Minn, n and e Wisc, Mich, uncommon in ne Ill and nw Ind. Circumboreal, s to NJ, Pa, n Ill and Mo; s in Rocky Mts to NM.

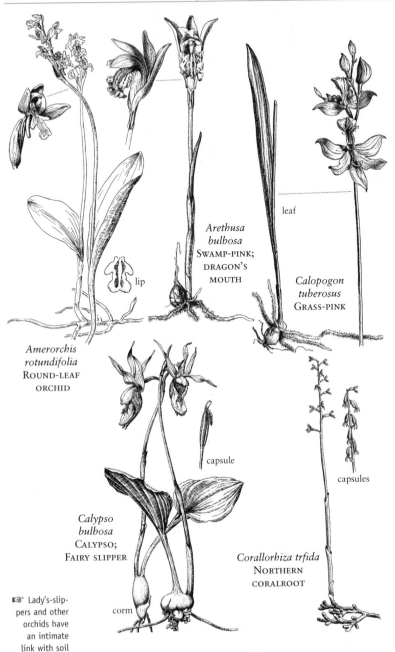

leaf

*Arethusa
bulbosa*
SWAMP-PINK;
DRAGON'S
MOUTH

lip

*Calopogon
tuberosus*
GRASS-PINK

*Amerorchis
rotundifolia*
ROUND-LEAF
ORCHID

capsule

capsules

*Calypso
bulbosa*
CALYPSO;
FAIRY SLIPPER

Corallorhiza trfida
NORTHERN
CORALROOT

corm

☞ Lady's-slip-
pers and other
orchids have
an intimate
link with soil
microorgan-
isms, making
successful
transplant to a
garden unlike-
ly. Digging-up
these plants is
also unethical—
and illegal for
most species!

▶Cypripedium L. / Lady's-slipper

Erect perennial herbs, from coarse, fibrous roots. **Stems** unbranched,
often clumped, hairy. **Leaves** 2 or more at base of plant or along stem,
broad. **Flowers** 1 or 2, large and mostly showy at ends of stems, white,
pink or yellow; lateral sepals similar to lateral petals, the sepals joined to
form a single appendage below the lip; lateral petals free and spreading,
lip inflated and pouchlike, projecting forward; stamens 2, 1 on each side
of column. **Fruit** a many-seeded capsule.

▶KEY TO CYPRIPEDIUM

1 Lip pouch pink to purple; leaves 2 at base of stem . . . . . . *C. acaule*
. . . . MOCCASIN-FLOWER; PINK LADY'S-SLIPPER
1 Lip pouch yellow or whitish; leaves 3 or more on stem **2**

2 Pouch yellow, sometimes brown- or purple-dotted **3**
2 Pouch white to pink, or pink with white patches **4**

3 Sepals and petals red-brown; lateral petals strongly twisted, brown-purple; pouch less than 4 cm long. . . . *C. calceolus* var. *parviflorum*
. . . . SMALL YELLOW LADY'S-SLIPPER
3 Sepals and petals yellow to brown-green; lateral petals wavy, green with red-brown streaks; pouch more than 4 cm long . . . .
. . . . . . *C. calceolus* var. *pubescens* / LARGE YELLOW LADY'S-SLIPPER

4 Pouch projected downward into a cone-shaped spur . . *C. arietinum*
. . . . RAM'S-HEAD LADY'S-SLIPPER
4 Pouch not spurred. **5**

5 Sepals and lateral petals white; lip 3–5 cm long . . . . *C. reginae*
. . . . SHOWY LADY'S-SLIPPER
5 Sepals and lateral petals green; lip 1.5–2 cm long . . . . *C. candidum*
. . . . WHITE LADY'S-SLIPPER

Cypripedium acaule Aiton
Moccasin-flower; Pink lady's-slipper   FACW

⚠
STATUS
Illinois - E

Perennial herb, from coarse rhizomes; roots long and cordlike. **Stems** leafless, 2–4 dm long, glandular-hairy. **Leaves** 2 at base of plant, opposite, oval to obovate, 1–2 dm long and 3–10 cm wide, thinly hairy, stalkless. **Flowers** 1, nodding at end of stem; sepals and lateral petals yellow-green to green-brown, the 2 lower sepals joined to form a single sepal below the lip; lip drooping, pink with red veins, 3–5 cm long, cleft along the upper side and hiding the opening. May–June. ⚘ Hummocks in conifer swamps; sites typically shaded, acidic and nutrient-poor, sometimes fairly dry; s in region also found on hummocks in open bogs. ⊕ Minn (but local in s), Wisc, Mich, occasional in ne Ill and nw Ind. Nfld and Que to Alberta, s to NJ, SC and Ala near coast; inland s to n Ind and n Ill.

Cypripedium arietinum R. Br.
Ram's-head lady's-slipper   FACW+

⚠
STATUS
Michigan - T
Minnesota - T
☞ **Ram's-head lady's-slipper** is the region's smallest and rarest lady's-slipper.

Perennial herb, from a coarse rhizome, roots long and cordlike. **Stems** slender, 1–4 dm long, thinly hairy. **Leaves** 3–5, above middle of stem, stalkless, oval, often folded, 5–10 cm long and 1.5–3 cm wide, finely hairy. **Flowers** 1 or sometimes 2 at ends of stems; sepals and lateral petals similar, green-brown; lip an inflated pouch, 1.5-2.5 cm long, white or pink-tinged, with prominent red-veins, extended downward to form a conical pouch. Late May–June. ⚘ Conifer swamps, wet forest openings (often with white cedar); also in drier, sandy, conifer and mixed conifer-deciduous forests, and on low dunes under conifers near shores of Great Lakes. ⊕ Rare in Minn, n and e Wisc (usually with tamarack near Lake Mich), UP and n and c LP of Mich. Que to Man, s to Mass, NY and Minn.

Cypripedium calceolus L. var. **parviflorum** (Salisb.) Fern.
Small yellow lady's-slipper   FAC+

Perennial herb, from rhizomes, roots long and numerous. **Stems** 1.5–6 dm long, glandular-hairy. **Leaves** 2–5, alternate along stem, ascending, oval, 5–18 cm long and 2–7 cm wide, sparsely hairy, stalkless. **Flowers** 1 (rarely 2) at ends of stems; sepals purple-brown, the lateral sepals joined below the lip, notched at tip; lateral petals linear, purple-brown, spirally twisted, 2–5 cm long; lip an inflated pouch, 1.5–3 cm long, yellow, often with purple veins and spots near opening. May–July. *C. parviflorum.* ☙ Conifer swamps, wet meadows, fens, and moist forests (often under cedar); sphagnum mosses are usually sparse; sites are shaded or sunny, with organic or mineral, often calcium-rich soil; s in region also in open, calcium-rich swales. ⊕ Minn, Wisc, Mich, ne Ill and nw Ind. Circumboreal, NS to Alaska, s to Ga, Ala, Tex, NM, Utah and Ore.

Cypripedium calceolus L. var. **pubescens** (Willd.) Correll
Large yellow lady's-slipper   FAC+

Perennial herb, from a rhizome, roots long and numerous. **Stems** 1.5–6 dm long, glandular-hairy. **Leaves** 3–6, alternate along stem, ascending, ovate to oval, 8–20 cm long and 3–8 cm wide, sparsely hairy. **Flowers** 1 (rarely 2) at ends of stems; sepals yellow-green, the lateral sepals joined below the lip, notched at tip; lateral petals linear, yellow-green, often streaked with red-brown, usually spirally twisted, 4–8 cm long; lip an inflated pouch, 3–6 cm long, yellow, often with purple veins near opening. May–July. *C. pubescens.* ☙ Conifer swamps, bogs, fens, prairies and thickets, especially where soils derived from limestone; also in moist hardwood forests. ⊕ Minn, Wisc, Mich, ne Ill and nw Ind. Circumboreal, NS to Alaska, s to Ga, Ala, Tex, NM, Utah and Ore.

Cypripedium candidum Muhl.
White lady's-slipper   OBL

Perennial herb, from a rhizome, roots long and cordlike. **Stems** 1.5–3 dm long, hairy. **Leaves** 2–4, upright, alternate along upper stem, oval, 5–15 cm long and 2–5 cm wide, sparsely glandular-hairy, stalkless; reduced to overlapping sheathing scales below. **Flowers** 1 at end of stems, the subtending bract leaflike, erect, 3–8 cm long; sepals and lateral petals green-yellow, often streaked with purple, the lateral sepals joined below lip, notched at tip; lateral petals linear lance-shaped, green-yellow, sometimes twisted, 2–4 cm long; lip a small inflated pouch, 1.5–2 cm long, white with faint purple veins. May–June. ☙ Calcium-rich wet meadows, low prairie, wet shores along Great Lakes, calcareous fens (often with **shrubby cinquefoil**, *Potentilla fruticosa*); usually where open and sunny. ⊕ s and w Minn, s Wisc (especially se), s LP of Mich, rare in ne Ill and nw Ind. NY to s Man, s to Pa, Ky, Mo and Neb.

Cypripedium reginae Walter
Showy lady's-slipper   FACW+

Perennial herb, from a coarse rhizome, roots many, long and cordlike. **Stems** 4–10 dm long, strongly glandular-hairy. **Leaves** 4–12, alternate along stem, spreading or ascending, broadly oval, 10–25 cm long, 4–12 cm wide, abruptly tapered to tip, nearly smooth to hairy, stalkless; reduced to sheaths at base. **Flowers** 1 or often 2 at ends of stems, the subtending bract leaflike, 6–12 cm long; sepals and lateral petals white, the lateral sepals joined to form an appendage under the lip, rounded at tip; lip an inflated pouch, 3–5 cm long, white, often infused with pink or purple. June–July. ☙ Conifer and hardwood swamps (especially balsam fir-cedar-tamarack swamps), bogs, calcareous fens, sedge meadows, floating

---

⚠ STATUS
Illinois - E

☞ In N Amer., C. calceolus has been divided into two varieties. In var. parviflorum, the lip is mostly 2–3 cm long, and the sepals and petals are dark red; in var. pubescens, the lip is mostly 3–6 cm long and the sepals and petals are yellow-green. However, apparent hybrids between the two vars. are fairly common.

⚠ STATUS
Illinois - T
Michigan - T
Wisconsin - T

⚠ STATUS
Illinois - E

☠ Avoid touching plants as the hairs are irritating to skin.

☞ Showy lady's-slipper is the region's largest lady's-slipper.

mats, wet openings, wet clayey slopes, ditches; especially where open and sunny; most abundant in openings in wet forests and swamps not dominated by sphagnum mosses. ⊕ Minn (where the official state flower), Wisc, Mich, rare in ne Ill and nw Ind. Newf and Que to Man, s to Ga, Ala, Mo and ND.

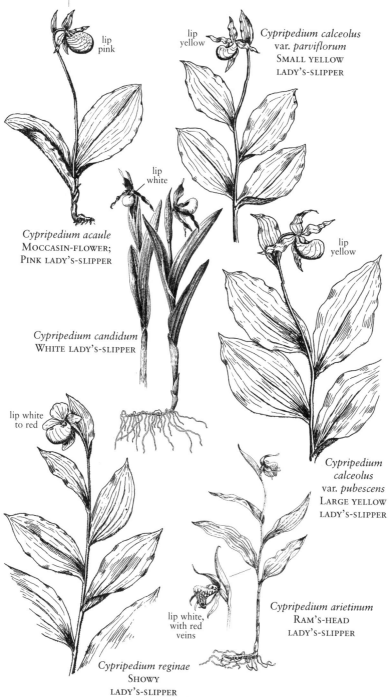

lip pink

lip yellow

Cypripedium calceolus var. *parviflorum* SMALL YELLOW LADY'S-SLIPPER

lip white

Cypripedium acaule MOCCASIN-FLOWER; PINK LADY'S-SLIPPER

lip yellow

Cypripedium candidum WHITE LADY'S-SLIPPER

lip white to red

Cypripedium calceolus var. *pubescens* LARGE YELLOW LADY'S-SLIPPER

Cypripedium arietinum RAM'S-HEAD LADY'S-SLIPPER

lip white, with red veins

Cypripedium reginae SHOWY LADY'S-SLIPPER

▶**Isotria** Raf. / Whorled pogonia

Isotria verticillata (Willd.) Raf.
  Larger whorled pogonia   FAC

Perennial herb; roots long, fleshy, covered with
hairs. **Stems** smooth, red-brown, hollow, 1–4 dm
long. **Leaves** 5–6 in a whorl at top of stem,
oblong lace-shaped, upright when young,
drooping with age, 3–9 cm long and
2–5 cm wide. **Flowers** 1–2 at end of
stems, on stalks 3–5 cm long; sepals green, purple-tinged, narrowly
lance-shaped, 4–6 cm long and 3–5 mm
wide; petals yellow-green, oval, shorter
and wider than sepals, 2–3 cm long and
4–6 mm wide; lip green-white, 3-lobed near
tip, 1.5–2.5 cm long and 1 cm wide. **Capsules**
erect, oval, 2–3 cm long. May–June. *Pogonia
verticillata.* ☙ In sphagnum and in partial
shade in tamarack and black spruce bogs;
also in moist, sandy woods. ⊕ Rare in s LP
of Mich and n Ind. Maine to Ont and Mich,
s to n Fla, Ark and e Tex; locally common
in parts of e portion of the species'
range, but rare in Gt Lakes region.

▶**Liparis** Rich. / Twayblade

Liparis loeselii (L.) Rich.
  Fen-orchid; Loesel's twayblade   FACW+
Small, smooth perennial herb, from a bulblike
base. **Stems** erect, 1–2.5 dm long, upper stem
somewhat angled in section. **Leaves** 2 from base
of plant, ascending, sheathing at base, shiny,
lance-shaped to oval, 4–15 cm long and 1–4 cm
wide. **Flowers** 2–15, yellow-green, small, upright,
in an open raceme 2–10 cm long and 1–2 cm
wide; sepals narrowly lance-shaped, 4–6 mm
long and 1–2 mm wide; petals linear, 3–5 mm
long, often twisted and bent forward under the
lip; lip yellow-green, obovate, 4–5 mm long and
2–3 mm wide, tipped with a short point.
Capsules persistent, short-cylindric, 8–12 mm
long. June–Aug. ☙ Conifer swamps, fens, floating
mats, streambanks, sandy shores, ditches; soils
peaty to mineral, acid to calcium-rich. ⊕ All but far
s Minn; Wisc, Mich, local in ne Ill and nw Ind. NS
and Que to Man, s to NJ, Ohio, Ala, and Neb, sporadically w to Mont and Wash.

▶**Listera** R. Br. / Twayblade

Perennial herbs. **Stems** with a pair of opposite leaves near middle, stems smooth below leaves, hairy above. **Leaves** broad, stalkless. **Flowers** small, green to purple, in a raceme at end of stem, the lip 2-lobed or deeply parted.

▶**KEY TO LISTERA**

1 Lip 3–5 mm long, divided to about middle into 2 narrow segments.
. . . . *L. cordata* / HEART-LEAVED TWAYBLADE
1 Lip 7–12 mm long, shallowly notched or divided 1/3 of length, the segments broad. **2**

2 Lip wide at base, with a pair of auricles. . . . . *L. auriculata*
. . . . AURICLED TWAYBLADE
2 Lip narrowed to base, auricles absent . . . . *L. convallarioides*
. . . . BROAD-LEAVED TWAYBLADE

Listera auriculata Wieg.
Auricled twayblade   FACW+

Perennial herb, roots fibrous. **Stems** 1–2 dm long, smooth below leaves, hairy above. **Leaves** 2 near middle of stem, opposite, ovate, 2–5 cm long and 2–4 cm wide. **Flowers** pale green, 8–15 in a raceme 4–8 cm long and 2–3 cm wide, on stalks 2–5 mm long; lip oblong, 6–10 mm long and 2–5 mm wide, the base with a pair of small clasping auricles, the tip cleft for about 1/4–1/3 of its length. June–Aug. ⚘ Alluvial sand along rivers, often under alders, occasionally in moist conifer or mixed conifer and deciduous forests; usually where shaded. ⊕ Rare in ne Minn, nw Wisc, UP of Mich. Nfld and Que to NH, NY and n Great Lakes.

Listera convallarioides (Swartz) Torr.
Broad-leaved twayblade   FACW

Perennial herb, roots fibrous. **Stems** 1–3 dm long, glandular-hairy above leaves, smooth below. **Leaves** 2, opposite near middle of stem, broadly ovate, 3–6 cm long and 2–5 cm wide, stalkless. **Flowers** yellow-green, 6–20 in a raceme 4–10 cm long and 2–3 cm wide; lip wedge-shaped, 9–11 mm long and to 6 mm wide at tip, usually with a small tooth on each side near the base, the tip shallowly 2-lobed. July–Aug. ⚘ Seeps in forests, cedar swamps, wet, mixed conifer-deciduous woods, streambanks. ⊕ Rare in ne Minn (but possibly extinct from state), far nw Wisc, UP and n LP of Mich. Nfld to Alaska, s to Mass, NY, Minn and Ariz.

Listera cordata (L.) R. Br.
Heart-leaved twayblade   FACW

Perennial herb, roots fibrous. **Stems** 1–3 dm long, glandular-hairy above leaves, smooth below. **Leaves** 2, opposite near middle of stem, 1–4 cm long and 1–3 cm wide, stalkless. **Flowers** green to red-purple, 6–20 in a raceme 3–12 cm long and 1–2 cm wide; lip slender, 3–5 mm long, with 2 teeth on side near base, the tip cleft halfway or more into spreading linear lobes. June–July. ⚘ Open bogs and conifer swamps, where usually on sphagnum moss hummocks; hemlock groves. ⊕ c and ne Minn, n and c Wisc, UP and n LP of Mich. Circumboreal, s to NY, Pa, NC, Minn and NM.

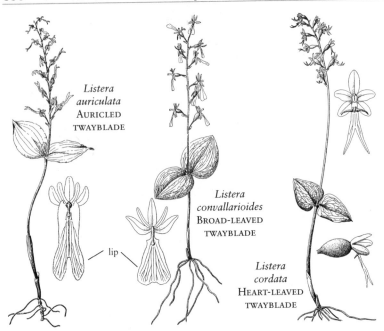

Listera auriculata AURICLED TWAYBLADE

Listera convallarioides BROAD-LEAVED TWAYBLADE

lip

Listera cordata HEART-LEAVED TWAYBLADE

▶**Malaxis** Sol. / Adder's mouth

Small perennial herbs. **Leaves** 1–5 from base of plant or single along stem. **Flowers** green-white, spaced or crowded in slender or cylindric racemes at ends of stems.

▶KEY TO MALAXIS

1 Leaves 2 or more from base of plant, the leaves less than 2 cm long; rare in n Minn. . . . . *M. paludosa* / BOG ADDER'S MOUTH
1 Leaves 1 along stem, 2.5 cm or more long; more widespread **2**

2 Flowers evenly spaced in a raceme 5–11 cm long . . *M. monophyllos* . . . . WHITE ADDER'S MOUTH
2 Flowers crowded near top of raceme, the raceme 2–5 cm long . . . . *M. unifolia* / GREEN ADDER'S MOUTH

Malaxis monophyllos Swartz
White adder's mouth   FACW

Perennial herb, from a bulblike base; roots few, fibrous. **Stems** smooth, 1–2 dm long. **Leaves** single, appearing to be attached well above base of stem, the leaf base clasping stem, ovate to oval, 3–7 cm long and 1.5–4 cm wide. **Flowers** small, green-white, 14–30 or more, in a long, slender, spikelike raceme 4–11 cm long and to 1 cm wide; on stalks 1–2 mm long, the flowers evenly spaced in the raceme; lip heart-shaped, bent downward, 2–3 mm long and 1–2 mm wide, narrowed at middle to form a long, lance-shaped tip, with a pair of lobes at base. June–Aug. Ours are var. *brachypoda. M. brachypoda.* ❦ Conifer swamps (cedar-balsam fir-spruce), especially in wet depressions and where soils are marly; sphagnum moss hummocks in conifer swamps, wet hardwood forests. ⊕ Uncommon in nc and ne Minn, n, c and se Wisc, local across most of Mich, rare in ne Ill. Circumboreal, s to NJ, Pa, Ill, Minn, Colo and Calif.

Malaxis paludosa (L.) Swartz

Bog adder's mouth OBL

Small perennial herb, from a bulblike base; roots few, fibrous. **Stems** leafless, smooth, 7–15 cm long. **Leaves** 2–5 from base of plant, obovate, 1–2 cm long and 0.5–1 cm wide, clasping stem at base. **Flowers** small, yellow-green, 10 or more in a slender, spikelike raceme 3–9 cm long and about 5 mm wide, the flowers evenly spaced in the raceme, twisted so that lip is uppermost in the flowers; lip very small, ovate, 1–1.5 mm long and 0.5 mm wide. July–Aug. *Hammarbya paludosa*. ⚘ Sphagnum moss hummocks in black spruce swamps, usually where somewhat open. ⊕ Rare in nc Minn. ± circumboreal, s in USA to n Minn.

Malaxis unifolia Michx.

Green adder's mouth FAC

Small perennial herb, from a bulblike base; roots few, fibrous. **Stems** smooth, 1–3 dm long. **Leaves** single, attached near middle of stem, ovate, 2–7 cm long and 1–4 cm wide. **Flowers** small, green, numerous in a cylindric raceme 1.5–6 cm long and 1–2 cm wide, the upper flowers crowded, the lower flowers more widely spaced; lowermost lip very small, 1–2 mm long, with 3 teeth at tip. June–Aug. ⚘ Sphagnum moss hummocks in swamps, sedge meadows, thickets; also in moist to dry forests. ⊕ n and c Minn, Wisc, Mich, rare in nw Ind. Nfld and Que to Man, s to Fla and Tex.

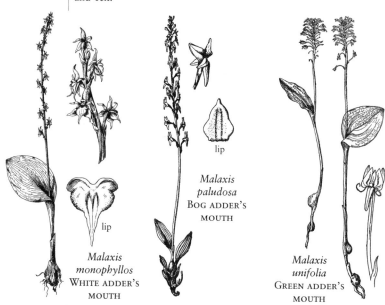

lip

*Malaxis
paludosa*
Bog adder's
mouth

*Malaxis
monophyllos*
White adder's
mouth

lip

*Malaxis
unifolia*
Green adder's
mouth

▶Platanthera L.C. Rich. / Rein-orchid

Perennial herbs, from a cluster of fleshy roots. **Stems** erect, smooth. **Leaves** mostly along the stem, upright, reduced to sheaths at base and upward on stem; leaves basal in large round-leaf orchid (*P. orbiculata*). **Flowers** white or green, several to many in a spike or raceme; upper sepal joined with petals to form a hood over the column; lateral sepals spreading; lip linear to ovate or 3-lobed, entire, toothed or fringed, extended backward into a spur, the spur commonly curved; stamens 1, the anther attached to the top of the short column. **Fruit** a many-seeded capsule.

▶KEY TO PLATANTHERA

1 Margin of lip fringed; flowers often large and showy **2**
1 Margin of lip entire, not fringed; flowers small. **6**

2 Flowers yellow-orange or pink-purple **3**
2 Flowers white or green-white. **4**

3 Flowers yellow-orange . . . . . . *P. ciliaris* / YELLOW FRINGED ORCHID
3 Flowers pink-purple. . . . . . . *P. psycodes* / PURPLE FRINGED ORCHID

4 Lip fringed but not lobed . . . . *P. blephariglottis*
. . . . WHITE FRINGED ORCHID
4 Lip fringed and 3–5 lobed **5**

5 Flowers creamy or green-yellow, in spikes to 3 cm wide; lip fringed
nearly to base. . . . . *P. lacera* / RAGGED FRINGED ORCHID
5 Flowers white, in spikes 4–5 cm wide; lip less deeply fringed . . . . .
. . . . *P. leucophaea* / PRAIRIE FRINGED ORCHID

6 Stems leafless; leaves 1–2 at base of stem **7**
6 Stems leafy; leaves 1 or more. **8**

7 Leaves 1, ascending; stems to 3 dm long . . . . *P. obtusata*
. . . . BLUNT-LEAF ORCHID
7 Leaves 2, prostrate; stems 3–6 dm long . . . . *P. orbiculata*
. . . . LARGE ROUND-LEAF ORCHID

8 Stem leaf 1, sometimes with several small leaves on upper stem . . .
. . . . *P. clavellata* / CLUB-SPUR ORCHID
8 Stem leaves 2 or more **9**

9 Lip wide, 2-lobed and fringed at base *P. flava* / PALE GREEN ORCHID
9 Lip narrow, neither lobed nor fringed. **10**

10 Flowers white; lip widened at base . . . . *P. dilatata*
. . . . TALL WHITE BOG-ORCHID; BOG CANDLES
10 Flowers green-white; lip narrowly lance-shaped . . . .
. . . . *P. hyperborea* / NORTHERN BOG-ORCHID

Platanthera blephariglottis (Willd.) Lindl.
White fringed orchid   OBL

Perennial herb, roots fleshy. **Stems** 2–10 dm long. **Leaves** 1–3, alternate
along stem, narrowly lance-shaped, 5–30 cm long and 1–5 cm wide;
upper several leaves smaller and bractlike. **Flowers** bright white, in a
compact, densely flowered raceme, 5–15 cm long and 4–5 cm wide; sepals nearly round, 5–11 mm long; lateral petals narrowly oblong; lip
oblong lance-shaped, fringed, 8–11 mm long; spur slender 1.5–4 cm
long. July–Aug. *Habenaria blephariglottis.* ✹ Open sphagnum bogs,
occasional in wet, open sandy areas. ⊕ n and w LP of Mich. Nfld and
Ont to Mich, irregularly s to Fla and Tex.

Platanthera ciliaris (L.) Lindl.
Yellow fringed orchid   FACW

Perennial herb, roots long and fleshy. **Stems** 3–10 dm long. **Leaves** 1–3,
alternate along stem, oblong lance-shaped, 6–30 cm long and 4–6 cm
wide; upper leaves abruptly reduced in size and bractlike. **Flowers**

⚠
STATUS
Illinois - E
Indiana - E

orange, many, in a densely flowered cylindric raceme 5–15 cm long and 5 cm wide; sepals broadly oval to obovate, 6–8 mm long, the lateral sepals spreading; lip oblong, 10–16 mm long, long-fringed, some fringes branched; spur slender, 2–3 cm long. July–Aug. *Habenaria ciliari*s. ❦ Open sphagnum bogs, moist sandy meadows; often with **white fringed orchid** (*P. blephariglottis*), and hybrids of the two are common. ⊕ Rare in s LP of Mich, ne Ill and nw Ind. Mass to Mich, n Ill and Mo, s to Fla and Tex.

Platanthera clavellata (Michx.) Luer
Club-spur orchid — OBL

Perennial herb, roots fleshy. **Stems** slender, 1–4 dm long. **Leaves** 1, near or just below middle of stem, oblong to lance-shaped, 5–15 cm long and 1–3 cm wide, usually with 1–3 bractlike leaves above. **Flowers** 5–20, green-yellow, spreading, in a short raceme, 2–6 cm long and 1.5–3 cm wide; sepals and lateral petals broadly ovate, 3–5 mm long; lip oblong, 3–5 mm long, shallowly 3-lobed or toothed at tip; spur curved, widened at tip, 8–12 mm long. June–Aug. *Habenaria clavellata*. ❦ In sphagnum moss of open bogs and floating mats, black spruce and tamarack swamps; also colonizing wet ditches. ⊕ Local in e Minn, Wisc, Mich, uncommon in ne Ill and nw Ind. Nfld to Ont and Minn, s to Fla and Tex.

Platanthera dilatata (Pursh) Lindl.
Tall white bog-orchid; Bog candles — FACW+

Perennial herb, clove-scented, roots fleshy. **Stems** stout or slender, to 1 m long. **Leaves** 3–6, alternate along stem, upright, lance-shaped, to 10–20 cm long and 1–3 cm wide, with 1–2 small, bractlike leaves above and 1 bladeless sheath at base of stem. **Flowers** 10–60, bright white, upright, in a raceme 1–2.5 dm long; lateral sepals lance-shaped, 4–9 mm long and 1–3 mm wide; lateral petals similar but joined with upper sepal to form somewhat of a hood over the column; lip lance-shaped, widened at base, 6–8 mm long; spur slender, 4–8 mm long. June–July. *Habenaria dilatata*. ❦ Wet, open bogs and floating mats, conifer swamps, streambanks, shores and seeps; often where sandy or calcium-rich (as in calcareous fens), not in deep sphagnum moss. ⊕ nc and ne Minn, local in n and e Wisc, Mich, rare in ne Ill and nw Ind. Iceland and Greenland to Alaska, s to NY, Pa, n Ind, Iowa, NM and Calif; ne Asia.

Platanthera flava (L.) Lindl.
Pale green orchid — FACW

Perennial herb, roots fleshy. **Stems** 3–7 dm long. **Leaves** 2–4, alternate along stem, lance-shaped or oval, to 5–15 cm long and 2–5 cm wide, with 1–3 bractlike leaves above. **Flowers** 15 or more, green-yellow or green, stalkless, in a raceme 5–15 cm long and 2–4 cm wide; sepals ovate, 2–3 mm long; lip bent downward, 3–6 mm long, the margin irregular, with a tooth near base on each side; spur 4–6 mm long. June–Aug. *Habenaria flava*. ❦ Wet depressions in hardwood swamps, alder thickets, sedge meadows, moist sand prairies; often where calcium-rich, sometimes where disturbed. ⊕ Rare in ec and se Minn, mostly c and s Wisc, LP of Mich, ne Ill and nw Ind. NS and s Que to Minn, s to Fla and Tex.

Platanthera hyperborea (L.) Lindl.
Northern bog-orchid — FACW+

Perennial herb, roots fleshy. **Stems** 2–8 dm long. **Leaves** 2–7, alternate on stem, linear to oblong, 5–30 cm long and 2–5 cm wide, with 1–3 smaller leaves above. **Flowers** small, green, erect, many in a raceme 4–25 cm long; lateral sepals ovate and spreading; lateral petals lance-shaped,

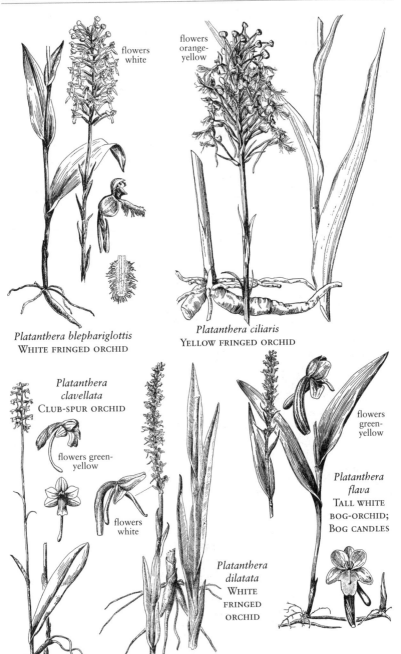

Platanthera blephariglottis
WHITE FRINGED ORCHID

Platanthera ciliaris
YELLOW FRINGED ORCHID

flowers white

flowers orange-yellow

Platanthera clavellata
CLUB-SPUR ORCHID

flowers green-yellow

flowers white

Platanthera dilatata
WHITE FRINGED ORCHID

flowers green-yellow

Platanthera flava
TALL WHITE BOG-ORCHID;
BOG CANDLES

curved upward and joined with upper sepal to form a loose hood over column; lip lance-shaped, 3–7 mm long, not abruptly widened at base; spur curved forward under the lip, about as long as lip, 3–7 mm long. June–Aug. *Habenaria hyperborea.* ≱ Moist to wet forests and swamps, thickets, streambanks, wet meadows, wet sand along Great Lakes shoreline, ditches. ⊕ Minn, mostly n and e Wisc (occasional in w), Mich, ne Ill and nw Ind. Greenland to Alaska, s to NJ, Pa, Ind, Iowa, Neb, NM and Ore; e Asia.

Platanthera lacera (Michx.) G. Don
Ragged fringed orchid   FACW

Perennial herb, roots fleshy. **Stems** 3–8 dm long. **Leaves** 3–7, alternate on stem, lance-shaped to oval, to 5–15 cm long and 1–4 cm wide; upper leaves much smaller. **Flowers** white or green-white, in a usually compact, many-flowered raceme, 5–20 cm long and 2–5 cm wide; sepals broadly oval, 4–7 mm long, the lateral ones deflexed behind the lip; lateral petals linear, entire; lip 10–16 mm long and 5–20 mm wide, deeply 3-lobed, each lobe fringed with a few long segments; spur curved, 1–2 cm long. June–Aug. *Habenaria lacera.* ❧ Hummocks in open sphagnum bogs, conifer bogs, swamps, wet meadows, sandy prairie, thickets, ditches. ⊕ n and ec Minn, Wisc (but local in sw), Mich, ne Ill and nw Ind. Nfld to se Man, s to SC, Ala, Ark and ne Okla.

Platanthera leucophaea (Nutt.) Lindl.
Prairie fringed orchid   FACW+

⚠ STATUS
Illinois - E
Michigan - E
Wisconsin - E
USA - T

☞

Platanthera praeclara, a species of sunny, moist to dry prairie swales of the Gt Plains (in our region in w and s Minn), is similar to the more eastern *P. leucophaea* (but larger). Because of its rarity and declining habitat, *Platanthera praeclara* is listed as federally threatened and state endangered in Minnesota.

Perennial herb; roots thick, fleshy. **Stems** 4–8 dm long, smooth. **Leaves** 5–10, alternate on stem, lance-shaped, 8–15 cm long and 1–4 cm wide, the upper leaves much smaller. **Flowers** white, large and showy, spreading, in a cylindric raceme 5–15 cm long and 5–9 cm wide; sepals 9–12 mm long, broadly ovate; lateral petals broadly obovate, ragged at tip, 10–15 mm long; lip deeply 3-lobed, the lobes fringed more than half way to base, 1.5–2.5 cm long and about as wide; spur curved, 2.5–5 cm long. June–July. *Habenaria leucophaea.* ❧ Open, calcium-rich wet meadows and low prairie, especially where soils are high in organic matter; occasionally in sedge meadows and on floating bog mats. ⊕ Rare and local in s half of Wisc, LP of Mich (mostly se), and ne Ill. NS and Ont to ND, s to Ohio, La and Kans.

Platanthera obtusata (Banks ex Pursh) Lindl.
Blunt-leaf orchid   FACW

Perennial herb, roots fleshy. **Stems** leafless, slender, 1–3 dm long. **Leaves** 1 at base of stem, ascending, persistent through flowering, obovate, 5–15 cm long and 1–4 cm wide, blunt-tipped, long-tapered to base. **Flowers** 4–20, green-white, in a raceme 3–12 cm long and 1–2 cm wide; lateral sepals ovate, spreading; petals ascending, widened below middle; lip lance-shaped, widened at base, 4–6 mm long; spur curved, tapered to a thin tip, 5–8 mm long. June–Aug. *Habenaria obtusata.* ❧ Shaded hummocks in conifer swamps (especially under cedar, black spruce or balsam fir), wet mixed conifer-deciduous forests, alder thickets. ⊕ n Minn, n Wisc, UP and n LP of Mich. Circumboreal, s to Mass, NY, Minn and Colo.

Platanthera orbiculata (Pursh) Lindl.
Large round-leaf orchid   FAC

Perennial herb, roots fleshy. **Stems** 2–6 dm long, leafless apart from 1–6 small bracts. **Leaves** 2, opposite at base of plant, spreading or lying flat on ground, ± round, shiny, 6–15 cm long and 4–15 cm wide. **Flowers** green-white, several in a raceme 5–20 cm long and 3–6 cm wide; sepals ovate, to 1 cm long; petals ovate, 6–7 mm long; lip entire, rounded at tip, 10–15 mm long and 2 mm wide; spur 2–3 cm long, somewhat widened at tip. Late June–Aug. *Habenaria orbiculata.* ❧ Shaded conifer swamps (white cedar, balsam fir, black spruce), especially where underlain by marl; also in drier conifer forests. ⊕ n Minn, n and e Wisc, Mich, rare in ne Ill. Labr to Alaska, s to NC, Tenn, Ill, Minn, Ore.

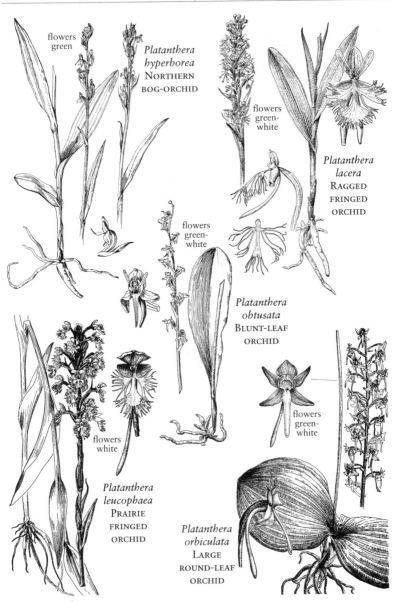

flowers
green

*Platanthera
hyperborea*
NORTHERN
BOG-ORCHID

flowers
green-
white

*Platanthera
lacera*
RAGGED
FRINGED
ORCHID

flowers
green-
white

*Platanthera
obtusata*
BLUNT-LEAF
ORCHID

flowers
green-
white

flowers
white

*Platanthera
leucophaea*
PRAIRIE
FRINGED
ORCHID

*Platanthera
orbiculata*
LARGE
ROUND-LEAF
ORCHID

Platanthera psycodes (L.) Lindl.
Purple fringed orchid   FACW

⚠
STATUS
Illinois - E

☞ The similar
but larger
*Platanthera
grandiflora*
occurs in e
Ohio and ne
USA and
Canada.

Perennial herb, roots thick and fleshy. **Stems** stout, 3–10 dm long. **Leaves**
4–12, alternate on stem, lance-shaped or oval, the upper much smaller
and narrow. **Flowers** rose-purple, in a densely flowered, cylindric raceme
4–20 cm long and 3–5 cm wide; sepals oval to obovate, 4–6 mm long;
petals spatula-shaped, finely toothed on margins; lip broad, 8–14 mm
wide, deeply 3-lobed, the lobes fan-shaped, fringed to less than half way
to base; spur curved, about 2 cm long. July–Aug. *Habenaria psycodes*. ⚘
Wetland margins, shores, wet forests, wet meadows, low prairie, roadside ditches; typically not on sphagnum moss. ⊕ n and e Minn, Wisc,
Mich, local in ne Ill and nw Ind. Nfld to n Man, s to Md, NC, Tenn, n
Ind and Neb.

▶**Pogonia** Juss. / Pogonia

Pogonia ophioglossoides (L.) Ker Gawler
  Rose pogonia; Snake-mouth   OBL

⚠
STATUS
Illinois - E

Perennial herb, spreading by surface runners (stolons) which send up a stem every 10 cm or more apart. **Stems** slender, smooth, 1.5–4 dm long. **Leaves** single, attached about halfway up stem, narrowly oval, 3–10 cm long and 1–2.5 cm wide, stalkless. **Flowers** pink to purple, usually 1 at end of stems; sepals widely spreading, petals oval, angled over the column; lip pink with purple veins, 1.5–2 cm long and 5–10 mm wide, fringed at tip, bearded with yellow bristles. June–July. ☙ Conifer swamps and open bogs in sphagnum moss, floating sedge mats, sedge meadows, sandy interdunal wetlands. ⊕ n and c Minn, Wisc, Mich, uncommon in ne Ill, nw Ind. Nfld to Minn, s to Fla and Tex.

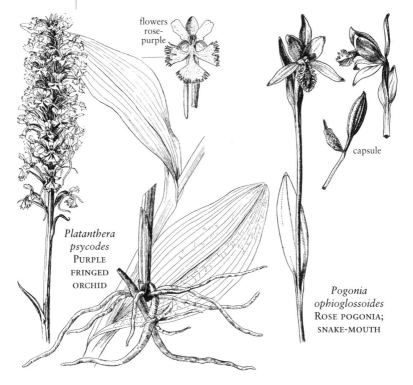

flowers
rose-
purple

capsule

Platanthera psycodes
Purple
fringed
orchid

Pogonia ophioglossoides
Rose pogonia;
snake-mouth

Spiranthes Rich. / Ladies' tresses

Perennial herbs, from a cluster of tuberous roots. **Stems** slender, erect. **Leaves** largest at base of plant, becoming smaller upward on stem, the stem leaves erect and sheathing. **Flowers** small, white or creamy, spirally twisted in a densely flowered, spikelike raceme; sepals and lateral petals similar, the lateral petals joined with all 3 sepals or with only the upper sepal to form a hood over lip and column; lip folded upward near middle so that margins embrace the column, curved downward beyond the middle, with a pair of bumps or thickenings at base; anthers 1, from back of the short column.

▶KEY TO SPIRANTHES

1 Lip of flower violin-shaped (constricted near middle and widened near tip) . . . . *S. romanzoffiana* / HOODED LADIES' TRESSES
1 Lip not violin-shaped. **2**

2 Lip bright yellow . . . . *S. lucida* / SHINING LADIES' TRESSES
2 Lip white or yellow-green in center . . . . *S. cernua*
. . . . NODDING LADIES' TRESSES

Spiranthes cernua (L.) L. C. Rich.
Nodding ladies' tresses   FACW-
Perennial herb, roots fleshy. **Stems** 1–5 dm long, upper stem short-hairy, lower stem smooth. **Leaves** mostly at base of plant, usually present at flowering time, linear to oblong lance-shaped, 6–25 cm long and 5–15 mm wide; upper stem leaves 3–5, much smaller and bractlike. **Flowers** white, in a spikelike raceme 3–15 cm long, with 2–4 vertical rows of flowers, the rows spirally twisted; sepals and petals hairy on outside; lateral petals joined with upper sepal to form a hood; lip white, yellow-green at center, 6–10 mm long and 3–6 mm wide, slightly narrowed at middle, curved downward, the tip curved inward toward stem, the tip wavy-margined or with small rounded teeth, the base of lip with a pair of backward-pointing bumps. Aug–Oct. ✺ Open, usually sandy wetlands such as wet meadows, lakeshores, moist prairies, ditches and roadsides. ✹ Minn (all but far n), Wisc, Mich, ne Ill and nw Ind. Newf and Que to e SD, s to Fla, Tex and NM; also Utah.

Spiranthes lucida (H. Eaton) Ames
Shining ladies' tresses   FACW+

⚠ STATUS Illinois - E

☞ Shining ladies' tresses often occurs with **meadow spikemoss** (*Selaginella apoda*).

Small perennial herb, roots fleshy. **Stems** slender, smooth to finely hairy above, 1–3 dm long. **Leaves** mostly at base of plant, oblong lance-shaped, shiny, 5–10 cm long and 5–15 mm wide; stem leaves usually 2, small and bractlike. **Flowers** white, nodding, in a spikelike raceme 2–7 cm long, the flowers in 1–2 vertical rows, the rows spirally twisted; upper sepal and petals forming a hood over the column; lip oblong, 5–6 mm long, the outer half bright yellow or yellow-orange, with white margins, bumps at base of lip small, less than 1 mm long. June–July. ✺ Streambanks, lakeshores, wet meadows, ditches; especially on calcium-rich soils and limestone gravels, often where somewhat disturbed. ✹ Local in c and s LP of Mich, uncommon in ne Ill and nw Ind. NS and NB to s Ont, Mich and n Ill, s to WVa and Ky.

Spiranthes romanzoffiana Cham.
Hooded ladies' tresses   FACW+

⚠ STATUS Illinois - E Indiana - E

Perennial herb, roots thick and fleshy. **Stems** 1–4 dm long, upper stem finely hairy. **Leaves** mostly from base of plant, present at flowering time, upright, linear to narrowly lance-shaped, 5–20 cm long and 3–9 mm wide, the stem leaves becoming smaller and bractlike. **Flowers** white or cream-colored, in a spikelike raceme 3–10 cm long, with 1–3 vertical rows of flowers, the rows spirally twisted; sepals and lateral petals joined to form a hood over the lip; lip ovate, strongly constricted near middle (violin-shaped), curved downward, the tip ragged and bent inward toward stem, the bumps at base very small. July–Sept. ✺ Open wetlands including wet meadows, fens, lakeshores, open swamps, ditches, seeps; usually in neutral or calcium-rich habitats. ✹ Minn (all but s), Wisc, Mich, uncommon in ne Ill and nw Ind. Labr and Newf to Alaska, s to Pa, Mich, Iowa, NM, Ariz and Calif; Ireland and Scotland.

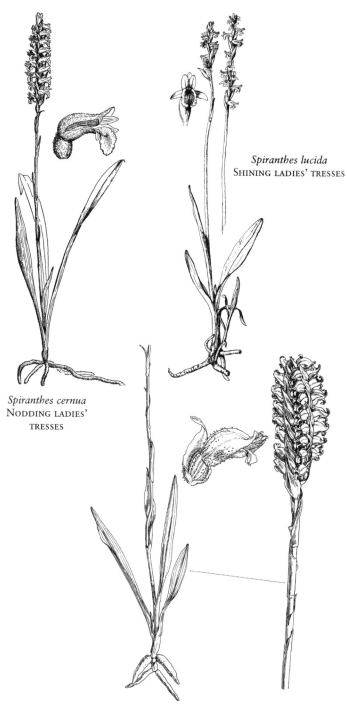

Spiranthes lucida
SHINING LADIES' TRESSES

Spiranthes cernua
NODDING LADIES'
TRESSES

Spiranthes romanzoffiana
HOODED LADIES' TRESSES

Showy lady's-slipper (Cypripedium reginae**).** The region's largest lady's-slipper is found in a variety of wet, partly shaded to open habitats across most of the Great Lakes region. The species is most common in openings in conifer swamps, especially those dominated by trees of northern white cedar (*Thuja occidenatlis*) and tamarack (*Larix laricina*), and where soils are neutral to alkaline in reaction. In favorable situations, colonies of thousands of plants may develop.

Poaceae
Grass Family

Perennial or annual herbaceous plants, clumped or spreading by rhizomes. **Stems** (culms) usually hollow, with swollen, solid nodes. **Leaves** long, linear, parallel-veined, alternate in 2 ranks or rows, sheathing the stem, the sheaths usually split vertically, sometimes joined and tubular as in brome (*Bromus*) and mannagrass (*Glyceria*); with a membranous or hairy ring (ligule) at top of sheath between blade and stem, or the ligule sometimes absent; a pair of projecting lobes (auricles) sometimes present at base of blade.   ▶**Flowers** (florets) small, usually perfect (with both male and female parts), or sometimes either male or female, the male and female flowers separate on the same or different plants.   ▶**Florets** grouped into spikelets, each spikelet with 1 to many florets, the florets stalkless and alternate along a small stem or axis (rachilla), with a pair of small bracts (glumes) at base of each spikelet (the glumes rarely absent); the glumes usually of different lengths, the lowermost (or first) glume usually smaller, the upper (or second) glume usually longer. ▶Within the **spikelet**, each floret subtended by 2 bracts, the larger one (lemma) containing the flower, the smaller one (palea) covering the flower; the lemma and palea often enclosing the ripe **fruit** (grain or caryopsis); stamens usually 3 or sometimes 6, usually exserted when flowering; ovary superior, never enclosed in a sac (as in sedges); styles 2–3-parted, the stigmas often feathery.   ▶**Spikelets** grouped in a variety of heads, most commonly in branching heads (panicles), or stalked along an unbranched stem (rachis) in a raceme, or the spikelets stalkless along an unbranched stem in a spike; spikelets breaking (disarticulating) either above or below the glumes when mature, the glumes remaining in the head if falling above the glumes, or the glumes falling with the florets if disarticulation is below the glumes.

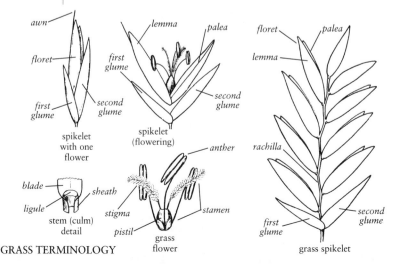

GRASS TERMINOLOGY

▶**KEY TO POACEAE GROUPS**

1 Stems often 2 m or more tall **2**
1 Stems usually less than 2 m tall **3**

2 Male and female flowers separate on same plant . . *Zizania aquatica*
. . . . ANNUAL WILDRICE
2 Flowers perfect . . . . *Phragmites australis* / COMMON REED

3 Spikelets breaking below the glumes, the glumes falling with the florets . . . . GROUP 1
3 Spikelets breaking above the glumes, the glumes remaining in the
head **4**

4 Each spikelet with 1 fertile floret. . . . . GROUP 2
4 Each spikelet with 2 or more fertile florets **5**

5 Spikelets in spikes or spikelike racemes . . . . GROUP 3
5 Spikelets in open or dense panicles . . . . GROUP 4

▶**KEY TO POACEAE GROUP 1**

Spikelets falling as entire unit (the glumes falling with the florets).

1 Spikelets falling with attached stalk and bristles . *Hordeum jubatum*
. . . . FOXTAIL BARLEY
1 Spikelets falling separately, without attached stalk **2**

2 Each spikelet with 2 florets . *Sphenopholis obtusata* / WEDGE-GRASS
2 Each spikelet with 1 perfect floret (sterile or male florets sometimes
present). **3**

3 Spikelets in a spike or raceme **4**
3 Spikelets in a panicle. **5**

4 Spikelets ± round in outline; first and second glumes of equal lengths
. . . . *Beckmannia syzigachne* / AMERICAN SLOUGHGRASS
4 Spikelets lance-shaped; first and second glumes of different lengths .
. . . . *Spartina* / CORDGRASS

5 Spikelets flattened on back sides **6**
5 Spikelets flattened along margins **7**

6 Spikelets awned; ligules absent . . . . *Echinochloa* / BARNYARD-GRASS
6 Spikelets not awned; ligules present. . . . . . . *Panicum* / PANIC-GRASS

7 Bracts below each spikelet 2; glumes absent . . . *Leersia* / CUT-GRASS
7 Bracts below each spikelet 3–4; glumes present. **8**

8 Panicle open . . . . *Cinna* / WOODREED
8 Panicle dense, cylinder-shaped and spikelike. . *Alopecurus* / FOXTAIL

▶**KEY TO POACEAE GROUP 2**

*Spikelets with 1 fertile floret, disarticulating above glumes (the glumes
remaining attached to the head).*

1 Florets stiff and shiny . . *Phalaris arundinacea* / REED CANARY-GRASS
1 Florets soft and papery, not shiny. **2**

2 Glumes much smaller than floret **3**
2 At least 1 glume about same length as spikelet **5**

3 Lemma 5-veined . . . . *Leersia* / CUT-GRASS
3 Lemma 3-veined **4**

4 Lemma not awned, the lemma veins running parallel to a blunt tip.
. . . . *Catabrosa aquatica* / BROOK-GRASS
4 Lemma usually awned, the veins converging to the tip . . . .
. . . . *Muhlenbergia* / MUHLY

5 Florets 3, the 2 lower florets male or reduced to scales **6**
5 Florets 1, with both male and female parts. **7**

6 Panicle dense and spikelike. . . . . *Phalaris arundinacea*
. . . . REED CANARY-GRASS
6 Panicle open. . . . . *Hierochloe odorata*
. . . . SWEET GRASS; HOLY GRASS; VANILLA GRASS

7 Stalk within spikelet (rachilla) elongate and bristlelike behind the
palea . . . . *Calamagrostis* / REEDGRASS
7 Rachilla not elongated. **8**

8 Lemmas with 3 pronounced veins and tipped with an awn . . . .
. . . . *Muhlenbergia* / MUHLY
8 Lemmas with 5 faint veins, awn (if present) from back of lemma . .
. . . . *Agrostis* / BENTGRASS

▶ **KEY TO POACEAE GROUP 3**

Head a spike.

1 Spikes several to many at ends of stems; 1-sided, the spikelets all in 2
rows on lower side of rachis *Leptochloa fascicularis* / SPRANGLETOP
1 Spikes single; spikelets on opposite sides of rachis. **2**

2 Spikelets in groups of 3 at nodes of spike, the 2 side spikelets reduced
and on short stalks about 1 mm long . . . . *Hordeum jubatum*
. . . . FOXTAIL BARLEY
2 Spikelets mostly 2 at each node, the spikelets all alike . . . . . *Elymus*
. . . . WILD RYE

▶ **KEY TO GROUP 4**

*Head a panicle; fertile florets more than 1; spikelets disarticulating
above the glumes (the glumes remaining attached to head).*

1 Glumes about as long as spikelet **2**
1 Glumes much shorter than spikelet **4**

2 Florets 3 or more; plant of w and sc Minn . . . *Scolochloa festucacea*
. . . . SPRANGLETOP; WHITETOP
2 Florets 2 . . . . **3**

3 Lemmas awned . . . . . . *Deschampsia cespitosa* / Tufted hairgrass
3 Lemmas awnless . . . . *Trisetum melicoides* / Purple false-oats

4 Lemmas with 3 prominent veins **5**
4 Lemmas with 5 or more prominent veins **6**

5 Each spikelet with 2 florets; lemma veins running parallel to a blunt tip . . . . *Catabrosa aquatica* / Brook-grass
5 Each spikelet with 3 florets; lemma veins converging at tip . . . . *Eragrostis* / Lovegrass

6 Edges of leaf sheaths joined for at least half of their length **7**
6 Edges of leaf sheaths joined only at base **8**

7 Lemmas awned . . . . *Bromus* / Brome
7 Lemmas awnless . . . . *Glyceria* / Mannagrass

8 Male and female flowers on separate plants; plant of brackish areas in w Minn and ne Ill . . . . *Distichlis spicata* / Inland saltgrass
8 Flowers perfect, with both male and female parts **9**

9 Lemmas with parallel veins extending to a blunt tip . . . . *Puccinellia* . . . . Alkali-grass
9 Lemmas tapered to a point, the veins converging at tip . . . . *Poa* . . . . Bluegrass

▶**Agrostis** L. / Bentgrass

Perennial grasses, clumped or spreading by rhizomes or sometimes by stolons. **Leaves** soft, flat. **Head** an open panicle. **Spikelets** small, 1-flowered, breaking above glumes; glumes ± equal length, 1-veined; floret shorter than glumes; lemma awnless or with a short straight awn; palea small or absent; stamens usually 3.

▶**KEY TO AGROSTIS**

1 Plants clumped; palea ± absent. . . . . *A. hyemalis* / Ticklegrass
1 Plants with rhizomes and/or stolons; palea present, about half as long as lemma . . . . *A. stolonifera* / Redtop; Spreading bentgrass

Agrostis hyemalis (Walter) BSP.
  Ticklegrass   FAC-
Clumped perennial grass. **Stems** slender, erect to reclining, 2–6 dm long. **Leaves** mostly at or near base of plant, upright to spreading, flat to inrolled, 1–2 mm wide, smooth or somewhat rough-to-touch; sheaths smooth, the ligule translucent, 1–2 mm long, rounded and usually ragged at tip. **Head** an open panicle, 1–3 dm long, the branches threadlike and spreading, the branches themselves branched and with spikelets only above their middle. **Spikelets** 1-flowered, often purple, 1–3 mm long; glumes lance-shaped, 1–3 mm long; lemma 1–2 mm long, unawned or with a short straight awn; palea absent. June–Aug. *A. scabra.* ❀ Wet meadows, bogs, ditches, streambanks, shores; more commonly in dry, sandy places. ⊕ n and e Minn, Wisc, Mich, ne Ill and nw Ind. Labr to Alaska, s to Fla and Mex.

Agrostis stolonifera L.

Redtop; Spreading bentgrass FACW

Perennial grass, spreading by rhizomes and also sometimes by stolons. **Stems** erect or ± horizontal at base, 3–10 dm or more long. **Leaves** ascending, 2–8 mm wide, rough-to-touch; sheaths smooth, the ligule translucent, usually splitting at tip, 2–5 mm long. **Head** an open panicle, 3–20 cm long, the branches spreading, branched and with spikelets along their entire length. **Spikelets** 1-flowered, usually purple, 2–4 mm long; glumes lance-shaped, 1.5–2.5 mm long; lemma 2/3 length of glumes, 1–2 mm long; palea present, about half as long as lemma. July–Sept. *A. alba*, *A. gigantea*, *A. palustris*. ≋ Wet meadows, ditches, streambanks and shores; disturbed areas. ⊕ Common; Minn, Wisc, Mich, ne Ill and nw Ind. Introduced from Europe as a pasture grass (and also native in part), naturalized throughout most of USA and s Can.

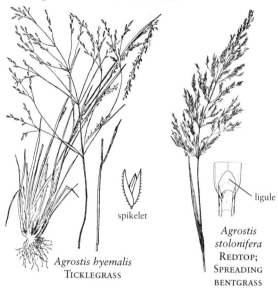

spikelet

Agrostis hyemalis TICKLEGRASS

ligule

Agrostis stolonifera REDTOP; SPREADING BENTGRASS

▶**Alopecurus** L. / Foxtail

Annual or perennial grasses. **Leaves** soft, flat. **Stems** erect or ± horizontal at base. **Heads** densely flowered, cylindric, spikelike panicles. **Spikelets** 1-flowered, flattened, breaking below the glumes; glumes equal length, 3-nerved, often silky hairy on back, awnless; lemma about as long as glumes or shorter, awned from the back, the awn shorter to longer than the glume tips; palea absent.

▶**KEY TO ALOPECURUS**

1 Plants single or in small clumps; spikes not bristly in outline; awns straight, shorter or to 1 mm longer than tip of glumes . . *A. aequalis* . . . . SHORT-AWN FOXTAIL
1 Plants densely clumped; spikes bristly in outline; awns bent, 2–4 mm longer than glume tips . . . . . . *A. carolinianus* / CLUMPED FOXTAIL

Alopecurus aequalis Sobol.

Short-awn foxtail OBL

Annual or short-lived perennial grass. **Stems** single or in small clumps, slender, erect to ± horizontal, 2–6 dm long, often rooting at the nodes.

Leaves 1–5 mm wide, finely rough-to-touch above; ligule membranous, rounded to elongate, 2–7 mm long. **Head** an erect, spikelike panicle, 2–7 cm long and 3–5 mm wide. **Spikelets** 1-flowered; glumes 2–3 mm long, blunt-tipped, hairy on the keel and veins; lemma about equaling the glumes, awned from back, the awn straight, to 1.5 mm longer than glume tips. June–Aug. ⚘ Shallow water or mud of wet meadows, marshes, ditches, springs, open bogs, fens, shores and streambanks; sometimes where calcium-rich. ⊕ Common to occasional; Minn, Wisc, Mich, ne Ill and nw Ind. Circumboreal, s to NJ, Pa, Ohio, Ill, Mo, Kans, NM and Calif.

Alopecurus carolinianus Walter
Clumped foxtail   FACW

Densely clumped annual grass. **Stems** erect to upright, 1–4 dm long. **Leaves** 1–3 mm wide, finely rough-to-touch above; ligule membranous, rounded to elongate, 1–5 mm long. **Head** a cylindric, spikelike panicle, 1–5 cm long and 3–5 mm wide. **Spikelets** 1-flowered; glumes 2–3 mm long, blunt-tipped, hairy on keel; lemma about as long as glumes, awned from back, the awn bent near middle and 2–3 mm longer than glume tips. May–July. ⚘ Mud flats, temporary ponds, wet meadows, marshes, low prairie, fallow fields. ⊕ wc and se Minn (especially along Minn River), sw Wisc; local in s LP of Mich, ne Ill and nw Ind. Mass to BC, s to Fla, La, Tex, Ariz and Calif.

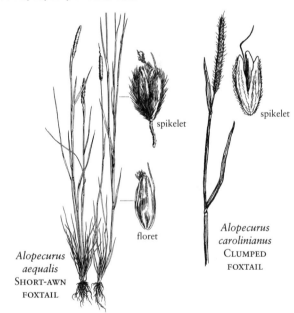

spikelet

spikelet

floret

Alopecurus carolinianus
CLUMPED
FOXTAIL

Alopecurus aequalis
SHORT-AWN
FOXTAIL

▶**Beckmannia** Host. / Sloughgrass

Beckmannia syzigachne (Steud.) Fernald
American sloughgrass   OBL

Stout annual grass. **Stems** single or in small clumps, 4–10 dm long. **Leaves** flat, 3–10 mm wide, rough-to-touch; sheaths overlapping, smooth, the upper sheath often loosely enclosing lower part of panicle; ligule membranous, rounded to acute, 3–6 mm long. **Head** of many 1-

sided spikes in a narrow panicle 10–30 cm long, the panicle branches erect, overlapping, 1–5 cm long; each spike 1–2 cm long, with several to many spikelets in 2 rows on the rachis. **Spikelets** 1–2-flowered, overlapping, nearly round, 2–4 mm long, straw-colored when mature, breaking below the glumes; glumes equal, broad, inflated along midvein, with a short, slender tip; lemma about as long as glumes but narrower; palea nearly as long as lemma. June–Sept. ❦ Wet meadows, marshes, ditches, shores and streambanks. ⊕ Minn, local in n and e Wisc, rare in Mich (Isle Royale and n and c LP only); rare in ne Ill. w NY to Man and Alaska, s to Ohio, Ill, n Kans, NM and Calif; e Asia.

Bromus L. / Brome

Perennial grasses. **Leaves** flat; sheaths closed to near top. **Head** a panicle of drooping spikelets. **Spikelets** with several to many flowers, breaking above the glumes; glumes shorter than lemmas; lemmas awned (in species included here); stamens usually 3.

▶ **KEY TO BROMUS**

1 Lemmas hairy across back . . . . . *B. altissimus* / EAR-LEAVED BROME
1 Lemmas smooth on back, lemma margins fringed with hairs. . . . . .
. . . . *B. ciliatus* / FRINGED BROME

Bromus altissimus Pursh.
Ear-leaved brome   FACW-
Perennial grass. **Stems** single or in small clumps, ± smooth, 6–15 dm long. **Leaves** flat, 8–20 along stem; 10–15 mm wide, with a pair of auricles at base; sheaths with a dense ring of hairs at top. **Head** a panicle 1–2 dm long, the branches spreading or drooping. **Spikelets** several-flowered, 2–3 cm long, first glume 5–8 mm long, awl-shaped, second glume wider, 6–10 mm long; lemmas 10–12 mm long, hairy, awned, the awn 2–7 mm long. *B. latiglumis.* ❦ Floodplain forests, thickets and streambanks, sometimes in rocky woods and slopes. ⊕ Minn (all but ne), Wisc, c and s LP of Mich, ne Ill and nw Ind. Maine to Mont, s to NC and Okla. ☞ Similar to **Canada brome** (*Bromus pubescens*), a species of mostly drier woods, but top of sheaths of ear-leaved brome have a ring of dense hairs, and leaf blades have well-developed auricles.

Bromus ciliatus L.
Fringed brome   FACW
Perennial grass, rhizomes absent. **Stems** single or few together, smooth or hairy at nodes, 5–12 dm long. **Leaves** flat, 4–10 mm wide, usually with long, soft hairs mainly on upper surface; sheaths usually with long hairs; ligule membranous, short, to 2 mm long, ragged across tip. **Head** a loose, open panicle 1–3 dm long, the branches usually drooping. **Spikelets** large, 4–10-flowered, 1.5–3 cm long and 5–10 mm wide; glumes usually ± smooth, lance-shaped, the first glume 4–9 mm long, the second glume 6–10 mm long, often tipped with a short awn; lemma 10–15 mm long, ± smooth on back, usually long-hairy along lower margins, tipped with an awn 2–6 mm long; palea about as long as body of lemma. July–Sept. ❦ Streambanks, shores, thickets, sedge meadows, fens, marshes; also in moist woods. ⊕ Minn (all but sw), Wisc, Mich occasional in ne Ill and nw Ind. Newf to Wash, s to NJ, Tenn, Iowa, Tex and Calif.

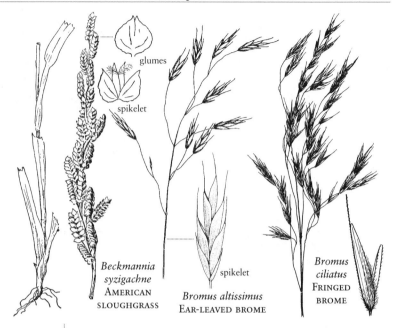

Beckmannia syzigachne
AMERICAN SLOUGHGRASS

Bromus altissimus
EAR-LEAVED BROME

Bromus ciliatus
FRINGED BROME

▶**Calamagrostis** Adans. / Reedgrass

Perennial grasses, spreading by rhizomes. **Stems** single or in clumps. **Leaves** flat or inrolled, green or waxy blue-green, smooth or rough-to-touch; sheaths smooth; ligule large, membranous, usually with an irregular, ragged margin. **Head** a loose and open, or dense and contracted panicle. **Spikelets** 1-flowered, breaking above glumes; glumes nearly equal, lance-shaped; lemma shorter than glumes, lance-shaped, awned from back, the awn about as long as lemma, the base of lemma (callus) bearded with a tuft of hairs, these shorter to as long as lemma; palea shorter than lemma; stamens 3.

▶KEY TO CALAMAGROSTIS

1 Panicle ± loose and open, the branches ascending to spreading; leaves ± lax, flat, 2–6 mm wide . . . . *C. canadensis* / BLUEJOINT
1 Panicle contracted, the branches short, ascending to appressed; leaves stiff, often inrolled, 1–4 mm wide when flattened . . . . . . *C. stricta* . . . . NARROW-SPIKE REEDGRASS

Calamagrostis canadensis (Michx.) P. Beauv.
Bluejoint   OBL
Perennial grass, from creeping rhizomes. **Stems** erect, in small clumps, 6–15 dm long, often rooting from lower nodes when partly underwater. **Leaves** flat, green to waxy blue-green, 3–8 mm wide, rough-to-touch on both sides; sheaths smooth; ligules 3–7 mm long. **Head** a ± open panicle, 8–20 cm long, the branches upright or spreading. **Spikelets** 1-flowered, 2–6 mm long; glumes ± equal, 2–4 mm long, smooth or finely rough-hairy on back; lemma ± smooth, awned from middle of back, the awn straight, base with dense callus hairs about as long as lemma. June–Aug. ☙ Wet meadows, shallow marshes, calcareous fens, streambanks, thickets. ⊕ Common to abundant; Minn, Wisc, Mich, n Ill and n Ind. Greenland to Alaska, s to NJ, WVa, NC, Mo, Kans, NM and Calif.

Calamagrostis stricta (Timm) Koeler

Narrow-spike reedgrass   FACW+

Perennial grass, spreading by rhizomes; plants waxy blue-green. **Stems** erect, 3–12 dm long. **Leaves** stiff, often inrolled, 1–4 mm wide when flattened. **Head** a narrow panicle, 5–15 cm long, the branches short, upright to erect. **Spikelets** 1-flowered; glumes 3–6 mm long, smooth or rough-hairy on back; lemma rough-hairy, 2–4 mm long, awned, the awn straight, from near middle of back, base with many callus hairs, half to as long as lemma. June–Sept. *C. inexpansa, C. neglecta.* ❧ Wet meadows, shallow marshes, shores, streambanks; rocky shore of Lake Superior. ⊕ Occasional to uncommon; Minn (all but far se), n and e Wisc, Mich, ne Ill and nw Ind. Greenland to Alaska, s to NY, Pa, Va, Ohio, Mo, Kans, NM, Ariz and Calif. ☞ Similar to **bluejoint** (*C. canadensis*), but the head narrow and crowded and the leaves often inrolled.

▶**Catabrosa** P. Beauv. / Brook-grass

Catabrosa aquatica (L.) P. Beauv.

Brook-grass   OBL

Loosely clumped or sprawling perennial grass. **Stems** thick, weak, often horizontal, 2–6 dm long, branching and rooting at nodes in mud or water. **Leaves** flat, smooth, mostly 10–15 cm long and 3–10 mm wide; sheaths smooth; ligule 1–4 mm long. **Head** an open, pyramid-shaped or oblong panicle 10–20 cm long. **Spikelets** mostly 2-flowered or sometimes mostly 1-flowered, the second floret (when present) well above the first, breaking above the glumes, golden brown, 2–4 mm long; glumes unequal, the first glume smaller, 1–2 mm long, the second glume ragged at tip; lemma smooth, ragged at tip, 2–3 mm long; palea similar to lemma. June–Sept. ❧ Shallow water or mud of streambanks, cold springs and seeps. ⊕ Rare in nw and c Wisc. Newf and Labr to Alberta, s to Wisc, Neb, Colo, Ariz, Nev and Wash; Eurasia.

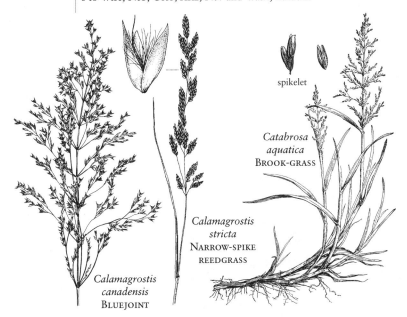

spikelet

*Catabrosa
aquatica*
BROOK-GRASS

*Calamagrostis
stricta*
NARROW-SPIKE
REEDGRASS

*Calamagrostis
canadensis*
BLUEJOINT

Cinna L. / Woodreed

Tall, perennial grasses, rhizomes weak or absent. **Leaves** wide, flat and lax; ligule brown, membranous, with an irregular, jagged margin. **Head** a large, closed to open panicle, the branches upright to spreading or drooping. **Spikelets** small, 1-flowered, laterally compressed, breaking below the glumes; glumes nearly equal, lance-shaped, keeled; lemma similar to glumes, with a short awn from just below the tip; palea shorter than lemma; stamens 1.

▶**KEY TO CINNA**

1 Panicle ± crowded and narrow, the branches upright; second glume 4–6 mm long . . . . *C. arundinacea* / COMMON WOODREED
1 Panicle open, the branches spreading to drooping; second glume 2–4 mm long . . . . *C. latifolia* / DROOPING REEDGRASS

Cinna arundinacea L.
Common woodreed   FACW

Perennial grass, rhizomes weak or absent. **Stems** 1 or few together, erect, 6–15 dm long, often swollen at base. **Leaves** 4–12 mm wide, margins rough-to-touch; sheaths smooth; ligule red-brown, 3–10 mm long. **Head** a narrow panicle, dull gray-green, 1–3 dm long, the branches upright. **Spikelets** 1-flowered; glumes narrowly lance-shaped, 3–5 mm long, the first glume 1-veined, the second glume 3-veined, usually rough-hairy; lemma 3–5 mm long, rough-hairy on back, usually with an awn to 0.5 mm long, attached just below tip and mostly shorter than lemma tip. Aug–Sept. ☙ Swamps, floodplain forests, streambanks, pond margins, moist woods. ⊕ c and se Minn, Wisc (all but far n), s LP of Mich, ne Ill and nw Ind. Mich to Mont, s to Ga and e Tex.

Cinna latifolia (Trevir.) Griseb.
Drooping reedgrass   FACW+

Perennial grass, with weak rhizomes. **Stems** single or in small groups, erect, 5–13 dm long, not swollen at base. **Leaves** 5–15 mm wide, usually rough-to-touch; sheaths smooth to finely roughened; ligule pale, 2–7 mm long. **Head** a loose, open panicle, pale green, satiny, 1–3.5 dm long, the branches spreading to drooping. **Spikelets** 1-flowered; glumes narrowly lance-shaped, 1-veined, 2–4 mm long; lemma 2–4 mm long, finely rough-hairy on back, usually with an awn to 1.5 mm long from just below the tip, the awn usually longer than the tip. July–Aug. ☙ Wet woods, swamps, springs. ⊕ n and ec Minn, Wisc (all but far s), UP, n and c LP of Mich. Newf to Alaska, s to NC, Tenn, Ill, SD, NM and Calif.

Deschampsia P. Beauv. / Hairgrass

Deschampsia cespitosa (L.) P. Beauv.
Tufted hairgrass   FACW+

Densely clumped perennial grass. **Stems** stiff, erect, 3–10 dm long. **Leaves** mostly from base of plant, usually shorter than head, flat or inrolled, 2–4 mm wide; sheaths smooth; ligule white, translucent, 3–10 mm long. **Head** a narrow to open panicle, 1–4 dm long, the panicle branches threadlike, upright to spreading, the lower branches in groups of 2–5, flowers mostly near branch tips. **Spikelets** 2-flowered, purple-tinged, fading to silver with age, 2–5 mm long, breaking above the glumes; glumes shiny, 2–5 mm long, the first glume slightly shorter than second glume; lemma smooth, 2–4-toothed across the flat tip, awned from near base on back, the awn shorter to about as long as lemma. June–July. ≱ Wet meadows, streambanks, shores, calcium-rich seeps and springs, rocky shores of Great Lakes. ⊕ ne and nw Minn, Wisc, Mich (especially Great Lakes shorelines), ne Ill and nw Ind. Greenland to Alaska, s to NJ, NC, Ohio, Ill, Minn, ND, NM, Ariz and Calif, Eurasia.

▸**Distichlis** Raf. / Saltgrass

Distichlis spicata (L.) Greene
  Inland saltgrass   UPL
Short perennial grass, spreading by scaly rhizomes and forming patches; the male and female flowers on separate plants. **Stems** stiff, erect, 1–3 dm long. **Leaves** upright, the upper often longer than the head, mostly inrolled, 5–10 cm long and 0.5–3 mm wide, smooth or with sparse hairs; sheaths overlapping, smooth or sparsely hairy, usually long-hairy at collar; ligule small. **Head** an unbranched, narrow, spikelike panicle, 3–7 cm long. **Spikelets** several to many, upright, 8–20 mm long; male spikelets straw-colored, female spikelets green-gray, breaking above the glumes; glumes unequal, 1–5 mm long; lemmas ovate, 3–6 mm long. June–Sept. *D. stricta*. ≱ Seasonally wet, brackish flats, shores and disturbed areas. ⊕ Far w Minn, introduced in ne Ill. w Minn to Sask and Wash, s to Tex, Calif and Mex.

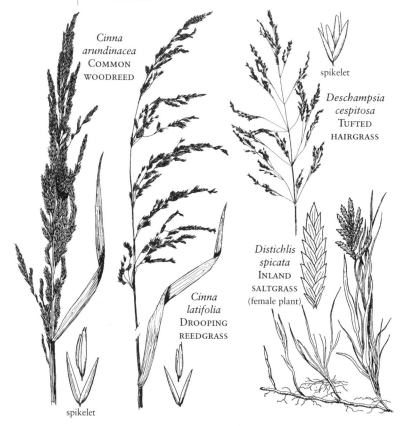

Cinna arundinacea COMMON WOODREED

spikelet

Deschampsia cespitosa TUFTED HAIRGRASS

Cinna latifolia DROOPING REEDGRASS

Distichlis spicata INLAND SALTGRASS (female plant)

spikelet

▶**Echinochloa** P. Beauv. / Barnyard-grass

Large, weedy, annual grasses. **Stems** single or several together, erect to ± horizontal, to 1 m or more long. **Leaves** flat, wide and smooth; sheaths smooth or hairy; ligules absent. **Head** a dense panicle, the branches crowded with spikelets forming racemes or spikes. **Spikelets** with 1 terminal fertile floret and 1 sterile floret, breaking below the glumes, nearly stalkless; glumes unequal, the first glume 3-veined, to half the length of second glume, the second glume 5-veined; sterile lemma similar to second glume, awned or awnless; fertile lemma smooth and shiny.

▶**KEY TO ECHINOCHLOA**

1 Lower leaf sheaths rough-hairy; spikelets each with 2 awns; s portion of region . . . . *E. walteri* / Saltmarsh cockspur grass
1 Leaf sheaths smooth; spikelets with usually 1 awn (from sterile lemma); widespread. **2**

2 Fertile lemma rounded or broadly tapered to a thin, membranous, withered beak . . . . *E. crusgalli* / Barnyard-grass
2 Fertile lemma tapered to a stiff, persistent beak. . . . . . . *E. muricata* . . . . Barnyard grass

Echinochloa crusgalli (L.) P. Beauv.
Barnyard-grass   FACW
Weedy annual grass. **Stems** 1 m or more long. **Leaves** 7–30 mm wide; sheaths smooth; ligule absent. **Head** an erect, green to purple panicle, 1–2.5 dm long; panicle branches spreading to erect, long-hairy, some of the hairs as long or longer than spikelets (excluding spikelet awns). **Spikelets** 3–5 mm long (excluding awns); glumes awnless; sterile lemma awnless or with an awn to 4 cm or more long; tip of fertile lemma firm, shiny, rounded or broadly tapered to a point, the beak usually green and withered, the lemma body and beak separated by a line of tiny hairs. July–Sept. ❦ Shores, wet meadows, ditches, streambanks, mud flats, moist disturbed areas. ⊕ Minn, Wisc (especially s), Mich (especially LP), ne Ill and nw Ind. Introduced from Europe, naturalized throughout much of s Can and most of USA, s to Mex.

Echinochloa muricata (P. Beauv.) Fernald
Barnyard-grass   OBL

☞ E. muricata is sometimes grouped with E. crusgalli (above) because of similarities in form and habitat.

Weedy annual grass. **Stems** 1 m or more long. **Leaves** 5–30 mm wide; sheaths smooth; ligule absent. **Head** a green to purple panicle, sometimes strongly purple, 1–3 dm long, panicle branches spreading, hairs on branches absent or to 3 mm long and shorter than spikelets. **Spikelets** 2–4 mm long (excluding awns); glumes awnless; sterile lemma awnless or with an awn 5–10 mm long; tip of fertile lemma firm, shiny, gradually tapered to the stiff beak, the lemma body and beak not separated by a line of tiny hairs (the beak itself often short-hairy). July–Sept. *E. pungans.* ❦ Shores, streambanks and ditches, where sometimes in shallow water. ⊕ Minn, Wisc, Mich, ne Ill and nw Ind. Que and NB to Alberta and Wash, s to Fla, Tex, Calif and into Mex.

Echinochloa walteri (Pursh) Heller
Saltmarsh cockspur grass   OBL
Tall annual grass. **Stems** usually erect, 1–2 m long. **Leaves** 10–25 mm wide; lower sheaths usually rough-hairy; ligule absent. **Head** a dense panicle, often nodding, 1–3 dm long. **Spikelets** ± hidden by awns, the

awns 1–3 cm long from sterile lemmas and 2–10 mm long from second glume; fertile lemma oval, with a small, withering tip, but not separated by a line of hairs as in *E. crusgalli.* Aug–Sept. ☙ Streambanks, lakeshores, ditches. ⊕ se Minn, Wisc (mostly s, especially along Fox River), s LP of Mich (locally common in Lake Erie marshes in se Mich), local in ne Ill and nw Ind. Atlantic coast from Mass to Fla and Tex; occasional inland to s Great Lakes, Iowa and Mo.

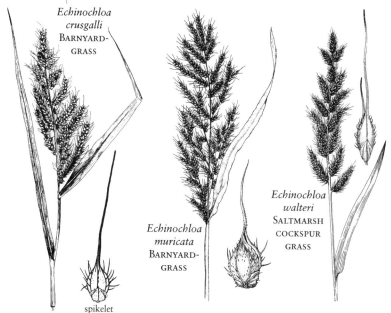

Echinochloa crusgalli BARNYARD-GRASS

Echinochloa muricata BARNYARD-GRASS

Echinochloa walteri SALTMARSH COCKSPUR GRASS

spikelet

▶**Elymus** L. / Wildrye

Clumped perennial grasses. **Leaves** flat; ligules short. **Head** a densely flowered spike. **Spikelets** usually 2 at each node of spike, breaking above glumes (*E. riparius*) or below glumes (*E. virginicus*); glumes narrow and awnlike; lemmas tipped with a long awn; stamens 3.

▶KEY TO ELYMUS

1 Spikes somewhat nodding; lemma awned, the awn longer than 1 cm; glumes not bowed-out at base . . *E. riparius* / STREAMBANK WILDRYE
1 Spikes erect; lemma unawned, or with a short awn to 1 cm long; glumes bowed-out at base . . . . . . *E. virginicus* / VIRGINIA WILDRYE

☞ Similar to **Canada wild rye** (*E. canadensis*), a species of drier, sandy places, but awns in streambank wildrye are straight rather than bent and curved.

Elymus riparius Wiegand
Streambank wildrye   FACW
Clumped perennial grass. **Stems** 1 m long or more. **Leaves** 8–10 along stem, 5–15 mm wide, upper surface smooth to rough; sheaths smooth; ligule short. **Head** a spike, 6–20 cm long, somewhat nodding. **Spikelets** mostly 2 at each node, 2–4-flowered, finely hairy, breaking above glumes; glumes narrow, to 1 mm wide at middle, not bowed-out at base; lemma finely hairy to smooth, tipped with a straight awn 2–3 cm long. ☙ Streambanks, floodplain forests. ⊕ Local in driftless area of sw Wisc, w UP, c and s LP of Mich, ne Ill and nw Ind. Maine to Wisc, Iowa and Neb, s to NC, Ill and Ark.

Elymus virginicus L.

Virginia wildrye   FACW-

Clumped perennial grass. **Stems** 6–12 dm long. **Leaves** flat, 5–15 mm wide, rough-to-touch on both sides; sheaths smooth. **Head** an erect spike, 5–15 cm long, the base of spike often covered by top of upper sheath. **Spikelets** usually 2 at each node, 2–4-flowered, breaking below glumes; glumes firm, 1–2 mm wide, yellowish, bowed-out at base, tapered to a straight awn about 1 cm long; lemmas 6–9 mm long, smooth to hairy, usually with a straight awn to 3 cm long. July–Aug. ♛ Floodplain forests, thickets, streambanks. ⊕ Common; Minn, Wisc, Mich, ne Ill and nw Ind. Nfld to Alberta, s to Fla and Ariz.

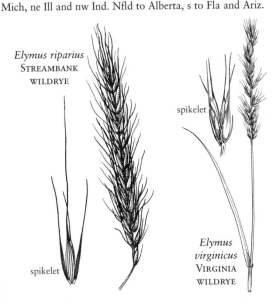

Elymus riparius
STREAMBANK
WILDRYE

spikelet

spikelet

*Elymus
virginicus*
VIRGINIA
WILDRYE

▶**Eragrostis** Wolf / Lovegrass

Annual grasses (those included here), perfect-flowered or with male and female flowers on different plants. **Stems** clumped, or spreading and rooting at lower nodes and with creeping stolons. **Leaves** with short, flat to folded blades; sheaths hairy near top; ligule a ring of short hairs. **Heads** usually many, in an open or narrow panicle. **Spikelets** few- to many-flowered, breaking above glumes, laterally compressed, the florets overlapping; glumes unequal; lemmas 3-veined; palea shorter than lemma, 2-veined.

▶KEY TO ERAGROSTIS

1 Plants mat-forming; base of stems lying along ground, rooting at lower nodes, the nodes bearded with hairs; spikelets 3–10 mm long
. . . . *E. hypnoides* / CREEPING LOVEGRASS

1 Plants not mat-forming; stems erect, not rooting at lower nodes, the nodes smooth; spikelets to 3 mm long . . . . *E. frankii*
. . . . SANDBAR LOVEGRASS

Eragrostis frankii C. A. Meyer

Sandbar lovegrass   FACW

Densely clumped annual grass. **Stems** branched, 1–5 dm long. **Leaves** smooth, 1–4 mm wide; sheaths smooth but long-hairy at top; ligule short-hairy. **Head** an open panicle, 5–20 cm long, the branches mostly ascending. **Spikelets** 3–6-flowered, 2–3 mm long and 1–2 mm wide. Aug–Sept. ❦ Wet, muddy areas, streambanks, sandbars, roadside ditches, cultivated fields. ⊕ se Minn, s Wisc, s LP of Mich, ne Ill and nw Ind. New Eng and s Que to s Minn, s to Fla and Ark.

Eragrostis hypnoides (Lam.) BSP.
Creeping lovegrass   OBL

Mat-forming annual grass. **Stems** mostly spreading and rooting at lower nodes, 5–15 cm long, smooth but short-hairy at nodes. **Leaves** flat to folded, 1–5 cm long and 1–3 mm wide, upper surface hairy; sheaths smooth except for hairs at top and sometimes along margins; ligule of short hairs about 0.5 mm long. **Head** a loose panicle, 2–6 cm long. **Spikelets** 10–35-flowered, linear, 3–10 mm long; glumes 1-veined, 0.5–1.5 mm long; lemma smooth and shiny, 1–2 mm long. July–Sept. ❦ Wet, sandy or muddy shores and streambanks, sand bars, mud flats. ⊕ Minn, c and s Wisc, c and s LP of Mich, ne Ill and nw Ind. Que to Wash, s throughout much of USA; s into Mex and S Amer.

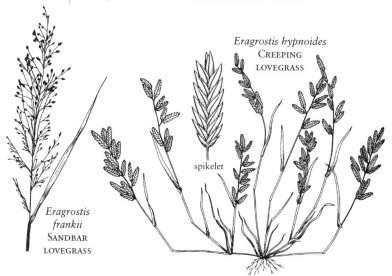

Eragrostis hypnoides
CREEPING
LOVEGRASS

spikelet

*Eragrostis
frankii*
SANDBAR
LOVEGRASS

▶**Glyceria** R. Br. / Mannagrass

Perennial grasses, loosely clumped or spreading by rhizomes. **Stems** upright, or reclining at base and often rooting at lower nodes. **Leaves** flat; sheaths tubular, the margins mostly closed. **Head** an open panicle. **Spikelets** 3-flowered, ovate to linear, ± round in section or somewhat flattened, breaking above the glumes; glumes unequal, shorter than lemmas, 1-veined; lemmas unawned, usually 7-veined; palea about as long as lemma; stamens 3 or 2.

▶**KEY TO GLYCERIA**

1 Spikelets linear-cylindric, 10 mm long or longer **2**
1 Spikelets ovate, 2 to 7 mm long **3**

2 Leaves less than 5 mm wide; lemmas ± smooth . . . . *G. borealis*
. . . . NORTHERN MANNAGRASS
2 Leaves 5 mm or more wide; lemmas finely hairy . *G. septentrionalis*
. . . . EASTERN MANNAGRASS

3 Spikelets 3–4 mm wide; veins of lemma not raised . . *G. canadensis*
. . . . Rattlesnake-mannagrass
3 Spikelets 2–2.5 mm wide; veins of lemma raised **4**

4 Spikelets 4–7 mm long . . . . . *G. grandis* / American mannagrass
4 Spikelets 2–4 mm long . . . . *G. striata* / Fowl-mannagrass

---

Glyceria borealis (Nash) Batchelder
Northern mannagrass   OBL

Perennial grass. **Stems** erect or reclining at base, often rooting from lower nodes, 6–12 dm long. **Leaves** flat or folded, 2–5 mm wide, smooth; sheaths smooth; ligule 3–10 mm long. **Head** a panicle, 2–4 dm long, with stiff, erect to ascending, branches to 8–12 cm long, each with several spikelets. **Spikelets** linear, mostly 6–12-flowered, 1–1.5 cm long; glumes rounded at tip, 2–3 mm long; lemmas 3–4 mm long, 7-veined. June–Aug. ❀ Marshes, ponds, stream, ditches, often in shallow water or mud. ⊕ Minn, Wisc (but uncommon in sw), Mich, rare in ne Ill and nw Ind. Newf to Alaska, s to NJ, Pa, Ill, Minn, SD, NM, Ariz and Calif.

Glyceria canadensis (Michx.) Trin.
Rattlesnake-mannagrass   OBL
Perennial grass. **Stems** single or few together, erect, 6–15 dm long. **Leaves** 3–7 mm wide, upper surface rough; ligule 2–5 mm long. **Head** an open panicle, 1–3 dm long, the branches drooping, with spikelets mostly near tips. **Spikelets** ovate, 5–10-flowered, 5–7 mm long, the florets spreading; glumes 2–3 mm long, the first glume lance-shaped, the second glume ovate; lemma veins not raised. ❀ Marshes, swamps, thickets, open bogs, fens. ⊕ Common; nc, ne and ec Minn, Wisc (especially n and c), Mich, ne Ill and nw Ind. Nfld to Minn, s to NJ, Ind and Ill.

Glyceria grandis S. Wats.
American mannagrass   OBL
Loosely clumped perennial grass. **Stems** erect, stout, 1–1.5 m long and 4–6 mm wide. **Leaves** flat, smooth, 6–12 mm wide; sheaths smooth; the ligule translucent, 3–6 mm long. **Head** a large, open, much-branched panicle, 2–4 dm long, usually nodding at tip, branches lax and drooping when mature. **Spikelets** ovate, purple, slightly flattened, 5–9-flowered, 4–7 mm long; glumes pale or white, 1–3 mm long; lemmas purple, 2–3 mm long. June–Sept. ❀ Marshes, ditches, streams, lakes and ponds, open bogs, fens; usually in shallow water or mud. ⊕ Minn, Wisc, Mich and ne Ill. Que and NS to Alaska, s to Va, Tenn, La, Neb, NM, Ariz and Wash.

Glyceria septentrionalis A. Hitchc.
Eastern mannagrass   OBL
Perennial grass. **Stems** somewhat fleshy, often ± horizontal at base and rooting from lower nodes, 1–1.5 m long. **Leaves** 6–10 mm wide; sheaths smooth; ligule large. **Head** a narrow panicle, 2–4 dm long, the branches to 10 cm long, each with several spikelets. **Spikelets** 1–2 cm long, 8–14-flowered; glumes 2–4 mm long; lemmas green or pale, 4–5 mm long, spreading when mature; palea often longer than lemma. June–Aug. ❀ Swamps, thickets, shallow water of pond margins, wet depressions in forests. ⊕ Common; c and s Wisc, LP of Mich (especially s), ne Ill and nw Ind. Mass to Wisc, s to SC and Tex.

Glyceria striata (Lam.) A. Hitchc.
Fowl-mannagrass OBL

Loosely clumped perennial grass; plants pale green. **Stems** erect, slender, 3–10 dm long. **Leaves** flat or folded, smooth, 2–6 mm wide; sheaths smooth; ligule 1–3 mm long. **Head** an open, loose panicle, 1–2 dm long, the branches lax, drooping. **Spikelets** ovate, often purple, 3–7-flowered, 3–4 mm long; glumes 0.5–1.5 mm long; lemma 2 mm long, strongly 7-veined. June–Aug. ❧ Swamps, thickets, low areas in forests, wet meadows, springs, streambanks. ⊕ Common; Minn, Wisc, Mich, ne Ill, nw Ind. Newf and Labr to BC, s to Fla, Tex and Calif.

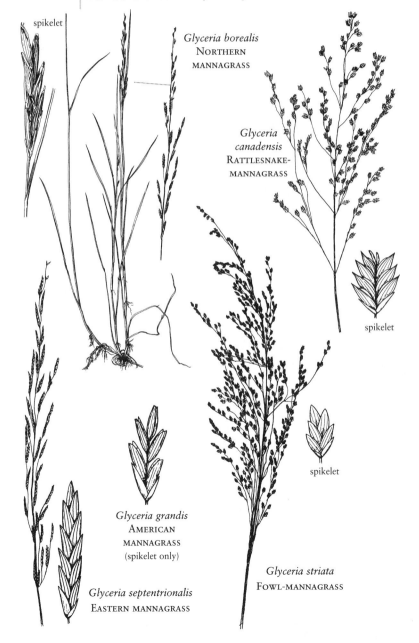

spikelet

Glyceria borealis
NORTHERN
MANNAGRASS

Glyceria canadensis
RATTLESNAKE-
MANNAGRASS

spikelet

Glyceria grandis
AMERICAN
MANNAGRASS
(spikelet only)

Glyceria septentrionalis
EASTERN MANNAGRASS

spikelet

Glyceria striata
FOWL-MANNAGRASS

▶**Hierochloe** R. Br. / Sweetgrass

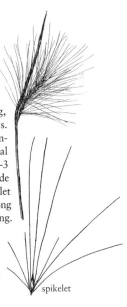

spikelet

Hierochloe odorata (L.) P. Beauv.

Sweetgrass; Holy grass; Vanilla grass   FACW

Perennial grass, from creeping rhizomes; plants sweet-scented, especially when dried. **Stems** erect, 2–6 dm tall, smooth. **Leaves** flat, 2–6 mm wide, smooth or short-hairy; stem leaves short, 1–4 cm long, leaves on sterile shoots much longer; sheaths smooth or short-hairy at top; ligule membranous, 1–4 mm long. **Head** a pyramid-shaped panicle, 5–10 cm long, the branches spreading to drooping. **Spikelets** 3-flowered, the lower 2 florets male, the terminal spikelet perfect, golden brown, or green or purple at base and golden near tips, 5 mm long, breaking above the glumes; glumes ovate, shiny, 4–6 mm long; lemmas 3–4 mm long, the male lemma hairy. May–July. ❦ Wet meadows, shores, low prairie; often where sandy. ⊕ Minn, Wisc (especially ec and se, uncommon in far w), Mich, ne Ill and nw Ind. Circumboreal, Labr to Alaska, s to NJ, Ohio, Ill, Iowa, SD, Ariz and Wash.

☞ Hierchloe odorata is an important plant of Native American ceremonies, but likely declining due to over-collecting and habitat loss.

▶**Hordeum** L. / Barley

Hordeum jubatum L.

Foxtail barley   FAC+

Clumped perennial grass; plants smooth to densely hairy. **Stems** erect or reclining at base, 2–7 dm long. **Leaves** usually flat, 2–5 mm wide; ligule less than 1 mm long. **Head** a terminal spike, erect to nodding, 3–10 cm long, appearing bristly due to the long, spreading awns from glumes and lemmas. **Spikelets** 1-flowered, 3 at each node, the center spikelet fertile, stalkless, the 2 lateral spikelets sterile, short-stalked, reduced to 1–3 spreading awns; the 3 spikelets at each node falling as a unit; glumes of fertile spikelet awnlike; lemma lance-shaped, tipped by a long awn; the glume and lemma awns 2–7 cm long. June–Sept. ❦ Wet meadows, ditches, shores, shallow marshes, disturbed areas; often where brackish. ⊕ Minn, Wisc, Mich, ne Ill and nw Ind. Newf to Alaska, s to Md, Ky, Mo, Tex, Calif and Mex.

spikelet

▶**Leersia** Swartz / Cut-grass

Perennial grasses, spreading by long rhizomes. **Stems** slender, somewhat weak. **Leaves** flat, smooth to hairy or rough-to-touch; ligules membranous, short. **Head** an open panicle. **Spikelets** 1-flowered, laterally compressed, falling as a unit from the stalk; glumes absent; lemmas smooth to bristly hairy, 5-veined; palea narrow, about as long as lemma; stamens 2–3 (Great Lakes species).

▶KEY TO LEERSIA

1 Spikelets ovate, 3–4 mm wide . . . . *L. lenticularis* / CATCHFLY GRASS
1 Spikelets linear, 1–2 mm wide **2**

2 Stems round in section; leaves very rough-to-touch; spikelets 4–6 mm
long . . . . *L. oryzoides* / RICE CUT-GRASS
2 Stems flattened in section; leaves smooth or finely roughened;
spikelets to 3.5 mm long . . . . *L. virginica* / WHITE GRASS

Leersia lenticularis Michx.
Catchfly grass   OBL
Perennial grass, from creeping rhizomes. **Stems** 1–1.5 m long. **Leaves** lax, smooth to soft-hairy, 1–2 cm wide; sheaths smooth, or hairy at top; ligule flat-topped, 1 mm long. **Head** a panicle, 1–2 dm long, often drooping, the branches spreading, each branch with 1–4 spikelike racemes 1–2 cm long. **Spikelets** 1-flowered, pale, flat, nearly round in section, 4–5 mm long, short-stalked, closely overlapping one another; glumes absent; lemma 4–6 mm long, the veins and keel fringed with bristly hairs. ❀ River floodplains. ✜ Local in se Minn and sw Wisc, especially along Miss and lower Wisc Rivers; ne Ill and nw Ind. Atlantic coast from Va to Fla and Tex, n in Miss River valley to Wisc and Minn, n Ill and n Ind.

Leersia oryzoides (L.) Swartz
Rice cut-grass   OBL
Loosely clumped perennial grass, from creeping rhizomes. **Stems** weak and sprawling, rooting at nodes, 1–1.5 m long. **Leaves** flat, 2–3 dm long and 5–10 mm wide, rough-to-touch, the margins fringed with short spines; sheaths rough-hairy; ligule flat-topped, 1 mm long. **Head** an open panicle at end of stem and from leaf axils (these often partly enclosed by leaf sheaths), 1–2 dm long, the branches ascending to spreading. **Spikelets** 1-flowered, oval, 5 mm long and 1–2 mm wide, compressed, pale green, turning brown with age; glumes absent; lemma covered with bristly hairs. July–Sept. ❀ Muddy or sandy streambanks, shores, swales and marshes; sometimes forming large patches. ✜ Common to occasional; Minn, Wisc (all but ne), Mich, ne Ill and nw Ind. Que and NS to BC, s to Fla, Tex and Calif; Europe and e Asia.

Leersia virginica Willd.
White grass   FACW
Perennial grass, spreading by rhizomes. **Stems** slender and weak, often ± horizontal at base and rooting at nodes, 5–12 dm long. **Leaves** rough-hairy, especially along margins, 5–20 cm long and 5–15 mm wide; sheaths smooth or finely hairy; ligule short, flat-topped. **Head** an open panicle, 1–2 dm long, the branches separated along the rachis, stiffly spreading, the spikelets from middle to tip of branches. **Spikelets** oblong, barely overlapping one another, 3 mm long and 1 mm wide, sparsely hairy; glumes absent; lemma 3–4 mm long, the keel and margins sparsely hairy. July–Sept. ❀ Swamps, floodplain forests, shaded forest depressions, streambanks. ✜ Common; c and s Minn and Wisc, s LP of Mich, ne Ill and nw Ind. Que to Minn, s to Fla and Tex.

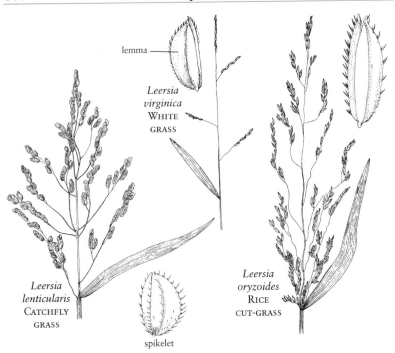

lemma

Leersia virginica WHITE GRASS

Leersia lenticularis CATCHFLY GRASS

Leersia oryzoides RICE CUT-GRASS

spikelet

▶**Leptochloa** P. Beauv. / Sprangletop

Leptochloa fascicularis (Lam.) A. Gray

Sprangletop   OBL

Clumped annual grass. **Stems** erect to spreading, branched from base, 2–10 dm long, somewhat fleshy. **Leaves** flat to loosely inrolled, 1–3 mm wide, finely rough-to-touch; sheaths ± smooth, often purple, the upper sheath often partly sheathing the head; ligule 3–5 mm long. **Head** a ± cylindric panicle, 5–20 cm long and 2–5 cm wide, composed of several to many branches, the branches upright and bearing spikelets in racemes. **Spikelets** 6–12-flowered, 5–10 mm long, breaking above the glumes; glumes unequal, lance-shaped, 1-veined, the first glume 2–4 mm long, the second glume 4–5 mm long; lemma 4–5 mm long, 3-veined, tipped with an awn 4–5 mm long; palea about as long as lemma. July–Sept. *Diplachne acuminata.* ❦ Shores, streambanks, muddy or sandy flats, usually where flooded part of year, often where brackish. ⊕ Local in s and far w Minn, uncommon in s LP of Mich. New Eng to ND, s to Fla, La and Tex; w USA in Wash and Ore, s to Ariz and Calif; c and S Amer.

spikelets

▶**Muhlenbergia** Schreber / Muhly

Perennial grasses, clumped or with creeping rhizomes. **Stems** erect or reclining at base, often branching from base. **Leaves** smooth to hairy, ligules membranous. **Head** a panicle, usually narrow and spikelike, sometimes open and spreading, at ends of stems and sometimes also from leaf axils. **Spikelets** 1-flowered, breaking above glumes; glumes usually nearly equal in length, 1-veined, the tip often awned; lemma lance-shaped, 3-veined, sometimes awned, some species with long, soft hairs at lemma base; palea about as long as lemma.

▶**KEY TO MUHLENBERGIA**

1 Panicle open and loose, 4 cm wide or more **2**
1 Panicle slender and densely flowered, less than 2.5 cm wide **3**

2 Plants spreading by rhizomes . . . . . *M. asperifolia* / ALKALI MUHLY
2 Plants clumped, rhizomes absent . . . . *M. unifolia* / BOG MUHLY

3 Leaf blades usually inrolled, to1 mm wide; panicles few-flowered, the heads not round in outline . . . . *M. richardsonis* / MAT-MUHLY
3 Leaf blades flat, 2–7 mm wide; panicles usually densely flowered, the heads ± round in outline **4**

4 Stems smooth and shiny . . . . *M. frondosa* / WIRESTEM MUHLY
4 Stems dull, finely hairy (at least below the nodes) **5**

5 Panicle stiffly erect, 5–10 mm wide; glumes longer than lemma. . . .
. . . . *M. glomerata* / MARSH-MUHLY
5 Panicle bent or nodding, less than 5 mm wide; glumes shorter or equal to lemma **6**

6 Panicle silvery green; lemmas with awn 5 mm or more long . . . . . .
. . . . *M. sylvatica* / FOREST MUHLY
6 Panicle pale green or purple-tinged; lemmas unawned or with short awn less than 5 mm long . . . . *M. mexicana* / WIRESTEM-MUHLY

Muhlenbergia asperifolia (Nees & Meyen) L. Parodi
Alkali muhly · FACW
Perennial grass, from slender, scaly rhizomes. **Stems** 1–5 dm long, becoming ± horizontal near base, rooting and branching from lower nodes, the branches spreading, waxy. **Leaves** upright, flat, 2–6 cm long and 1–3 mm wide, rough-to-touch; sheaths smooth; ligule ragged, to 0.5 mm long. **Head** an open panicle, 5–15 cm long, the branches threadlike, widely spreading. **Spikelets** 1-flowered (sometimes 2-flowered), single on the branches, purple or dark gray, 1–2 mm long; glumes nearly equal, half to nearly as long as spikelet; lemma unawned, 1–2 mm long. July–Sept. ✾ In w Minn, wet meadows, seeps, shores and mudflats, often where brackish. In ne Ill and nw Ind, weedy in disturbed areas such as roadside ditches and along railroads. Ind and Ill to BC, s to Tex, Calif and Mex.

Muhlenbergia frondosa (Poiret) Fern.
Wirestem muhly · FACW
Perennial grass, from stout, scaly rhizomes. **Stems** 4–10 dm long, unbranched and erect when young, becoming branched and sprawling with age, smooth and shiny between nodes. **Leaves** lax, smooth, 3–10 cm long and 2–6 mm wide; ligule fringed, 1–2 mm long. **Head** a narrow pan-

icle, to 10 cm long, from ends of stems and leaf axils (where partly enclosed by sheaths), the branches erect to spreading, with spikelets from near base to tip. **Spikelets** 1-flowered; glumes 2–3 mm long, tipped with a short awn; lemma 3–4 mm long, usually with an awn to 1 cm long, short-hairy at base. Aug–Sept. ✹ Floodplain forests, streambanks, thickets, shores; also somewhat weedy in disturbed areas such as along railroads. ⊕ Minn, Wisc, Mich, ne Ill and nw Ind. NB to ND, s to Ga and Tex.

Muhlenbergia glomerata (Willd.) Trin.
Marsh-muhly   FACW+
Perennial grass, spreading from rhizomes. **Stems** upright, 3–9 dm long, sometimes with a few branches from base, dull and finely hairy between nodes. **Leaves** flat, lax, 5–15 cm long and 2–6 mm wide; sheaths smooth; ligule fringed, to 0.5 mm long. **Head** a narrow, crowded, cylindric panicle, 2–10 cm long and 5–10 mm wide, the lower clusters of spikelets often separate from one another. **Spikelets** 1-flowered, often purple-tinged, 5–6 mm long; glumes nearly equal, longer than the floret, tipped with an awn 1–5 mm long; lemma lance-shaped, 2–3 mm long, with long, soft hairs at base. Aug–Sept. ✹ Swamps, wet meadows, marshes, springs, open bogs, fens, calcareous shores. ⊕ Minn, Wisc (but uncommon in sw), Mich (especially s LP), ne Ill and nw Ind. Newf and Que to NW Terr and BC, s to WVa, Ind, Iowa, Neb, Colo, Utah and Ore.

Muhlenbergia mexicana (L.) Trin.
Wirestem muhly   FACW
Perennial grass, from scaly rhizomes. **Stems** upright, 2–8 dm long, sometimes branched from base; dull and finely hairy between nodes. **Leaves** flat, lax, 5–20 cm long and 2–5 mm wide; sheaths smooth; ligule entire to fringed, to 1 mm long. **Head** a narrow, densely flowered panicle, 5–15 cm long and 2–10 mm wide, from ends of stems and leafy branches. **Spikelets** 1-flowered, green or purple, 2–3 mm long; glumes nearly equal, lance-shaped, 3–4 mm long, about as long as floret, tipped with a short awn about 1 mm long; lemma lance-shaped, 2–3 mm long, unawned or with an awn to 7 mm long. Aug–Sept. *M. foliosa.* ✹ Swamps, floodplain forests, thickets, wet meadows, marshes, springs, fens and streambanks. ⊕ Common; Minn, Wisc, Mich, ne Ill and nw Ind. Wisc to Alberta, s to Ind, Ill, Okla, NM and Ariz.

Muhlenbergia richardsonis (Trin.) Rydb.
Mat-muhly   FAC+

⚠
STATUS
Michigan - T

Loosely clumped perennial grass, rooting from lower nodes and forming mats. **Stems** very slender, erect or ± horizontal at base, 2–6 dm long. **Leaves** upright, usually inrolled, 1–5 cm long and 1–2 mm wide; sheaths smooth; ligule 2–3 mm long. **Head** a narrow panicle, 2–8 cm long. **Spikelets** 1-flowered, uncrowded, green or gray-green, 2–3 mm long; glumes nearly equal, ovate, to half as long as floret; lemma lance-shaped, smooth, 2–3 mm long tipped with a short point. July–Sept. ✹ Low prairie, wet meadows, marshes and seeps; often where brackish. ⊕ w and s Minn, uncommon in s LP of Mich. NB and Maine to Alberta, s to Mich, Minn, Neb, NM, Ariz and Baja Calif.

Muhlenbergia sylvatica Torr.
Forest muhly   FACW
Perennial grass, spreading by rhizomes. **Stems** erect, or sprawling when old, 4–10 dm long, coarse-hairy between nodes. **Leaves** flat, lax, upright to spreading, 5–15 cm long and 2–6 mm wide; sheaths smooth; ligule fringed, 1–3 mm long. **Head** a slender panicle, often nodding, 5–20 cm long and 2–7 mm wide. **Spikelets** 1-flowered, 2–4 mm long, at ends of

stalks about 3 mm long; glumes nearly equal, sharp-tipped, shorter than lemma; lemma 2–4 mm long, short hairy at base, tipped with an awn 5–15 mm long. Aug–Sept. ❦ Streambanks, shaded wet areas. ⊕ Local in e Minn, s Wisc, s LP of Mich, uncommon in ne Ill and nw Ind. Maine and Que to Minn, s to NC, Ill, Ark and Tex.

Muhlenbergia uniflora (Muhl.) Fernald
Bog muhly OBL
Clumped perennial grass. **Stems** very slender, 2–4 dm long, often ± horizontal and rooting at base. **Leaves** flat, crowded near base of plant, 5–10 cm long and to 1 mm wide; sheaths ± smooth, compressed; ligule ragged, about 1 mm long. **Head** a loose, open panicle, 7–20 cm long and 2–4 cm wide, the branches threadlike. **Spikelets** 1-flowered (rarely 2-flowered), oval, purple-tinged, 1–2 mm long; glumes about equal, ovate, to half the length of spikelet; lemma 1–2 mm long, unawned. ❦ Wetland margins, exposed sandy shores. ⊕ Uncommon in ne Minn, local in nw and c Wisc, more common in UP and n LP of Mich. Nfld to w Ont, s to NJ, Mich and n Minn.

▶Panicum L. / Panic-grass

Annual or perennial grasses. **Heads** narrow to open panicles (ours). **Spikelets** small, with 1 fertile flower; glumes usually unequal, the first glume membranous, usually very small, second glume green, about as long as spikelet; sterile lemma similar to second glume, enclosing the palea and sometimes a male flower, fertile lemma whitish, smooth.

▶KEY TO PANICUM

1 Spikelets smooth **2**
1 Spikelets at least sparsely hairy **4**

2 Sheaths hairy . . . . *P. flexile* / WIRY WITCH-GRASS
2 Sheaths ± smooth **3**

3 Spikelets smooth, nerves evident . . . . . *P. rigidulum* / MUNRO GRASS
3 Spikelets covered with bumps, nerves ± absent . . . . . *P. verrucosum*
. . . . WARTY PANIC-GRASS

4 Larger stem leaves more than 15 mm wide . . . . *P. clandestinum*
. . . . DEER-TONGUE GRASS
4 Stem leaves less than 15 mm wide **5**

5 Spikelets 2–3 mm long; ligule absent or a ring of hairs to 1 mm long
. . . . *P. boreale* / NORTHERN PANIC-GRASS
5 Spikelets less than 2 mm long; ligule a ring of hairs 2–3 mm long . .
. . . . *P. spretum* / SAND PANIC-GRASS

Panicum boreale Nash
Northern panic-grass FAC

⚠ STATUS Illinois - E

Perennial grass, in small clumps. **Stems** upright, 2–6 dm long. **Leaves** upright to spreading, 5–20 cm long and 1–2 cm wide, smooth or sometimes hairy on underside, base of leaf often fringed with hairs; sheaths hairy; ligule absent or a fringe of short hairs. **Head** an open panicle, 5–12 cm long, the branches spreading or upright. **Spikelets** oval in outline, finely hairy, about 2 mm long, on long stalks with 1 fertile flower; first glume to half as long as second glume; second glume and lemma purple-

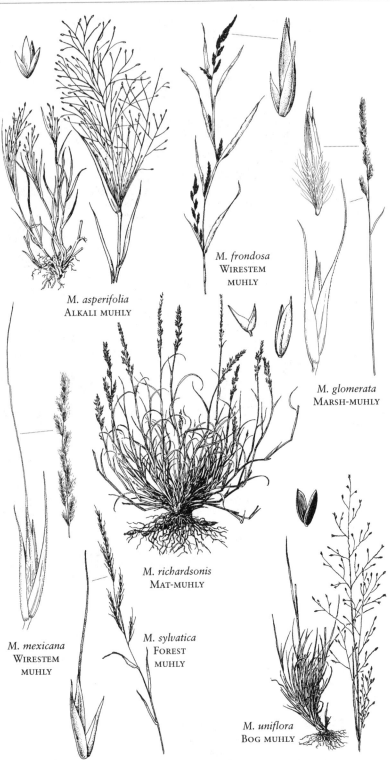

M. frondosa
WIRESTEM
MUHLY

M. asperifolia
ALKALI MUHLY

M. glomerata
MARSH-MUHLY

M. richardsonis
MAT-MUHLY

M. mexicana
WIRESTEM
MUHLY

M. sylvatica
FOREST
MUHLY

M. uniflora
BOG MUHLY

MUHLENBERGIA

tinged, about equal, and as long as fruit. June–Aug. *Dichanthelium bore-ale.* ⚘ Local in wet prairies and tamarack bogs. ⊕ ne and ec Minn, s Wisc, Mich, ne Ill and nw Ind. Que and Nfld to Minn, s to NJ and n Ill.

Panicum clandestinum L.

Deer-tongue grass   FACW

Clumped perennial grass, often forming large colonies. **Stems** stout, erect, 6–15 dm long, hairy at least at nodes. **Leaves** flat, spreading, smooth to hairy, 5–20 cm long and 1–3 cm wide, often fringed with hairs at base; sheaths hairy to smooth. **Head** an open panicle, 5–15 cm long, the branches spreading or upright. **Spikelets** oblong, finely hairy, about 3 mm long, with 1 fertile flower; first glume to half as long as second glume; second glume shorter than sterile lemma and fruit. June–July. *Dichanthelium clandestinum.* ⚘ Floodplain forests, alder thickets, ditches; especially where sandy. ⊕ c and s LP of Mich, ne Ill and nw Ind. NS and Que to Mich, Ill, Mo and Okla, s to Fla and Tex.

Panicum flexile (Gattinger) Scribn.

Wiry witch-grass   FACW+

Slender annual grass. **Stems** erect, 2–7 dm long, branched from base, hairy at nodes. **Leaves** erect, smooth or sparsely hairy, 10–30 cm long and 2–6 mm wide. **Head** a narrow panicle, 10–20 cm long and about a third as wide, the branches threadlike, upright to spreading. **Spikelets** lance-shaped, 3–4 mm long, with 1 fertile flower; first glume about half as long as second glume and sterile lemma. Aug–Sept. ⚘ Sandy and gravelly shores, marshes; often where calcium-rich. ⊕ se Wisc, LP of Mich, ne Ill and nw Ind. NY and s Ont to Wisc, s to Fla and Tex.

Panicum rigidulum Nees

Munro grass   FACW

Densely clumped perennial grass. **Stems** 5–15 dm long. **Leaves** crowded near base, upright, 2–4 dm long and 510 mm wide, sometimes longer than the panicle, margins finely rough-hairy; sheaths smooth, flattened; ligule membranous, ragged. **Head** a narrow to open panicle, 1–3 dm long, from ends of stems and leaf axils, the spikelet-bearing branches mostly on upper sides of panicle branches. **Spikelets** lance-shaped, green to purple, 2–3 mm long, with 1 fertile flower; glumes and sterile lemma pointed at tip, with conspicuous veins; first glume about half as long as spikelet; second glume and sterile lemma about equal, longer than the fruit. July–Aug. *P. agrostoides.* ⚘ Pond margins, streambanks, ditches and swales. ⊕ Local in s LP of Mich, ne Ill and nw Ind. Maine to Mich and ne Ill, s to Fla and Tex.

Panicum spretum Schultes

Sand panic-grass   (OBL)

Loosely clumped perennial grass. **Stems** erect, smooth, 3–8 dm long. **Leaves** firm, upright, 5–10 cm long and 3–5 mm wide, fringed with sparse hairs at base; sheaths ± smooth; ligule a fringe of hairs 2–3 mm long. **Head** a narrow panicle, 8–12 cm long. **Spikelets** oval, hairy, 1–2 mm long, with 1 fertile flower; first glume short, about 0.5 mm long; second glume and sterile lemma nearly equal to fruit. June–Aug. ⚘ Moist to wet sandy shores and flats. ⊕ sw LP of Mich, nw Ind. Atlantic coast from NS to Fla and Tex, inland in s Ont, Mich and nw Ind.

Panicum verrucosum Muhl.

Warty panic-grass   FACW

Annual grass; plants bright green. **Stems** erect or spreading, single or few together, smooth, 3–10 dm long. **Leaves** flat, lax, 5–20 cm long and 5–10 mm wide, fringed with sparse hairs at base; sheaths ± smooth; ligule a fringe of hairs 2–3 mm long. **Head** an open, spreading panicle, 5–25 cm long, often with smaller panicles from leaf axils. **Spikelets** with 1 fertile flower, obovate, about 2 mm long, covered with small bumps; first glume triangular, less than 1 mm long; second glume and sterile lemma nearly equal to fruit. Aug–Sept. ❦ Moist sandy shores. ⊕ Rare in sw LP of Mich and nw Ind. Atlantic coast from Mass to Fla and Tex, occasional inland to ne Ind and sw Mich.

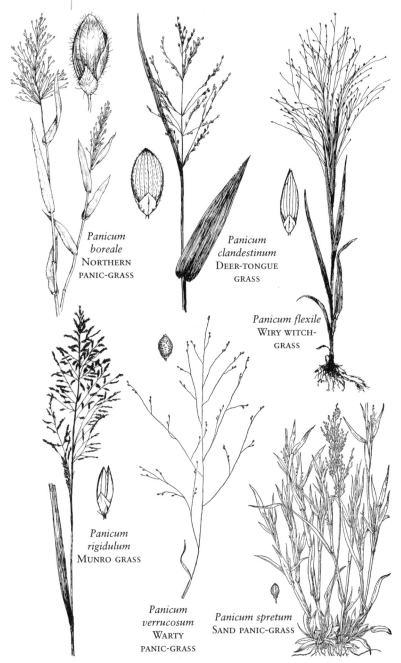

Panicum boreale
NORTHERN PANIC-GRASS

Panicum clandestinum
DEER-TONGUE GRASS

Panicum flexile
WIRY WITCH-GRASS

Panicum rigidulum
MUNRO GRASS

Panicum verrucosum
WARTY PANIC-GRASS

Panicum spretum
SAND PANIC-GRASS

spikelet

☞ **Reed canary-grass** is an aggressive, highly competitive wetland species, to the detriment of other plants. Most populations are probably non-native strains, originally introduced from Eurasia as a pasture plant and now widely naturalized.

▶**Phalaris** L. / Canary-grass

Phalaris arundinacea L.
Reed canary-grass   FACW+

Tall perennial grass, spreading by rhizomes and typically forming large, dense colonies. **Stems** stout, smooth, 5–15 dm long. **Leaves** flat, smooth, 1–2 dm long and 1–2 cm wide; sheaths smooth; ligule membranous, 3–8 mm long. **Head** a narrow, densely flowered panicle, 5–25 cm long, often purple-tinged, becoming straw-colored with age, the branches short and upright to ascending. **Spikelets** 4–6 mm long, breaking above glumes, with 1 fertile flower and 2 small sterile lemmas below; glumes nearly equal, longer than fertile floret, lance-shaped, tapered to tip or short-awned, 3-veined; fertile lemma ovate, 3 mm long, shiny; palea as long as lemma. June–July. ☙ Wet meadows, shallow marshes, ditches, shores and stream-banks. ⊕ Common to abundant; Minn, Wisc, Mich, ne Ill and nw Ind. Circumboreal, Newf to Alaska, s to NC, Mo, Okla, NM, Ariz and Calif.

▶**Phragmites** Adans. / Common reed

spikelet

Phragmites australis (Cav.) Trin.
Common reed   FACW+

Tall, stout perennial reed, from deep, scaly rhizomes, or the rhizomes sometimes exposed and creeping over the soil; often forming large colonies. **Stems** erect, hollow, 2–4 m long and 5–15 mm wide near base, the internodes often purple. **Leaves** flat, long, 1–3 cm wide; sheaths open; ligule white, 1 mm long. **Head** a large, plumelike panicle, purple when young, turning yellow-brown with age, 15–40 cm long, much-branched, the branches angled or curved upward. **Spikelets** 3–7-flowered, linear, 10–15 mm long, breaking above the glumes; the stem within the spikelet (rachilla) cov-ered with long silky hairs, these longer than the florets and becoming exposed as the lem-mas spread after flowering; glumes unequal, the first glume half the length of second glume. **Grain** (seed) seldom produced. Aug–Sept. *P. communis.* ☙ Fresh to brackish marshes, shores, streams, ditches, occasional in tamarack swamps; sometimes in shallow water. ⊕ Common; Minn, Wisc, Mich, ne Ill and nw Ind. Nearly worldwide.

▶**Poa** L. / Bluegrass

Perennial, loosely clumped or rhizomatous grasses. **Leaves** mostly near base, flat to folded, the tip keeled similar to the bow of a boat; sheaths partly closed, ligules membranous. **Head** an open panicle. **Spikelets** small, with 2 to several flowers breaking above the glumes; glumes nearly equal, the first glume usually 1-veined, the second glume 3-veined; lemmas often with a tuft of distinctive cobwebby hairs at base; palea nearly as long as lemma.

▶**KEY TO POA**

1 Keel of lemma silky-hairy; lemma nerves without hairs. . . *P. alsodes* . . . . GROVE BLUEGRASS

1 Keel of lemma and some or all nerves hairy **2**

2 Plants with rhizomes . . . . *P. pratensis* / KENTUCKY BLUEGRASS
2 Plants without rhizomes **3**

3 Panicle branches single or in groups of 2; sheaths rough-to-touch; ligules less than 2 mm long; rare. *P. paludigena* / MARSH BLUEGRASS
3 Panicle branches in groups of 3–5; sheaths smooth; ligules 3–5 mm long; widespread . . . . *P. palustris* / FOWL BLUEGRASS

Poa alsodes A. Gray
Grove Bluegrass
FACW-

Loosely clumped perennial grass, rhizomes absent. **Stems** slender, 3–8 dm long. **Leaves** lax, 5–20 cm long and 2–5 mm wide; sheaths smooth, ligule 1–3 mm long. **Head** a lax, open panicle, 10–20 cm long, the branches becoming widely spreading, mostly in groups of 4–5, with 1 to few spikelets near tip of branch; base of panicle sometimes remaining enclosed by sheath. **Spikelets** ovate, 2–3-flowered, 3–5 mm long; glumes nearly equal, 2–4 mm long; lemmas 2–4 mm long, with cobwebby hairs at base. May–July. ⚘ Alder thickets, swamp hummocks, most common in moist deciduous or mixed conifer-deciduous forests. ⊕ ec and ne Minn (especially along Lake Superior), n and c Wisc, Mich, s Ill, nw Ind. NS and Maine to Mich, Ind and Minn, s to Del, NC and Tenn.

⚠️
STATUS
Illinois - T

Poa paludigena Fernald & Wieg.
Marsh bluegrass
OBL

Perennial grass, without rhizomes. **Stems** single or in small clumps, slender and weak, 2–6 dm long. **Leaves** upright, to 10 cm long and 1–2 mm wide; sheaths finely rough-hairy; ligule flat-topped, about 1 mm long. **Head** a loose, open panicle, 5–12 cm long, the lower branches in groups of 2, with a few spikelets above middle. **Spikelets** 2–5-flowered, 4–5 mm long, glumes lance-shaped, the first glume to 2 mm long, the second glume 2–3 mm long; lemma 3–4 mm long, with cobwebby hairs at base. June–July. ⚘ Swamps, alder thickets, sedge meadows, open bogs, cold springs; usually in sphagnum moss and often under **black ash** (*Fraxinus nigra*). ⊕ Rare in ec Minn, nw, c and e Wisc, c and s LP of Mich, nw Ind. NY and Pa to Wisc and Minn, s to n Ind.

⚠️
STATUS
Michigan - T
Minnesota - T
Wisconsin - T

Poa palustris L.
Fowl bluegrass
FACW+

Loosely clumped perennial grass. **Stems** smooth, 4–12 dm long, reclining at base and rooting from lower nodes, lower portion often purple-tinged. **Leaves** flat, upright to spreading, 1–4 mm wide, rough-to-touch; sheaths smooth; ligule 2–5 mm long. **Head** a loosely spreading panicle (narrow when emerging from sheath), 1–3 dm long, the branches in mostly widely separated groups along panicle stem (rachis). **Spikelets** 2–4-flowered, 2–5 mm long and 1–2 mm wide; glumes nearly equal, lance-shaped, 2–3 mm long, often purple; lemma 2–3 mm long, often purple on sides, with cobwebby hairs at base. June–Sept. ❦ Wet meadows, marshes, shores, streambanks, ditches and low prairie; also moist woods. ⊕ Common to occasional; Minn, Wisc, Mich, ne Ill and nw Ind. Newf and Que to Alaska, s to Va, Mo, Neb, NM and Calif; Eurasia.

Poa pratensis L.
Kentucky bluegrass   FAC-

☞ **Kentucky bluegrass** was introduced from Europe for lawns and pastures but may be native in part (especially in n portions of region).

Perennial grass, spreading by rhizomes and forming a sod. **Stems** erect, 3–10 dm long. **Leaves** flat or folded, 1–4 mm wide, margins sometimes somewhat rough-to-touch; sheaths smooth; ligule 0.5–2 mm long. **Head** an open, pyramid-shaped panicle, 5–15 cm long, the branches spreading to ascending, the lowest branches in groups of 4–5. **Spikelets** 2–5-flowered, green or purple-tinged, compressed, 3–5 mm long and 2–3 mm wide; glumes unequal, lance-shaped, 2–4 mm long, roughened on keels; lemma 2–4 mm long, with an obvious tuft of cobwebby hairs at base, often purple-tinged on sides. May–Aug. ❦ All types of moist to dry places; not usually in very wet situations. ⊕ Common throughout Gt Lks region; Minn, Wisc, Mich, n Ill and n Ind. Most of Canada and USA.

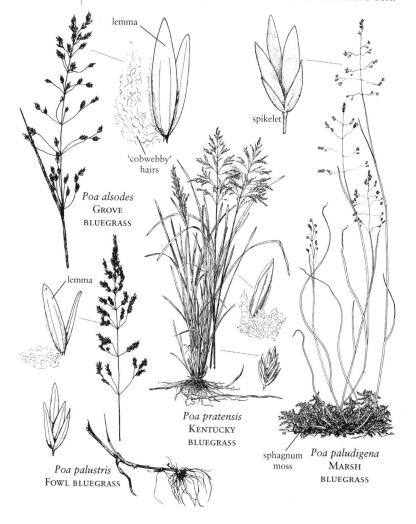

lemma

spikelet

'cobwebby' hairs

Poa alsodes
GROVE
BLUEGRASS

lemma

Poa palustris
FOWL BLUEGRASS

Poa pratensis
KENTUCKY
BLUEGRASS

sphagnum moss

Poa paludigena
MARSH
BLUEGRASS

▶**Puccinellia** Parl. / Alkali-grass

Clumped, smooth perennial grasses, usually in brackish habitats (except *P. pallida*). **Leaves** mostly from base of plants, flat to inrolled. **Head** an open panicle, the branches upright to spreading. **Spikelets** several-flowered, oval to linear, nearly round in section, breaking above the glumes; glumes unequal, the first glume 1-veined, the second glume 3-veined; lemmas rounded on back, often short-hairy at base; palea shorter to about as long as lemma.

▶**KEY TO PUCCINELLIA**

1 Plants not in brackish wetlands; lemma with 5 prominent veins . . . . *P. pallida* / Pale alkali-grass
1 Plants of brackish wetlands and along salted highways; lemma only faintly veined **2**

2 Lower panicle branches horizontal or angled downward when mature; lemma broad, not tapered to the blunt or rounded tip . . . . *P. distans* / European alkali-grass
2 Lower panicle branches usually angled upward; lemma narrow, tapered to a rounded tip . . *P. nuttalliana* / Nuttall's alkali-grass

---

Puccinellia distans (Jacq.) Parl.
European alkali-grass   OBL
Clumped, smooth perennial grass. **Stems** erect or reclining at base, 1–5 dm long. **Leaves** flat to slightly inrolled, 1–3 mm wide; ligule about 1 mm long. **Head** a loose, pyramid-shaped panicle, 5–15 cm long, the branches in groups, the lower branches angled downward. **Spikelets** 3–7-flowered, 4–6 mm long; glumes ovate, 1–2 mm long; lemmas about 2 mm long, smooth or short-hairy at base. May–Aug. ⚘ Occasional in brackish waste areas and ditches along salted highways. ⊕ s Minn, Wisc Mich, ne Ill and nw Ind. Introduced from Eurasia, in N Amer along the Atlantic coast from NB to Del, inland to Great Lakes and Great Plains; also Yukon and n BC, s to Calif.

Puccinellia nuttalliana (Schultes) A. Hitchc.
Nuttall's alkali-grass   OBL
Clumped perennial grass. **Stems** slender, erect, 2–8 dm long. **Leaves** flat or often inrolled, 1–3 mm wide; ligule 1–3 mm long, **Head** an open panicle, 5–25 cm long, the branches ascending to spreading, rough-to-touch, to 10 cm long, the spikelets mostly above middle of branch. **Spikelets** 3–9-flowered, slender, 4–7 mm long, glumes lance-shaped, 1–3 mm long; lemmas oblong, 2–3 mm long, with tiny hairs at base. June–July. *P. airoides.* ⚘ Moist flats, sometimes in shallow water, often where salty or disturbed. ⊕ Far w Minn, Wisc. Minn to BC, s to Kans, NM, Calif and n Mex.

Puccinellia pallida (Torr.) R. T. Clausen
Pale alkali-grass   OBL

STATUS
Illinois - E

Perennial grass. **Stems** slender, weak, usually reclining at base, 3–10 dm long. **Leaves** flat, soft, 3–8 mm wide; sheaths open; ligule 3–9 mm long. **Head** a pale green, open panicle, 5–15 cm long, the branches upright, becoming spreading. **Spikelets** 4–7-flowered, oval in outline, 5–7 mm long; glumes rounded at tip, 1–3 mm long; lemmas 2–3 mm long, 5-veined, finely hairy, the tip rounded and ragged. June–Aug. *Glyceria pallida, P. fernaldii.* ⚘ Marshes, pond margins, alder thickets, forest depressions; often in shallow water. ⊕ nc and ne Minn, n and c Wisc, s Mich (and uncommon in UP), s Ill, nw Ind. Nfld to Minn, s to NC, Ind and Mo.

▶**Scolochloa** Link / Sprangletop

Scolochloa festucacea (Willd.) Link

Sprangletop; Whitetop OBL

Tall perennial grass, spreading by thick rhizomes and forming colonies. **Stems** erect, hollow, 1–2 m long and 3–5 mm wide near base, usually with a few suckers and roots from lower nodes. **Leaves** flat or slightly inrolled, 3–10 mm wide, tapered to a sharp tip, upper surface rough-to-touch; sheaths smooth; ligule white, ragged at tip, 4–7 mm long. **Head** a loose, open panicle, 15–20 cm long, the branches ascending, the lowest branches much longer than upper. **Spikelets** 3–4-flowered, purple or green, becoming straw-colored, 7–10 mm long, breaking above glumes; glumes unequal, lance-shaped, the first glume 3-veined, 4–7 mm long, the second glume 5-veined, 6–9 mm long; lemmas lance-shaped, about 6 mm long; palea as long as lemma. June–July. *Fluminea festucacea.* ⊮ Shallow water, marshes. Introduced as a forage plant and sometimes mowed for hay during dry periods. ⊕ w and sc Minn. Man to BC, s to n Iowa, Neb and e Ore; n Eurasia.

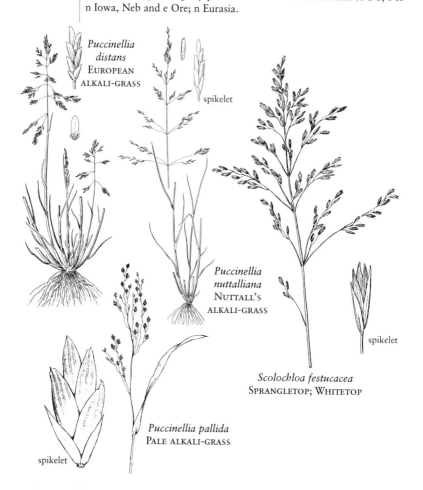

*Puccinellia
distans*
EUROPEAN
ALKALI-GRASS

spikelet

*Puccinellia
nuttalliana*
NUTTALL'S
ALKALI-GRASS

spikelet

Scolochloa festucacea
SPRANGLETOP; WHITETOP

Puccinellia pallida
PALE ALKALI-GRASS

spikelet

▶**Spartina** Schreber / Cordgrass

Coarse perennial grasses, spreading by long scaly rhizomes. **Stems** stout and erect. **Leaves** flat to inrolled, tough, rough-to-touch; sheaths smooth; ligule a fringe of hairs. **Head** of several to many 1–sided spikes in racemes at ends of stem, the spikes upright to appressed. **Spikelets** 1-flowered, flattened, overlapping in 2 rows on 1 side of the rachis, breaking below the glumes; glumes unequal, 1–2-veined, with rough hairs on the keel; lemma with pronounced midvein and 2 faint lateral veins; palea about as long as lemma.

▶**KEY TO SPARTINA**

1 Plants 1–2 m tall; leaf blades flat (at least near base), more than 5 mm wide . . . . *S. pectinata* / Prairie cordgrass
1 Plants to 1 m tall; leaf blades inrolled or flat, 2–5 mm wide **2**

2 Leaf blades usually flat; spikes erect; wc Minn . . . . *S. gracilis*
. . . . Alkali cordgrass
2 Leaf blades usually inrolled; spikes ascending or spreading; se Mich
. . . . *S. patens* / Saltmeadow cordgrass

Spartina gracilis Trin.
Alkali cordgrass   FACW

Perennial grass, from rhizomes. **Stems** 4–8 dm long. **Leaves** usually inrolled, 10–20 cm long and 2–4 mm wide. **Head** a spikelike raceme of 4–8, 1-sided spikes, the spikes 2–5 cm long, appressed to the raceme stem (rachis). **Spikelets** 1-flowered, 6–9 mm long; glumes and lemma fringed with hairs on keel, the first glume half as long as second; lemma nearly as long as second glume. July–Sept. ⚘ Wet meadows, shores, flats and seeps; often where brackish. ⊕ Far wc Minn. Man to BC, s to Kans, NM, Ariz and Calif. c Man to BC, s to Kans, NM, Ariz and Calif.

Spartina patens (Aiton) Muhl.
Saltmeadow cordgrass   FACW

☞ In e USA along the Atlantic coast, this species is the main source of eastern salt hay.

Perennial grass, from long rhizomes. **Stems** slender, tough, 3–9 dm long. **Leaves** inrolled or flat near base, 5–30 cm long and 1–4 mm wide. **Head** a raceme of 2–7 spikes, the spikes 1.5–5 cm long, upright but not appressed, somewhat separate from one another along the raceme stem (rachis). **Spikelets** 1-flowered, 8–12 mm long, fringed with hairs on keels; first glume 2–6 mm long, half as long as floret, second glume lance-shaped, 8–12 mm long; lemma 5–8 mm long. *S. juncea.* ⚘ Uncommon in salt marshes in se Mich. ⊕ Atlantic coast from Que to Fla and Tex; inland in c NY, s Ont and se Mich.

Spartina pectinata Link
Prairie cordgrass   FACW+

Perennial grass, with scaly rhizomes. **Stems** tough, 1–2 m long. **Leaves** flat to inrolled, 3–10 mm wide, margins very rough. **Head** a spikelike raceme of mostly 10–30, 1-sided spikes, the spikes upright to sometimes appressed, 3–10 cm long. **Spikelets** 1-flowered, 8–11 mm long, fringed with hairs on keels; first glume nearly as long as floret, tapered to tip or with an awn 1–5 mm long, second glume longer than floret, tipped with an awn 2–8 mm long; lemma 7–9 mm long, shorter than second glume. July–Sept. ⚘ Shallow marshes, wet meadows, sandy shores, ditches, low prairie. ⊕ Minn, Wisc (especially s and w), LP and c UP of Mich, common in ne Ill and nw Ind. Newf and Que to Alberta, Wash and Ore, s to NC, Ark, Tex and NM.

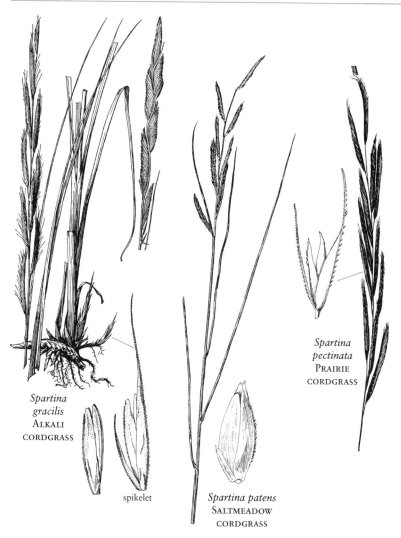

Spartina gracilis
ALKALI
CORDGRASS

spikelet

Spartina patens
SALTMEADOW
CORDGRASS

Spartina pectinata
PRAIRIE
CORDGRASS

▶**Sphenopholis** Scribn. / Wedge-grass

Sphenopholis obtusata (Michx.) Scribn.
Wedge-grass   FAC

Clumped perennial (sometimes annual) grass; plants smooth to rough-hairy. **Stems** slender, 2–10 dm long. **Leaves** upright to spreading, flat, rough-to-touch, 2–7 mm wide; ligule membranous, ragged at tip, 1–4 mm long. **Head** a dense, shiny, spikelike panicle, 5–20 cm long, the spikes often (in part) separate from one another. **Spikelets** 2-flowered, 3–4 mm long, unawned, breaking below the glumes; glumes 2–3 mm long, the first glume linear, 1-veined, the second glume broader, 3–5-veined; lemma 2–3 mm long, 1-veined; palea linear, about as long as lemma. June–Aug. *S. intermedia.* 🌿 Low prairie, wet meadows, gravelly shores, streambanks, wetland margins; also in moist woods. ⊕ Minn (all but far ne), Wisc, Mich, ne Ill and nw Ind. Maine to BC, s to Fla, Mex and Calif, W Indies.

▶Trisetum Pers. / False-oats

Trisetum melicoides (Michx.) Scribn.
Purple false-oats   FACW

Clumped perennial grass. **Stems** smooth or finely hairy, 4–9 dm long.
Leaves flat, 3–6 mm wide, sparsely long-hairy; sheaths smooth or hairy;
ligule membranous, ragged at tip. **Head** a slender, nodding panicle,
10–20 cm long, the branches upright to drooping, to 6 cm long, the
spikelets mostly above middle of branch. **Spikelets** 2-flowered, 6–7 mm
long, finely hairy; glumes somewhat unequal, 4–7 mm long, the first
glume l-veined, the second glume 3-veined; lemma unawned; stalk within spikelet (rachilla) and base of lemma white-hairy. ❦ Cedar swamps,
gravelly shores. ⊕ Uncommon near Lake Mich in Wisc; Mich (especially s LP). Nfld and Que to Ont, s to Mich and Wisc.

▶Zizania L. / Wildrice

Zizania aquatica L.
Annual wildrice   OBL

☞ Zizania
aquatica is the
source of com-
mercial wild
rice. Harvesting
is most wide-
spread in
Minnesota,
especially by
Native
Americans
where large
areas of lakes
and shallow
marshes may
be dominated
by this plant.
The grain is
also an excel-
lent food for
waterfowl.
Many popula-
tions are intro-
ductions to
intentionally
spread the
species.

Large annual emergent grass, with fleshy yellow roots. **Stems** single or
few together, 1–3 m long. **Leaves** flat, 1–3 mm wide, smooth or finely
hairy, usually floating on water surface early in season, becoming
upright; sheaths short-hairy at top, smooth below; ligule membranous,
entire or with a jagged margin, 10–15 mm long. **Head** a panicle, 3–6 dm
long, the branches 10–20 cm long; male and female flowers separate on
same plant, the male flowers on lower panicle branches, female flowers
on upper branches, the male portion becoming spreading, branches of
female portion remaining upright. **Spikelets** 1-flowered, round in section,
breaking as a unit from the stalk; glumes absent; **male spikelets** straw-
colored to purple, 6–12 mm long, hanging downward from branches,
lemma linear, tapered to tip or tipped with an awn to 3 mm long, early
deciduous; **female spikelets** linear, purple or light green, lemma awl-
shaped, 1–2 cm long, tapered to a slender awn 3–6 cm long. **Grain** cylindric, dark brown to black, 1–2 cm long. July–Sept. Includes *Z. palustris*.
❦ Shallow water (up to 1 m deep) or mud of streams, rivers, lakes,
ponds; where water is slightly flowing and not stagnant; soils vary from
muck to silt, sand, or gravel, with best establishment of plants on a layer
of soft silt or muck several cm thick. ⊕ Minn (especially n and c), Wisc,
Mich (especially LP, local in UP), local in ne Ill and nw Ind. e Que and
NS to Man, s to Fla, La and Neb.   ☞ *Zizania aquatica* var. *aquatica* is
listed as threatened by the state of Michigan. It is a tall plant (to 3 m)
with leaves 1–4.5 cm wide, and occurs in s LP. Var. *angustifolia* occurs
throughout the state, and is generally shorter, with narrower leaves.
However, distinctions between the two vars. are not always clear.

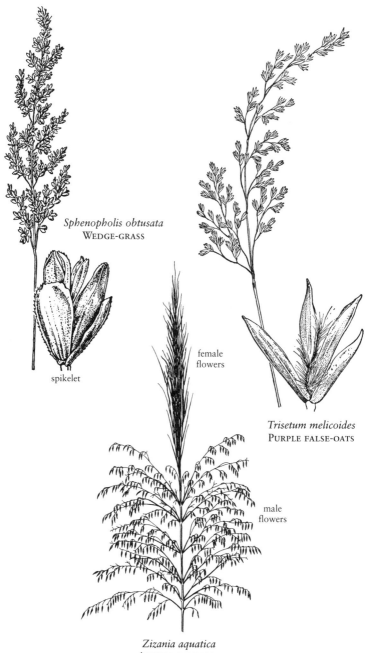

Sphenopholis obtusata
WEDGE-GRASS

spikelet

Trisetum melicoides
PURPLE FALSE-OATS

female
flowers

male
flowers

Zizania aquatica
ANNUAL WILDRICE

Pontederiaceae
Water-Hyacinth Family

Mostly perennial, aquatic or emergent herbs. **Leaves** alternate, stalkless and straplike, or with a petiole and broad blade. **Flowers** perfect (with both male and female parts), regular or irregular, single from leaf axils or in spikes or panicles, subtended by leaflike bracts (spathes), light yellow, white or blue-purple, perianth of 6 petal-like lobes, usually joined near base to form a tube; stamens 3–6, the filaments attached to throat of perianth tube; ovary superior, 3-chambered, style 1. **Fruit** a many-seeded capsule inside the spathe, or a 1-seeded, achene-like utricle.

▶**KEY TO PONTEDERIACEAE**

1 Flowers 2-lipped, each lip 3-lobed, the 3 lower lobes spreading; stamens 6, 3 longer than petals, 3 shorter; fruit 1-seeded . . . . *Pontederia cordata* / PICKEREL-WEED
1 Flowers regular, the lobes ± equal; stamens 3, all longer than petals; fruit a many-seeded capsule. **2**

2 Flowers blue-purple or white; leaves with a petiole and blade, emersed or floating . *Heteranthera limosa* / SMALLER MUD-PLANTAIN
2 Flowers light yellow; leaves linear and straplike, not differentiated into petiole and blade, usually underwater. . . . . *Zosterella dubia* . . . . WATER STAR-GRASS

▶**Heteranthera** Ruiz & Pavon / Mud-plantain

Heteranthera limosa (Swartz) Willd.
Smaller mud-plantain   OBL

⚠
STATUS
Minnesota - T

Small annual herb. **Stems** much-branched from base, 1–3 dm long, short when exposed, longer and sprawling when in water. **Leaves** with blade and petiole, the blades usually emersed, ovate to oval, 2–6 cm long and 1–3 cm wide, tapered to a rounded tip, base rounded or flat across; petioles 5–15 cm long, with a membranous sheath at base. **Flowers** 1, enclosed by a spathe; spathe folded, 2–4 cm long, abruptly narrowed at tip, enclosing the tubular portion of the perianth, the flower and spathe at end of a stout stalk arising from stem; perianth segments usually blue-purple, sometimes white, lance-shaped, 5–10 mm long, the perianth tube 1–4 cm long, the lobes ± equal, 5–15 mm long, the 3 upper lobes with a yellow spot at base; stamens 3, the 2 lateral stamens short, yellow, the center stamen longer and blue or yellow. June–Sept. ≋ Shallow water or mud of ponds and marshes. ⊕ Rare in far sw Minn. Ky to Minn and SD, s to Miss, Tex, Ariz and Mex.

▶**Pontederia** L. / Pickerel-weed

flower detail

Pontederia cordata L.
Pickerel-weed OBL

Perennial emergent herb, spreading from rhizomes and forming colonies. **Stems** stout, upright, to 12 dm long, with 1 leaf. **Leaves** lance-shaped to ovate, 5–20 cm long and 2–15 cm wide, heart-shaped at base; petioles 3–7 cm long, sheathing on stem. **Flowers** blue-purple (rarely white), many in a spike 5–15 cm long, subtended by a bractlike spathe 3–6 cm long; perianth funnel-like, the tube 6 mm long, 2-lipped above, upper lip with 3 ovate lobes, lower lip with 3 slender, spreading lobes, the lobes 7–10 mm long. **Fruit** a 1-seeded utricle, 5–10 mm long. June–Sept. *P. lanceolata.* ⬙ Shallow water (to 1 m deep) of lakes, ponds, rivers and swamps. ⊕ e Minn, Wisc, Mich (but local in UP), ne Ill and nw Ind. NS to Ont and Minn, s to S Amer.

▶**Zosterella** Small / Water star-grass

☞ **Water star-grass** is distinguished from the **pondweeds** (*Potamogeton*) by lack of a leaf midrib.

Zosterella dubia (Jacq.) Small
Water star-grass OBL

Aquatic perennial herb, with lax stems and leaves, or plants sometimes exposed and forming small, leafy rosettes. **Stems** slender, forked, often rooting at lower nodes, to 1 m long. **Leaves** alternate, linear, flat, translucent, rounded at tip or tapered to a point, 2–12 cm long and 2–6 mm wide, the midrib and veins inconspicuous; petioles absent. **Flowers** 1, opening on water surface, light yellow, enclosed in a spathe from upper leaf axils, the spathe membranous, 2–5 cm long, surrounding much of the slender perianth tube; perianth tube often curved, 2–8 cm long, the 6 perianth segments linear, 4–6 mm long; stamens 3, all alike. **Fruit** a many-seeded capsule about 1 cm long. July–Sept. *Heteranthera dubia.* ⬙ Shallow water, muddy shores of ponds, lakes, streams and marshes. ⊕ Minn (all but extreme nw), Wisc, Mich (especially LP), ne Ill and nw Ind. Que to ND and Wash, s to Fla, Tex, Calif and Mex.

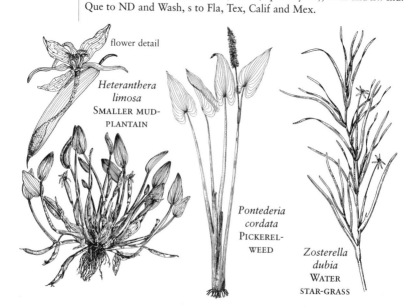

flower detail

Heteranthera limosa
SMALLER MUD-PLANTAIN

Pontederia cordata
PICKEREL-WEED

Zosterella dubia
WATER STAR-GRASS

Potamogetonaceae
Pondweed Family

▶**Potamogeton** L. / Pondweed

☞ The narrow-leaved pondweeds (leads 7-18 in Group 1 key) are important foods for waterfowl, but often difficult to distinguish from one another.

Aquatic perennial herbs; leaves all submerged or with leaves both submerged and floating leaves, from rhizomes or tubers, sometimes reproducing and over-wintering by free-floating winter buds (turions). **Stems** long, wavy, anchored to bottom by roots and rhizomes. **Leaves** alternate, or becoming opposite upward in some species, simple, with an open or closed sheath at their base. **Underwater leaves** usually linear and thread-like, sometimes broader, margins often wavy, usually stalkless. **Floating leaves**, if present, oval or ovate, stalked, with a waxy upper surface. **Flowers** perfect, regular, green to red, in stalked spikes at ends of stems or from leaf axils, usually raised above water surface, the spikes with few to many small flowers; perianth of 4 sepal-like bracts; stamens 4. **Fruit** a group of 4 beaked achenes.

▶KEY TO POTAMOGETON

1 Plants with underwater leaves only, these all alike . . . . **GROUP 1**
1 Plants with 2 kinds of leaves: broad floating leaves and broad or narrow underwater leaves . . . . **GROUP 2**

▶KEY TO POTAMOGETON GROUP 1

Plants with underwater leaves only, these all alike.

1 Leaves broad, lance-shaped to oval or ovate, never linear **2**
1 Leaves linear **7**

2 Leaf margins wavy-crisped, finely toothed . . . . *P. crispus*
. . . . CURLY PONDWEED
2 Leaf margins flat or sometimes wavy, entire (or rarely finely toothed at tip) **3**

3 Base of leaf blade tapered, not clasping stem **4**
3 Base of leaf blade clasping stem **5**

4 Plants green, upper leaves stalked, leaf margins finely toothed near tip
. . . . *P. illinoensis* / ILLINOIS PONDWEED
4 Plants red-tinged, upper leaves ± stalkless, leaf margins entire . . . . .
. . . . *P. alpinus* / RED PONDWEED

5 Stems whitish; leaves 10–30 cm long; fruit 4–5 mm long . . . .
. . . . *P. praelongus* / WHITESTEM-PONDWEED
5 Stems green; leaves 1–12 cm long; fruit 2–4 mm long **6**

6 Leaves ovate, mostly 1–5 cm long, margins flat; stipules small or absent; plants drying olive-green. . . . . *P. perfoliatus*
. . . . REDHEAD-GRASS; CLASPING-LEAVED PONDWEED
6 Leaves lance-shaped, mostly more than 5 cm long; margins wavy-crisped; stipules conspicuous, persisting as shreds; plants drying light green . . . . *P. richardsonii* / CLASPING-LEAVED PONDWEED

typical
Group 1
species

7 Stipules joined with lower part of leaf to form a sheath at least 1 cm long **8**
7 Stipules free from leaf, or rarely joined to leaf base for only 1–2 mm **11**

8 Leaves 4–8 mm wide, auricled at base, margins finely toothed . . . . *P. robbinsii* / FERN-PONDWEED
8 Leaves threadlike, rarely to 3 mm wide, not auricled, margins entire **9**

9 Leaves gradually tapered to tip; rhizomes tuber-bearing; stigmas raised on a tiny style . . . . *P. pectinatus* / SAGO-PONDWEED
9 Leaves rounded, blunt-tipped or tipped with a short, sharp point, stigmas inconspicuous, broad and not raised **10**

10 Plants short, to 0.5 m long; sheaths tight around stem; spikes with 2–5 whorls of flowers . . . . . *P. filiformis* / THREADLEAF-PONDWEED
10 Plants large and coarse, 2–5 m long; sheaths enlarged to 2–5 times diameter of stem; spikes with 5–12 whorls of flowers . *P. vaginatus* . . . . BIGSHEATH-PONDWEED

11 Plants with slender creeping rhizomes. **12**
11 Plants with short rhizomes or rhizomes absent (plants often rooting at lower nodes of stem) **13**

12 Flower clusters on stalks at ends of stems, the stalks mostly 5–25 cm long; leaves threadlike, narrower than stems . . . . . . *P. confervoides* . . . . ALGA PONDWEED
12 Flower clusters on stalks from leaf axils, the stalks less than 3 cm long; leaves linear, wider than stems . *P. foliosus* / LEAFY PONDWEED

13 Leaves 9- to many-veined (with 1–2 main veins and many finer ones) . . . . *P. zosteriformis* / FLATSTEM-PONDWEED
13 Leaves 1–7-veined **14**

14 Leaves without glands at base. . . . . . *P. foliosus* / LEAFY PONDWEED
14 At least some of leaves with pair of glands at base **15**

15 Leaves with 5–7 nerves . . . . *P. friesii* / FRIES' PONDWEED
15 Leaves with 3 (rarely 1 or 5) nerves **16**

16 Leaves gradually tapered to a bristlelike tip **17**
16 Leaves rounded at tip or tapered to a point, not bristle-tipped . . **18**

17 Leaf margins rolled under; widespread species . . . . . . *P. strictifolius* . . . . STRAIGHT-LEAVED PONDWEED
17 Leaf margins flat, not rolled under; n LP of Mich. . . . . *P. hillii* . . . . HILL'S PONDWEED

18 Leaves 1–4 mm wide, rounded at tip; body of achene 2.5–4 mm long . . . . *P. obtusifolius* / BLUNTLEAF-PONDWEED
18 Leaves to 2.5 mm wide, usually tapered to a sharp tip; body of achene to 2 mm long . . . . . *P. pusillus* / SLENDER OR SMALL PONDWEED

typical
Group 2
species

▶**KEY TO POTAMOGETON GROUP 2**

Plants with 2 kinds of leaves: broad floating leaves and broad or narrow underwater leaves.

1 Underwater leaves broad, never narrowly linear **2**
1 Underwater leaves linear or threadlike **7**

2 Floating leaves with 30–55 nerves; underwater leaves with 30–40 nerves . . . . *P. amplifolius* / BIGLEAF PONDWEED
2 Floating leaves with fewer than 30 nerves; underwater leaves with less than 30 nerves **3**

3 Underwater leaves with more than 7 nerves, all leaves stalked. . . . **4**
3 Underwater leaves mostly with 7 nerves, at least the lower leaves stalkless **5**

4 Base of floating leaves ± heart-shaped . . . . *P. pulcher* . . . . SPOTTED PONDWEED
4 Base of floating leaves tapered or rounded, not heart-shaped . . . . *P. nodosus* / LONGLEAF PONDWEED

5 Margins of underwater leaves finely toothed near tip . . *P. illinoensis* . . . . ILLINOIS PONDWEED
5 Margins of underwater leaves entire. **6**

6 Plants red-tinged; underwater leaves 5–20 cm long and at least as wide as floating leaves, mostly on main stem . . . . *P. alpinus* . . . . RED PONDWEED
6 Plants green; underwater leaves 3–8 cm long and narrower than floating leaves, often numerous on short branches from leaf axils . . . . *P. gramineus* / VARIABLE PONDWEED

7 Spikes of 1 kind only; fruits not (or only slightly) compressed; stipules not joined with leaf base **8**
7 Spikes of 2 kinds: those in axils of lower underwater leaves on short stalks; those in axils of upper or floating leaves often emersed on long stalks; fruit flattened; stipules of leaves (or at least some of lower leaves) joined with leaf base. **12**

8 Floating leaves less than 1 cm wide and less than 2 cm long *P. vaseyi* . . . . VASEY'S PONDWEED
8 Floating leaves more than 1 cm wide and more than 2 cm long. . . **9**

9 Underwater leaves flat and tapelike, 2–10 mm wide . . . *P. epihydrus* . . . . RIBBONLEAF-PONDWEED
9 Underwater leaves round in cross-section, often reduced to a petiole, mostly less than 1.5 mm wide **10**

10 Blade of floating leaves oval, tapered to base; fruit 3-keeled . . . . *P. nodosus* / LONGLEAF PONDWEED
10 Blade of floating leaves ovate to nearly heart-shaped at base; fruit barely keeled. **11**

11 Floating leaves mostly 3–10 cm long; spikes 3–6 cm long . *P. natans* . . . . FLOATING PONDWEED
11 Floating leaves 2–5 cm long; spikes 1–3 cm long . . . . *P. oakesianus* . . . . OAKES' PONDWEED

12 Underwater leaves blunt-tipped; floating leaves with a small notch at tip . . . . *P. spirillus* / NORTHERN SNAILSEED PONDWEED

12 Underwater leaves tapered to a pointed tip; floating leaves not notched at tip . . . *P. diversifolius* / COMMON SNAILSEED PONDWEED

Potamogeton alpinus Balbis.

Red pondweed   OBL

Aquatic perennial herb; plants red-tinged. **Stems** round in section, unbranched or sometimes branched above, to 1 m long and 1–2 mm wide. **Underwater leaves** linear lance-shaped, 4–20 cm long and 5–15 mm wide, 7–9-veined, usually rounded at tip, narrowed to a stalkless base. **Floating leaves** often absent, if present, thin, obovate, 4–6 cm long and 1–2 cm wide, 7- to many-veined, rounded at tip, tapered to a narrow base; stipules not joined to leaf base, membranous, 1–3 cm long and to 1.5 cm wide. **Flowers** in cylindric spikes, 1–3 cm long, with 5–9 whorls of flowers, on stalks 6–15 cm long and about as thick as stem. **Achene** yellow-brown to olive, flattened, 3 mm long, the beak short. July–Sept. ❦ Shallow to deep (usually cold) water of lakes and streams. ⊕ nc and ne Minn, n and c Wisc, UP and n and c LP of Mich. Circumboreal, from Newf to Alaska, s to Mass, NY, Wisc, Minn, SD, Colo and Calif.

Potamogeton amplifolius Tuckerman

Bigleaf pondweed   OBL

Aquatic perennial herb. **Stems** round in section, usually unbranched, to 1 m or more long and 2–4 mm wide. **Upper underwater leaves** ovate, folded and sickle-shaped, 8–20 cm long and 2–7 cm wide, many-veined; **lower underwater leaves** lance-shaped, to 2 cm wide, often not folded, usually decayed by fruiting time, many-veined; petioles 1–5 cm long. **Floating leaves** usually present at flowering time, ovate 5–10 cm long and 3–6 cm wide, many-veined, rounded at tip or abruptly tapered to a sharp tip, rounded at base; petioles 5–15 cm long; stipules open and free of the petioles, 5–12 cm long, long-tapered to a sharp tip. **Flowers** in dense cylindric spikes, 3–6 cm long in fruit, on stalks 6–20 cm long, widening near tip. **Achene** green-brown to brown, 4–5 mm long, beak to 1 mm long. July–Aug. ❦ Shallow to deep water of lakes and rivers. ⊕ Minn (especially ne), Wisc, Mich, ne Ill and nw Ind. Que to BC, s to Ala, Okla and Calif.

Potamogeton confervoides Reichenb.

Alga pondweed   OBL

⚠
STATUS
Michigan - T
Wisconsin - T

☞ **Alga pondweed** is unique among our pondweeds in its much-branched stems with linear leaves and the flower spike atop an elongate, leafless stalk.

Aquatic perennial herb, from a long rhizome. **Stems** slender, to 8 dm long, branched, the branches forking. **Leaves** many, all underwater, delicate, flat, bright green, 2–5 cm long and about 0.3 mm wide, tapered to a hairlike tip, l-veined; stipules short-lived, 1–5 cm long. **Flowers** in a short spike 5–10 mm long, at end of an erect stalk 5–20 cm long. **Achene** 2–3 mm long, with a sharp keel. June–Aug. ❦ Shallow water of lakes, kettle-hole ponds and peatlands. ⊕ nc Wisc, local in c and e UP of Mich.

Potamogeton crispus L.

Curly pondweed   OBL

Aquatic perennial herb. **Stems** compressed, with few branches, to 8 dm long and 1–2 mm wide. **Leaves** all underwater, oblong, 3–9 cm long and 5–10 mm wide, rounded at tip, slightly clasping at base, stalkless, 3–5-veined, margins wavy-crisped, finely toothed; stipules 4–10 mm long, slightly joined at base, early shredding. **Flowers** in dense cylindric spikes,

1–2 cm long, appearing bristly in fruit from long achene beaks; on stalks 2–6 cm long. **Achene** brown, 2–3 mm long, with a beak 2–3 mm long. April–June. ≋ Shallow to deep water of lakes (including Great Lakes) and rivers; pollution-tolerant. ⊕ se Minn, Wisc, Mich (local in UP), ne Ill and nw Ind. Native of Europe; established across most of N Amer.

Potamogeton diversifolius Raf.

Common snailseed pondweed   OBL

STATUS
Michigan - T
Minnesota - E

Aquatic perennial herb. **Stems** slender, flattened or round in section, branched, to 15 dm long and 1 mm wide. **Underwater leaves** linear, flat, 1–10 cm long and 0.2–1.5 mm wide, 1-veined (sometimes 3-veined), stalkless; stipules 2–18 mm long, joined to leaf blade for less than half their length. **Floating leaves** sometimes absent, oval, leathery, 5–40 mm long and 4–20 mm wide, acute to rounded at tip, rounded at base, 3- to many-veined, the veins sunken on leaf underside; petioles 1–3 cm long; stipules not joined to leaf base, 5–20 mm long. **Flowers** in spikes of 2 types, the **underwater spikes** 3–6 mm long, on stalks 2–10 mm long; **emersed spikes** cylindric, 1–3 cm long, on stalks 5–30 mm long. **Achene** olive to yellow, round and flattened, spiraled on surface, winged, the beak tiny. June–Sept. Includes *P. bicupulatus* and *P. capillaceus*. ≋ Shallow water of ponds. ⊕ Rare in ec Minn, Wisc, rare in wc LP of Mich, uncommon in ne Ill and nw Ind. Conn to Mont and Ore, s to Fla, Tex, Ariz, Calif and Mex.

Potamogeton epihydrus Raf.

Ribbonleaf-pondweed   OBL

STATUS
Indiana - E

Aquatic perennial herb. **Stems** slender, compressed, sparingly branched, to 2 m long and 1–2 mm wide. **Underwater leaves** linear, ribbonlike, 10–20 cm long and 3–8 mm wide, with a translucent strip on each side of midvein forming a band 1–3 mm wide, 5–13-veined, stalkless; stipules 1–3 cm long, not joined to leaf. **Floating leaves** usually present and numerous, opposite, oval to obovate, 3–8 cm long and 1–2 cm wide, mostly obtuse to bluntly abruptly short-awned at the tip, 11–25-veined, tapered to flattened petioles; stipules free, 1–3 cm long. **Flowers** in dense, cylindric spikes 2–3 cm long, on stalks 2–6 cm long and about as thick as stem. **Achene** olive to brown, 2–3 mm long; beak tiny. July–Sept. ≋ Water to 2 m deep in lakes, ponds and rivers. ⊕ ne and c Minn, Wisc, Mich and nw Ind. Newf and Que to Alaska, s to Ga, Mo, SD, Colo, Idaho and Calif.

Potamogeton filiformis Pers.

Threadleaf-pondweed   OBL

Aquatic perennial herb, from a long, tuber-bearing rhizome. **Stems** ± round in section, branched from base, mostly unbranched above, 1–5 dm or more long and 1 mm wide. **Leaves** all underwater, narrowly linear, 5–10 cm long and 0.2–2 mm wide, 1-veined; stipules 1–3 cm long, joined to base of leaf blade, forming a tight sheath around stem. **Flowers** in underwater spikes, 1–5 cm long, with 2–5 separated whorls of flowers, on slender stalks 2–12 cm long. **Achene** olive-green, 2–3 mm long, the beak flat, tiny. July–Aug. ≋ Mostly shallow water (to 1 m) in lakes (including Great Lakes) and rivers. ⊕ Local in n and c Minn, Wisc, Mich. Circumboreal, s to Maine, Pa, Mich, Minn, Neb, Colo, Ariz and Calif.

Potamogeton foliosus Raf.

Leafy pondweed   OBL

Aquatic perennial herb. **Stems** compressed, much-branched, to 8 dm long and 1 mm wide. **Leaves** all underwater, linear, 1–8 cm long and 1–2 mm wide, 1–3-veined, stalkless; stipules free, 0.5–2 cm long, glands usually

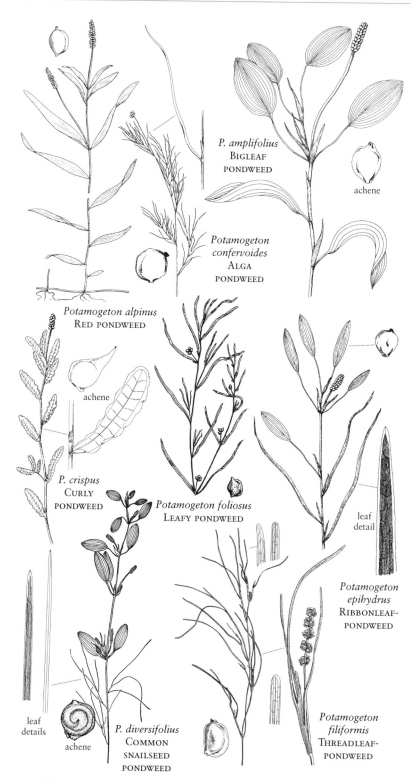

P. amplifolius
BIGLEAF
PONDWEED

achene

Potamogeton
confervoides
ALGA
PONDWEED

Potamogeton alpinus
RED PONDWEED

achene

P. crispus
CURLY
PONDWEED

Potamogeton foliosus
LEAFY PONDWEED

leaf
detail

Potamogeton
epihydrus
RIBBONLEAF-
PONDWEED

leaf
details

achene

P. diversifolius
COMMON
SNAILSEED
PONDWEED

Potamogeton
filiformis
THREADLEAF-
PONDWEED

absent at base of stipules. **Flowers** in rounded to short-cylindric spikes, 2–7 mm long, with 1–2 whorls of flowers, on stalks 5–12 mm long, widened at tip. **Achene** green-brown, 1.5–3 mm long, winged, the beak to 0.5 mm long. June–Aug. ⚘ Shallow to deep water of lakes, ponds, rivers and streams. ⊕ Occasional to common; Minn, Wisc, Mich, ne Ill and nw Ind. Newf to BC, s throughout most of USA, Mex and c Amer.

Potamogeton friesii Rupr.
Fries' pondweed   OBL

⚠
STATUS
Indiana - E

Aquatic perennial herb. **Stems** compressed, branched, 1–1.5 m long and to 1 mm wide. **Leaves** all underwater, linear, 3–7 cm long and 1.5–3 mm wide, tip rounded with a short slender point, tapered to the base, 5–7-veined, stalkless, margins flat or becoming rolled under; stipules free, 5–20 mm long, fibrous, often shredding above, 2 glands present at base of stipule. **Flowers** in cylindric spikes, 8–16 mm long, with 2–5 whorls of flowers, on stalks 1.5–6 cm long. **Achene** olive-green to brown, 2–3 mm long, beak flat, short. June–Aug. ⚘ Shallow to deep water of lakes, ponds, rivers and streams. ⊕ Minn, Wisc, Mich (but local in w UP), local in ne Ill and nw Ind. Newf to Alaska, s to Pa, n Ind, Iowa, Neb and Utah.

Potamogeton gramineus L.
Variable pondweed   OBL

⚠
STATUS
Illinois - T

Aquatic perennial herb. **Stems** slender, slightly compressed, much-branched, to 8 dm long and 1 mm wide. **Underwater leaves** variable, linear to lance-shaped or oblong lance-shaped, 3–9 cm long and 3–12 mm wide, 3–7-veined, tapered to a stalkless base. **Floating leaves** usually present, oval, 2–6 cm long and 1–3 cm wide, 11–19-veined, rounded at base; petioles 2–10 cm long, shorter to longer than blade; stipules free, persistent, 1–4 cm long. **Flowers** in dense, cylindric spikes, 1.5–4 cm long, the stalks thicker than stem, 2–10 cm long. **Achene** dull green, 2–3 mm long. June–Aug. ⚘ Shallow to deep water of streams, ponds and lakes (including Great Lakes). ⊕ Minn (all but far s), Wisc, Mich, occasional in ne Ill and nw Ind. Circumboreal, s to NY, Iowa, Neb and Calif.

Potamogeton hillii Morong
Hill's pondweed   OBL

⚠
STATUS
Michigan - T

Aquatic perennial herb, rhizomes ± absent. **Stems** slender, slightly compressed, much-branched, to 1 m long. **Leaves** all underwater, linear, 3–7 cm long and 1–2 mm wide, 3-veined, the lateral veins nearer margins than midvein; stipules white or cream-colored, free, 1–2 cm long, becoming fibrous. **Flowers** in rounded spikes, 4–8 mm long, with 1 (sometimes 2) whorls of flowers, on stalks 5–15 mm long. **Achene** flattened, 2–4 mm long, the beak 0.5 mm long. ⚘ Shallow water of ponds and streams, often where calcium-rich. ⊕ Rare and local in n LP of Mich. New Eng and Pa to Ont, Mich and Ohio.

Potamogeton illinoensis Morong
Illinois pondweed   OBL

Aquatic perennial herb. **Stems** nearly round in section, usually branched, to 2 m long and 2–5 mm wide. **Underwater leaves** lance-shaped to obovate, 6–20 cm long, 2–4 cm wide, 9–17-veined, tapered to a broad, flat petiole, 2–4 cm long; stipules free, persistent, 3–8 cm long. **Floating leaves** sometimes absent, opposite, lance-shaped to oval, 5–14 cm long and 2–6 cm wide, 13- to many-veined, often short-awned from the rounded tip, rounded to wedge-shaped at base; petioles 3–10 cm long, shorter than blades. **Flowers** in dense cylindric spikes, 2–6 cm long, on stalks 4–20 cm long, usually wider than stem. **Achene** olive-green, 3–4 mm long, the beak short, blunt. July–Sept. *P. angustifolius.* ⚘ Shallow to deep water of lakes and rivers. ⊕ c Minn, Wisc, Mich, occasional in ne Ill and nw Ind. NS to Ont and BC, s to Fla, Kans, Calif and into Mex.

Potamogeton natans L.
Floating pondweed OBL

Aquatic perennial herb. **Stems** slightly compressed, usually unbranched, 0.5–2 m long and 1–2 mm wide. **Underwater leaves** reduced to linear, bladeless, expanded petioles (phyllodes), these often absent by flowering time, 10–30 cm long and 1–2 mm wide. **Floating leaves** ovate to oval, 4–10 cm long and 2–5 cm wide, usually tipped with a short point, rounded to heart-shaped at base, many-veined; petioles usually much longer than blades, the blade often angled at juncture with petiole; stipules free, 4–10 cm long, persistent or shredding with age. **Flowers** in dense cylindric spikes, 2–5 cm long, stalks thicker than the stem, 6–14 cm long. **Achene** green-brown to brown, 3–5 mm long, with a loose, shiny covering, the beak short. June–Aug. ❀ Usually shallow water (to 2 m deep) of ponds, lakes, rivers and peatlands. ⊕ n and c Minn, Wisc, Mich, ne Ill and nw Ind. Circumboreal, s to Pa, Ind, Iowa, n Kans, NM, Ariz and Calif.

Potamogeton nodosus Poiret
Longleaf pondweed OBL

Aquatic perennial herb. **Stems** round in section, branched, to 2 m long and 1–2 mm wide. **Underwater leaves** commonly decayed by fruiting time, lance-shaped to linear, translucent, 10–30 cm long and 1–3 cm wide, 7–15-veined, gradually tapered to a petiole 4–10 cm long. **Floating leaves** oval, thin, 5–12 cm long and 1–5 cm wide, tapered at both ends, many-veined; petioles somewhat winged, 5–20 cm long and 2–3 mm wide, usually longer than blades; stipules free, those of underwater leaves often absent by flowering time, those of floating leaves persistent, 3–10 cm long. **Flowers** in dense cylindric spikes, 2–6 cm long, on stalks 3–15 cm long and thicker than stem. **Achene** red-brown to brown, 3–4 mm long, the beak short. July–Aug. ❀ Shallow water to 2 m deep, mostly in rivers; lakes. ⊕ Occasional to common; Minn (all but nw), Wisc, mostly c and s LP of Mich, ne Ill and nw Ind. Cosmopolitan.

Potamogeton oakesianus J. W. Robbins
Oakes' pondweed OBL

⚠
STATUS
Indiana - E
☞ Similar to
**floating
pondweed**
(*P. natans*) but
plants smaller
and the fruit
± smooth on
the sides (vs.
depressed in *P.
natans*).

Aquatic perennial herb. **Stems** slender, often much-branched, to 1 m long. **Underwater leaves** bladeless, petiolelike, 0.5–1 mm wide, often persistent. **Floating leaves** oval, 3–6 cm long and 1–2 cm wide, rounded at base, 12- to many-veined; petioles 5–15 cm long; stipules free, 2.5–4 cm long. **Flowers** in cylindric spikes, 1.5–3 cm long, on stalks 3–8 cm long and wider than stem. **Achene** 2–4 mm long, with a tight, dull covering, the beak flat. ❀ Ponds and streams, peatland pools. ⊕ n and c Wisc; Mich UP, local in w LP; Ind. Nfld and Que to Wisc, s to Pa and NJ.

Potamogeton obtusifolius Mert. & Koch
Bluntleaf-pondweed OBL

Aquatic perennial herb, rhizomes ± absent. **Stems** very slender, compressed, much-branched, to 1 m long. **Leaves** all underwater, linear, stalkless, often red-tinged, 3–10 cm long and 1–4 mm wide, rounded at tip, the midvein broad, base usually with pair of translucent glands; stipules free, white, 1–2 cm long. **Flowers** in thick cylindric spikes, 8–14 mm long, on slender, upright stalks 1–3 cm long. **Achene** 2–3 mm long, the beak rounded, 0.5 mm long ❀ Lakes, ponds and streams, peatland pools. ⊕ Local in n and c Minn, n and c Wisc, UP and n LP of Mich. Que and NS to BC, s to NJ, n Great Lakes and Wyo.

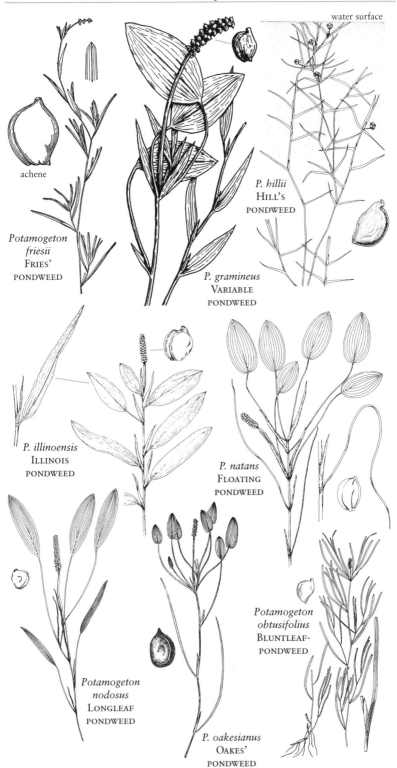

water surface

achene

Potamogeton friesii FRIES' PONDWEED

P. gramineus VARIABLE PONDWEED

P. hillii HILL'S PONDWEED

P. illinoensis ILLINOIS PONDWEED

P. natans FLOATING PONDWEED

Potamogeton nodosus LONGLEAF PONDWEED

P. oakesianus OAKES' PONDWEED

Potamogeton obtusifolius BLUNTLEAF-PONDWEED

Potamogeton pectinatus L.

Sago-pondweed OBL

Aquatic perennial herb, the rhizomes tipped with a white tuber. **Stems** slender, round in section, 3–10 dm long and 1–2 mm wide much-branched and forking above, fewer branched near base. **Leaves** all underwater, threadlike to narrowly linear, 3–12 cm long and 0.5–1.5 mm wide, stalkless; stipules joined to base of blade for 1–3 cm, forming a sheath around stem. **Flowers** on underwater, cylindric spikes 1–5 cm long, with 2–5 whorls of flowers, on lax, threadlike stalks to 15 cm long. **Achene** yellow-brown, 3–4 mm long, the beak to 0.5 mm long; the large fruits an important waterfowl food. June–Sept. ⚘ Shallow to deep water of lakes, ponds and streams; tolerant of brackish water. ⊕ Common; Minn, Wisc, Mich, ne Ill and nw Ind. Nearly worldwide.

Potamogeton perfoliatus L.

Redhead-grass; Clasping-leaved pondweed OBL

Aquatic perennial herb. **Stems** slender, to 2.5 m long, often much-branched. **Leaves** all underwater, ovate to nearly round or sometimes lance-shaped, 1–7 cm long and 5–30 mm wide, tip often very finely toothed, base heart-shaped and clasping stem, stalkless; stipules free, soon decaying. **Flowers** on underwater cylindric spikes, 1–5 cm long, on upright stalks 1–7 cm long and about as wide as stem. **Achene** 2–3 mm long, the beak short, curved. ⚘ Lakes and streams. ⊕ Uncommon in c UP and c and s LP of Mich.

Potamogeton praelongus Wulfen

Whitestem-pondweed OBL

⚠

STATUS
Illinois - E
Indiana - E

Aquatic perennial herb. **Stems** white-tinged, compressed, branched, to 2–3 m long and 2–4 mm wide, the shorter internodes often zigzagged. **Leaves** all underwater, lance-shaped, 10–30 cm long and 1–4 cm wide, with 3–5 main veins, rounded and hoodlike at tip, base ± heart-shaped and clasping stem, stalkless, margins entire and gently wavy; stipules free, white, 1–3 cm long, fibrous at tip. **Flowers** in dense, cylindric spikes 2–5 cm long; stalks erect, 1–4 dm long, as wide as stems. June–Aug. ⚘ Shallow to deep water of lakes (including Great Lakes), streams. ⊕ Minn (all but far w), Wisc, Mich, rare in ne Ill and nw Ind. Circumboreal, s to Conn, NY, Ind, Minn, Neb, Colo, Utah and Calif.

Potamogeton pulcher Tuckerman

Spotted pondweed OBL

⚠

STATUS
Illinois - E
Indiana - E
Michigan - T
Wisconsin - E

Aquatic perennial herb. **Stems** round in section, unbranched, black-spotted, usually less than 5 dm long. **Underwater leaves** thin, narrowly lance-shaped, 8–15 cm long and 1–3 cm wide, base tapered to a short petiole, margins wavy; the lowest leaves often thick and spatula-shaped. **Floating leaves** alternate, clustered at top of stem on short branches, ovate, 4–8 cm long and 2–5 cm wide, many-veined, the base somewhat heart-shaped; petioles black-spotted, 2–8 cm long; stipules free, to 6 cm long. **Flowers** in dense cylindric spikes, 2–4 cm long, on stalks 5–10 cm long and slightly wider than stem. **Achene** 4–5 mm long, the beak broad and blunt. ⚘ Muddy shores and shallow water of lakes. ⊕ Rare in n and c Wisc, Mich (known only from several locations in n and s LP), ne Ill and nw Ind.

Potamogeton pusillus L.

Slender or Small pondweed OBL

Aquatic perennial herb, rhizomes ± absent. **Stems** very slender, round in section, usually freely branched, 2–10 dm long and about 0.5 mm wide. **Leaves** all underwater, linear, 1–7 cm long and 0.5–2 mm wide, tapered to a stalkless base, the midvein broad; stipules free, boat-shaped, brown-green, 4–10 mm long and 2x width of leaf base, soon decaying, glands sometimes present at stipule base. **Flowers** in short-cylindric spikes 2–10 mm long, the flowers in 1–3 whorls, on slender, upright stalks 1–5 cm long. **Achene** green to brown, 1–2 mm long, the beak flat. June–Aug. ❦ Shallow water (to 2 m deep) of lakes and ponds, occasionally in streams. ⊕ Minn, Wisc, w UP and c and s LP of Mich, ne Ill and nw Ind. Newf to NW Terr, s throughout most of USA and into Mex; Eurasia.

Potamogeton richardsonii (Ar. Benn.) Rydb.
Clasping-leaved pondweed   OBL

Aquatic perennial herb. **Stems** brown to yellow-green, round in section, sparingly to freely branched, mostly 3–10 dm long and 1–2.5 mm wide, the shorter internodes rarely zigzagged. **Leaves** all underwater, lance-shaped, 5–12 cm long and 1–2.5 cm wide, with 13 or more prominent veins, base heart-shaped and clasping stem, stalkless, margins entire and gently wavy; stipules free, 1–2 cm long, soon shredding into white fibers. **Flowers** in dense cylindric spikes 1.5–4 cm long, on stalks 2–20 cm long, the stalks strongly curved when in fruit. **Achene** green to brown, 2–4 mm long, the beak short. July–Aug. ❦ Shallow to deep water of lakes (including Great Lakes), streams. ⊕ Occasional to common; Minn, Wisc, Mich, ne Ill and nw Ind. Labr to Alaska, s to Pa, Ind, Iowa, Neb, Colo, Utah and Calif.

Potamogeton robbinsii Oakes
Fern-pondweed   OBL

Aquatic perennial herb, rhizomes not tuberous. **Stems** few-branched below, much-branched above, to 1 m long. **Leaves** all underwater, crowded in 2 ranks, linear, 4–10 cm long and 3–7 mm wide, tapered to a pointed tip, abruptly narrowed at base, with rounded auricles where joined with stipule, midvein pronounced, margins pale; stipules joined to leaf for 5–15 mm, soon decaying into fibers. **Flowers** on underwater, cylindric spikes 1–2 cm long, with 3–5 separated whorls of flowers, the inflorescence often branched into 5–20 stalks, 2–5 cm long, at ends of stems. **Achenes** rarely produced, 3–5 mm long, the beak thick, somewhat curved; reproduction most commonly by stem fragments which root from the nodes. July–Aug. ❦ Shallow to deep water of lakes, ponds and streams. ⊕ n and ec Minn, Wisc, Mich, rare and local in ne Ill and nw Ind.

Potamogeton spirillus Tuckerman
Northern snailseed pondweed   OBL

Aquatic perennial herb. **Stems** compressed, to 1 m long, branched, the branches short and often curved. **Underwater leaves** 1–8 cm long and 0.5–2 mm wide, rounded at tip, stalkless; stipules joined for most of length. **Floating leaves**, if present, 1–4 cm long and 5–12 mm wide, 5–13-veined, the veins sunken on underside of blade, petioles 2–4 cm long; stipules free. **Flowers** in 2 types of spikes, the underwater spikes round, with 1–8 fruits, ± stalkless in the leaf axils; emersed spikes longer, cylindric, to 8–12 mm long, on stalks from leaf axils. **Achene** 1–3 mm long, flattened, winged, spiraled on surface, the beak absent. ❦ Shallow water of lakes and ponds. ⊕ Minn (mostly ne), Wisc, local in UP and n LP of Mich. Nfld and Que to sw Ont, s to Va and Mich.

Potamogeton strictifolius Ar. Bennett
Straight-leaved pondweed   OBL

Aquatic perennial herb. **Stems** slender, slightly compressed, unbranched or branched above, to 1 m long and 0.5 mm wide. **Leaves** all underwa-

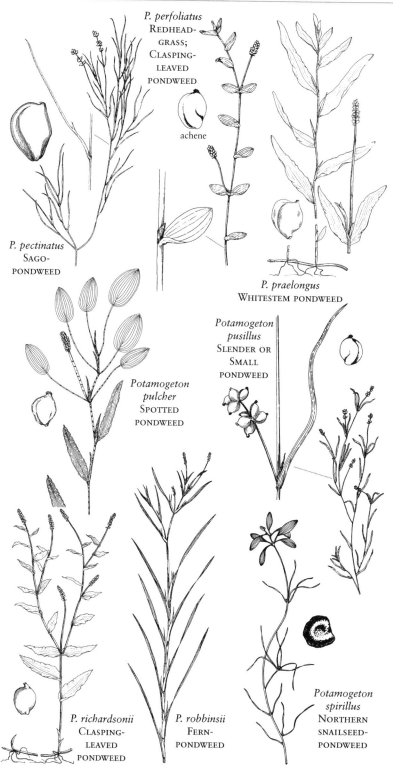

P. perfoliatus
REDHEAD-
GRASS;
CLASPING-
LEAVED
PONDWEED

achene

P. pectinatus
SAGO-
PONDWEED

P. praelongus
WHITESTEM PONDWEED

Potamogeton pulcher
SPOTTED
PONDWEED

Potamogeton pusillus
SLENDER OR
SMALL
PONDWEED

P. richardsonii
CLASPING-
LEAVED
PONDWEED

P. robbinsii
FERN-
PONDWEED

Potamogeton spirillus
NORTHERN
SNAILSEED-
PONDWEED

590 MONOCOTS **Pondweed Family**

ter, linear, upright, 1–6 cm long and 0.5–2 mm wide, 3–5-veined, the veins prominent on underside, tapered to stalkless base, margins often rolled under; stipules free, white, shredding at tip, 5–20 mm long; 2 glands present at base of stipules. **Flowers** in cylindric spikes 6–15 mm long, with 3–5 whorls of flowers, on stalks 1–5 cm long. **Fruit** green-brown, 2 mm long, the beak broad, rounded. June–Aug. ⚘ Shallow to deep water of lakes and rivers. ⊕ Minn, Wisc, Mich, local in ne Ill and nw Ind. Newf and Que to Alberta and NW Terr, s to NY, Ohio, n Ind, Minn, n Neb, Wyo and n Utah.

Potamogeton vaginatus Turcz.
Bigsheath-pondweed OBL

⚠
STATUS
Wisconsin - T

Aquatic perennial herb, rhizomes tipped by a tuber 3–5 cm long. **Stems** round in section, much-branched above, to 1.5 m long and 1–2 mm wide. **Leaves** all underwater, crowded in 2 ranks, threadlike to narrowly linear, 2–20 cm long and 0.5–2 mm wide, with 1 main vein; stipules joined to base of leaf for 1–5 cm and sheathing stem, the sheaths on main stem inflated 2–4x wider than the stem. **Flowers** in spikes 3–6 cm long, with 5–12 spaced whorls of flowers, on lax, slender stalks to 10 cm long, the stalks often much shorter than upper leaves. **Fruit** dark green, 3 mm long, the beak short or nearly absent. July–Aug. *P. interruptus.* ⚘ Cold-water streams and lakes. ⊕ Uncommon in ne and c Minn, sc Wisc, local in e UP and n LP of Mich. Newf to Alaska, s to NY, Wisc, Minn, SD, Wyo and Ore; also Eurasia and Africa.

Potamogeton vaseyi Robbins
Vasey's pondweed OBL

⚠
STATUS
Illinois - E
Indiana - E
Michigan - T

Aquatic perennial herb. **Stems** threadlike, 2–10 dm long, much-branched, the upper branches short. **Underwater leaves** transparent, linear, 2–6 cm long and to 1 mm wide, tapered to a sharp tip, 1-veined or rarely with 2 weak lateral nerves, stalkless; stipules free, linear, white, 1–2 cm long, sometimes with 2 glands at base. **Floating leaves** on flowering plants only, opposite, obovate, leathery, 8–15 mm long and 4–7 mm wide, 5–9-veined, the veins sunken on underside, petiole about as long as blade. **Flowers** in cylindric spikes 3–8 mm long, with 1–4 whorls of flowers, on stems 1–3 cm long. **Fruit** 2–3 mm long, the beak short. *P. lateralis.* ⚘ Shallow to deep water of ponds. ⊕ Local in ne Minn along US-Canada border, Wisc, uncommon in s LP of Mich and ne Ill. NB and Que to n Minn, s to Pa, Ind and Ill.

Potamogeton zosteriformis Fernald
Flatstem-pondweed OBL

Aquatic perennial herb, rhizomes ± absent. **Stems** strongly flattened, sometimes winged, freely branched, to 1 m long and 1–3 mm wide. **Leaves** all underwater, linear, 5–20 cm long and 3–5 mm wide, 15- to many-veined, tapered to a tip, or sometimes with a short, sharp point, slightly narrowed to the stalkless base; stipules free, white, shredding with age, 1–4 cm long. **Flowers** in cylindric spikes, 1–2.5 cm long, with 7–11 whorls of flowers, on curved stalks 2–6 cm long. **Fruit** dark green to brown, 4–5 mm long, the beak short and blunt. July–Aug. ⚘ Shallow to deep water of lakes (including Great Lakes) and streams. ⊕ Minn, Wisc, Mich, ne Ill and nw Ind. Que and NB to BC, s to Va, Ind, Iowa, Neb, Mont, Idaho and n Calif.

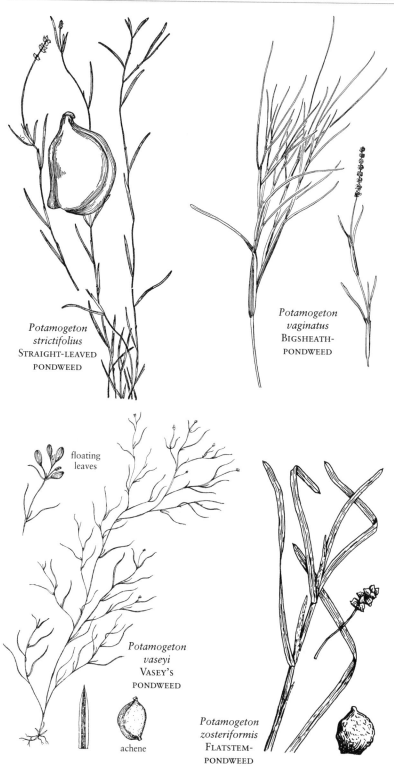

Potamogeton strictifolius STRAIGHT-LEAVED PONDWEED

Potamogeton vaginatus BIGSHEATH-PONDWEED

floating leaves

Potamogeton vaseyi VASEY'S PONDWEED

achene

Potamogeton zosteriformis FLATSTEM-PONDWEED

Ruppiaceae
Ditch-Grass Family

▶**Ruppia** L. / Ditch-grass; Widgeon-grass

Ruppia maritima L.
Ditch-grass; Widgeon-grass   OBL

Aquatic perennial herb. **Stems** slender, round in section, white-tinged, wavy, to 6 dm long, branching at base and with short branches above, the internodes often zigzagged. **Leaves** simple, alternate or opposite, stalkless, threadlike, mostly 5–25 cm long and 0.5 mm wide, 1-veined, with a sheathing stipule at base. **Flowers** very small, perfect, in small, 2-flowered spikes from leaf axils, the spikes enclosed by the leaf sheath at flowering time, the flower stalks elongating and usually coiling as fruits mature; sepals and petals absent; stamens 2; pistils typically 4 (varying from 2–8), raised on a slender stalk in fruit and becoming umbel-like. **Fruit** an olive-green to black, ovate drupelet, 2–3 mm long. July–Aug. 🌱 Lakes and ponds, often where brackish. ⊕ Uncommon in wc Minn and se Wisc, in Mich known only from Mackinac County in e UP, rare in ne Ill. Coastal marshes from N Amer to S Amer and Eurasia, inland throughout s Can and much of USA.

Ruppia maritima
Ditch-grass;
Widgeon-grass

Scheuchzeriaceae
Scheuchzeria Family

▶**Scheuchzeria** L. / Pod-grass

Scheuchzeria palustris L.
Pod-grass   OBL

Perennial rushlike herb, from creeping rhizomes. **Stems** 1 to several, 1–4 dm long, remains of old leaves often persistent at base of plant. **Leaves** alternate, several from base and 1–3 along stem, 1–3 dm long and 1–3 mm wide, the stem leaves smaller; lower part of blade half-round in section, with an expanded sheath at base, upper portion of blade flat, with a small pore at leaf tip. **Flowers** perfect, regular, green-white, in a several-flowered raceme 3–10 cm long, the flowers on stalks 1–2.5 cm long; tepals 6, in 2 series, ovate, 2–3 mm long; stamens 6. **Fruit** a group of 3 (rarely to 6) spreading follicles, 5–10 mm long, each with 1–2 seeds; seeds brown-black, 4–5 mm long. May–June. ⚘ Wet, sphagnum moss peatlands. ⊕ n and c Minn, occasional in n and e Wisc, Mich, rare in ne Ill and nw Ind. Circumboreal, s to NJ, Ind, Iowa, ND, Idaho, and n Calif.

Scheuchzeria palustris
POD-GRASS

Sparganiaceae
Bur-Reed Family

▶**Sparganium** L. / Bur-reed

Perennial sedgelike herbs, floating or emergent in shallow water, from rhizomes and forming colonies. **Stems** stout, usually erect, unbranched, round in section. **Leaves** long, broadly linear, sheathing stem at base. **Flowers** crowded in round heads, the heads with either male or female flowers; male heads few to many, borne above female heads in a unbranched or sparsely branched inflorescence; the female heads 1 to several, from leaf axils or borne above axils on upper stem; sepals and petals reduced to chaffy, spatula-shaped scales, these appressed to the achenes in the mature female heads; male flowers with mostly 3–5 stamens; female flowers with a 1–2-chambered pistil, stigmas 1 or 2. **Fruit** a beaked, nutletlike achene, stalkless or short-stalked.

▶**KEY TO SPARGANIUM**

1 Plants large, about 1 m tall; leaves usually erect; stigmas 2; achenes broadly oblong pyramid-shaped . . . . *S. eurycarpum*
. . . . COMMON OR GIANT BUR-REED
1 Plants smaller, leaves erect or floating; stigmas 1; achenes slender . **2**

2 Fruiting heads about 1 cm wide; male head 1 (often absent by fruiting time); achene beaks less than 1 mm long . . . . *S. minimum*
. . . . SMALL BUR-REED
2 Fruiting heads 1.5 cm or more wide; male heads 2 or more; achene beaks 2 mm or more long **3**

3 Fruiting heads 1.5–2 cm wide; leaves mostly flat. **4**
3 Fruiting heads larger mostly 2–3 cm wide; leaves often keeled. . . . **5**

4 Male heads several, separate from the female heads; achene not shiny
. . . . *S. fluctuans* / FLOATING BUR-REED
4 Male heads usually 1 (sometimes 2) and near upper female head; a-chene shiny . . . . *S. glomeratum* / CLUSTERED BUR-REED

5 Fruiting heads or branches all from leaf axils **6**
5 At least some fruiting heads or branches borne above leaf axils . . **7**

6 Inflorescence unbranched or the branches short and sometimes with 1–2 male heads; achenes dull, with a beak 3–4 mm long. . . . .
. . . . *S. americanum* / AMERICAN BUR-REED
6 Inflorescence branched, the branches jointed, with 3 or more male heads; achenes shiny, with a beak 5–7 mm long . . . *S. androcladum*
. . . . BRANCHED BUR-REED

7 Leaves floating; achene beak 1–3 mm long. . . . . . . *S. angustifolium*
. . . . NARROW-LEAVED BUR-REED
7 Leaves usually stiffly erect and emersed; achene beak 3–5 mm long.
. . . . *S. chlorocarpum* / DWARF BUR-REED

Sparganium americanum Nutt.

American bur-reed OBL

Perennial herb. **Stems** stout, erect, mostly unbranched, 3–10 dm long. **Leaves** linear, flat to somewhat keeled, to 1 m long and 4–12 mm wide; leaflike bracts on upper stem shorter than leaves, widened at base. **Inflorescence** usually unbranched, or with a few, straight branches; **female heads** stalkless, 2–4 on main stem, sometimes with 1–3 on branches, 2 cm wide when mature; scales widest at tip; **male heads** 3–10 on main stem, sometimes with 1–5 on branches. **Achenes** widest at middle, tapered to both ends, dull brown, 3–5 mm long, the beak straight, 2–4 mm long. July–Aug. ❀ Marshes, shallow water, streambanks. ⊕ ne and c Minn, Wisc, Mich, local in ne Ill and nw Ind. Nfld and Que to Minn, s to Fla and La.

Sparganium androcladum (Engelm.) Morong

Branched bur-reed OBL

Perennial herb. **Stems** stout, erect, branched, 4–10 dm long. **Leaves** linear, keeled, triangular in section near base, 4–8 dm long and 5–12 mm wide; bracts leaflike, upright, shorter than leaves, slightly widened at base. **Inflorescence** often branched, the branches zigzagged; **female heads** stalkless, 2–4 on main stem, absent or occasionally 1 near base of branches, 3 cm wide when mature; scales spatula-shaped, widest at tip; **male heads** 5–8 on main stem, 3 or more on branches. **Achenes** oval, shiny light brown, 5–7 mm long, often slightly narrowed at middle, the beak straight, 4–6 mm long. July–Aug. *S. lucidum.* ❀ Marshes, lakeshores, fens. ⊕ ne Minn, Wisc, uncommon in LP of Mich, ne Ill and nw Ind. Que s to Va, and Ohio to Ill, Wisc, Minn and Mo.

Sparganium angustifolium Michx.

Narrow-leaved bur-reed OBL

Perennial herb. **Stems** long and usually floating. **Leaves** floating, mostly 2–3 mm wide, often wider at base. **Inflorescence** unbranched; **female heads** 1–3, shiny, about 2 cm wide, the lowest stalked, the upper female heads stalkless; scales spatula-shaped, ragged at tip; **male heads** 2–6, close together above female heads. **Achenes** spindle-shaped, 5–7 mm long, dull brown except at red-brown base, abruptly contracted to a beak 1–3 mm long. July–Aug. *S. emersum.* ❀ Lakes, ponds and shores. ⊕ n Minn, n Wisc, UP and n and c LP of Mich. Nfld to Alaska, s to NJ, Mich, Minn and Calif.

Sparganium chlorocarpum Rydb.

Dwarf bur-reed OBL

Perennial herb. **Stems** usually erect, sometimes lax and trailing in water, 2–6 dm long. **Leaves** linear, yellow-green, flat to keeled, 3–7 dm long and 3–6 mm wide, usually longer than stems; bracts leaflike, erect, barely widened at base. **Inflorescence** unbranched, 1–2 dm long; **female heads** 1–4, stalkless or lowest head often stalked, at least 1 head on stem above leaf axils, 1.5–2.5 cm wide when mature; scales spatula-shaped, widest at tip; **male heads** usually 2–5, 1.5–2 cm wide at flowering time. **Achenes** widest at middle, tapered to both ends, 4–5 mm long, shiny olive-green, the beak 3–5 mm long. June–Aug. ❀ Shallow water or mud of marshes, streams, ditches, open bogs, ponds. ⊕ n and e Minn, Wisc, Mich, ne Ill and nw Ind. Newf and Que to n Idaho, s to WVa, Ind, Iowa, SD and Mont.

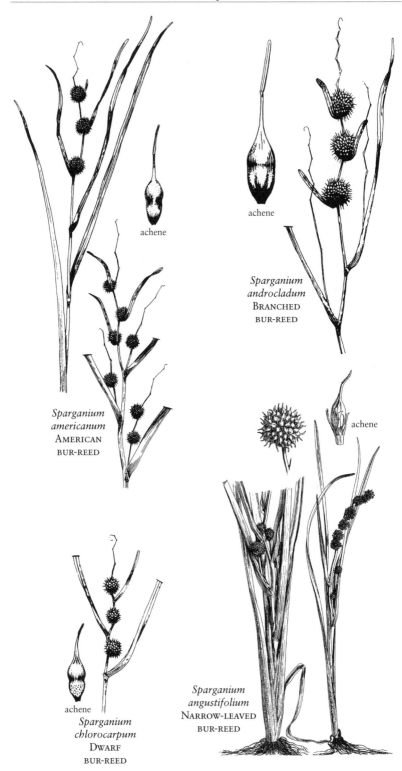

achene

achene

Sparganium androcladum
BRANCHED
BUR-REED

Sparganium americanum
AMERICAN
BUR-REED

achene

Sparganium chlorocarpum
DWARF
BUR-REED

achene

Sparganium angustifolium
NARROW-LEAVED
BUR-REED

Sparganium eurycarpum Engelm.
Common or Giant bur-reed
OBL

Perennial herb. **Stems** stout, branched, 4–10 dm long. **Leaves** linear, bright green, keeled, 8–10 dm long and 5–12 mm wide; bracts leaflike, slightly widened at base. **Inflorescence** 1–3 dm long, branched from the bract axils; lower branches with 1 female head and several male heads, main stem and upper branches with 6–10 male heads; **female heads** 2–6, 1.5–2.5 cm wide in fruit, scales spatula-shaped; **male heads** numerous, 1–2 cm wide. **Achenes** oblong pyramid-shaped, 6–8 mm long, the top flattened, 4–7 mm wide, brown to golden-brown, the beak 2–4 mm long. June–Aug. ⚘ Usually in shallow water of marshes, streams, ditches, ponds and lakes, often with **cat-tails** (*Typha*). ⊕ Minn, Wisc, Mich, ne Ill and nw Ind. Newf to BC, s to NJ, Ohio, Ind, Mo, Okla, Ariz and Calif.

Sparganium fluctuans (Morong) Robinson
Floating bur-reed
OBL

Perennial herb. **Stems** slender, floating, to 15 dm long. **Leaves** floating, linear, flat, translucent, 3–10 mm wide, underside with netlike veins; bracts leaflike, short, widened at base. **Inflorescence** usually branched, the main stem with 2–4 male heads, the branches with 1 female head near base and 2–3 male heads above; **female heads** 2–4, 1.5–2 cm wide when mature, scales oblong; **male heads** to 1 cm wide. **Achenes** obovate, 3–4 mm long, sometimes narrowed near middle, brown, the beak curved, 2–3 mm long. ⚘ In shallow water of ponds and lakes. ⊕ ne and nc Minn, n Wisc, UP of Mich. Nfld and Que to Wisc and Minn, s to Conn, Pa and Mich.

Sparganium glomeratum Laest.
Clustered bur-reed
OBL

Perennial herb. **Stems** stout, floating or erect, 2–4 dm long. **Leaves** linear, ± flat, 3–8 mm wide; bracts leaflike, widened at base. **Inflorescence** usually unbranched; **female heads** several, clustered on the stem, stalkless, 1.5–2 cm wide when mature, scales narrowly oblong; **male heads** 1–2 above the female heads and continuous with them on stem. **Achenes** widest at middle, tapered to both ends, 3–8 mm long, slightly narrowed below the middle, shiny brown, the beak ± straight, 1–2 mm long. ⚘ Shallow water of marshes and bogs. ⊕ Uncommon in ne Minn. In N Amer, ne Minn and Que; n Europe.

Sparganium minimum (Hartman) Fries
Small bur-reed
OBL

Perennial herb. **Stems** usually long and floating, sometimes shorter and upright, 1–3 dm or more long. **Leaves** linear, dark green, thin, flat, 2–6 mm wide; bracts leaflike, short, somewhat widened at base. **Inflorescence** unbranched; **female heads** 2–3, from bract axils, stalkless or the lowest sometimes short-stalked, 1 cm wide when mature; scales spatula-shaped, widest at tip; **male heads** usually 1 (rarely 2). **Achenes** broadly oval, 3–4 mm long, dull green-brown, the beak 1–2 mm long. ⚘ Shallow water, pond margins. ⊕ nc and ne Minn, n and c Wisc, Mich. Circumboreal, s to NJ, Pa, Mich and NM.

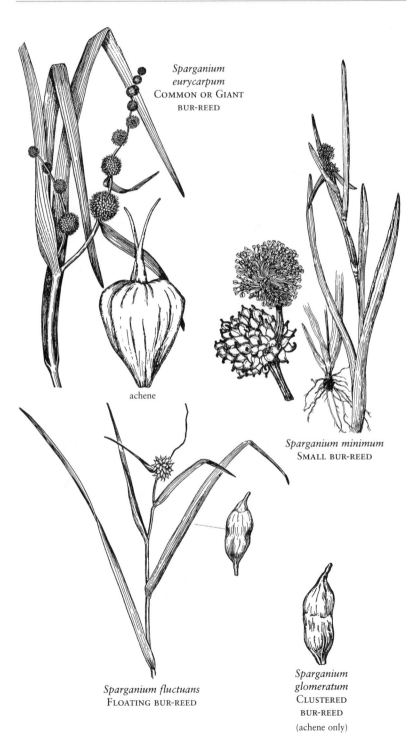

Sparganium eurycarpum
COMMON OR GIANT
BUR-REED

achene

Sparganium minimum
SMALL BUR-REED

Sparganium fluctuans
FLOATING BUR-REED

Sparganium glomeratum
CLUSTERED
BUR-REED
(achene only)

Typhaceae
Cat-tail Family

▶Typha L. / Cat-tail-tail

Large reedlike perennials, from fleshy rhizomes and forming colonies. **Stems** erect, unbranched, round in section, sheathed for most of length by overlapping leaf sheaths. **Leaves** mostly near base of plant, alternate in 2 ranks, erect, linear, spongy. **Flowers** tiny, either male or female, separate on same plant; petals and sepals reduced to bristles. **Male flowers** usually of 3–5 stamens, bristles absent or 1–3 or more. **Female flowers** intermixed with some sterile flowers; pistil 1, raised on a short stalk (gynophore), with numerous bristles near base, the bristles longer than pistil; small bracts (bractlets) also sometimes present, these intermixed with the bristles, slender but with a widened brown tip. **Heads** in a single, dense, cylindric spike, with male flowers above female, the male and female portions of the spike unlike, contiguous in **common cat-tail** (*T. latifolia*) or separated in **narrow-leaved cat-tail** (*T. angustifolia*); the mature spike brown and fuzzy in appearance due to the crowded stigmas and gynophore bristles. **Fruit** a yellow-brown achene, 1–2 mm long, the style persistent, long and slender with an expanded stigma.

☞ A hybrid between *T. angustifolia* and *T. latifolia* is termed *Typha* x *glauca* Godr. Usually larger than either parent, male and female portions of hybrid plants are usually separated by a space to 4 cm long. The male portion of the spike is light brown, 0.5–2 dm long and about 1 cm wide at flowering time; the female portion is dark brown, 10–20 cm long and 1–2 cm wide. Since *Typha* x *glauca* is sterile, reproduction is vegetative from rhizomes. The hybrid occurs in Gt Lakes region in s Wisc, LP of Mich (especially common in Lake Erie marshes of se Mich), ne Ill and nw Ind, and may be found wherever populations of *T. angustifolia* and *T. latifolia* overlap.

▶KEY TO TYPHA

1 Male and female portions of spike usually separated; leaves to 1 cm wide; stigmas long and slender, pale brown . . . . *T. angustifolia* . . . . NARROW-LEAVED CAT-TAIL
1 Male and female portions of spike usually contiguous, not separated; leaves mostly 1–2 mm wide; stigmas broad and flattened, dark brown . . . . *T. latifolia* / COMMON CAT-TAIL

Typha angustifolia L.
Narrow-leaved cat-tail   OBL

Perennial emergent herb. **Stems** erect, 1–2 m long. **Leaves** upright, flat, 4–10 mm wide. **Flowers** either male or female, on separate portions of the spike, separated by an interval of 2–10 cm; male portion 7–20 cm long and 7–15 mm wide, male bractlets brown; female portion of spike dark brown, 10–20 cm long and 1–2 cm wide; each flower with 1 bristle-like bractlet, these flat and brown at the widened tip, gynophore hairs brown-tinged at tips; stigmas pale brown, linear, 1 mm long. **Fruit** 5–7 mm long, subtended by many fine hairs, the hairs slightly widened and brown at tip. June. ❦ Marshes, lakeshores, streambanks, roadside ditches, pond margins, usually in shallow water; more tolerant of brackish conditions than **common cat-tail** (*Typha latifolia*). ⊕ Minn (all but ne), Wisc, Mich (especially LP), ne Ill and nw Ind. Nearly cosmopolitan; in N Amer from Maine to Man and s Mont, s to SC, Ky, Mo, and Tex; c Calif.

Typha latifolia L.
Common cat-tail   OBL

Perennial emergent herb. **Stems** erect, 1–2.5 m long. **Leaves** upright, mostly 1–2 cm wide. **Flowers** either male or female, the male and female portions of spike normally contiguous, rarely separated by 3–4 mm; male portion 5–15 cm long and 1.5–2 cm wide at flowering time, male bractlets white; female portion of spike dark brown, 10–15 cm long and 2–3 cm wide when mature, female bractlets absent, gynophore hairs white; stigma lance-shaped, becoming dark brown, less than 1 mm long. **Fruit** 1 cm long, with many white, linear hairs from base. June. ❦ Marshes, lakeshores, streambanks, ditches, pond margins, usually in shallow water; less tolerant of brackish conditions than **narrow-leaved cat-tail** (*T. angustifolia*). ⊕ Common; Minn, Wisc, Mich, ne Ill and nw Ind. s Can to c Alaska, throughout USA and into Mex; Eurasia and n Africa.

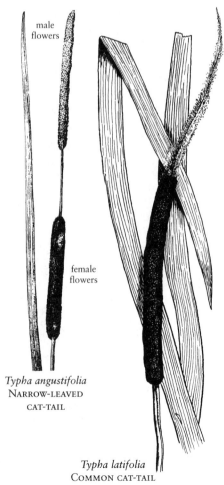

male
flowers

female
flowers

Typha angustifolia
Narrow-leaved
cat-tail

Typha latifolia
Common cat-tail

Xyridaceae
Yellow-Eyed Grass Family

▶**Xyris** L. / Yellow-eyed grass

Perennial rushlike herbs. **Stems** erect, leafless, straight or sometimes ridged. **Leaves** all from base of plant, upright to spreading, linear, often twisted, usually dark green. **Flowers** small, perfect, yellow, from base of tightly overlapping bracts or scales, in rounded or cylindric heads at ends of stems; sepals 3, petals 3; stamens 3; style 3-parted. **Fruit** an oblong, 3-chambered capsule.

▶**KEY TO XYRIS**

1 Plants swollen and hard at base . . . . *X. torta*
. . . . TWISTED YELLOW-EYED GRASS
1 Plants flattened and soft at base. **2**

2 Leaves 5 mm or more wide; upper flower scales with a green spot, 2–3 mm long, near center . *X. difformis* / COMMON YELLOW-EYED GRASS
2 Leaves to 2 mm wide; flower scales without central green spot . . . .
. . . . *X. montana* / NORTHERN YELLOW-EYED GRASS

Xyris difformis Chapman
Common yellow-eyed grass   OBL

⚠ STATUS
Indiana - T

Perennial herb. **Stems** leafless, 1.5–6 dm long, lower stem round in section and twisted, upper stem compressed and straighter, with 2 prominent ridges. **Leaves** linear, not twisted, l–5 dm long and 5–15 mm wide, widened to a soft base. **Flowers** yellow, in round to ovate spikes 0.5–1 cm long; scales ovate, entire; lateral sepals shorter than scales, the margins finely fringed from middle to tip; petals obovate, 4 mm long. **Seeds** 0.5 mm long. July–Aug. ❦ Sandy or peaty lakeshores, sphagnum peatlands, floating sedge mats. ⊕ Mich (mostly wc and s LP), local in nw Ind. Atlantic coast from Maine to Fla and Tex; occasional inland to Mich and Ind.

Xyris montana H. Ries
Northern yellow-eyed grass   OBL

Densely clumped perennial herb. **Stems** leafless, 0.5–3 dm long, round in section, straight or lower part of stem slightly twisted. **Leaves** narrowly linear, flat or only slightly twisted, 5–20 cm long and 1–2 mm wide, rough, dark green, red-purple at base. **Flowers** yellow, in ovate spikes less than 1 cm long; scales obovate, finely fringed at tip; lateral sepals about as long as scales, linear, margins entire or finely hairy near tip. **Seeds** 1 mm long. ❦ Wet, sandy shores, pools in sphagnum peatlands. ⊕ Local in nc and ne Minn, n Wisc, UP and n LP of Mich. NS to s Ont and Minn, s to Pa, Mich and Wisc.

Xyris torta J. E. Smith
Twisted yellow-eyed grass   OBL

⚠ STATUS
Minnesota - E

Perennial herb. **Stems** leafless, 1.5–8 dm long, spirally twisted, ridged. **Leaves** linear, twisted, 2–5 dm long and 2–5 mm wide; outer leaves shorter, tinged purple-brown and swollen and bulblike at base. **Flowers** yellow, in cylindric spikes 1–2.5 cm long; scales oblong; lateral sepals linear, about as long as scales, tips of scales and lateral sepals with tuft of short, red-brown hairs; petals obovate, 4 mm long. **Seeds** 0.5 mm long. June–Aug. ❦ Wet sandy shores. ⊕ Rare in ec Minn; Wisc, c and s LP of Mich, local in ne Ill and nw Ind. New Eng to Minn, s to Va, Ga and Tex.

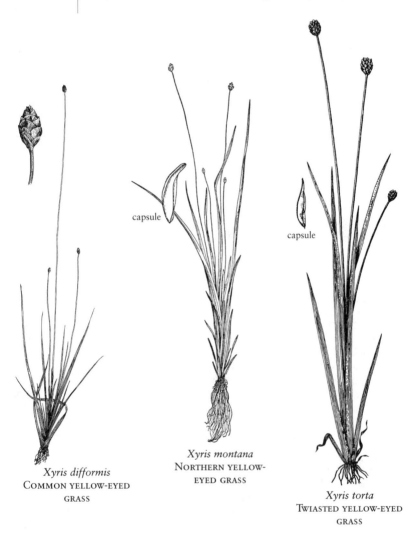

capsule

capsule

Xyris difformis
COMMON YELLOW-EYED
GRASS

Xyris montana
NORTHERN YELLOW-
EYED GRASS

Xyris torta
TWIASTED YELLOW-EYED
GRASS

Zannichelliaceae
Horned Pondweed Family

▶**Zannichellia** L. / Horned pondweed

Zannichellia palustris L.
Horned pondweed   OBL

⚠
STATUS
Indiana - E

Perennial aquatic herb, with creeping rhizomes and often forming extensive underwater mats. **Stems** slender and delicate, wavy, 0.5–5 dm long,
branched from base. **Leaves** simple, opposite (or upper leaves appearing
whorled), threadlike, 2–8 cm long and 0.5 mm wide, stalkless; stipules
membranous and soon deciduous. **Flowers** small, produced underwater,
either male or female, separate on plant but from same leaf axil, with 1
male flower and usually 4 (varying from 1–5) female flowers at each
node, surrounded by a membranous, spathelike bract; petals and sepals
absent; male flower a single anther. **Fruit** a brown to red-brown, cres-
cent-shaped nutlet, gently wavy on margins, 2–3
mm long, tipped by a beak 1–2 mm long; the fruits
mostly 2–6 per node. June–Aug. ≽ Submerged in
fresh or brackish water of streams,
reservoirs, muddy lake and pond bottoms, marshes and ditches. ⊕
Occasional to common, w and s Minn,
Wisc, LP of Mich (and local in sc UP); local
in ne Ill and nw Ind. Coastal and inland N
Amer; S Amer, Eurasia and Africa.

nutlet

Zannichellia palustris
Horned pondweed

References
& Illustration Credits

Barnes, B., and W. Wagner. 1981. MICHIGAN TREES. The University of Michigan Press. Ann Arbor, MI. 383 p.

Billington, C. 1952. FERNS OF MICHIGAN. Cranbrook Institute of Science Bulletin No. 32. Bloomfield Hills, MI 240 p.

Case, F., Jr. 1987. ORCHIDS OF THE WESTERN GREAT LAKES REGION. Cranbrook Institute of Science Bulletin No. 48. Bloomfield Hills, MI. 240 p.

Chadde, S.W. 1998. A GREAT LAKES WETLAND FLORA. A COMPLETE, ILLUSTRATED GUIDE TO THE AQUATIC AND WETLAND PLANTS OF THE UPPER MIDWEST. PocketFlora Press, Calumet, MI. 569 p.

Cody, W., and D. Britton. 1989. FERNS AND FERN ALLIES OF CANADA. Publication 1829/E. Research Branch, Agriculture Canada. Ottawa, Canada. 430 p.

Cowardin, L., V. Carter, F. Golet, and E. LaRoe. 1979. CLASSIFICATION OF WETLANDS AND DEEPWATER HABITATS OF THE UNITED STATES. U.S. Department of the Interior, Fish and Wildlife Service. Washington, DC. 103 p.

Crow, G., and C. Hellquist. 2000. AQUATIC AND WETLAND PLANTS OF NORTHEASTERN NORTH AMERICA (2 VOLS.). University of Wisconsin Press. Madison, WI.

Crum, H. 1976. MOSSES OF THE GREAT LAKES FOREST. University Herbarium, University of Michigan, Ann Arbor, MI. 404 p.

Crum, H. 1988. A FOCUS ON PEATLANDS AND PEAT MOSSES. The University of Michigan Press. Ann Arbor, MI. 306 p.

Crum, H., and L. Anderson. 1981. MOSSES OF EASTERN NORTH AMERICA (2 vols). Columbia Univ. Press. New York, NY.

Curtis, J. 1971. THE VEGETATION OF WISCONSIN. The University of Wisconsin Press. Madison, WI. 657 p.

Eastman, J. 1995. THE BOOK OF SWAMP AND BOG: TREES, SHRUBS, AND WILDFLOWERS OF EASTERN FRESHWATER WETLANDS. Stackpole Books. Mechanicsburg, PA. 237 p.

Eggers, S., and D. Reed. 1997. WETLAND PLANTS AND PLANT COMMUNITIES OF MINNESOTA AND WISCONSIN (2ND ED.). U.S. Army Corps of Engineers, St. Paul District. 264 p.

Fassett, N. 1957. A MANUAL OF AQUATIC PLANTS. The University of Wisconsin Press. Madison, WI. 405 p.

Flora of North America Editorial Committee. 1993. FLORA OF NORTH AMERICA NORTH OF MEXICO. VOLUME 2: PTERIDOPHYTES AND GYMNOSPERMS. Oxford University Press. New York, NY. 475 p.

Flora of North America Editorial Committee. 1997. FLORA OF NORTH AMERICA NORTH OF MEXICO. VOLUME 3: MAGNOLIOPHYTA: MAGNOLIIDAE AND HAMAMELIDAE. Oxford University Press. New York, NY. 590 p.

Flora of North America Editorial Committee. 2000. FLORA OF NORTH AMERICA NORTH OF MEXICO. VOLUME 22: MAGNOLIOPHYTA: ALISMATIDAE, ARECIDAE, COMMELINIDAE (IN PART), AND ZINGIBERIDAE. Oxford University Press. New York, NY. 352 p.

Gleason, H., and A. Cronquist. 1991. MANUAL OF VASCULAR PLANTS OF NORTHEASTERN UNITED STATES AND ADJACENT CANADA (2nd Ed.). The New York Botanical Garden. Bronx, NY. 910 p.

Holmgren, N. (editor). 1998. ILLUSTRATED COMPANION TO GLEASON AND CRONQUIST'S MANUAL. New York Botanical Garden. Bronx, NY. 937 p.

Kartesz, J.T. 1999. A SYNONYMIZED CHECKLIST AND ATLAS WITH BIOLOGICAL ATTRIBUTES FOR THE VASCULAR FLORA OF THE UNITED STATES, CANADA, AND GREENLAND. First Edition. In: Kartesz, J.T., and C.A. Meacham. Synthesis of the North American Flora, Version 1.0. North Carolina Botanical Garden, Chapel Hill, NC.

Ownbey, G., and T. Morley. 1991. VASCULAR PLANTS OF MINNESOTA: A CHECKLIST AND ATLAS. The University of Minnesota Press. Minneapolis, MN. 306 p.

Reed, P. 1988. NATIONAL LIST OF PLANT SPECIES THAT OCCUR IN WETLANDS: NORTH CENTRAL (REGION 3). Biological Report 88(26.3). U.S. Department of the Interior, Fish and Wildlife Service. Washington, DC. 99 p.

Smith, W. 1993. ORCHIDS OF MINNESOTA. The University of Minnesota Press. Minneapolis, MN. 172 p.

Soper, J., and M. Heimburger. 1982. SHRUBS OF ONTARIO. The Royal Ontario Museum. Toronto, Ontario. 495 p.

Swink, F., and G. Wilhelm. 1994. PLANTS OF THE CHICAGO REGION (4th Ed.). Indiana Academy of Science. Indianapolis, IN. 921 p.

Tryon, R. 1980. FERNS OF MINNESOTA (2nd Ed.). The University of Minnesota Press. Minneapolis, MN. 165 p.

Tryon, R., N. Fassett, D. Dunlop, and M. Diemer. 1953. THE FERNS AND FERN ALLIES OF WISCONSIN. The University of Wisconsin Press. Madison, WI. 158 p.

Voss, E.G. 1972. MICHIGAN FLORA, PART I GYMNOSPERMS AND MONOCOTS. Cranbrook Institute of Science Bulletin 55 and University of Michigan Herbarium. 488 p.

Voss, E.G. 1985. MICHIGAN FLORA, PART II DICOTS (SAURURACEAE–CORNACEAE). Cranbrook Institute of Science Bulletin 59 and University of Michigan Herbarium. 724 p.

Voss, E.G. 1996. MICHIGAN FLORA, PART III DICOTS (PYROLACEAE–COMPOSITAE). Cranbrook Institute of Science Bulletin 61 and University of Michigan Herbarium. 622 p.

Wetter, A.W, T.S. Cochrane, M.R. Black, H.H. Iltis, P.E. Berry. 2001. CHECKLIST OF THE VASCULAR PLANTS OF WISCONSIN. Tech. Bulletin No. 192. Dept. Natural Resources, Madison, WI. 258 p.

Wright, H., B. Coffin, and N. Aaseng (editors). 1992. THE PATTERNED PEATLANDS OF MINNESOTA. University of Minnesota Press. Minneapolis, MN. 327 p.

Illustrations were obtained from a number of public domain sources. Special acknowledgment is given to FLORA OF WEST VIRGINIA by P.D. Strausbaugh and Earl L. Core (4 parts, published from 1952-1964 by West Virginina University); A MANUAL OF MARSH AND AQUATIC VASCULAR PLANTS OF NORTH CAROLINA WITH HABITAT DATA (1977), by E.O. Beal, published by North Carolina Agricultural Experiment Station; and NORTH AMERICAN CARICEAE (1940) by K.K. Mackenzie, published by NY Botanical Garden.

Appendix A
Glossary

achene   A one-seeded, dry, indehiscent fruit with the seed coat not attached to the mature wall of the ovary.

acid   Having more hydrogen ions than hydroxyl (OH) ions; a pH less than 7.

acute   Gradually tapered to a tip.

alkaline   Having more hydroxyl ions than hydrogen ions; a pH more than 7.

alluvial   Pertaining to the deposits of rivers and streams.

alternate   Borne singly at each node, as in leaves on a stem.

ament   Spikelike inflorescence of same-sexed flowers (either male or female); same as catkin.

angiosperm   A plant producing flowers and bearing seeds in an ovary.

annual   A plant that completes its life cycle in one growing season, then dies.

anther   Pollen-bearing part of stamen.

appressed   Lying flat to or parallel to a surface.

aquatic   Living in water.

areole   In leaves, the spaces between small veins.

aromatic   Strongly scented.

ascending   Angled upward.

asymmetrical   Not symmetrical.

auricle   An ear-shaped appendage to a leaf or stipule.

awl-shaped   Tapering gradually from a broad base to a sharp point.

awn   A bristle-like organ.

axil   Angle between a stem and the attached leaf.

barb   Downward pointing projections.

basal   From base of plant.

basic   A pH greater than 7.

beard   Covering of long or stiff hairs.

berry   Fruit with the seeds surrounded by fleshy material.

biennial   A plant that completes its life cycle in two growing season, typically flowering and fruiting in the second year, then dying.

blade   Expanded, usually flat part of a leaf or petiole.

bog   A wet, acidic, nutrient-poor peat-land characterized by sphagnum and other mosses, shrubs and sedges. Technically, a type of peatland raised above its surroundings by peat accumulation and receiving nutrients only from precipitation.

boreal   Far northern latitudes.

brackish   Salty.

bract   An accessory structure at the base of some flowers, usually appearing leaflike.

bractlet   A secondary bract (*Typha*).

branchlets   A small branch.

bristle   A stiff hair.

bulblet   Small bulb borne above ground, as in a leaf axil.

calcareous fen   An uncommon wetland type associated with seepage areas, and which receive groundwater enriched with primarily calcium and magnesium bicarbonates.

calcium-rich   Refers to wetlands underlain by limestone or receiving water enriched by calcium compounds.

calyx   Collectively, all the sepals of a flower.

capsule   A dry, dehiscent fruit splitting into 3 or more parts.

carpel   Fertile leaf of an angiosperm, bearing the ovules. A pistil is made up of one or more carpels.

caryopsis   The dry, indehiscent seed of grasses.

catkin   Spikelike inflorescence of same-sexed flowers (either male or female); same as ament.

chaff   Thin, dry scales; in the Asteraceae, sometimes found as chaffy bracts on the receptacle.

circumboreal   Refers to a species distribution pattern which circles the earth's boreal regions.

clasping   Leaves that partially encircle the stem at the base.

cleistogamous   Type of flower that remains closed and is self-pollinated.

clumped   Having the stems grouped closely together; tufted.

colony-forming   A group of plants of the same species, produced either vegetatively or by seed.

column   The joined style and filaments

in the Orchidaceae.

coma   A tuft of fine hairs, especially at the tip of a seed.

composite   An inflorescence that is made up of many tiny florets crowded together on a receptacle; members of the Composite Family (Asteraceae).

compound   A leaf with two or more leaflets.

concave   Curved inward.

cone   The dry fruit of conifers composed of overlapping scales.

conifer   Cone-bearing woody plants.

convex   Curved outward.

corm   An enlarged, rounded, underground stem, usually covered with papery scales or modified leaves.

corolla   Collectively, all the petals of a flower.

corymb   A flat-topped or convex inflorescence.

crisped   An irregularly crinkled or curled leaf margin.

crown   Persistent base of a plant, especially a grasses.

culm   The stem of a grass or grasslike plant, especially a stem with the inflorescence.

cyme   A type of inflorescence in which the central flowers open first.

deciduous   Not persistent.

dehiscent   Splitting open at maturity.

dicots   One of two main divisions of the Angiosperms (the other being the Monocots); plants having 2 seed leaves (cotyledons), net-venation, and flower parts in 4s or 5s (or multiples of these numbers).

disarticulation   Spikelets breaking either above or below the glumes when mature, the glumes remaining in the head if disarticulation above the glumes, or the glumes falling with the florets if disarticulation is below the glumes.

discoid   In composite flowers (Asteraceae), a head with only disk (tubular) flowers, the ray flowers absent.

disjunct   A population of plants widely separated from its main range.

disk   In the Asteraceae, the central part of the head, composed of tubular flowers.

dissected   Leaves divided into many smaller segments.

disturbed   Natural communities altered by human influences.

divided   Leaves which are lobed nearly to the midrib.

dolomite   A type of limestone consisting of calcium magnesium carbonate.

driftless area   In our region, portions of sw Wisconsin, ne Iowa, and se Minnesota that are not covered by glacial drift.

drupe   A fleshy fruit with a single large seed such as a cherry.

elliptic   Broadest at the middle, gradually tapering to both ends.

emergent   Growing out of and above the water surface.

emersed leaf   Growing above the water surface or out of water.

endangered   A species in danger of extinction throughout all or most of its range if current trends continue.

endemic   A species restricted to a particular region.

entire   With a smooth margin.

erect   Stiffly upright.

escape   A cultivated plant which establishes itself outside of cultivation.

evergreen   Plant retaining its leaves throughout the year.

exserted   Extending beyond the mouth of a structure such as stamens extending out from the mouth of the corolla.

Facultative (FAC)   An indicator status category of the US Fish and Wildlife Service for species equally likely to occur in wetlands or non-wetlands (estimated probability 34%–66%).

Facultative Wetland (FACW)   An indicator status category of the US Fish and Wildlife Service for a species that usually occurs in wetlands (estimated probability 67%–99%), but is occasionally found in non-wetlands (estimated probability 1%–33%).

Facultative Upland (FACU)   An indicator status category of the US Fish and Wildlife Service for plants that usually occur in non-wetlands (estimated probability 67%–99%), but is occasionally found in wetlands (estimated probability 1%–33%).

fen   An open wetland usually dominated by herbaceous plants, and fed by in-flowing, often calcium- and/or magnesium-rich water; soils vary from peat to clays and silts.

fern   Perennial plants with spore-bearing leaves similar to the vegetative leaves and bearing sporangia on their underside, or the spore-bearing leaves much modified (Pteridophyta order).

fibrous A cluster of slender roots, all with the same diameter.

filament The stalk of a stamen which supports the anther.

floating mat A feature of some ponds where plant roots form a carpet over some or all of the water surface.

floodplain That part of a river valley that is occasionally covered by flood waters.

floret A small flower in a dense cluster of flowers; in grasses the flower with its attached lemma and palea.

follicle A dry, dehiscent fruit that splits along one side when mature.

genus The first part of the scientific name for a plant or animal (plural genera).

gland An appendage or depression which produces a sticky or greasy substance.

glaucous Having a bluish appearance.

glumes A pair of small bracts at base of each spikelet the lowermost (or first) glume usually smaller the upper (or second) glume usually longer.

grain The fruit of a grass; the swollen seedlike protuberance on the fruit of some *Rumex*.

gymnosperm Plants in which the seeds are not produced in an ovary, but usually in a cone.

gynophore The central stalk of some flowers, especially in cat-tails (*Typha*).

hardwoods Loosely used to contrast most deciduous trees from conifers.

herb A herbaceous, non-woody plant.

herbaceous Like an herb; also, leaflike in appearance.

hummock A small, raised mound formed by certain species of sphagnum moss.

humus Dark, well-decayed organic matter in soil.

hybrid A cross-breed between two species.

hypanthium A ring, cup, or tube around the ovary; the sepals, petals and stamens are attached to the rim of the hypanthium.

indehiscent Not splitting open at maturity.

indusium In ferns, a membranous covering over the sorus (plural indusia).

inferior The position of the ovary when it is below the point of attachment of the sepals and petals.

inflorescence A cluster of flowers.

insectivorous Refers to the insect trapping and digestion habit of some plants as a nutrition supplement.

interdunal swale Low-lying areas between sand dune ridges.

internode Portion of a stem between two nodes.

introduced A non-native species.

involucral bract A single member of the involucre; sometimes called phyllary in composite flowers (Asteraceae)

involucre A whorl of bracts, subtending a flower or inflorescence.

irregular flower Not radially symmetric; with similar parts unequal.

joint A node or section of a stem where the branch and leaf meet.

keel A central rib like the keel of a boat.

lance-shaped Broadest near the base, gradually tapering to a narrower tip.

lateral Borne on the sides of a stem or branch.

lax Loose or drooping.

leaf axil The point of the angle between a stem and a leaf.

leaflet One of the leaflike segments of a compound leaf.

lemma In grasses, the lower bract enclosing the flower (the upper, smaller bract is the palea).

lens-shaped Biconvex in shape (like a lentil).

lenticel Blisterlike openings in the epidermis of woody stems, admitting gases to and from the plant, and often appearing as small oval dots on bark.

ligulate Having a ligule; in the Asteraceae, the strap-shaped corolla of a ray floret.

ligule In grasses and grasslike plants, the membranous or hairy ring at top of sheath between the blade and stem.

linear Narrow and flat with parallel sides.

lip Upper or lower part of a 2-lipped corolla; also the lower petal in most orchid flowers.

lobed With lobes; in leaves divisions usually not over halfway to the midrib.

local Occurring sporadically in an area.

low prairie Wet and moist herbaceous plant communities, typically dominated by grasses.

margin   The outer edge of a leaf.

marl   A calcium-rich clay.

marsh   Wetland dominated by herbaceous plants, with standing water for part or all the growing season, then often drying at the surface.

megaspore   Large, female spores.

microspore   Small, male spores.

midrib   The prominent vein along the main axis of a leaf.

mixed forest   A type of forest composed of both deciduous and conifer trees.

moat   The open water area ringing the outer edge of a peatland or floating mat.

monocots   One of two main divisions of the Angiosperms (the other being the Dicots); plants with a single seed leaf (cotyledon); typically having narrow leaves with parallel veins, and flower parts in 3s or multiples of 3.

muck   An organic soil where the plant remains are decomposed to the point where the type of plants forming the soil cannot be determined.

mucro   A sharp point at termination of an organ or other structure.

naked   Without a covering; a stalk or stem without leaves.

native   An indigenous species.

naturalized   An introduced species that is established and persistent in an ecosystem.

needle   A slender leaf, as in the Pinaceae.

nerve   A leaf vein.

neutral   A pH of 7.

node   The spot on a stem or branch where leaves originate.

nutlet   A small dry fruit that does not split open along a seam.

oblanceolate   Reverse lance-shaped; broadest at the apex, gradually tapering to the narrower base.

Obligate (OBL)   An indicator status category of the US Fish and Wildlife Service for a species that almost always occurs in wetlands (greater than 99% probability).

oblong   Broadest at the middle, and tapering to both ends, but broader than elliptic.

obovate   Broadly rounded at the apex, becoming narrowed below.

ocrea   A tube-shaped stipule or pair of stipules around the stem; characteristic of the Smartweed Family (Polygonaceae).

opposite   Leaves or branches which are paired opposite one another on the stem.

organic   Soils composed of decaying plant remains.

oval   Elliptical.

ovary   The lower part of the pistil that produces the seeds.

ovate   Broadly rounded at the base, becoming narrowed above; broader than lanceolate.

palea   The uppermost of the two inner bracts subtending a grass flower (the lower bract is the lemma).

palmate   Divided in a radial fashion, like the fingers of a hand.

panicle   An arrangement of flowers consisting of several racemes.

pappus   The modified sepals of a composite flower which persist atop the ovary as bristles, scales or awns.

parallel-veined   With several veins running from base of leaf to leaf tip, characteristic of most monocots.

peat   An organic soil formed of partially decomposed plant remains.

peatland   A wetland whose soil is composed primarily of organic matter (mosses, sedges, etc.); a general term for bogs and fens.

pepo   A fleshy, many-seeded fruit with a tough rind, as a melon.

perennial   Living for 3 or more years.

perfect   A flower having both male (stamens) and female (pistils) parts.

perianth   Collectively, all the sepals and petals of a flower.

perigynium   A sac-like structure enclosing the pistil in *Carex*. (plural perigynia).

petal   An individual part of the corolla, often white or colored.

petiole   The stalk of a leaf.

phyllary   An involucral bract subtending the flower head in composite flowers (Asteraceae).

phyllode   An expanded petiole.

pinna   The primary or first division in a fern frond or leaf (plural pinnae).

pinnate   Divided once along an elongated axis into distinct segments.

pinnule   The pinnate segment of a pinna.

pistil   The seed-producing part of the flower, consisting of an ovary and one or more styles and stigmas.

pith   A spongy central part of stems and branches.

pollen   The male spores in an anther.

prairie   An open plant community dominated by herbaceous species, especially grasses.

prostrate   Lying flat on the ground.

raceme   A grouping of flowers along an elongated axis where each flower has its own stalk.

rachilla   A small stem or axis.

rachis   The central axis or stem of a leaf or inflorescence.

radiate heads   In composite flowers, heads with both ray and disk flowers (Asteraceae).

ray flower   A ligulate or strap-shaped flower in the Asteraceae, where often the outermost series of flowers in the head.

receptacle   In the Asteraceae, the enlarged summit of the flower stalk to which the sepals, petals, stamens, and pistils are usually attached.

recurved   Curved backward.

regular   Flowers with all the similar parts of the same form; radially symmetric.

rhizome   An underground, horizontal stem.

rib   A pronounced vein or nerve.

rootstock   Similar to rhizome but referring to any underground part that spreads the plant.

rosette   A crowded, circular clump of leaves.

samara   A dry, indehiscent fruit with a well-developed wing.

saprophyte   A plant that lives off of dead organic matter.

scale   A tiny, leaflike structure; the structure that subtends each flower in a sedge (Cyperaceae).

scape   A naked stem (without leaves) bearing the flowers.

section   Cross-section.

secund   Flowers mostly on 1 side of a stalk or branch.

sedge meadow   A community dominated by sedges (Cyperaceae) and occurring on wet, saturated soils.

seep   A spot where water oozes from the ground.

sepal   A segment of the calyx; usually green in color.

sheath   Tube-shaped membrane around a stem, especially for part of the leaf in grasses and sedges.

shrub   A woody plant with multiple stems.

silicle   Short fruit of the Mustard Family (Brassicaceae), normally less than 2x longer as wide.

silique   Dry, dehiscent, 2-chambered fruit of the Mustard Family (Brassicaceae), longer than a silicle.

simple   An undivided leaf.

sinus   The depression between two lobes.

smooth   Without teeth or hairs.

sorus   Clusters of spore containers (plural sori).

spadix   A fleshy axis in which flowers are embedded.

spathe   A large bract subtending or enclosing a cluster of flowers.

spatula-shaped   Broadest at tip and tapering to the base.

sphagnum moss   A type of moss common in peatlands and sometimes forming a continuous carpet across the surface; sometimes forming layers several meters thick; also loosely called peat moss.

spike   A group of unstalked flowers along an unbranched stalk.

spikelet   A small spike; the flower cluster (inflorescence) of grasses (Poaceae) and sedges (Cyperaceae).

sporangium   The spore-producing structure (plural sporangia).

sporophyll   A modified, spore-bearing leaf.

spreading   Widely angled outward.

spring   A place where water flows naturally from the ground.

spur   A hollow, pointed projection of a flower.

stamen   The male or pollen-producing organ of a flower.

staminode   An infertile stamen.

stem   The main axis of a plant.

stigma   The terminal part of a pistil which receives pollen.

stipe   A stalk.

stipule   A leaflike outgrowth at the base of a leaf stalk.

stolon   A horizontal stem lying on the surface of the soil.

style   The stalklike part of the pistil between the ovary and the stigma.

subspecies   A subdivision of the species forming a group with shared traits which differ from other members of the species (subsp.).

subtend   Attached below and extending upward.

succulent   Thick, fleshy and juicy.

superior   Referring to the position of the ovary when it is above the point of attachment of sepals, petals, stamens, and pistils.

swale   A slight depression.

swamp   Wooded wetlands dominated by trees or shrubs; soils are typically wet for much of year or sometimes inundated.

talus   Fallen rock at the base of a slope or cliff.

taproot   A main, downward-pointing root.

tendril   A threadlike appendage from a stem or leaf that coils around other objects for support (as in Lathyrus).

tepal   Sepals or petals not differentiated from one another.

terminal   Located at the end of a stem or stalk.

thallus   A small, flattened plant structure, without distinct stem or leaves.

thicket   A dense growth of woody plants.

threatened   A species likely to become endangered throughout all or most of its range if current trends continue.

translucent   Nearly transparent.

tree   A large, single-stemmed woody plant.

tuber   An enlarged portion of a root or rhizome.

tubercle   Base of style persistent as a swelling atop the achene different in color and texture from achene body

tundra   Treeless plain in arctic regions, having permanently frozen subsoil.

turion   A specialized type of shoot or bud that overwinters and resumes growth the following year.

umbel   A cluster of flowers in which the flower stalks arise from the same level.

umbelet   A small, secondary umbel in an umbel, as in the Apiaceae.

Upland (UPL)   An indicator status category of the US Fish and Wildlife Service for a species that almost always occur in non-wetlands (greater than 99% probability).

upright   Erect or nearly so.

utricle   A small, one-seeded fruit with a dry, papery outer covering.

valve   A segment of a dehiscent fruit; the wing of the fruit in Rumex.

variety   Taxon below subspecies and differing from other varieties within the same subspecies (var.).

vein   A vascular bundle, as in a leaf.

velum   The membranous flap that partially covers the sporangium in Isoetes.

vine   A trailing or climbing plant, dependent on other objects for support.

wavy   Undulating.

whorl   A group of 3 or more parts from one point on a stem.

wing   A thin tissue bordering or surrounding an organ.

woody   Xylem tissue (the vascular tissue which conducts water and nutrient.

Appendix B
Abbreviations & Symbols

Botanical
subsp. subspecies
var. variety

Conservation Status
E endangered
T threatened

Measurements
mm millimeter
cm centimeter
dm decimeter
m meter
x times
± more or less

Geographical
c central
e east
n north
s south
w west

States and Provinces
Ala Alabama
Appal Appalachia
Ariz Arizona
Ark Arkansas
BC British Columbia
c Amer central America
Calif California
Can Canada
Colo Colorado
Conn Connecticut
Daks North and South Dakota
DC District of Columbia
Del Delaware
Fla Florida
Ga Georgia
Ill Illinois
Ind Indiana
Kans Kansas
Ky Kentucky
La Louisiana
Lab Labrador
LP Lower Peninsula of Michigan
Man Manitoba
Mass Massachusetts
Md Maryland
Mex Mexico

Mich Michigan
Minn Minnesota
Miss Mississippi
Mo Missouri
Mont Montana
N Amer North America
NB New Brunswick
NC North Carolina
ND North Dakota
Neb Nebraska
New Eng New England
Nev Nevada
Nfld Newfoundland
NH New Hampshire
NJ New Jersey
NM New Mexico
NS Nova Scotia
NWT Northwest Territories
NY New York
Okla Oklahoma
Ont Ontario
Ore Oregon
Pa Pennsylvania
PEI Prince Edward Island
Que Quebec
RI Rhode Island
S Amer South America
Sask Saskatchewan
SC South Carolina
SD South Dakota
Tenn Tennessee
Tex Texas
UP Upper Peninsula of Michigan
USA United States
Va Virginia
Vt Vermont
Wash Washington
Wisc Wisconsin
WVa West Virginia
Wyo Wyoming

Symbols

≽ Habitat

⊕ Range

⚠ Species of conservation concern
(endangered or threatened)

☞ Note

☒ Toxic

Appendix C
Wetland Indicator Status

APPENDIX C lists the **wetland indicator status** for all species included in the Flora. These rankings are provided for use when delineating jurisdictional wetlands using methods prescribed by federal or state agencies. The indicator status rankings, defined below, are based on the NATIONAL LIST OF PLANT SPECIES THAT OCCUR IN WETLANDS: NORTH CENTRAL (REGION 3) (Reed 1988).

Species in *italics* are **introduced species**, or plants not considered part of the original native flora of the Great Lakes region.

Species with an indicator status in parentheses were not ranked for Region 3 by Reed (1988), but tentative assignments are given based on a plant's reported wetland status in surrounding regions, or were assigned by the author based on a species' apparent occurrence in wetlands of the Great Lakes region. Rankings in parentheses are provided for informational purposes only and should not be used in jurisdictional wetland delineation or determination studies.

Obligate Wetland (OBL)   A species that almost always occurs (under natural conditions) in wetlands (greater than 99% estimated probability).

Facultative Wetland (FACW)   A species that usually occurs in wetlands (estimated probability 67%–99%), but is occasionally found in non-wetlands.

Facultative (FAC)   A species that is equally likely to occur in wetlands or non-wetlands (estimated probability 34%–66%).

Facultative Upland (FACU)   A species that usually occurs in non-wetlands (estimated probability 67%–99%), but is occasionally found in wetlands (estimated probability 1%–33%).

Obligate Upland (UPL)   A species that almost always occurs in non-wetlands (greater than 99% probability).

No Indicator (NI)   A species for which there was insufficient information to provide an indicator determination.

A positive (+) sign indicates that the species has a tendency toward the higher end of the category (for example, FACW+ indicates a species occuring more frequently in wetlands). A negative sign (-) indicates a tendency toward the lower end of the category.

Abies balsamea . . . . .FACW
Acer
 negundo . . . . .FACW-
 rubrum . . . . .FAC
 saccharinum . . . . .FACW
Aconitum noveboracense . . . . .NI
Acorus calamus . . . . .OBL
Aesculus glabra . . . . .NI
Agalinis
 purpurea . . . . .FACW
 skinneriana . . . .(FACW)
 tenuifolia . . . . .FACW
Agrostis
 hyemalis . . . . .FAC-
 stolonifera . . . . .FACW
Alisma
 gramineum . . . . .OBL
 plantago-aquatica . . . . .OBL
Alnus
 glutinosa . . . . .FACW-
 incana . . . . .OBL
 viridis . . . . .OBL
Alopecurus
 aequalis . . . . .OBL
 carolinianus . . . . .FACW
Amaranthus tuberculatus . . . . . .OBL
Amelanchier bartramiana . . . . . .FAC
Amerorchis rotundifolia . . . . . . .OBL
Ammannia robusta . . . . .OBL
Amorpha fruticosa . . . . .FACW+
Andromeda glaucophylla . . . . . .OBL
Anemone canadensis . . . . .FACW
Angelica atropurpurea . . . . .OBL
Apios americana . . . . .FACW
Arethusa bulbosa . . . . .OBL
Arisaema
 dracontium . . . . .FACW
 triphyllum . . . . .FACW-
Armoracia lacustris . . . . .OBL
Aronia melanocarpa . . . . .FACW-
Artemisia biennis . . . . .FACW-
Asclepias incarnata . . . . .OBL
Aster
 borealis . . . . .OBL
 brachyactis . . . . .FAC
 dumosus . . . . .FAC+
 firmus . . . . .FACW+
 lanceolatus . . . . .FACW
 lateriflorus . . . . .FACW-
 longifolius . . . . .FACW
 nemoralis . . . . .OBL
 novae-angliae . . . . .FACW
 ontarionis . . . . .FAC
 pilosus . . . . .FACU+
 praealtus . . . . .FACW
 puniceus . . . . .OBL
 subulatus . . . . .OBL

 umbellatus . . . . .FACW
Astragalus agrestis . . . . .FACW-
Athyrium filix-femina . . . . .FAC
Atriplex patula . . . . .FACW-
Azolla mexicana . . . . .OBL

Bacopa rotundifolia . . . . .OBL
Barbarea orthoceras . . . . .OBL
Bartonia
 paniculata . . . . .OBL
 virginica . . . . .FACW+
Beckmannia syzigachne . . . . .OBL
Berula erecta . . . . .OBL
Betula
 alleghaniensis . . . . .FAC
 nigra . . . . .FACW
 pumila . . . . .OBL
Bidens
 aristosa . . . . .FACW
 cernua . . . . .OBL
 comosa . . . . .FACW
 connata . . . . .OBL
 coronata . . . . .OBL
 discoidea . . . . .FACW
 frondosa . . . . .FACW
 vulgata . . . . .FACU
Boehmeria cylindrica . . . . .OBL
Boltonia asteroides . . . . .FACW
Botrychium
 lanceolatum . . . . .FACW
 lunaria . . . . .FACW
 virginianum . . . . .FACU
Brasenia schreberi . . . . .OBL
Bromus
 altissimus . . . . .FACW-
 ciliatus . . . . .FACW
Butomus umbellatus . . . . .OBL

Cabomba caroliniana . . . . .OBL
Cacalia
 plantaginea . . . . .OBL
 suaveolens . . . . .OBL
Calamagrostis
 canadensis . . . . .OBL
 stricta . . . . .FACW+
Calla palustris . . . . .OBL
Callitriche
 hermaphroditica . . . . .OBL
 heterophylla . . . . .OBL
 palustris . . . . .OBL
Calopogon tuberosus . . . . .OBL
Caltha
 natans . . . . .OBL
 palustris . . . . .OBL
Calypso bulbosa . . . . .FACW
Campanula aparinoides . . . . .OBL
Cardamine

douglassii . . . . .FACW
pensylvanica . . . . .FACW+
pratensis . . . . .OBL
rhomboidea . . . . .OBL
Carex
  alata . . . . .OBL
  albolutescens . . . . .FACW
  alopecoidea . . . . .FACW+
  aquatilis . . . . .OBL
  arcta . . . . .OBL
  atherodes . . . . .OBL
  atlantica . . . . .FACW
  aurea . . . . .FACW+
  bebbii . . . . .OBL
  bromoides . . . . .FACW+
  brunnescens . . . . .FACW
  buxbaumii . . . . .OBL
  canescens . . . . .OBL
  capillaris . . . . .FACW
  castanea . . . . .FACW+
  chordorrhiza . . . . .OBL
  comosa . . . . .OBL
  conjuncta . . . . .FACW
  conoidea . . . . .FACW+
  crawei . . . . .FACW
  crawfordii . . . .(FAC+)
  crinita . . . . .FACW+
  cristatella . . . . .FACW+
  crus-corvi . . . . .OBL
  cryptolepis . . . . .OBL
  davisii . . . . .FAC+
  debilis . . . . .FACW
  deflexa . . . .(NI)
  deweyana . . . . .FACU-
  diandra . . . . .OBL
  dioica . . . . .OBL
  disperma . . . . .OBL
  echinata . . . . .OBL
  emoryi . . . . .OBL
  exilis . . . . .OBL
  flava . . . . .OBL
  folliculata . . . . .OBL
  frankii . . . . .OBL
  granularis . . . . .FACW+
  grayi . . . . .FACW+
  gynandra . . . . .FACW+
  haydenii . . . . .OBL
  heleonastes . . . .(OBL)
  hyalinolepis . . . . .OBL
  hystericina . . . . .OBL
  interior . . . . .OBL
  intumescens . . . . .FACW+
  lacustris . . . . .OBL
  laeviconica . . . . .OBL
  laevivaginata . . . . .OBL
  lanuginosa . . . . .OBL
  lasiocarpa . . . . .OBL

lenticularis . . . . .OBL
leptalea . . . . .OBL
limosa . . . . .OBL
livida . . . . .OBL
longii . . . . .OBL
lupuliformis . . . . .FACW+
lupulina . . . . .OBL
lurida . . . . .OBL
michauxiana . . . . .OBL
muskingumensis . . . . .OBL
normalis . . . . .FACW
norvegica . . . . .FACW
oligosperma . . . . .OBL
parryana . . . .(FACW)
pauciflora . . . . .OBL
paupercula . . . . .OBL
praegracilis . . . . .FACW
prairea . . . . .FACW+
prasina . . . . .OBL
projecta . . . . .FACW+
pseudocyperus . . . . .OBL
retrorsa . . . . .OBL
rostrata . . . . .OBL
sartwellii . . . . .FACW+
scabrata . . . . .OBL
schweinitzii . . . . .OBL
scirpoidea . . . . .FACU
scoparia . . . . .FACW
seorsa . . . . .FACW+
squarrosa . . . . .OBL
sterilis . . . . .OBL
stipata . . . . .OBL
straminea . . . . .OBL
stricta . . . . .OBL
suberecta . . . . .OBL
sychnocephala . . . . .FACW+
tenera . . . . .FAC+
tenuiflora . . . . .OBL
tetanica . . . . .FACW
tribuloides . . . . .FACW+
trichocarpa . . . . .OBL
trisperma . . . . .OBL
tuckermanii . . . . .OBL
typhina . . . . .OBL
utriculata . . . . .OBL-
vaginata . . . . .OBL
vesicaria . . . . .OBL
viridula . . . . .OBL
vulpinoidea . . . . .OBL
weigandii . . . .(OBL)
Carya laciniosa . . . . .FACW
Catabrosa aquatica . . . . .OBL
Cephalanthus occidentalis . . . . . . .OBL
Ceratophyllum
  demersum . . . . .OBL
  echinatum . . . . .OBL
Chamaedaphne calyculata . . . . . . .OBL

Chelone
    glabra . . . . .OBL
    obliqua . . . . .OBL
Chenopodium
    glaucum . . . . .FACW
    rubrum . . . . .OBL
Chrysosplenium americanum . . . . .OBL
Cicuta
    bulbifera . . . . .OBL
    maculata . . . . .OBL
Cinna
    arundinacea . . . . .FACW
    latifolia . . . . .FACW+
Circaea alpina . . . . .FACW
Cirsium
    arvense . . . . .FACU
    muticum . . . . .OBL
    palustre . . . . .NI
Cladium mariscoides . . . . .OBL
Conioselinum chinense . . . .(OBL)
Conium maculatum . . . . .FACW
Coptis trifolia . . . . .FACW
Corallorrhiza trifida . . . . .FACW-
Cornus
    alternifolia . . . .(FAC-)
    amomum . . . . .FACW+
    canadensis . . . . .FACW-
    drummondii . . . . .FACW-
    racemosa . . . . .FACW-
    sericea . . . . .FACW
Crassula aquatica . . . . .OBL
Crepis runcinata . . . . .FACW
Cyperus
    acuminatus . . . . .OBL
    bipartitus . . . . .FACW+
    dentatus
    diandrus . . . . .FACW+
    erythrorhizos . . . . .OBL
    esculentus . . . . .FACW
    flavescens . . . . .OBL
    odoratus . . . . .FACW
    squarrosus . . . . .OBL
    strigosus . . . . .FACW
Cypripedium
    acaule . . . . .FACW
    arietinum . . . . .FACW+
    calceolus . . . . .FAC+
    candidum . . . . .OBL
    reginae . . . . .FACW+
Cystopteris bulbifera . . . . .FACW-

Decodon verticillatus . . . . .OBL
Deparia acrostichoides . . . . .FAC
Deschampsia cespitosa . . . . . . .FACW+
Didiplis diandra . . . . .OBL
Distichlis spicata . . . . .NI

Drosera
    anglica . . . .(OBL)
    intermedia . . . . .OBL
    linearis . . . . .OBL
    rotundifolia . . . . .OBL
Dryopteris
    carthusiana . . . . .FACW-
    celsa . . . . .OBL
    clintoniana . . . . .FACW+
    cristata . . . . .OBL
    goldiana . . . . .FAC
    intermedia . . . . .FAC
Dulichium arundinaceum . . . . . .OBL

Echinochloa
    crusgalli . . . . .FACW
    muricata . . . . .OBL
    walteri . . . . .OBL
Echinocystis lobata . . . . .FACW-
Eclipta prostrata . . . . .FACW
Elatine
    minima . . . . .OBL
    triandra . . . . .OBL
Eleocharis
    acicularis . . . . .OBL
    caribaea . . . . .FACW
    compressa . . . . .FACW
    equisetoides . . . . .OBL
    flavescens . . . . .OBL
    intermedia . . . . .FACW
    macrostachya . . . . .OBL
    melanocarpa . . . . .FACW+
    ovata . . . . .OBL
    palustris . . . . .OBL
    parvula . . . . .OBL
    pauciflora . . . . .OBL
    quadrangulata . . . . .OBL
    robbinsii . . . . .OBL
    rostellata . . . . .OBL
    tenuis . . . . .FACW
    tricostata . . . . .OBL
    wolfii . . . . .OBL
Elodea
    canadensis . . . . .OBL
    nuttallii . . . . .OBL
Elymus
    riparius . . . . .FACW
    virginicus . . . . .FACW-
Empetrum
    nigrum . . . . .FACW-
Epilobium
    ciliatum . . . . .FACU
    coloratum . . . . .OBL
    hirsutum . . . . .FACW+
    leptophyllum . . . . .OBL
    palustre . . . . .OBL
    parviflorum . . . .(OBL)

strictum . . . . .OBL
Equisetum
    arvense . . . . .FAC
    fluviatile . . . . .OBL
    hyemale . . . . .FACW-
    laevigatum . . . . .FACW
    palustre . . . . .FACW
    pratense . . . . .FACW
    scirpoides . . . . .FAC+
    sylvaticum . . . . .FACW
    variegatum . . . . .FACW
Eragrostis
    frankii . . . . .FACW
    hypnoides . . . . .OBL
Erigeron
    hyssopifolius . . . . .FACW
    lonchophyllus . . . . .FACW-
    philadelphicus . . . . .FACW
Eriocaulon aquaticum . . . . .OBL
Eriophorum
    angustifolium . . . . .OBL
    chamissonis . . . . .OBL
    gracile . . . . .OBL
    tenellum . . . . .OBL
    vaginatum . . . . .OBL
    virginicum . . . . .OBL
    viridicarinatum . . . . .OBL
Eupatorium
    fistulosum . . . . .OBL
    maculatum . . . . .OBL
    perfoliatum . . . . .FACW+
    rugosum . . . . .UPL
Euthamia graminifolia . . . . . . .FACW-
Filipendula rubra . . . . .FACW+
Fimbristylis
    autumnalis . . . . .FACW+
    puberula . . . . .OBL
Fraxinus
    nigra . . . . .FACW+
    pennsylvanica . . . . .FACW
    profunda . . . . .OBL
Fuirena pumila . . . . .OBL

Galium
    asprellum . . . . .OBL
    boreale . . . . .FAC
    labradoricum . . . . .OBL
    obtusum . . . . .FACW+
    tinctorium . . . . .OBL
    trifidum . . . . .FACW+
    triflorum . . . . .FACU+
Gaultheria hispidula . . . . .FACW
Gaylussacia baccata . . . . .FAC
Gentiana
    andrewsii . . . . .FACW
    linearis . . . . .NI
    rubricaulis . . . . .OBL

Gentianella
    amarella . . . . .OBL
    quinquefolia . . . . .FAC
Gentianopsis
    crinita . . . . .FACW+
    procera . . . . .OBL
Geocaulon lividum . . . . .FACW-
Geum
    allepicum . . . . .FAC+
    laciniatum . . . . .FACW
    macrophyllum . . . . .FACW+
    rivale . . . . .OBL
Glaux maritima . . . . .OBL
Glyceria
    borealis . . . . .OBL
    canadensis . . . . .OBL
    grandis . . . . .OBL
    septentrionalis . . . . .OBL
    striata . . . . .OBL
Gnaphalium
uliginosum . . . . .FAC
Gratiola
    aurea . . . . .OBL
    neglecta . . . . .OBL
    virginiana . . . . .OBL

Halenia deflexa . . . . .FAC
Helenium autumnale . . . . . . .FACW+
Helianthus
    giganteus . . . . .FACW
    grosseserratus . . . . .FACW-
Hemicarpha micrantha . . . . .OBL
Heracleum lanatum . . . . .FACW
Heteranthera limosa . . . . .OBL
Hibiscus
    laevis . . . . .OBL
    moscheutos . . . . .OBL
Hierochloe odorata . . . . .FACW
Hippuris vulgaris . . . . .OBL
Hordeum jubatum . . . . .FAC+
Hydrocotyle
    americana . . . . .OBL
    umbellata . . . . .OBL
Hypericum
    boreale . . . . .OBL
    canadense . . . . .FACW
    ellipticum . . . . .OBL
    kalmianum . . . . .FACW-
    majus . . . . .FACW
    mutilum . . . . .FACW
    pyramidatum . . . . .FAC+
Hypoxis hirsuta . . . . .FAC

Ilex verticillata . . . . .FACW+
Impatiens
    capensis . . . . .FACW
    pallida . . . . .FACW

Iodanthus pinnatifidus . . . . .FACW

Iris
    pseudacorus . . . . .OBL
    versicolor . . . . .OBL
    virginica . . . . .OBL

Isoetes
    echinospora . . . . .OBL
    engelmannii . . . . .OBL
    lacustris . . . . .OBL
    melanopoda . . . . .OBL

Isotria verticillata . . . . .FAC

Juncus
    acuminatus . . . . .OBL
    alpinoarticulatus . . . . .OBL
    arcticus . . . . .OBL
    articulatus . . . . .OBL
    brachycarpus . . . . .FACW
    brachycephalus . . . . .OBL
    brevicaudatus . . . . .OBL
    bufonius . . . . .FACW+
    canadensis . . . . .OBL
    compressus . . . . .OBL
    effusus . . . . .OBL
    ensifolius . . . . .NI
    filiformis . . . . .FACW
    gerardii . . . . .OBL
    longistylis . . . . .FACW
    marginatus . . . . .FACW
    militaris . . . . .OBL
    nodosus . . . . .OBL
    pelocarpus . . . . .OBL
    scirpoides . . . . .FACW+
    stygius . . . . .OBL
    tenuis . . . . .FAC
    torreyi . . . . .FACW
    vaseyi . . . . .FACW

Justicia americana . . . . .OBL

Kalmia
    angustifolia . . . . .FAC
    polifolia . . . . .OBL

Laportea canadensis . . . . .FACW
Larix laricina . . . . .FACW
Lathyrus palustris . . . . .FACW
Ledum groenlandicum . . . . .OBL

Leersia
    lenticularis . . . . .OBL
    oryzoides . . . . .OBL
    virginica . . . . .FACW

Lemna
    minor . . . . .OBL
    perpusilla . . . . .OBL
    trisulca . . . . .OBL
    valdiviana . . . . .OBL

Leptochloa fascicularis . . . . .OBL

Liatris
    pycnostachya . . . . .FAC-
    spicata . . . . .FAC

Lilium philadelphicum . . . . .FAC-
Limosella aquatica . . . . .OBL
Lindera benzoin . . . . .FACW-
Lindernia dubia . . . . .OBL
Linnaea borealis . . . . .FAC

Linum
    medium . . . .(FACW)
    striatum . . . . .FACW-

Liparis loeselii . . . . .FACW+

Listera
    auriculata . . . . .FACW+
    convallarioides . . . . .FACW
    cordata . . . . .FACW

Littorella uniflora . . . . .OBL

Lobelia
    cardinalis . . . . .OBL
    dortmanna . . . . .OBL
    kalmii . . . . .OBL
    siphilitica . . . . .FACW+
    spicata . . . . .FAC

Lonicera
    caerulea . . . . .FACW
    oblongifolia . . . . .OBL

Ludwigia
    alternifolia . . . . .OBL
    palustris . . . . .OBL
    polycarpa . . . . .OBL
    sphaerocarpa . . . . .OBL

Lycopodium
    appressum . . . . .NI
    inundatum . . . . .OBL
    lucidulum . . . . .FAC+
    selago . . . . .FACU-

Lycopus
    americanus . . . . .OBL
    amplectens . . . .(OBL)
    asper . . . . .OBL
    europaeus . . . . .OBL
    rubellus . . . . .OBL
    uniflorus . . . . .OBL
    virginicus . . . . .OBL

Lygodium palmatum . . . . .NI

Lysimachia
    ciliata . . . . .FACW
    hybrida . . . . .OBL
    nummularia . . . . .FACW+
    quadriflora . . . . .OBL
    terrestris . . . . .OBL
    thyrsiflora . . . . .OBL

Lythrum
    alatum . . . . .OBL
    salicaria . . . . .OBL

Megalodonta
    beckii . . . . .OBL
Maianthemum canadense . . . . . . .UPL
Malaxis
    monophyllos . . . . .FACW
    paludosa . . . . .OBL
    unifolia . . . . .FAC
Marsilea
    quadrifolia . . . . .OBL
    vestita . . . . .OBL
Matteuccia struthiopteris . . . . . .FACW
Melampyrum lineare . . . . .FAC-
Mentha arvensis . . . . .FACW
Menyanthes trifoliata . . . . .OBL
Mertensia virginica . . . . .FACW
Mimulus
    alatus . . . . .OBL
    glabratus . . . . .OBL
    guttatus . . . . .OBL
    moschatus . . . . .OBL
    ringens . . . . .OBL
Mitella nuda . . . . .FACW
Moneses uniflora . . . . .FAC
Montia chamissoi . . . . .OBL
Muhlenbergia
    asperifolia . . . . .FACW
    frondosa . . . . .FACW
    glomerata . . . . .FACW+
    mexicana . . . . .FACW
    racemosa . . . . .FACW
    richardsonis . . . . .FAC+
    sylvatica . . . . .FACW
    uniflora . . . . .OBL
Myosotis
    laxa .OBL
    scorpioides . . . . .OBL
Myosurus minimus . . . . .FACW
Myrica gale . . . . .OBL
Myriophyllum
    alterniflorum . . . . .OBL
    farwellii . . . . .OBL
    heterophyllum . . . . .OBL
    sibiricum . . . . .OBL
    spicatum . . . . .OBL
    tenellum . . . . .OBL
    verticillatum . . . . .OBL

Najas
    flexilis . . . . .OBL
    gracillima . . . . .OBL
    guadalupensis . . . . .OBL
    marina . . . . .OBL
    minor . . . . .OBL
Napaea dioica . . . . .FACW-
Nelumbo lutea . . . . .OBL
Nemopanthus mucronatus . . . . . .OBL
Nuphar

advena . . . . .OBL
    microphylla . . . . .OBL
    variegata . . . . .OBL
Nymphaea
    odorata . . . . .OBL
    tetragona . . . . .OBL
Nyssa sylvatica . . . . .NI

Onoclea sensibilis . . . . .FACW
Ophioglossum vulgatum . . . . .FACW
Oplopanax horridus . . . . .FACW
Osmunda
    cinnamomea . . . . .FACW
    claytoniana . . . . .FAC+
    regalis . . . . .OBL
Oxalis acetosella . . . . .FACU
Oxypolis rigidior . . . . .OBL

Panicum
    clandestinum . . . . .FACW
    flexile . . . . .FACW+
    rigidulum . . . . .FACW
    spretum . . . .(OBL)
Parnassia
    glauca . . . . .OBL
    palustris . . . . .OBL
    parviflora . . . . .OBL
Pedicularis lanceolata . . . . . . .FACW+
Peltandra virginica . . . . .OBL
Penthorum sedoides . . . . .OBL
Petasites
    frigidus . . . . .FACW
    sagittatus . . . . .OBL
Phalaris arundinacea . . . . . . .FACW+
Phlox
    glaberrima . . . . .FACW
    maculata . . . . .FACW+
Phragmites australis . . . . .FACW+
Phyla lanceolata . . . . .OBL
Physocarpus opulifolius . . . . . .FACW-
Physostegia
    virginiana . . . . .FACW
Picea
    glauca . . . . .FACU
    mariana . . . . .FACW
Pilea
    fontana . . . . .FACW
    pumila . . . . .FACW
Pinguicula vulgaris . . . . .OBL
Plantago
    cordata . . . . .OBL
    elongata . . . . .FACW
Platanthera
    blephariglottis . . . . .OBL
    ciliaris . . . . .FACW
    clavellata . . . . .OBL
    dilatata . . . . .FACW+

flava . . . . .FACW
hyperborea . . . . .FACW+
lacera . . . . .FACW
leucophaea . . . . .FACW+
obtusata . . . . .FACW
orbiculata . . . . .FAC
praeclara . . . . .FACW+
psycodes . . . . .FACW
Platanus occidentalis . . . . .FACW
Poa
    alsodes . . . . .FACW-
    paludigena . . . . .OBL
    palustris . . . . .FACW+
    pratens . . . . .FAC-
Podostemum ceratophyllum . . . . .OBL
Pogonia ophioglossoides . . . . . . .OBL
Polemonium occidentale . . . . . . .OBL
Polygala cruciata . . . . .FAC-
Polygonum
    amphibium . . . . .OBL
    arifolium . . . . .OBL
    careyi . . . . .FACW+
    hydropiper . . . . .OBL
    hydropiperoides . . . . .OBL
    lapathifolium . . . . .FACW+
    pensylvanicum . . . . .FACW+
    persicaria . . . . .FACW
    punctatum . . . . .OBL
    sagittatum . . . . .OBL
Pontederia cordata . . . . .OBL
Populus
    balsamifera . . . . .FACW
    deltoides . . . . .FAC+
    heterophylla . . . . .OBL
Potamogeton
    alpinus . . . . .OBL
    amplifolius . . . . .OBL
    confervoides . . . . .OBL
    crispus . . . . .OBL
    diversifolius . . . . .OBL
    epihydrus . . . . .OBL
    filiformis . . . . .OBL
    foliosus . . . . .OBL
    friesii . . . . .OBL
    gramineus . . . . .OBL
    hillii . . . . .OBL
    illinoensis . . . . .OBL
    natans . . . . .OBL
    nodosus . . . . .OBL
    oakesianus . . . . .OBL
    obtusifolius . . . . .OBL
    pectinatus . . . . .OBL
    perfoliatus . . . . .OBL
    praelongus . . . . .OBL
    pulcher . . . . .OBL
    pusillus . . . . .OBL
    richardsonii . . . . .OBL

robbinsii . . . . .OBL
spirillus . . . . .OBL
strictifolius . . . . .OBL
vaginatus . . . . .OBL
vaseyi . . . . .OBL
zosteriformis . . . . .OBL
Potentilla
    anserina . . . . .FACW+
    fruticosa . . . . .FACW
    palustris . . . . .OBL
    paradoxa . . . . .FACW+
    rivalis . . . . .FACW+
Prenanthes racemosa . . . . .FACW
Primula mistassinica . . . . .FACW
Proserpinaca
    palustris . . . . .OBL
    pectinata . . . . .NI
Prunella vulgaris . . . . .FAC
Puccinellia
    distans . . . . .OBL
    nuttalliana . . . . .OBL
    pallida . . . . .OBL
Pycnanthemum virginianum . . .FACW+
Pyrola asarifolia . . . . .FACW

Quercus
    bicolor . . . . .FACW+
    palustris . . . . .FACW

Ranunculus
    abortivus . . . . .FACW-
    acris . . . . .FACW-
    cymbalaria . . . . .OBL
    flabellaris . . . . .OBL
    flammula . . . . .FACW
    gmelinii . . . . .FACW+
    hispidus . . . . .FACW+
    lapponicus . . . . .OBL
    longirostris . . . . .OBL
    macounii . . . . .OBL
    pensylvanicus . . . . .OBL
    recurvatus . . . . .FACW
    sceleratus . . . . .OBL
    subrigidus . . . . .OBL
Rhamnus
    alnifolia . . . . .OBL
    cathartica . . . . .FACU
    frangula . . . . .FAC+
    lanceolata . . . .(OBL)
Rhexia
    marina . . . . .OBL
    virginica . . . . .OBL
Rhynchospora
    alba . . . . .OBL
    capillacea . . . . .OBL
    capitellata . . . . .OBL
    fusca . . . . .OBL

globularis . . . . .FACW
macrostachya . . . . .OBL
scirpoides . . . . .OBL
Ribes
americanum . . . . .FACW
cynosbati . . . . .UPL
glandulosum . . . . .FACW
hirtellum . . . . .FACW
hudsonianum . . . . .OBL
lacustre . . . . .FACW
oxyacanthoides . . . . .NI
triste . . . . .OBL
Rorippa
nasturtium-officinale . . . . . . .OBL
palustris . . . . .OBL
sessiliflora . . . . .OBL
sinuata . . . . .FACW
sylvestris . . . . .OBL
Rosa palustris . . . . .OBL
Rotala ramosior . . . . .OBL
Rubus
acaulis . . . . .OBL
flagellaris . . . . .FACW
hispidus . . . . .FACW
idaeus . . . . .FACW-
pubescens . . . . .FACW+
setosus . . . . .FACW-
Rudbeckia
fulgida . . . . .OBL
laciniata . . . . .FACW+
Rumex
altissimus . . . . .FACW-
crispus . . . . .FAC+
maritimus . . . . .FACW+
obtusifolius . . . . .FACW
orbiculatus . . . . .OBL
salicifolius . . . . .OBL
stenophyllus . . . . .FACW
verticillatus . . . . .OBL
Ruppia maritima . . . . .OBL

Sabatia angularis . . . . .FAC+
Sagittaria
brevirostra . . . . .OBL
calycina . . . . .OBL
cuneata . . . . .OBL
graminea . . . . .OBL
latifolia . . . . .OBL
rigida . . . . .OBL
Salicornia rubra . . . . .OBL
Salix
alba . . . . .FACW
amygdaloides . . . . .FACW
bebbiana . . . . .FACW+
candida . . . . .OBL
discolor . . . . .FACW
eriocephala . . . . .FACW

exigua . . . . .OBL
lucida . . . . .FACW+
myricoides . . . . .FACW
nigra . . . . .OBL
pedicellaris . . . . .OBL
pellita . . . . .FACW
petiolaris . . . . .FACW+
planifolia . . . . .OBL
purpurea . . . . .FACW
pyrifolia . . . . .FACW+
sericea . . . . .OBL
serissima . . . . .OBL
Sambucus
canadensis . . . . .FACW-
racemosa . . . . .FACU+
Samolus floribundus . . . . .OBL
Sanguisorba canadensis . . . . . .FACW+
Sarracenia purpurea . . . . .OBL
Saururus cernuus . . . . .OBL
Saxifraga
pensylvanica . . . . .OBL
Scheuchzeria palustris . . . . .OBL
Scirpus
acutus . . . . .OBL
atrovirens . . . . .OBL
cespitosus . . . . .OBL
cyperinus . . . . .OBL
expansus . . . . .OBL
fluviatilis . . . . .OBL
heterochaetus . . . . .OBL
hudsonianus . . . . .OBL
maritimus . . . . .NI
microcarpus . . . . .OBL
pendulus . . . . .OBL
pungens . . . . .OBL
smithii . . . . .OBL
subterminalis . . . . .OBL
supinus . . . . .OBL
torreyi . . . . .OBL
validus . . . . .OBL
Scleria
reticularis . . . . .OBL
verticillata . . . . .OBL
Scolochloa festucacea . . . . .OBL
Scutellaria
galericulata . . . . .OBL
lateriflora . . . . .OBL
Selaginella
apoda . . . . .FACW+
selaginoides . . . . .FACW+
Senecio
aureus . . . . .FACW
congestus . . . . .FACW+
indecorus . . . . .FACW*
pseudaureus . . . . .FACW
Senna hebecarpa . . . . .FACW
Sicyos angulatus . . . . .FACW-

Silene nivea . . . . .FACW
Silphium
    perfoliatum . . . . .FACW-
    terebinthinaceum . . . . .FACU
Sisyrinchium
    atlanticum . . . . .FACW
    montanum . . . . .FAC+
    mucronatum . . . . .FACW-
Sium suave . . . . .OBL
Smilacina trifolia . . . . .OBL
Solidago
    gigantea . . . . .FACW
    houghtonii . . . . .OBL
    ohioensis . . . . .OBL
    patula . . . . .OBL
    riddellii . . . . .OBL
    uliginosa . . . . .OBL
Sparganium
    americanum . . . . .OBL
    androcladum . . . . .OBL
    chlorocarpum . . . . .OBL
    eurycarpum . . . . .OBL
    fluctuans . . . . .OBL
    glomeratum . . . . .OBL
    minimum . . . . .OBL
Spartina
    gracilis . . . . .FACW
    patens . . . . .FACW
    pectinata . . . . .FACW+
Spergularia
    marina . . . . .OBL
    media . . . . .NI
Sphenopholis obtusata . . . . .FAC
Spiraea
    alba . . . . .FACW+
    tomentosa . . . . .FACW
Spiranthes
    cernua . . . . .FACW-
    lucida . . . . .FACW+
    romanzoffiana . . . . .FACW+
Spirodela polyrhiza . . . . .OBL
Stachys
    hispida . . . . .FACW+
    hyssopifolia . . . . .FACW+
    palustris . . . . .OBL
    tenuifolia . . . . .OBL
Stellaria
    alsine . . . .(FACW)
    aquatica . . . . .OBL
    borealis . . . . .OBL
    crassifolia . . . . .NI
    longifolia . . . . .FACW+
    longipes . . . . .OBL
Styrax americanus . . . . .OBL
Suaeda calceoliformis . . . . .FACW
Subularia aquatica . . . . .OBL
Symplocarpus foetidus . . . . .OBL

Teucrium canadense . . . . .FACW-
Thalictrum
    dasycarpum . . . . .FACW-
    revolutum . . . . .FAC
    venulosum . . . . .FACW
Thelypteris
    palustris . . . . .FACW+
    phegopteris . . . . .UPL
    simulata . . . . .FACW
Thuja occidentalis . . . . .FACW
Tofieldia glutinosa . . . . .OBL
Toxicodendron
    radicans . . . . .FAC+
    vernix . . . . .OBL
Triadenum
    fraseri . . . . .OBL
    virginicum . . . . .OBL
Triglochin
    maritimum . . . . .OBL
    palustre . . . . .OBL
Trisetum melicoides . . . . .FACW
Typha
    angustifolia . . . . .OBL
    latifolia . . . . .OBL

Ulmus americana . . . . .FACW-
Urtica dioica . . . . .FAC+
Utricularia
    cornuta . . . . .OBL
    geminiscapa . . . . .OBL
    gibba . . . . .OBL
    intermedia . . . . .OBL
    minor . . . . .OBL
    purpurea . . . . .OBL
    radiata . . . . .OBL
    resupinata . . . . .OBL
    subulata . . . . .OBL
    vulgaris . . . . .OBL

Vaccinium
    angustifolium . . . . .FACU
    corymbosum . . . . .FACW
    macrocarpon . . . . .OBL
    myrtilloides . . . . .FACW-
    oxycoccos . . . . .OBL
    vitis-idaea . . . . .FAC
Valeriana
    edulis . . . . .FACW+
    uliginosa . . . .(OBL)
Vallisneria americana . . . . .OBL
Verbena hastata . . . . .FACW+
Verbesina alternifolia . . . . .FACW
Vernonia fasciculata . . . . .FACW
Veronica
    americana . . . . .OBL
    anagallis-aquatica . . . . .OBL
    peregrina . . . . .FACW+

scutellata . . . . .OBL
Veronicastrum virginicum . . . . . . .FAC
Viburnum
    edule . . . . .FACW
    nudum . . . . .FACW
    opulus . . . . .FACW
Viola
    affinis . . . . .FACW
    blanda . . . . .FACW-
    cucullata . . . . .OBL
    labradorica . . . . .FAC
    lanceolata . . . . .OBL
    macloskeyi . . . . .OBL
    nephrophylla . . . . .FACW+
    primulifolia . . . . .FACW+
    renifolia . . . . .FACW
    sororia . . . . .FACW
    striata . . . . .FACW
Vitis riparia . . . . .FACW-

Wolffia
    columbiana . . . . .OBL
    papulifera . . . . .OBL
    punctata . . . . .OBL
Woodwardia virginica . . . . .OBL

Xanthium strumarium . . . . .FAC
Xyris
    difformis . . . . .OBL
    montana . . . . .OBL
    torta . . . . .OBL

Zannichellia palustris . . . . .OBL
Zigadenus elegans . . . . .FACW
Zizania aquatica . . . . .OBL
Zosterella dubia . . . . .OBL

Appendix D
Common Plant Species of Great Lakes Wetland Types

APPENDIX D lists some of the more common or typical plants associated with each of the major wetland types present in the Great Lakes region. These lists are not comprehensive but may serve to help identify at least the dominant plants in a given type of wetland.

▶Open Water Communities

Free-floating plants
Ceratophyllum demersum (Hornwort; Coontail)
Chara (Muskgrass; a species of algae of mineral-rich waters)
Lemna minor (Lesser duckweed)
Myriophyllum (Water-milfoil)
Ranunculus aquatilis (White water-crowfoot)
Utricularia vulgaris (Common bladderwort)

Submergent plants
Brasenia schreberi (Water-shield)
Elodea canadensis (Common water-weed)
Isoetes echinospora (Spiny-spored quillwort)
Najas flexilis (Northern water-nymph)
Nelumbo lutea (American lotus-lily)
Nuphar variegata (Yellow water-lily)
Nyphaea odorata (White water-lily)
Potamogeton (Pondweeds)
[*P. amplifolius* (Bigleaf pondweed), *P. illinoensis* (Illinois pondweed), *P. natans* (Floating pondweed), *P. pectinatus* (Sago-pondweed), *P. zosteriformis* (Flatstem-pondweed)]
Vallisneria americana (Tape-grass; Eel-grass; Water-celery)

▶Marshes

Grasses and grasslike plants
Carex aquatilis (Water sedge)
Carex atherodes (Slough sedge)
Carex comosa (Bristly sedge)
Carex hystericina (Porcupine sedge)
Carex lacustris (Common lakeshore sedge)
Eleocharis acicularis ((Least spike-rush)
Glyceria borealis (Northern-mannagrass)
Glyceria canadensis (Rattlesnake-mannagrass)
Glyceria grandis (American mannagrass)
Juncus effusus (Soft rush)
Phragmites australis (Common reed)
Scirpus acutus (Hardstem bulrush)
Scirpus fluviatilis (River-bulrush)
Scipus pungens (Common threesquare)
Scirpus validus (Softstem-bulrush)

Sparganium eurycarpum (Giant bur-reed)
Zizania aquatica (Annual wildrice)

Other herbaceous plants
Alisma plantago-aquatica (Water-plantain)
Equisetum fluviatile (Water-horsetail)
Iris versicolor (Northern blue flag)
Iris virginica (Southern blue flag)
Lemna minor (Lesser duckweed)
Lythrum salicaria (Purple loosestrife)
Polygonum amphibium (Water smartweed)
Pontederia cordata (Pickerelweed)
Sagittaria latifolia (Common arrowhead)
Typha angustifolia (Narrow-leaved cat-tail)
Typha latifolia (Common cat-tail)
Utricularia vulgaris (Common bladderwort)

▶Sedge Meadows

Northern Sedge Meadows
Grasses and grasslike plants
Calamagrostis canadensis (Bluejoint)
Carex lanuginosa (Woolly sedge)
Carex stricta (Common tussock sedge)
Carex utriculata (Beaked sedge)
Carex vesicaria (Inflated sedge)
Glyceria canadensis (Rattlesnake-mannagrass)
Poa palustris (Fowl bluegrass)
Scirpus atrovirens (Black bulrush)
Scirpus cyperinus (Wool-grass)

Other herbaceous plants
Asclepias incarnata (Swamp-milkweed)
Aster lanceolatus (Eastern lined aster)
Campanula aparinoides (Marsh-bellflower)
Eupatorium maculatum (Spotted joe-pye-weed)
Eupatorium perfoliatum (Boneset)
Iris versicolor (Northern blue flag)
Lycopus americanus (American water-horehound)
Lycopus uniflorus (Northern water-horehound)
Mentha arvensis (Field-mint)
Potentilla palustris (Marsh-cinquefoil)
Scutellaria galericulata (Marsh or Hooded skullcap)
Thelypteris palustris (Marsh fern)
Typha latifolia (Common cat-tail)

Southern Sedge Meadows
Grasses and grasslike plants
Calamagrostis canadensis (Bluejoint)
Carex stricta (Common tussock sedge)
Glyceria striata (Fowl-mannagrass)
Phalaris arundinacea (Reed canary-grass)
Spartina pectinata (Prairie cordgrass)

Other herbaceous plants
Anemone canadensis (Canada anemone)

Angelica atropurpurea (Purplestem-angelica)
Asclepias incarnata (Swamp-milkweed)
Aster firmus (Shining aster)
Aster lanceolatus (Eastern lined aster)
Equisetum arvense (Common or Field horsetail)
Eupatorium maculatum (Spotted joe-pye-weed)
Impatiens capensis (Orange-touch-me-not; Jewelweed)
Iris virginica (Southern blue flag)
Lathyrus palustris (Marsh-pea)
Lycopus americanus (American water-horehound)
Solidago gigantea (Smooth goldenrod)
Stachys palustris (Marsh hedge-nettle)
Thalictrum dasycarpum (Purple meadow-rue)
Typha latifolia (Common cat-tail)

▶Wet Meadows

Grasses and grasslike plants
Agrostis stolonifera (Redtop)
Calamagrostis canadensis (Bluejoint)
Carex vulpinoidea (Brown fox sedge)
Juncus tenuis (Path-rush)
Juncus canadensis (Canada rush)
Phalaris arundinacea (Reedcanary-grass)
Poa pratensis (Kentucky bluegrass)

Other herbaceous plants
Aster firmus (Shining aster)
Aster lanceolatus (Eastern lined aster)
Aster puniceus (Bristly aster)
Helenium autumnale (Common sneezeweed)
Solidago gigantea (Smooth goldenrod)
Verbena hastata (Common vervain)

▶Low Prairie

Grasses and grasslike plants
Carex bebbii (Bebb's oval sedge)
Calamagrostis canadensis (Bluejoint)
Spartina pectinata (Prairie cordgrass)

Other herbaceous plants
Angelica atropurpurea (Purplestem-angelica)
Aster novae-angliae (New England aster)
Helianthus grosseserratus (Sawtooth sunflower)
Pycnanthemum virginianum (Virginia mtn.-mint)
Silphium terebinthinaceum (Rosin-weed)
Solidago gigantea (Smooth goldenrod)
Solidago riddellii (Riddell's goldenrod)
Thalictrum dasycarpum (Purple meadow-rue)
Veronicastrum virginicum (Culver's root)

▶Calcareous Fens

Shrubs
Potentilla fruticosa (Shrubby cinquefoil)
Salix candida (Hoary or Sage-leaved willow)

Grasses and grasslike plants
Andropogon gerardii (Big bluestem)
Carex sterilis (Fen star sedge)
Cladium mariscoides (Twig-rush)
Eleocharis rostellata (Beaked spike-rush)
Eriophorum angustifolium (Thin-scale cotton-grass)
Muhlenbergia glomerata (Marsh-muhly)
Scirpus acutus (Hardstem bulrush)
Scirpus cespitosus (Clumped bulrush)
Sorghastrum nutans (Indian grass)

Other herbaceous plants
Cirsium muticum (Swamp-thistle)
Gentianopsis procera (Lesser fringed gentian)
Lobelia kalmii (Brook lobelia)
Parnassia glauca (American grass-of-parnassus)
Solidago ohioensis (Ohio goldenrod)
Spiranthes cernua (Nodding ladies' tresses)
Valeriana edulis (Common valerian; Tobacco-root)

▶Open Bogs

Trees
Larix laricina (Tamarack)
Picea mariana (Black spruce)

Shrubs
Andromeda glaucophylla (Bog-rosemary)
Chamaedaphne calyculata (Leatherleaf)
Kalmia polifolia (Bog-laurel)
Ledum groenlandicum (Labrador-tea)
Vaccinium angustifolium (Lowbush blueberry)
Vaccinium macrocarpon (Cranberry)
Vaccinium oxycoccos (Small cranberry)

Grasses and grasslike plants
Carex lasiocarpa (Slender sedge)
Carex oligosperma (Running bog sedge)
Carex pauciflora (Few-flowered bog sedge)
Carex paupercula (Poor sedge)
Carex trisperma (Three-seeded bog sedge)
Dulichium arundinaceum (Three-way sedge)
Eriophorum angustifolium (Thin-scale cotton-grass)
Eriophorum vaginatum (Tussock cotton-grass)
Eriophorum virginicum (Tawny cotton-grass)

Other herbaceous plants
Calla palustris (Water-arum)
Drosera rotundifolia (Round-leaved sundew)
Sarracenia purpurea (Pitcher-plant)
Smilacina trifolia (False Solomon's seal)

▶Conifer Bogs

Trees
Picea mariana (Black spruce)
Larix laricina (Tamarack)

Shrubs
Alnus incana (Speckled or Tag alder)
Betula pumila (Bog birch)
Chamaedaphne calyculata (Leatherleaf)
Ledum groenlandicum (Labrador-tea)

Grasses and grasslike plants
Carex lasiocarpa (Slender sedge)
Carex oligosperma (Running bog sedge)
Carex trisperma (Three-seeded bog sedge)
Eriophorum vaginatum (Tussock cotton-grass)

Other herbaceous plants
Calopogon tuberosus (Grass-pink)
Sarracenia purpurea (Pitcher plant)

▶Shrub-Carrs

Shrubs
Cornus ammomum (Silky dogwood)
Cornus sericea (Red-osier dogwood)
Ilex verticillata (Winterberry)
Myrica gale (Sweet gale)
Salix bebbiana (Bebb's willow)
Salix discolor (Pussy willow)
Salix exigua (Sandbar willow)
Spiraea alba (Meadowsweet)

Non-native shrubs
Rhamnus cathartica (Common buckthorn)
Rhamnus frangula (European alder-buckthorn)

Grasses and grasslike plants
Carex stipata (Common fox sedge)

Other herbaceous plants
Habenaria psycodes (Purple fringed orchid)

▶Alder Thickets

Shrubs
Alnus incana (Speckled or Tag alder)
Cornus sericea (Red-osier dogwood)
Ilex verticillata (Winterberry)
Myrica gale (Sweet gale)
Spiraea alba (Meadowsweet)
Viburnum opulus (High-bush cranberry)

Grasses and grasslike plants
Calamagrostis canadensis (Bluejoint)

Scirpus atrovirens (Black bulrush)

Other herbaceous plants
Aster lanceolatus (Eastern lined aster)
Campanula aparinoides (Marsh-bellflower)
Eupatorium maculatum (Spotted joe-pye-weed)
Eupatorium perfoliatum (Boneset)
Onoclea sensibilis (Sensitive fern)
Polygonum sagittatum (Arrow-leaved tearthumb)
Thelypteris palustris (Marsh fern)

▶Hardwood Swamps

Trees
Fraxinus nigra (Black ash)
Acer rubrum (Red maple)
Betula alleghaniensis (Yellow birch)
Acer saccharinum (Silver maple)
Thuja occidentalis (Northern white cedar)
Ulmus americana (American elm)

Shrubs
Cornus canadensis (Bunchberry)
Gaultheria hispidula (Creeping snowberry)
Vaccinium myrtilloides (Velvetleaf-blueberry)

Grasses and grasslike plants
Carex trisperma (Three-seeded bog sedge)

Other herbaceous plants
Caltha palustris (Common marsh-marigold)
Coptis trifolia (Alaska goldthread)
Impatiens capensis (Orange touch-me-not; Jewelweed)
Matteuccia struthiopteris (Ostrich fern)
Symplocarpus foetidus (Skunk-cabbage)
Viola macloskeyi (Wild white violet)

▶Conifer Swamps

Trees
Abies balsamea (Balsam fir)
Betula alleghaniensis (Yellow birch)
Larix laricina (Tamarack)
Picea mariana (Black spruce)
Thuja occidentalis (Northern white cedar)

Shrubs
Alnus incana (Speckled or Tag alder)
Gaultheria hispidula (Creeping snowberry)
Chamaedaphne calyculata (Leatherleaf)
Cornus canadensis (Bunchberry)
Ledum groenlandicum (Labrador-tea)
Linnaea borealis (Twinflower)
Vaccinium angustifolium (Lowbush blueberry)
Vaccinium myrtilloides (Velvetleaf-blueberry)

Grasses and grasslike plants
Carex disperma (Two-seeded sedge)
Carex trisperma (Three-seeded bog sedge)
Eriophorum virginicum (Tawny cotton-grass)

Other herbaceous plants
Coptis trifolia (Alaska goldthread)
Equisetum sylvaticum (Woodland horsetail)
Maianthemum canadense (Canada mayflower)
Osmunda cinnamomea (Cinnamon fern)
Smilacina trifolia (False Solomon's seal)
Viola macloskeyi (Wild white violet)

▶Floodplain Forests

Trees
Acer negundo (Boxelder)
Acer saccharinum (Silver maple)
Fraxinus pensylvanica (Green ash)
Betula nigra (River birch)
Thuja occidentalis (Northern white cedar)
Populus deltoides (Eastern cottonwood)
Salix nigra (Black willow)
Ulmus americana (American elm)

Vines
Vitis riparia (Riverbank grape)

Grasses and grasslike plants
Elymus virginicus (Virginia wildrye)
Carex typhina (Common cat-tail sedge)
Cinna arundinacea (Common woodreed)
Leersia virginica (White grass)
Muhlenbergia frondosa (Wirestem muhly)

Other herbaceous plants
Impatiens capensis (Orange touch-me-not; Jewelweed)
Laportea canadensis (Wood-nettle)
Pilea pumila (Clearweed)
Teucrium canadense (American germander)
Urtica dioica (Stinging nettle)

▶Seasonally Flooded Basins

Grasses and grasslike plants
Cyperus erythrorhizos (Red-root flatsedge)
Echinochloa crus-galli (Barnyard-grass)

Other herbaceous plants
Bidens (Beggarticks)
Eleocharis ovata (Blunt spike-rush)
Polygonum (Smartweeds)
Rumex (Dock)

Index

The index includes the scientific and common name of each family and genus treated in the Flora. Common names for most species are also listed. Synonyms are listed in *italic* type.

Order Form

HOW TO ORDER

• Visit our website at www.pocketflora.com for secure online ordering.

• E-mail your order to: orders@pocketflora.com

• Mail a copy of this form to:

PocketFlora Press
436 Hecla Street
Laurium, MI 49913

• Telephone: (906) 337-0716

• Fax: (586) 314-4295

Visa, MasterCard, American Express and Discover accepted.
Quantity discounts available.

TITLE	NO. COPIES	PRICE	TOTAL
A Great Lakes Wetland Flora A complete guide to the aquatic and wetland plants of the Upper Midwest (Second Edition) (ISBN 0-9651385-5-0)		$30.95	

Sales tax (retail orders)
Please add 6% for books shipped to Michigan addresses.
Shipping: 1-2 copies, add $5.20 per order
(for USPS Priority Mail; larger orders shipped via UPS).

NAME AND ADDRESS

Name

Address

City   State   Zip

Telephone   E-mail

PAYMENT

❏ Check   ❏ Purchase Order No.

Credit card: ❏ VISA   ❏ MasterCard   ❏ American Express   ❏ Discover

Card number

Cardholder   Exp. date   /

Signature